৪৭৮

METHODS OF ADVANCED CALCULUS

Methods of
Advanced Calculus

BY

PHILIP FRANKLIN, Ph.D.

Professor of Mathematics
Massachusetts Institute of Technology

FIRST EDITION
SEVENTH IMPRESSION

McGRAW-HILL BOOK COMPANY, Inc.

NEW YORK AND LONDON

1944

87826

THE MAPLE PRESS COMPANY, YORK, PA.

PREFACE

This book has two principal objectives: first, to refresh and improve the reader's technique in applying elementary calculus; second, to present those methods of advanced calculus which are most needed in applied mathematics. The reader is assumed to have a working knowledge of calculus, but he needs no greater facility in this subject than that usually acquired and retained from a first course in the subject. Thus the book may serve for reference or self-study by practicing engineers or applied scientists who need a steppingstone to the more formidable specialized mathematical treatises. As a textbook, it is suitable for a course in advanced calculus of a type now taken by many students whose major field of interest is engineering, mathematics, or science.

The earlier chapters of the book deal with topics touched on to some extent in elementary calculus, namely, Taylor's series, partial differentiation and its geometrical applications, and integration. Incidentally, they strengthen the reader's knowledge of elementary calculus. But the treatment here includes partial derivatives of implicit functions and Jacobians, the vector notation and its uses in kinematics and differential geometry, hyperbolic functions, line and multiple integrals, and the use of complex variable methods to simplify systematic integration, to evaluate certain definite integrals, and to calculate types of fluid flow.

The later chapters deal with special higher functions, Fourier series, ordinary and partial differential equations, vector analysis, and the calculus of variations. For each special function some graphs are drawn, and a method is given for computing numerical values of the functions from convergent or, where more convenient, asymptotic series. The use of available tables is also explained, so that results can be reduced to numerical form. A simple method, new in detail, of reducing elliptic integrals of the first and second kinds to the tabulated normal forms is given, starting with radicands either in polynomial or trigonometric form. In connection with Bessel functions, of real or imaginary arguments, the practical determination of the change of variable that reduces a related differential equation to the standard form is indicated.

The author's extensive contact with engineering colleagues and students at the Massachusetts Institute of Technology has taught him what sort of mathematics interests students, as well as what they most often need. This has led him to omit from this book all existence proofs or similar discussions that seem superfluous to the practical-minded. Results like the mean value theorem and the expression for the area of a curved surface are accompanied by a brief discussion relying on geometric intuition, of a nature to carry conviction and enable the reader to recall the results by retracing the argument. Finally, a few results easy to understand and use, but whose proofs are relatively long and difficult, like the theorems connecting power series and analytic functions, a sufficient condition for the convergence of Fourier series, and several of the more involved asymptotic expansions, are stated without proof.

On the other hand, loose statements are annoying to a conscientious mathematics teacher and misleading to the few students who will proceed to more refined theoretical treatments. For this reason the author has taken pains to formulate all statements of mathematical theorems correctly. He further clearly indicates each case where a result is suggested by a heuristic discussion rather than proved, where a statement is made without proof, or where a rule is merely valid for all practical purposes and not mathematically universal. Moreover, references to more rigorous and complete discussions are given at the end of each chapter.

Since the author had already published a comprehensive *Treatise on Advanced Calculus*, which included a rigorous discussion of the foundations, he could resist any temptation to include material of that nature in the present book. And the exclusion of such material has provided space for the comparatively extensive treatment of advanced techniques in a volume of moderate size.

The attempt to prove everything often leads to the use of roundabout methods in the beginning of a book. This fixes inefficient techniques in the reader's mind, even when better methods are presented later. In this book the author has given the simplest known method of solving each type of problem the first time it appears, even when this means quoting a theorem from an advanced branch of mathematics without proof.

Each chapter is followed by a number of problems, arranged in an order corresponding to the development of the text. There are a large number, averaging nearly 100 per chapter, and they range from routine exercises to elaborate applications to science and engineering. For any that offer real difficulties not explained in the text, the outline of a solution follows the problem. Answers to all problems are given at the end of the book.

A list of the works referred to in the text, together with a few additional books that have been consulted, is found in the bibliography.

Philip Franklin.

Cambridge, Mass.,
June, 1944.

CONTENTS

METHODS OF ADVANCED CALCULUS

CHAPTER I

ELEMENTARY FUNCTIONS FOR COMPLEX VALUES AND TAYLOR'S SERIES

In this chapter we shall discuss the elementary functions and their fundamental properties. Since many calculations may be simplified by the use of complex quantities, we briefly describe the complex number system and define the elementary functions for complex values of the variable. We include the Taylor's expansions of the elementary functions, the manipulation of such expansions, and their application to the evaluation of indeterminate forms and certain computations.

1. Elementary Functions. The basic elementary functions are the integral power function $y = x^n$, the exponential function $y = e^x$, and the trigonometric functions $y = \sin x$ and $y = \cos x$. A polynomial,

$$y = P(x) = a_n x^n + a_{n-1} x^{n-1} + \cdots + a_1 x + a_0, \qquad (1)$$

is formed from a finite number of powers and constants by the algebraic operations of multiplication and addition. Since the constants may be negative, the use of subtraction gives nothing new. However, the use of division leads to the rational functions. A rational function can always be expressed as the quotient of two polynomials,

$$y = R(x) = \frac{P(x)}{Q(x)} = \frac{a_n x^n + a_{n-1} x^{n-1} + \cdots + a_1 x + a_0}{b_n x^n + b_{n-1} x^{n-1} + \cdots + b_1 x + b_0}. \qquad (2)$$

The integral root function is the inverse of the power function. That is, $y = x^{1/n}$ if $x = y^n$. Similarly, the logarithmic function is the inverse of the exponential function. That is, $y = \log x$ if $x = e^y$.

The trigonometric functions $\tan x$, $\cot x$, $\sec x$, and $\csc x$ are defined in terms of $\sin x$ and $\cos x$ by the quotients

$$\tan x = \frac{\sin x}{\cos x}, \qquad \cot x = \frac{\cos x}{\sin x}, \qquad \sec x = \frac{1}{\cos x},$$

$$\csc x = \frac{1}{\sin x}. \tag{3}$$

Each of the six inverse trigonometric functions is the function inverse to the corresponding direct function. For example, $y = \sin^{-1} x$ if $x = \sin y$.

The functions that can be obtained as a finite combination of the functions just described are the elementary functions. In all first courses in the calculus, rules are derived that enable us to express the derivative of any elementary function as a second elementary function.

2. Complex Values. Many mathematical results may be stated more simply, and obtained more readily, by the use of complex quantities in the intermediate stages, even if the final applications involve real numbers only. We recall that a complex number is an expression of the form $a + bi$, where a and b are real numbers and i is the imaginary unit;

$$i = \sqrt{-1} \qquad \text{and} \qquad i^2 = -1. \tag{4}$$

For the most part, the rules for manipulating complex numbers are the same as those for real numbers. One useful principle is that, if a, b, a', and b' are all real, then the equation

$$a + bi = a' + b'i \qquad \text{implies that } a = a' \text{ and } b = b'. \tag{5}$$

Thus, in any equation simplified to this form, we may equate the real and imaginary parts separately.

For a complex variable $z = x + iy$, the power function z^n is defined by repeated multiplication. Polynomials and rational functions of z are then defined in terms of the four fundamental operations. One practical method of dividing complex numbers is illustrated by the following calculation:

$$\frac{a + bi}{c + di} = \frac{(a + bi)(c - di)}{(c + di)(c - di)} = \frac{(ac + bd) + (-ad + bc)i}{c^2 + d^2}$$

$$= \frac{ac + bd}{c^2 + d^2} + \frac{-ad + bc}{c^2 + d^2} i. \tag{6}$$

The functions e^z, $\sin z$, and $\cos z$ are defined by the infinite power series,

$$e^z = 1 + z + \frac{z^2}{2!} + \frac{z^3}{3!} + \cdots , \tag{7}$$

$$\sin z = z - \frac{z^3}{3!} + \frac{z^5}{5!} - \frac{z^7}{7!} + \cdots , \tag{8}$$

and

$$\cos z = 1 - \frac{z^2}{2!} + \frac{z^4}{4!} - \frac{z^6}{6!} + \cdots . \tag{9}$$

These series are similar in form to the MacLaurin's series which represent the functions e^x, $\sin x$, and $\cos x$ for all real values of x. This shows that, when $y = 0$, so that $z = x + iy = x$, the values obtained from the new definition will agree with those previously used for real values of the variable.

The series (7), (8), and (9) converge for all complex values of z. Convergent series of this type may be multiplied and added together in the same way that polynomials are combined. It follows that the functions defined by the series satisfy the relation

$$e^{z_1} \cdot e^{z_2} = e^{z_1 + z_2}, \tag{10}$$

as well as the addition theorems

$$\sin (z_1 + z_2) = \sin z_1 \cos z_2 + \cos z_1 \sin z_2, \tag{11}$$

and

$$\cos (z_1 + z_2) = \cos z_1 \cos z_2 - \sin z_1 \sin z_2, \tag{12}$$

and the identity

$$\cos^2 z + \sin^2 z = 1. \tag{13}$$

Similarly, it follows from the series that

$$e^{iz} = \cos z + i \sin z \tag{14}$$

and

$$e^{-iz} = \cos z - i \sin z. \tag{15}$$

We may solve these for $\sin z$ and $\cos z$ and so obtain

$$\sin z = \frac{e^{iz} - e^{-iz}}{2i}, \tag{16}$$

and

$$\cos z = \frac{e^{iz} + e^{-iz}}{2}. \tag{17}$$

The definitions of the remaining trigonometric functions are similar in form to Eqs. (3). For example,

$$\tan z = \frac{\sin z}{\cos z}, \tag{18}$$

so that from Eqs. (16) and (17),

$$\tan z = \frac{1}{i}\frac{e^{iz} - e^{-iz}}{e^{iz} + e^{-iz}} = -i\frac{e^{2iz} - 1}{e^{2iz} + 1}. \tag{19}$$

Equations (16) and (17) show that, after the exponential function has been defined for complex values of the variable, we may omit the trigonometric functions from our list of basic functions. More specifically, we may take Eq. (7) as the definition of e^z, and Eq. (10) as its fundamental property. Then Eqs. (16) and (17) may be used to define $\sin z$ and $\cos z$, and the series (8) and (9) then follow from (16) and (17) combined with (7) and (4). From this point of view Eqs. (11), (12), and (13) and all other trigonometric identities become a consequence of Eqs. (16), (17), and (7).

The usual proof for real values shows that, for any positive integer n,

$$\frac{d(az^n)}{dz} = anz^{n-1}. \tag{20}$$

Moreover, series of the type considered here may be differentiated termwise. Consequently, it follows from the series (7), (8), and (9) that

$$\frac{d(e^z)}{dz} = e^z, \tag{21}$$

$$\frac{d(\sin z)}{dz} = \cos z, \tag{22}$$

and

$$\frac{d(\cos z)}{dz} = -\sin z. \tag{23}$$

The rule for differentiating composite functions

$$\frac{dw}{dz} = \frac{dw}{du} \cdot \frac{du}{dz} \tag{24}$$

also remains valid in the complex case, and we may use this to deduce that

$$\frac{d(e^{iz})}{dz} = ie^{iz} \quad \text{and} \quad \frac{d(e^{-iz})}{dz} = -ie^{-iz}. \tag{25}$$

Using these, we may derive Eqs. (22) and (23) from Eqs. (16) and (17).

3. Evaluation of Functions of z. If $z = x + iy$, we find from Eqs. (10) and (14) that

$$e^z = e^{x+iy} = e^x \cdot e^{iy} = e^x(\cos y + i \sin y)$$
$$= e^x \cos y + ie^x \sin y. \tag{26}$$

This enables us to compute the value of e^z from tables of values of the real functions e^x, $\cos y$, and $\sin y$ with y in radian measure.

To compute $\sin z$ and $\cos z$ we have from Eqs. (11) and (12)

$$\sin z = \sin (x + iy) = \sin x \cos iy + \cos x \sin iy, \tag{27}$$
$$\cos z = \cos (x + iy) = \cos x \cos iy - \sin x \sin iy. \tag{28}$$

But from Eqs. (16) and (17) we have

$$\sin iy = \frac{e^{-y} - e^y}{2i} = i\left(\frac{e^y - e^{-y}}{2}\right), \tag{29}$$

$$\cos iy = \frac{e^y + e^{-y}}{2}. \tag{30}$$

This suggests that we tabulate the real functions

$$\cosh y = \frac{e^y + e^{-y}}{2} \quad \text{and} \quad \sinh y = \frac{e^y - e^{-y}}{2}, \tag{31}$$

read *hyperbolic cosine* and *hyperbolic sine*. We may then compute the functions $\sin z$ and $\cos z$ from

$$\sin z = \sin x \cosh y + i \cos x \sinh y, \tag{32}$$
$$\cos z = \cos x \cosh y - i \sin x \sinh y. \tag{33}$$

4. Hyperbolic Functions. Let us study the hyperbolic functions defined by

$$\sinh y = \frac{e^y - e^{-y}}{2} \quad \text{and} \quad \cosh y = \frac{e^y + e^{-y}}{2}. \tag{34}$$

It follows from Eqs. (29), (30), and (34) that

$$\sin iy = i \sinh y \quad \text{and} \quad \cos iy = \cosh y. \tag{35}$$

These relations may be used to deduce formulas for the hyperbolic functions from those for the trigonometric functions. For example, if we replace z_1 by iy_1 and z_2 by iy_2 in Eq. (11), we find

$$\sin i(y_1 + y_2) = \sin iy_1 \cos iy_2 + \cos iy_1 \sin iy_2. \qquad (36)$$

But from this by Eq. (35), we may derive

$$i \sinh (y_1 + y_2) = i \sinh y_1 \cosh y_2 + \cosh y_1(i \sinh y_2), \qquad (37)$$

so that, if we divide by i,

$$\sinh (y_1 + y_2) = \sinh y_1 \cosh y_2 + \cosh y_1 \sinh y_2. \qquad (38)$$

In this way we show that

$$\cosh (y_1 + y_2) = \cosh y_1 \cosh y_2 + \sinh y_1 \sinh y_2, \qquad (39)$$

and that

$$\cosh^2 y - \sinh^2 y = 1. \qquad (40)$$

By analogy with the defining relations (3), we define the hyperbolic tangent, hyperbolic cotangent, hyperbolic secant, and hyperbolic cosecant by the equations

$$\tanh y = \frac{\sinh y}{\cosh y}, \qquad \coth y = \frac{\cosh y}{\sinh y} = \frac{1}{\tanh y}, \qquad (41)$$

$$\operatorname{sech} y = \frac{1}{\cosh y}, \qquad \operatorname{csch} y = \frac{1}{\sinh y}. \qquad (42)$$

These additional functions may be expressed in terms of exponential functions by using Eq. (34). For example,

$$\tanh y = \frac{e^y - e^{-y}}{e^y + e^{-y}} = \frac{e^{2y} - 1}{e^{2y} + 1}. \qquad (43)$$

For the derivatives of $\sinh y$ and $\cosh y$, we may deduce from Eqs. (35), (22), (23), and (24) that

$$\frac{d(\sinh y)}{dy} = \cosh y \qquad \text{and} \qquad \frac{d(\cosh y)}{dy} = \sinh y. \qquad (44)$$

These also follow directly from Eqs. (34) and (21).

The power series for $\sinh y$ and $\cosh y$ may be obtained by combining Eqs. (35) with (8) and (9), or more directly from

Eqs. (34) and (7). The results are

$$\sinh y = y + \frac{y^3}{3!} + \frac{y^5}{5!} + \frac{y^7}{7!} + \cdots , \tag{45}$$

$$\cosh y = 1 + \frac{y^2}{2!} + \frac{y^4}{4!} + \frac{y^6}{6!} + \cdots . \tag{46}$$

All the formulas of this section hold for y complex, if we use these two series as the definitions. For complex values, the hyperbolic functions may be computed from

$$\cosh (x + iy) = \cosh x \cos y + i \sinh x \sin y, \tag{47}$$
$$\sinh (x + iy) = \sinh x \cos y + i \cosh x \sin y. \tag{48}$$

5. The Logarithmic Function. If $\log z$ is the function inverse to the exponential function, the relation

$$\log (x + iy) = u + iv \tag{49}$$

implies that

$$x + iy = e^{u+iv} = e^u(\cos v + i \sin v), \tag{50}$$

where the last form is similar to Eq. (26). Consequently,

$$x = e^u \cos v \quad \text{and} \quad y = e^u \sin v, \tag{51}$$

since x, y, u, and v are all real. It follows that

$$e^u = \sqrt{x^2 + y^2} \quad \text{and} \quad v = \tan^{-1} (y/x), \tag{52}$$

so that e^u and v may be used as the polar coordinates of a point in a plane with Cartesian or rectangular coordinates x and y. Let us denote a possible choice of polar coordinates with positive radius vector by r, θ so that

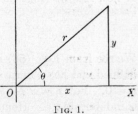

$$r = + \sqrt{x^2 + y^2};$$
$$x = r \cos \theta;$$
$$y = r \sin \theta. \tag{53}$$

Fig. 1.

The number r is called the *absolute value* of $z = x + iy$ and we write

$$|z| = |x + iy| = r = \sqrt{x^2 + y^2}. \tag{54}$$

We find from Eqs. (51), (52), and (53) that

$$u = \log r, \quad v = \theta, \tag{55}$$

leads to a value for the logarithm,

$$\log (x + iy) = \log r + i\theta. \tag{56}$$

Since θ is determined only to within an integral multiple of 2π, a complex number has an infinite number of possible logarithms. A particular value of θ may be determined from a knowledge of the sign of any two of the functions

$$\tan \theta = \frac{y}{x}, \qquad \cos \theta = \frac{x}{r}, \qquad \sin \theta = \frac{y}{r}, \qquad (57)$$

and the numerical value of any one. The simplest method of checking a value of θ is to plot the point (x,y). The proper quadrant and a rough estimation of θ may then be read from the diagram. If θ_0 is any one value, all of the possible values are given by

$$\theta = \theta_0 + 2k\pi, \qquad \text{where } k = 0, 1, 2, \cdots \text{ or } -1, -2, \cdots . \qquad (58)$$

The rule for differentiating inverse functions,

$$\frac{dw}{dz} = \frac{1}{dz/dw} \qquad (59)$$

remains valid in the complex case. But

$$w = \log z \text{ implies that } z = e^w. \qquad (60)$$

Consequently, by Eq. (21),

$$\frac{dz}{dw} = e^w = z. \qquad (61)$$

It now follows from the last three numbered equations that

$$\frac{d(\log z)}{dz} = \frac{1}{z}. \qquad (62)$$

We see from Eqs. (56) and (62) that the logarithmic function is defined and has a finite derivative for all finite values of z except $z = 0$. For $z = x + iy = 0$, $r = 0$ so that $\log r = -\infty$ and θ is indeterminate. Hence we do not define $\log z$ for $z = 0$.

The fundamental property of the logarithm

$$\log (z_1 z_2) = \log z_1 + \log z_2 \qquad (63)$$

follows from Eqs. (60) and (10). It is true in the sense that, if any two of the logarithms are given, with particular choices of k in Eq. (58), some possible value of the third logarithm will make the equation true.

6. The Complex Plane. In the last section we were lead to associate the complex number $z = x + iy$ with the point P in a plane where $P = (x,y)$. We may think of the point P, or the vector OP, as representing the complex number. The four fundamental operations on complex numbers then correspond to simple geometric operations on the vectors that represent them. We refer to P as the point z. If

$$z_1 = x_1 + iy_1, \qquad z_2 = x_2 + iy_2, \tag{64}$$

then

$$z_1 + z_2 = (x_1 + x_2) + i(y_1 + y_2). \tag{65}$$

Thus OQ, the vector sum of OP_1 and OP_2 according to the paral-

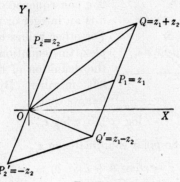

Fig. 2.

lelogram law, represents the algebraic sum of z_1 and z_2. Similarly OQ', the vector difference $OP_1 - OP_2$, obtained by adding OP_2 reversed or $OP_2' = -z_2$ to OP_1 vectorially, represents $z_1 - z_2$.

For products and quotients, we introduce the polar coordinates shown in Fig. 1. Then by Eqs. (53) and (14) we have

$$z_1 = r_1(\cos \theta_1 + i \sin \theta_1) = r_1 e^{i\theta_1}, \tag{66}$$
$$z_2 = r_2(\cos \theta_2 + i \sin \theta_2) = r_2 e^{i\theta_2}. \tag{67}$$

It follows that for the product

$$z_1 z_2 = r_1 r_2 e^{i(\theta_1 + \theta_2)} = r_1 r_2 [\cos (\theta_1 + \theta_2) + i \sin (\theta_1 + \theta_2)]. \tag{68}$$

Furthermore for the quotient

$$\frac{z_1}{z_2} = \frac{r_1}{r_2} e^{i(\theta_1 - \theta_2)} = \frac{r_1}{r_2} [\cos (\theta_1 - \theta_2) + i \sin (\theta_1 - \theta_2)]. \tag{69}$$

These results also follow from Eqs. (56) and (63).

Equation (68) shows that, if OP is the vector for the product and if OU is the vector to the point $1 = 1 + 0i$, then the triangle OP_2P is similar in sense and shape to the triangle OUP_1. Equation (69) shows that if OQ is the vector for the quotient, then the triangle OP_2Q is similar in sense and shape to the triangle OP_1U. This fact may be used as the basis for a geometric method of multiplying and dividing complex numbers.

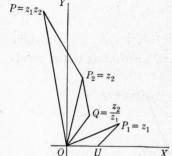

FIG. 3.

7. Powers and Roots. The relation

$$(e^w)^a = e^{aw} \qquad (70)$$

is a consequence of Eq. (10) when a is an integer or rational number. For other values of a, real or complex, this equation may be used as the definition of the power in the left member. By Eq. (60), it follows that

$$\log (z^a) = a \log z. \qquad (71)$$

If we introduce the polar coordinates of z,

$$z = r(\cos \theta + i \sin \theta) = re^{i\theta}. \qquad (72)$$

And, by Eqs. (56) and (58)

$$\log z = \log r + i(\theta_0 + 2k\pi). \qquad (73)$$

Hence

$$\log (z^a) = a \log z = a[\log r + i(\theta_0 + 2k\pi)]. \qquad (74)$$

If a is an irrational or complex number, each value of k will lead to a distinct value of z^a, and there will be an infinite number of values of the power.

If n is an integer, positive or negative, kn is an integer and

$$\log (z^n) = n \log r + in\theta = n \log r + i(n\theta_0 + 2kn\pi). \qquad (75)$$

Thus only one value of the power is obtained, namely,

$$z^n = r^n e^{in\theta} = r^n(\cos n\theta + i \sin n\theta), \\ n = 0, 1, 2, \cdots \text{ or } -1, -2, \cdots. \qquad (76)$$

This is known as *De Moivre's theorem* and could have been obtained directly from Eq. (72).

If m is a positive integer, for the mth root or $(1/m)$th power we have

$$\log (z^{1/m}) = \frac{1}{m} \log r + i\,\frac{\theta}{m} = \frac{1}{m} \log r + i\left(\frac{\theta_0 + 2k\pi}{m}\right). \quad (77)$$

This makes

$$z^{1/m} = r^{1/m}\left(\cos\frac{\theta_0 + 2k\pi}{m} + i\,\sin\frac{\theta_0 + 2k\pi}{m}\right),$$
$$m \text{ is a positive integer, } k = 0, 1, 2, 3, \cdots, m - 1. \quad (78)$$

This choice leads to m distinct values, and every other integral value of k leads to a value of the root equal to one of these. Thus a complex number ($\neq 0$) has m distinct mth roots.

For example, if $m = 4$ and $z = -16$, we have

$$z = -16 = 16(\cos\pi + i\,\sin\pi) = 16e^{i\pi}. \quad (79)$$

With $\theta_0 = \pi$, the four values of θ in Eq. (78) are

$$\frac{\pi}{4}, \frac{3\pi}{4}, \frac{5\pi}{4}, \frac{7\pi}{4} \text{ radians or, in degrees, } 45°, 135°, 225°, 315°. \quad (80)$$

Thus the four values of the fourth root of -16 are

$$\sqrt{2} + i\,\sqrt{2}. \qquad -\sqrt{2} + i\,\sqrt{2}, \qquad -\sqrt{2} - i\,\sqrt{2},$$
and
$$\sqrt{2} - i\,\sqrt{2}. \quad (81)$$

8. Inverse Trigonometric Functions. If $\sin^{-1} z$ is the function inverse to the function $\sin z$, then

$$w = \sin^{-1} z \qquad \text{implies that } z = \sin w. \quad (82)$$

Hence, by Eq. (16),

$$z = \frac{e^{iw} - e^{-iw}}{2i} \qquad \text{and} \qquad e^{iw} - 2iz - e^{-iw} = 0. \quad (83)$$

We may write this in the form

$$(e^{iw})^2 - 2iz(e^{iw}) - 1 = 0, \quad (84)$$

a quadratic equation in e^{iw}, whose solution is

$$e^{iw} = iz + \sqrt{1 - z^2}. \quad (85)$$

This shows that

$$\sin^{-1} z = -i \log (iz + \sqrt{1 - z^2}). \quad (86)$$

By a similar procedure we may deduce from Eq. (17) that

$$\cos^{-1} z = -i \log (z + \sqrt{z^2 - 1}), \tag{87}$$

and from Eq. (19) that

$$\tan^{-1} z = \frac{i}{2} \log \frac{1 - iz}{1 + iz}. \tag{88}$$

The rules of differentiation for these functions are similar in form to those which hold when the variables are real, namely,

$$\frac{d(\sin^{-1} z)}{dz} = \frac{1}{\sqrt{1 - z^2}}, \quad \text{where } \sqrt{1 - z^2} = \cos (\sin^{-1} z), \tag{89}$$

$$\frac{d(\cos^{-1} z)}{dz} = \frac{-1}{\sqrt{1 - z^2}}, \quad \text{where } \sqrt{1 - z^2} = \sin (\cos^{-1} z), \tag{90}$$

$$\frac{d(\tan^{-1} z)}{dz} = \frac{1}{1 + z^2}. \tag{91}$$

These may be derived either from Eqs. (86), (87), and (88) or by using Eq. (59) and the relations of the type of Eq. (82). The latter method of reasoning shows that in Eq. (89)

$$\sqrt{1 - z^2} = \cos w,$$

and in Eq. (90) $\sqrt{1 - z^2} = \sin w$. These supplementary relations determine which square root is to be taken.

9. Inverse Hyperbolic Functions. A discussion like that of Sec. 8, based on Eqs. (34) and (43) shows that

$$\sinh^{-1} z = \log (z + \sqrt{1 + z^2}), \tag{92}$$

$$\cosh^{-1} z = \log (z + \sqrt{z^2 - 1}), \tag{93}$$

$$\tanh^{-1} z = \frac{1}{2} \log \frac{1 + z}{1 - z}, \tag{94}$$

and that their derivatives are given by

$$\frac{d(\sinh^{-1} z)}{dz} = \frac{1}{\sqrt{1 + z^2}}, \quad \text{where } \sqrt{1 + z^2} = \cosh (\sinh^{-1} z), \tag{95}$$

$$\frac{d(\cosh^{-1} z)}{dz} = \frac{1}{\sqrt{z^2 - 1}}, \quad \text{where } \sqrt{z^2 - 1} = \sinh (\cosh^{-1} z), \tag{96}$$

$$\frac{d(\tanh^{-1} z)}{dz} = \frac{1}{1 - z^2}. \tag{97}$$

The additional conditions in Eqs. (95) and (96) determine which square root is to be used. For z and w real, the positive root is always to be taken in Eqs. (92) and (95). For z real and greater than unity, $\cosh^{-1} z$ is usually taken as positive and this leads to the positive root in Eq. (96).

10. Mean Value Theorems. It is a geometric fact that on any arc of a smooth plane curve, there is always some intermediate point at which the tangent is parallel to the chord. If the arc is part of the graph of $y = f(x)$, with end points P and Q, we may write

$$P = a, f(a); \qquad Q = b, f(b). \qquad (98)$$

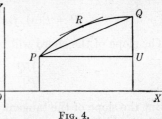

For the slope of the chord we have

$$\frac{UQ}{PU} = \frac{f(b) - f(a)}{b - a}. \qquad (99)$$

Fig. 4.

But the slope of the tangent to the curved arc at any point $x, f(x)$ is $dy/dx = f'(x)$. Hence if ξ is the x coordinate of one point R where the tangent is parallel to the chord or has the same slope, we shall have

$$\frac{f(b) - f(a)}{b - a} = f'(\xi). \qquad (100)$$

That *there is always some ξ with $a < \xi < b$ satisfying this relation for any differentiable function $f(x)$* is known as the *mean value theorem*.

When $f(a) = f(b) = 0$, there is some ξ with $a < \xi < b$ and such that $f'(\xi) = 0$. This special case is known as *Rolle's theorem*.

If we set

$$b = a + h \qquad \text{and} \qquad \xi = a + \theta h, \qquad (101)$$

we have

$$b - a = h > 0. \qquad (102)$$

Also the relation

$$a < \xi < b \qquad \text{implies that } 0 < \theta h < h. \qquad (103)$$

Hence

$$0 < \theta < 1. \qquad (104)$$

By using Eqs. (101) and (102) we may rewrite Eq. (100) in

the form

$$f(a + h) - f(a) = hf'(a + \theta h). \tag{105}$$

That *there always is some θ with $0 < \theta < 1$ satisfying this relation for any differentiable function $f(x)$* is known as the *law of finite increments*.

If the arc in Fig. 4 is part of a curve with parametric equations

$$x = F(t), \qquad y = f(t) \tag{106}$$

with $t = a$ at P and $t = b$ at Q, we shall have

$$P = F(a), f(a); \qquad Q = F(b), f(b). \tag{107}$$

The slope of the chord will be

$$\frac{UQ}{PU} = \frac{f(b) - f(a)}{F(b) - F(a)}. \tag{108}$$

But the slope of the tangent to the curved arc at any point $F(t)$, $f(t)$ at which $F'(t) \neq 0$, is

$$\frac{dy}{dx} = \frac{dy/dt}{dx/dt} = \frac{f'(t)}{F'(t)}. \tag{109}$$

Let us assume that for all t with $a < t < b$, $F'(t) \neq 0$. Then, if $t = \xi$ at one point R where the tangent is parallel to the chord, with $a < \xi < b$, we shall have $F'(\xi) \neq 0$ and

$$\frac{f(b) - f(a)}{F(b) - F(a)} = \frac{f'(\xi)}{F'(\xi)}. \tag{110}$$

That *there is always some ξ with $a < \xi < b$ satisfying this relation for any two differentiable functions $f(t)$ and $F(t)$ with $F'(t) \neq 0$ for $a < t < b$* is known as *Cauchy's generalized mean value theorem*.

A generalization of the law of finite increments [Eq. (105)], applicable to functions possessing derivatives of all orders, is

$$f(a + h) = f(a) + hf'(a) + \frac{h^2}{2!}f''(a) + \cdots + \frac{h^n}{n!}f^{(n)}(a)$$

$$+ \frac{h^{n+1}}{(n + 1)!}f^{(n+1)}(a + \theta h), \qquad \text{with } 0 < \theta < 1. \tag{111}$$

If we change variables in accordance with Eq. (101), we may write it as follows:

$$f(b) = f(a) + (b - a)f'(a) + \frac{(b - a)^2}{2!} f''(a) + \cdots$$

$$+ \frac{(b - a)^n}{n!} f^{(n)}(a) + \frac{(b - a)^{n+1}}{(n + 1)!} f^{(n+1)}(\xi), \quad \text{with } a < \xi < b. \quad (112)$$

This relation may be established by applying Rolle's theorem to the function

$$F(x) = -f(b) + f(x) + (b - x)f'(x) + \frac{(b - x)^2}{2!} f''(x) + \cdots$$

$$+ \frac{(b - x)^n}{n!} f^{(n)}(x) + \frac{(b - x)^{n+1}}{(n + 1)!} A, \quad (113)$$

where A is a constant defined by the relation

$$0 = F(a) = -f(b) + f(a) + (b - a)f'(a) + \frac{(b - a)^2}{2!} f''(a)$$

$$+ \cdots + \frac{(b - a)^n}{n!} f^{(n)}(a) + \frac{(b - a)^{n+1}}{(n + 1)!} A. \quad (114)$$

The value of the derivative of $F(x)$ is

$$F'(x) = \frac{(b - x)^n}{n!} f^{(n+1)}(x) - \frac{(b - x)^n}{n!} A, \quad (115)$$

since the other terms cancel in pairs.

But when $x = b$, $F(b)$ is zero by Eq. (113). And when $x = a$, $F(a)$ is zero by Eq. (114). Hence we may apply Rolle's theorem to $F(x)$ and deduce that for some ξ such that $a < \xi < b$, $F'(\xi) = 0$. Consequently by Eq. (115),

$$0 = F'(\xi) = \frac{(b - \xi)^n}{n!} [f^{(n+1)}(\xi) - A] \quad \text{and} \quad A = f^{(n+1)}(\xi). \quad (116)$$

If we now insert this value of A in Eq. (114), we have merely to transpose $f(b)$ to obtain Eq. (112).

This proves Eq. (112) as well as Eq. (111), which differed from it only by a change of variable.

In Eq. (112) we may think of b as a variable, replace it by x, and rewrite the equation in the form

$$f(x) = f(a) + (x - a)f'(a) + \frac{(x - a)^2}{2!} f''(a) + \cdots$$

$$+ \frac{(x - a)^n}{n!} f^{(n)}(a) + \frac{(x - a)^{n+1}}{(n + 1)!} f^{(n+1)}(\xi), \quad \text{with } a < \xi < x. \quad (117)$$

This expansion, or the equivalent form (111), is known as *Taylor's theorem with the remainder.*

An alternative form is obtained by starting with

$$\int_0^{b-a} f'(b-x)dx = -f(b-x)\Big|_0^{b-a} = f(b) - f(a), \quad (118)$$

and integrating the left member by parts,

$$\int_0^{b-a} f'(b-x)dx = f'(b-x)x \Big|_0^{b-a} + \int_0^{b-a} f''(b-x)x \, dx$$

$$= f'(a)(b-a) + \int_0^{b-a} f''(b-x)x \, dx. \quad (119)$$

If we repeatedly apply integration by parts, we find

$$f(b) = f(a) + (b-a)f'(a) + \frac{(b-a)^2}{2!} f''(a) + \cdots$$

$$\dashv \frac{(b-a)^n}{n!} f^{(n)}(a) + \int_0^{b-a} f^{(n+1)}(b-x)\frac{x^n}{n!} dx. \quad (120)$$

By using the change of variables (101) we may rewrite this in the form

$$f(a+h) = f(a) + hf'(a) + \frac{h^2}{2!} f''(a) + \cdots$$

$$+ \frac{h^n}{n!} f^{(n)}(a) + \int_0^h f^{(n+1)}(a+h-x)\frac{x^n}{n!} dx. \quad (121)$$

Either of the two preceding equations is an expression of the alternative form of Taylor's theorem with the remainder that we were seeking.   In each of Eqs. (111), (112), (120), and (121) the last term is known as the *remainder term.*

11. Taylor's Series for Complex Values. In a few simple cases it may be shown that as n becomes infinite, the remainder term in Eq. (117) approaches zero.   In this way it may be shown that, for all real values of x,

$$e^x = 1 + x + \frac{x^2}{2!} + \frac{x^3}{3!} + \cdots, \quad (122)$$

$$\sin x = x - \frac{x^3}{3!} + \frac{x^5}{5!} - \frac{x^7}{7!} + \cdots, \quad (123)$$

$$\cos x = 1 - \frac{x^2}{2!} + \frac{x^4}{4!} - \frac{x^6}{6!} + \cdots. \quad (124)$$

However, there is a simple process for determining a circle C which is applicable to many of the series met in practice.

Let us first suppose that, in the power series,

$$A_0 + A_1(z - \alpha) + A_2(z - \alpha)^2 + A_3(z - \alpha)^3 + \cdots, \quad (146)$$

the absolute value of the ratio of successive coefficients $|A_n/A_{n-1}|$ approaches a finite limit L, not zero, as n increases indefinitely. Thus

$$\lim_{n \to \infty} \left| \frac{A_n}{A_{n-1}} \right| = L \neq 0. \quad (147)$$

Then the series (146) will converge for any z such that

$$|z - \alpha| < \frac{1}{L}. \quad (148)$$

For this makes the limit of the ratio of the numerical values of successive terms in the series (146)

$$\lim_{n \to \infty} \frac{|A_n(z - \alpha)^n|}{|A_{n-1}(z - \alpha)^{n-1}|} = L|z - \alpha| < 1, \quad (149)$$

and is related to the fact that the geometric series

$$a + ar + ar^2 + \cdots + ar^n + \cdots, \quad (150)$$

with ratio of terms constantly equal to r, converges when $|r| < 1$.

Incidentally, just as the foregoing series (150) fails to converge when $|r| > 1$, so the series (146) diverges if $|z - \alpha| > 1/L$. Thus $1/L$ is the radius of the largest possible circle C.

For example, each of the series (125), (126), and (127) has $L = 1$ and hence will converge if $|x| < 1$.

If the series (146) is such that

$$\lim_{n \to \infty} \left| \frac{A_n}{A_{n-1}} \right| = 0, \quad (151)$$

then the series will converge for all values of the variable. The series (122) is an example.

If certain terms of the series are missing and the terms from the mth on are

$$A_m(z - \alpha)^m + A_{m+k}(z - \alpha)^{m+k}$$
$$+ A_{m+2k}(z - \alpha)^{m+2k} + \cdots, \quad (152)$$

And, for all real x with $|x| < 1$,

$$\frac{1}{1 + x} = 1 - x + x^2 - x^3 + \cdots, \quad (125)$$

$$\log(1 + x) = x - \frac{x^2}{2} + \frac{x^3}{3} - \frac{x^4}{4} + \cdots, \quad (126)$$

$$(1 + x)^k = 1 + kx + \frac{k(k - 1)}{2!} x^2 + \frac{k(k - 1)(k - 2)}{3!} x^3 + \cdots. \quad (127)$$

In the last case the series reduces to a finite sum if k is a positive integer, since all terms after the $(k + 1)$st contain the factor $k - k = 0$.

However, a much deeper insight into the behavior of Taylor's series may be gained by using some results of the theory of functions of a complex variable, which we shall briefly recapitulate.

We begin with some definitions.

Let $\alpha = a + bi$ be any point of the complex plane, and let C denote a circle of radius R with center at α. Then the condition for any point $z = x + iy$ to be inside the circle C is

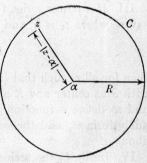

FIG. 5.

$$(x - a)^2 + (y - b)^2 < R^2. \quad (128)$$

But, since

$$z - \alpha = x + iy - (a + bi) = (x - a) + i(y - b), \quad (129)$$

by Eq. (54) its absolute value is given by

$$|z - \alpha| = \sqrt{(x - a)^2 + (y - b)^2}. \quad (130)$$

Consequently relation (128), the condition that z be inside C, may be written

$$|z - \alpha| < R. \quad (131)$$

A function of a complex variable z, $f(z)$, is said to be analytic in the circle C if a single value of $f(z)$ is defined for each z inside the circle C, and the function $f(z)$ has a finite derivative $f'(z)$ at each point z.

A function is said to be analytic at z if it is analytic in some circle C including z as an interior point.

The results referred to, which we shall state here as theorems without proof, are

I. If a function is analytic at z, it has higher derivatives of all orders at z.

II. If a function is analytic in C, for all points in C the Taylor's series about the center α converges to the function, so that

$$f(z) = f(\alpha) + f'(\alpha)(z - \alpha) + \frac{f''(\alpha)}{2!}(z - \alpha)^2 + \frac{f'''(\alpha)}{3!}(z - \alpha)^3 + \cdots, \quad (132)$$

for all z such that $|z - \alpha| < R$.

A power series is a series of the form,

$$A_0 + A_1(z - \alpha) + A_2(z - \alpha)^2 + A_3(z - \alpha)^3 + \cdots. \quad (133)$$

III. If a power series (133) converges for any one value of z, say z_2, where $z_2 \neq \alpha$, and

$$R = |z_2 - \alpha|, \quad (134)$$

then for all z_1 such that $|z_1 - \alpha| < R$, that is inside the circle C with α as center and R as radius, the series (133) will converge and so define a function $f(z)$. This function $f(z)$ is necessarily analytic in C, and the series (133) must be its Taylor's series about α.

IV. Inside C the series (133) may be differentiated or integrated termwise. That is, if

$$f(z) = A_0 + A_1(z - \alpha) + A_2(z - \alpha)^2 + A_3(z - \alpha)^3 + \cdots, \quad (135)$$

then

$$f'(z) = A_1 + 2A_2(z - \alpha) + 3A_3(z - \alpha)^2 + \cdots \quad (136)$$

and

$$\int_\alpha^z f(z)dz = A_0(z - \alpha) + \frac{A_1}{2}(z - \alpha)^2 + \frac{A_2}{3}(z - \alpha)^3 + \cdots. \quad (137)$$

In the last equation the integral is defined by

$$\int_\alpha^z f(z)dz = F(z)\Big|_\alpha^z = F(z) - F(\alpha), \quad (138)$$

where $F(z)$ is any function such that for all z inside C,

$$f(z) = F'(z) = \frac{dF}{dz}. \quad (13$$

The statement in Theorem III that a power series is nece sarily the Taylor's series of its sum function may be deduced fro the possibility of termwise differentiation mentioned in Theore IV. For, if Eq. (135) holds, we may deduce Eq. (136) and b repeated differentiation obtain

$$f''(z) = 2A_2 + 3 \cdot 2A_3(z - \alpha) + \cdots, \quad (14($$
$$f'''(z) = 3 \cdot 2A_3 + \cdots, \quad (14$$
$$\cdots \cdots \cdots \cdots \cdots$$

Let us next put $z = \alpha$ in each of Eqs. (135), (136), (140), an (141). The results are

$$f(\alpha) = A_0, \quad f'(\alpha) = A_1, \quad f''(\alpha) = 2!A_2, \quad f'''(\alpha) = 3!A_3 \cdots \quad (14$$

These equations show that

$$A_0 = f(\alpha), \quad A_1 = f'(\alpha), \quad A_2 = \frac{f''(\alpha)}{2!},$$
$$A_3 = \frac{f'''(\alpha)}{3!}, \quad \cdots \quad (14$$

But, if these values are substituted in Eq. (135), it becom identical with Eq. (132).

Since a power series is always the Taylor's series of its su all methods of expanding a function in a series of increasi powers of $(z - \alpha)$ will lead to the same series. In particul we may conclude from an equation of the type

$$A_0 + A_1(z - \alpha) + A_2(z - \alpha)^2 + \cdots = B_0 + B_1(z - \alpha) + B_2(z - \alpha)^2 + \cdots, \quad (14$$

that

$$A_0 = B_0, \quad A_1 = B_1, \quad A_2 = B_2, \quad \cdots \quad (14$$

In fact, the same conclusion holds if the relation (144) is kno to be true when α and z are restricted to real values.

We can often determine possible circles C for a given pow series from Theorem II, if the properties of the sum function known. Or we may use Theorem III, if a value z_2 can be fou

with

$$\lim_{n \to \infty} \left| \frac{A_{m+nk}}{A_{m+(n-1)k}} \right| = L_k, \qquad (153)$$

the series will converge if

$$\lim_{n \to \infty} \frac{|A_{m+nk}(z - \alpha)^{m+nk}|}{|A_{m+(n-1)k}(z + \alpha)^{m+(n-1)k}|} = L|z - \alpha|^k < 1. \qquad (154)$$

That is, if

$$|z - \alpha| < L_k^{-1/k} \qquad \text{when } L_k \neq 0, \qquad (155)$$

and for all values of z if $L_k = 0$. The series (123) and (124) are examples of the last case, with $L_2 = 0$.

The discussion of the function e^z in Sec. 2 is consistent with the results of this section. For example, Eq. (21) shows that e^z is analytic for all finite values of z and that the higher derivatives of Theorem I are

$$f'(z) = f''(z) = f'''(z) = \cdots = e^z. \qquad (156)$$

In particular

$$f'(0) = f''(0) = f'''(0) = \cdots = e^0 = 1. \qquad (157)$$

Consequently for $\alpha = 0$, the Taylor's development (132) of Theorem II reduces to

$$e^z = 1 + z + \frac{z^2}{2!} + \frac{z^3}{3!} + \cdots , \qquad (158)$$

or the defining Eq. (7).

On the other hand, if it is known that the series in the right member of Eq. (122) converges for all, and hence for arbitrarily large, real values of x, it follows from Theorem III that the right member of Eq. (158) equals a function analytic for all values of z and having this as its Taylor's expansion. This explains why it was practical to use this series as the definition of e^z for complex values of z.

Similar considerations apply to the functions $\sin z$ and $\cos z$. Like e^z, these are analytic for all finite values of z.

12. Singular Points. For a given function, a value of z that cannot be included in any circle C where the function is analytic is called a *singular point*. The function is said to have a *singularity* at this point. For the elementary functions the singular points include those values which make the function or its derivative infinite owing to the presence of a zero in the denominator. For example, $z = 0$ is a singular point of $1/z$, and also of $\log z$ which has $1/z$ as its derivative. For each of these functions $z = 0$ is the only finite singular point. For any nonintegral power, z^a as defined in Sec. 7 has $z = 0$ as a singular point. For, by Eq. (71),

$$z^a = e^{a \log z}. \tag{159}$$

It follows from this by Eqs. (21), (24), and (62) that

$$\frac{d(z^a)}{dz} = e^{a \log z} \cdot a \cdot \frac{1}{z} = az^{a-1}. \tag{160}$$

Consequently, the kth derivative is

$$\frac{d^k(z^a)}{dz^k} = a(a - 1)(a - 2) \cdots (a - k + 1)z^{a-k}. \tag{161}$$

This has z^{k-a} in the denominator, and this is zero for $z = 0$ if k is sufficiently large. Hence z^a must have a singularity at 0, since if it were analytic at 0 it would have all its higher derivatives finite for $z = 0$ by Theorem I. The function z^a has no other finite singularity.

More complicated composite elementary functions will always be analytic for any value of z that does not make some denominator, function raised to a power, or one whose logarithm is taken, equal to zero. Such functions will usually have singularities at the excepted places, although sometimes this is not the case. For example,

$$\left(\frac{1}{z}\right)z^2 = z \qquad \text{and} \qquad (z^{1/2})^4 = z^2 \tag{162}$$

are each analytic at $z = 0$, although this is a singularity of $1/z$ and $z^{1/2}$. We here assume either that no inverse trigonometric or hyperbolic functions occur or, if they are present to begin with, that they are expressed in terms of logarithms and roots by the formulas in Secs. 8 and 9.

Let us apply the remarks just made to the inverse functions themselves. From Eqs. (86), (87), and (88) we see that $\sin^{-1} z$ and $\cos^{-1} z$ have singularities at $z = \pm 1$, while $\tan^{-1} z$ has singularities at $z = \pm i$. This could also be deduced from Eqs. (89), (90), and (91). Similarly, by using Eqs. (92,) (93), and (94) or

Eqs. (95), (96), and (97) we see that $\sinh^{-1} z$ has singularities at $\pm i$, $\cosh^{-1} z$ has singularities at ± 1, and $\tanh^{-1} z$ has singularities at ± 1. Either argument shows that the inverse functions have no other finite singularities.

If $f(z)$ has a singularity at z_0, we must take α different from z_0 in the Taylor's expansion (132). Suppose that there are no singularities inside the circle C about α of radius $|z_0 - \alpha|$. Then the expansion will converge to the function $f(z)$ for all z in C. It may or may not converge for a point on the circumference of C. However, if it does converge at such a point it will equal $f(z)$ at that point. The expansion cannot converge at any point outside of the circle C, since in that case by Theorem III it would define a function equal to $f(z)$ inside of C and having no singularity at z_0, contrary to our hypothesis.

The argument just given shows that the function $1/z$ cannot be expanded about zero but that, if it is expanded about 1, the resulting series will converge for $|z - 1| < |0 - 1|$ or 1. To save writing, let us put

$$z - 1 = Z \quad \text{and} \quad \frac{1}{z} = \frac{1}{1 + Z}. \tag{163}$$

Then we have the Taylor's expansion

$$\frac{1}{1 + Z} = 1 - Z + Z^2 - Z^3 + \cdots, \quad \text{for } |Z| < 1. \tag{164}$$

For z real and $z - 1 = Z$ replaced by x, this reduces to Eq. (125).

Similar considerations apply to Eqs. (126) and (127) if in the latter k is not a positive integer. The expansion (126) may be obtained from Eq. (125) by termwise integration, using Theorem IV, Eq. (137). Again, let us put $Z = x^2$ in Eq. (164), obtaining

$$\frac{1}{1 + x^2} = 1 - x^2 + x^4 - x^6 + \cdots, \quad \text{for } |x| < 1. \tag{165}$$

We note that the function on the left has singularities when the denominator is zero, so that

$$1 + x^2 = 0 \quad \text{and} \quad x = i \text{ or } -i. \tag{166}$$

Each of these points is at unit distance from the origin, which explains why the series converges only for $|x| < 1$. Since the function is analytic for all real values of x, these limitations on x

cannot be predicted by considering the function for real values only. By integrating the series (165) termwise in accordance with Eq. (137), we find

$$\tan^{-1} x = x - \frac{x^3}{3} + \frac{x^5}{5} - \frac{x^7}{7} + \cdots, \qquad \text{for } |x| < 1. \quad (167)$$

13. Operations with Taylor's Series. By starting with the series (122) through (127) and operating as we would with polynomials, we may derive the following expansions:

$$\sin^2 x = x^2 - \frac{x^4}{3} + \cdots, \tag{168}$$

$$\sin^3 x = x^3 - \frac{x^5}{2} + \cdots, \tag{169}$$

$$e^{x^2} = 1 + x^2 + \frac{x^4}{2!} + \frac{x^6}{3!} + \cdots, \tag{170}$$

and

$$\cos(\sin x) = 1 - \frac{x^2}{2} + \frac{5}{24} x^4 + \cdots. \tag{171}$$

These are valid for all values of x. Also,

$$\cos^k x = 1 - \frac{k}{2} x^2 + \frac{k(3k-2)}{24} x^4 + \cdots, \qquad |x| < \frac{\pi}{2}. \quad (172)$$

Here we obtain (168) by multiplying the right member of (123) by itself, and then (169) by multiplying the result by the original right member. Again, if we replace the x in Eq. (122) by x^2, we obtain (170). To obtain Eq. (171), we replace the x in Eq. (124) by $\sin x$, and then express $\sin x$ and its powers in terms of powers of x by using Eqs. (123), (168), and (169). Finally, if we replace the x in Eq. (127) by the terms that follow the 1 in Eq. (124), we obtain Eq. (172). The powers of the series are found by successive multiplication in a manner similar to that used for Eqs. (168) and (169). The restriction on x in Eq. (172) follows from the fact that unless k is 0 or a positive integer, $\cos^k x$ has singular points for all values of x which make $\cos x = 0$, and of these the values $\pm\pi/2$ are nearest to 0.

For quotients of expansions, we may use either ordinary long division or the expansion (125). For example, from Eqs. (124)

and (125) we find

$$\sec x = \frac{1}{\cos x} = 1 + \frac{x^2}{2} + \frac{5}{24} x^4 + \cdots, \qquad |x| < \frac{\pi}{2}. \quad (173)$$

This may be checked by putting $k = -1$ in Eq. (172).

We may deduce from Eqs. (123) and (173) by multiplication the expansion

$$\tan x = \sin x \cdot \frac{1}{\cos x} = x + \frac{x^3}{3} + \cdots, \qquad |x| < \frac{\pi}{2}. \quad (174)$$

The method used to derive Eq. (172) from Eqs. (124) and (127) may be used for any function of a function. However, to expand $f[g(x)]$ in powers of $(x - a)$, we must first expand $f(u)$ in powers of $(u - b)$ where $b = g(a)$. For this makes $u - b = g(x) - g(a)$, which is zero when $x = a$. Consequently the expansion of $u - b$ in powers of $(x - a)$ will have no constant term. For example, let us find the series for $e^{\cos x}$ in powers of x. Here $a = 0$ and $b = \cos 0 = 1$. Hence we require the series for e^u in powers of $(u - 1)$, or

$$e^u = e \cdot e^{u-1} = e \left[1 + (u - 1) + \frac{(u - 1)^2}{2!} + \frac{(u - 1)^3}{3!} + \cdots \right]. \quad (175)$$

The right member, here obtained by using Eqs. (10) and (7), could of course be calculated directly by using Eqs. (132) and (21). We next deduce from Eq. (124) that

$$u - 1 = \cos x - 1 = -\frac{x^2}{2!} + \frac{x^4}{4!} - \frac{x^6}{6!} + \cdots. \quad (176)$$

If we now calculate the successive powers of this and insert them in the right member of Eq. (175), we find that

$$e^{\cos x} = e \left(1 - \frac{x^2}{2!} + 4 \frac{x^4}{4!} - 31 \frac{x^6}{6!} + \cdots \right). \quad (177)$$

This is the desired expansion and is valid for all x.

Some power series may be conveniently found by the method of undetermined coefficients or by use of the principle expressed in Eqs. (144) and (145). We shall illustrate this for the function inverse to $y(x)$. If $y = a$ when $x = b$, there will be a development

$$y - a = B_1(x - b) + B_2(x - b)^2 + \cdots, \quad (178)$$

which we assume to be known.

To obtain the development for the inverse function, we assume the expansion

$$(x - b) = A_1(y - a) + A_2(y - a)^2 + \cdots \qquad (179)$$

with unknown coefficients. We substitute this in the known development (178) and so deduce

$$(y - a) = B_1[A_1(y - a) + A_2(y - a)^2 + \cdots]$$
$$+ B_2[A_1{}^2(y - a)^2 + \cdots] + \cdots . \qquad (180)$$

We may now equate coefficients of like powers of $(y - a)$ to obtain

$$1 = B_1 A_1, \qquad 0 = B_1 A_2 + B_2 A_1{}^2, \cdots . \qquad (181)$$

These equations determine the unknown A_i successively as

$$A_1 = \frac{1}{B_1}, \qquad A_2 = -\frac{B_2}{B_1{}^3}, \qquad \cdots . \qquad (182)$$

As a specific example, with $a = b = 0$, from

$$y = \sin x = x - \frac{x^3}{3!} + \cdots , \qquad (183)$$

we may obtain the development for the inverse function

$$x = \sin^{-1} y = y + \frac{y^3}{3!} + \cdots , \qquad |y| < 1. \qquad (184)$$

The limitation on y is found from the singularities of $\sin^{-1} y$.

We may check the last expansion by termwise integration of the series

$$\frac{1}{\sqrt{1 - y^2}} = (1 - y^2)^{-\frac{1}{2}} = 1 + \frac{y^2}{2} + \cdots , \qquad |y| < 1. \quad (185)$$

This last series may be found either directly from Eq. (132) or by putting $x = y^2$ and $k = -\frac{1}{2}$ in Eq. (127).

14. Newton's Method of Solving Equations. The development of inverse functions given by Eqs. (179) and (182) may be applied to the problem of solving any equation in one variable involving algebraic or transcendental functions, provided that the functions are analytic for values of the variable near the root sought. We assume the equation written in the form

$$f(x) = 0, \tag{186}$$

where $f(x)$ is an analytic function.

Let us suppose that r_1 is a known approximate value of the root. Then if we write $y = f(x)$, we may form the Taylor's expansion about r_1, namely,

$$y = f(x) = f(r_1) + f'(r_1)(x - r_1) + \frac{f''(r_1)}{2!}(x - r_1)^2 + \cdots . \tag{187}$$

Using the method applied to Eq. (179), we may deduce from this that

$$x - r_1 = \frac{1}{f'(r_1)}[y - f(r_1)] - \frac{f''(r_1)}{2[f'(r_1)]^3}[y - f(r_1)]^2 \cdots . \tag{188}$$

If the exact value of the root approximated by r_1 is r,

$$f(r) = 0, \quad \text{and} \quad y = 0, x = r \tag{189}$$

are values satisfying Eq. (187), and hence (188). On substituting these values in the latter equation, we find

$$r - r_1 = -\frac{f(r_1)}{f'(r_1)} - \frac{f''(r_1)}{2[f'(r_1)]^3}[f(r_1)]^2 + \cdots . \tag{190}$$

Since r_1 is an approximation to r, $f(r_1)$ will approximate zero and hence be small compared with unity. Consequently the higher powers of $f(r_1)$ will be small compared with the first power. Neglecting these higher powers, and denoting the resulting solution of Eq. (190) for r by r_2, we find

$$r_2 = r_1 - \frac{f(r_1)}{f'(r_1)}, \tag{191}$$

as a second approximation to the root. The process may be repeated for increased accuracy. Usually, if r_1 is correct to n decimal places, $f(r_1)/f'(r_1)$ will be less than $1/10^n$. Hence $[f(r_1)/f'(r_1)]^2$ will be less than $1/10^{2n}$, and the new approximation will be correct to nearly $2n$ decimal places.

We illustrate the procedure for the algebraic equation

$$x^2 = 2. \tag{192}$$

Here we have

$$x^2 - 2 = 0, \qquad f(x) = x^2 - 2, \qquad f'(x) = 2x. \qquad (193)$$

Thus Eq. (191) for calculating improved approximations becomes

$$r_2 = r_1 - \frac{r_1{}^2 - 2}{2r_1} = \frac{r_1}{2} + \frac{1}{r_1}. \qquad (194)$$

Beginning with $r_1 = 1$, we find for the successive approximations

$$r_1 = 1, \qquad r_2 = 1.5, \qquad r_3 = 1.417, \qquad r_4 = 1.414216,$$
$$r_5 = 1.414214. \qquad (195)$$

The method is valid for complex roots, provided that an approximate value for a root r_1 can be found which makes $|f(r_1)|$ small.

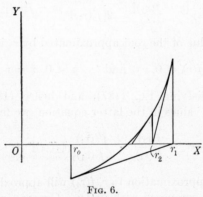

Fig. 6.

In the real case, a rough graph of $y = f(x)$ will usually provide a good approximation to take as r_1. The graph will also show whether it is better to take r_1 in excess or in defect of the true root. In Fig. 6, if we start with r_1, the successive approximations will rapidly decrease to the root. If we start with r_0, the second approximation would be as poor as the first but, since it would be r_1 in the figure, from this point on the approximations would improve. The figure also illustrates the geometric significance of Eq. (191) in that r_2 is the intersection with the x axis of the tangent to $y = f(x)$ at the point for which $x = r_1$.

15. Taylor's Series and the Indeterminate Form 0/0. If $f(x)$ and $F(x)$ each approach zero when x approaches a, the quotient $f(x)/F(x)$ may or may not approach a limit as x approaches a.

Whether there is a limit, and its value if there is one, cannot be predicted without further information about the functions. This situation is briefly described as the indeterminate form 0/0.

Let us first assume that $f(x)$ and $F(x)$ are each analytic at $x = a$ and that $F'(a) \neq 0$. Then on replacing the functions by their Taylor's series, we find

$$\frac{f(x)}{F(x)} = \frac{f(a) + (x - a)f'(a) + \dfrac{(x - a)^2}{2!} f''(a) + \cdots}{F(a) + (x - a) F'(a) + \dfrac{(x - a)^2}{2!} F''(a) + \cdots} \cdot \quad (196)$$

Since $f(x) \to 0$ and $F(x) \to 0$ when $x \to a$, in the Taylor's expansions we must have $f(a) = F(a) = 0$. If we omit these terms and assume that $x \neq a$, we may cancel the factor $(x - a)$ to obtain

$$\frac{f(x)}{F(x)} = \frac{f'(a) + \dfrac{(x - a)}{2!} f''(a) + \cdots}{F'(a) + \dfrac{(x - a)}{2!} F''(a) + \cdots} \cdot \quad (197)$$

It follows from this that

$$\lim_{x \to a} \frac{f(x)}{F(x)} = \frac{f'(a)}{F'(a)}, \qquad \text{when } f(a) = F(a) = 0, F'(a) \neq 0. \quad (198)$$

This is one form of *l'Hospital's rule* for evaluating indeterminate forms.

If $f'(a)$ and $F'(a)$ are also both zero while $F''(a) \neq 0$, we may cancel the factor $(x - a)^2/2!$ in Eq. (196) and deduce that

$$\lim_{x \to a} \frac{f(x)}{F(x)} = \frac{f''(a)}{F''(a)}, \qquad \text{when } f(a) = F(a) = f'(a) = F'(a) = 0,$$
$$F''(a) \neq 0. \quad (199)$$

A similar argument shows that

$$\lim_{x \to a} \frac{f(x)}{F(x)} = \frac{f^{(n)}(a)}{F^{(n)}(a)}, \qquad \text{when } F^{(n)}(a) \neq 0 \quad (200)$$

but

$$f(a) = f'(a) = \cdots = f^{(n-1)}(a) = 0$$

and

$$F(a) = F'(a) = \cdots = F^{(n-1)}(a) = 0.$$

Whenever we have to go beyond the first derivative, if the Taylor's series for $f(x)$ and $F(x)$ are either known or obtainable from known series by the methods of Sec. 13, it is practically simpler to use these directly, as in Eq. (196). For example, from the Taylor's series about zero we find

$$\frac{\sin (x^3) - x^3}{\tan^{-1} (x^3) - x^3} = \frac{x^3 - x^9/3! + \cdots - x^3}{x^3 - x^9/3 + \cdots - x^3}, \tag{201}$$

so that

$$\lim_{x \to 0} \frac{\sin (x^3) - x^3}{\tan^{-1} (x^3) - x^3} = \frac{-1/3!}{-1/3} = \frac{1}{2}. \tag{202}$$

If we had solved this example by means of Eq. (200), it would have been necessary to differentiate nine times.

Since the methods of this section depend on Taylor's series, they are valid for complex values of a or for approach to real values of a through complex values of x.

16. The Indeterminate Form 0/0. If a is a singular point of either $f(x)$ or $F(x)$, the argument of Sec. 15 no longer applies, since a function has no Taylor's expansion about a singularity. However, if a is real and x approaches a through real values greater than a, indicated by writing $x \to a+$, it is true that, if

$$\lim_{x \to a+} f(x) = 0, \qquad \lim_{x \to a+} F(x) = 0, \tag{203}$$

and

$$\lim_{x \to a+} \frac{f'(x)}{F'(x)} = L, \tag{204}$$

then

$$\lim_{x \to a+} \frac{f(x)}{F(x)} = L. \tag{205}$$

We may prove this as follows. By Eq. (204), in some interval $a < x < a + h$, the functions $f(x)$ and $F(x)$ will be differentiable and the arc with

$$x = F(t), \qquad y = f(t) \tag{206}$$

will be smooth. By Eq. (203) its end point at a will be 0,0 and Eq. (206) will hold at $t = a$ if we define $f(a) = 0$ and $F(a) = 0$. We may then write

$$\frac{f(x)}{F(x)} = \frac{f(x) - f(a)}{F(x) - F(a)}. \tag{207}$$

Next we note that, for a suitable ξ with $a < \xi < x$,

$$\frac{f(x) - f(a)}{F(x) - F(a)} = \frac{f'(\xi)}{F'(\xi)}, \tag{208}$$

by Cauchy's generalized mean value theorem [Eq. (110)]. Since ξ is between a and x, when $x \to a+$, $\xi \to a+$. But by Eq. (204),

$$\lim_{\xi \to a+} \frac{f'(\xi)}{F'(\xi)} = L, \tag{209}$$

so that in consequence of the preceding three equations

$$\lim_{x \to a+} \frac{f(x)}{F(x)} = L, \tag{210}$$

as we stated.

The rule of l'Hospital as stated in Eqs. (203), (204), and (205) continues to hold if we replace $x \to a+$ by $x \to a-$ throughout, where $x \to a-$ indicates that x approaches a through real values less than a. Or we may write throughout $x \to a$ to mean that there is no restriction on the sign of $x - a$. Likewise we may apply the rule when $x \to +\infty$, $x \to -\infty$, or $x \to \infty$. This may be shown by putting $y = 1/x$. This makes $y \to 0+$ when $x \to +\infty$ and

$$\lim_{x \to +\infty} \frac{f(x)}{F(x)} = \lim_{y \to 0+} \frac{f\left(\dfrac{1}{y}\right)}{F\left(\dfrac{1}{y}\right)} = \lim_{y \to 0+} \frac{\dfrac{d}{dy} f\left(\dfrac{1}{y}\right)}{\dfrac{d}{dy} F\left(\dfrac{1}{y}\right)}, \tag{211}$$

from the original rule for $y \to 0+$. But if

$$\frac{d}{dx} f(x) = f'(x), \qquad \frac{d}{dy} f\left(\frac{1}{y}\right) = -\frac{1}{y^2} f'\left(\frac{1}{y}\right) = -x^2 f'(x). \tag{212}$$

A similar result holds for $F(x)$. Hence

$$\lim_{y \to 0+} \frac{\dfrac{d}{dy} f\left(\dfrac{1}{y}\right)}{\dfrac{d}{dy} F\left(\dfrac{1}{y}\right)} = \lim_{x \to +\infty} \frac{f'(x)}{F'(x)}. \tag{213}$$

This proves that the rule holds for $x \to +\infty$.

17. The Indeterminate Form ∞ / ∞. If, when $x \to a+$,

$$\lim_{x \to a+} f(x) = \infty, \qquad \lim_{x \to a+} F(x) = \infty, \tag{214}$$

and

$$\lim_{x \to a+} \frac{f'(x)}{F'(x)} = L, \tag{215}$$

then

$$\lim_{x \to a+} \frac{f(x)}{F(x)} = L. \tag{216}$$

This may be proved by noting that for any two values x_1 and x_2, by the Cauchy generalized mean value theorem [Eq. (110)], we have

$$\frac{f(x_2) - f(x_1)}{F(x_2) - F(x_1)} = \frac{f'(\xi)}{F'(\xi)}, \tag{217}$$

where ξ is a suitably chosen number with $x_1 < \xi < x_2$. Let us next write

$$\frac{f(x_2) - f(x_1)}{F(x_2) - F(x_1)} = \frac{f(x_1)}{F(x_1)} \left[\frac{1 - f(x_2)/f(x_1)}{1 - F(x_2)/F(x_1)} \right]. \tag{218}$$

It follows from the last two equations that

$$\frac{f(x_1)}{F(x_1)} = \frac{f'(\xi)}{F'(\xi)} \left[\frac{1 - F(x_2)/F(x_1)}{1 - f(x_2)/f(x_1)} \right]. \tag{219}$$

In view of Eq. (215), we may take x_2 so close to a that, for all x in the interval from a to x_2, the value of $f'(x)/F'(x)$ will be near its limit L. Then, if x_1 is any value between a and x_2, ξ which is

$$a \qquad\qquad x_1 \quad\ \xi \quad\ x_2$$

FIG. 7.

between x_1 and x_2 will be in the interval from a to x_2. Consequently $f'(\xi)/F'(\xi)$, the first factor in the right member of Eq. (219), will be near L. But, having fixed x_2 and hence $F(x_2)$, we may then take x_1 so close to a that $F(x_1)$ is large compared with $F(x_2)$, in view of condition (214). This will make $F(x_2)/F(x_1)$ near zero and $1 - [F(x_2)/F(x_1)]$ near 1. Similarly we may make

$$1 - \left[\frac{f(x_2)}{f(x_1)} \right]$$

near 1. Consequently, the right member of Eq. (219) will be near L when x_1 is sufficiently near to a. That is,

$$\lim_{x \to a+} \frac{f(x)}{F(x)} = L, \tag{220}$$

which is the conclusion stated in Eq. (216).

By similar reasoning the rule may be shown to hold when $x \to a+$ is replaced throughout by $x \to a-$, $x \to a$, $x \to +\infty$, $x \to -\infty$, or $x \to \infty$.

As an application, consider the evaluation of

$$\lim_{x \to +\infty} \frac{3 + \log (x + 1)}{\log (x^2 + 1)}. \tag{221}$$

Here the numerator and denominator each approach $+\infty$ when $x \to +\infty$ and

$$\frac{f'(x)}{F'(x)} = \frac{\dfrac{1}{x + 1}}{\dfrac{2x}{x^2 + 1}} = \frac{x^2 + 1}{2x^2 + 2x} = \frac{1 + \dfrac{1}{x^2}}{2 + \dfrac{2}{x}}. \tag{222}$$

Since $1/x^2$ and $1/x$ each approach 0 when $x \to \infty$, the required limit (221) is $\tfrac{1}{2}$.

The method of factoring out the highest power of x used in Eq. (222) is often useful in evaluating the limiting ratio of two polynomials for $x \to \infty$.

We may use the rule just proved and embodied in Eqs. (214), (215), and (216) to prove that, for $x \to +\infty$,

$$\lim_{x \to +\infty} \frac{x}{e^x} = 0 \quad \text{and} \quad \lim_{x \to +\infty} \frac{\log x}{x} = 0. \tag{223}$$

These relations are not disturbed if we raise the functions to any fixed positive powers. That is, if $a > 0$ and $b > 0$,

$$\lim_{x \to +\infty} \frac{x^a}{e^{bx}} = 0 \quad \text{and} \quad \lim_{x \to +\infty} \frac{(\log x)^a}{x^b} = 0. \tag{224}$$

These relations hold however large a may be and however small b may be.

If we apply our rule to the limits just written, we find

$$\lim_{x \to +\infty} \frac{x^a}{e^{bx}} = \lim_{x \to +\infty} \frac{ax^{a-1}}{be^{bx}}, \tag{225}$$

and

$$\lim_{x \to +\infty} \frac{(\log x)^a}{x^b} = \lim_{x \to +\infty} \frac{a(\log x)^{a-1} \dfrac{1}{x}}{bx^{b-1}} = \lim_{x \to +\infty} \frac{a(\log x)^{a-1}}{bx^b} \tag{226}$$

If $a \leq 1$, the last limits in Eqs. (225) and (226) are directly seen to equal zero. If not, these limits are a constant times an expression similar to the one we started with but with a decreased by 1. Consequently, after a sufficient number of repetitions of the process, we shall come to a fraction whose numerator contains either x or $\log x$ raised to a power which is either zero or a negative number. Since the denominator of the fraction contains the factor e^{bx} or x^b, the limit of the fraction is seen to be zero.

This proves the relations (224), including the special case (223). These relations show that for $x \to +\infty$, e^x is an essentially higher order of infinity than x, and that for $x \to +\infty$, $\log x$ is an essentially lower order.

18. Other Indeterminate Forms. The indeterminate forms indicated by $\infty - \infty$, $0 \cdot \infty$, 1^∞, 0^0, ∞^0 may often be reduced to cases where l'Hospital's rule applies by a simple transformation. For example, the last three types reduce to the second type, $0 \cdot \infty$, by taking logarithms. This type may be reduced to a fraction by putting either factor in the denominator, or it may be treated directly by using Taylor's series.

As an example, consider

$$\lim_{x \to 0} (1 + ax + bx^2)^{(c/x)+d}. \tag{227}$$

If we denote the expression whose limit is required by u, we may write

$$\log u = \left(\frac{c}{x} + d\right) \log (1 + ax + bx^2). \tag{228}$$

But, by Eq. (126),

$$\log (1 + ax + bx^2) = (ax + bx^2) - \tfrac{1}{2}(ax + bx^2)^2 \cdots , \tag{229}$$

so that

$$\log u = ac + (ad + bc - \tfrac{1}{2}a^2c)x + \cdots . \tag{230}$$

It follows from this that, when $x \to 0$,

$$\log u \to ac \quad \text{and} \quad u \to e^{ac}. \tag{231}$$

That is,

$$\lim_{x \to 0} (1 + ax + bx^2)^{(c/x)+d} = e^{ac}. \tag{232}$$

In fact, adding higher powers of x constituting either a polynomial or convergent power series either to the terms in the parentheses or to those in the exponent does not affect the result. For example,

$$\lim_{x \to 0} (\cos \sqrt{x})^{\cot x} = \lim_{x \to 0} \left(1 - \frac{x}{2} + \cdots\right)^{(1/x) - \cdots} = e^{-\frac{1}{2}}. \quad (233)$$

As an example of the form $\infty - \infty$, we have:

$$\lim_{x \to 0} \left(\frac{1}{x \sin x} - \frac{1}{x^2}\right). \quad (234)$$

This may be evaluated by noting that

$$\frac{1}{x \sin x} - \frac{1}{x^2} = \frac{x - \sin x}{x^2 \sin x} = \frac{x^3/3! - \cdots}{x^3 - \cdots} = \frac{1/6 - \cdots}{1 - \cdots}. \quad (235)$$

The omitted terms in the last fraction all contain positive powers of x and so approach 0 when $x \to 0$. Consequently the required limit (234) is $\frac{1}{6}$.

The examples just worked out illustrate that it is often simpler to use expansions in Taylor's series than to reduce the expression to a form that can be treated by l'Hospital's rule.

19. Computation. The error made by replacing a function by the first n terms of its Taylor's series, in the case of real variables, could be estimated by using one of the forms of Taylor's theorem with the remainder, such as Eq. (121), (111), or (117). However, for a function analytic at a, the series is known to converge to the function for sufficiently small values of $x - a = h$. And the practical computation of the function from the series is feasible only when relatively few, say less than 10, terms will give a good approximation. In this case the practical method of finding a result accurate to within say 2×10^{-n} is to compute each term to the $(n + 1)$st decimal place, including all terms that numerically exceed 1 in this place, and after calculating their algebraic sum, to round this off to n places.

Whereas Taylor's series or some equivalent process is needed to make an original table of the functions $\log x$, e^x, and the trigonometric functions, for most practical purposes the values of these functions will be read from tables already available. Occasionally, however, combinations of such functions occur which are very small, so that few significant figures can be found by a direct use of ordinary tables, while an accurate value can easily be found by means of series. For example, if we require

$$\sqrt{100 + x} - 10, \quad (236)$$

for $x = 1$, we find from four-place tables of square roots

$$10.05 - 10 = 0.05. \tag{237}$$

But if we use the binomial series [Eq. (127)] we find

$$\sqrt{100 + x} = 10 \left(1 + \frac{x}{100}\right)^{1/2} = 10 \left[1 + \frac{1}{2}\frac{x}{100} - \frac{1}{8}\left(\frac{x}{100}\right)^2 \right.$$
$$\left. + \frac{1}{16}\left(\frac{x}{100}\right)^3 + \cdots \right], \tag{238}$$

so that when $x = 1$,

$$\sqrt{100 + 1} - 10 = 0.05 - 0.000125 + 0.000001 - \cdots \tag{239}$$
$$= 0.049876,$$

which is a result containing five significant figures.

As a second example, consider

$$\frac{\sin (x^3) - x^3}{\tan^{-1}(x^3) - x^3} = \frac{x^3 - \dfrac{x^9}{3!} + \dfrac{x^{15}}{5!} - \cdots - x^3}{x^3 - \dfrac{x^9}{3} + \dfrac{x^{15}}{5} - \cdots - x^3}$$
$$= \frac{1}{2} + \frac{11}{40}x^6 + \cdots. \tag{240}$$

If we attempt to compute the expression on the left from four-place tables for $x = 0.1$ and for $x = 0.5$, we find the numerator and denominator each zero for the smaller value, and for the second value the result 0.5 with some doubt as to the first significant figure. However, the series on the right shows that the expression is 0.5000003 when $x = 0.1$, and is 0.5043 when $x = 0.5$.

20. Technique and Logic. In evaluating a result for a practical purpose, we often use methods that from one point of view involve circular reasoning. For example, we may use l'Hospital's rule to show that

$$\lim_{x \to 0} \frac{\sin x}{x} = \lim_{x \to 0} \frac{\cos x}{1} = 1. \tag{241}$$

Actually the value of the first limit was needed to prove that $d(\sin x)/dx = \cos x$, which we used here at an intermediate stage of the argument. Thus Eq. (241) could not be regarded as a fundamental proof. However, it is a correct calculation in the sense that we have used the consistency of our results to recall a theorem of elementary calculus.

The reader interested in a logical development of the subject is referred to the author's *Treatise on Advanced Calculus* for a treatment starting from first principles and free of circular reasoning. Among other things, it includes derivations of most of the results stated without proof in this chapter. In particular, the elementary functions are discussed at length for real values in Chap. III of the *Treatise*, and for complex values in Chap. V. Mean value theorems and Taylor's theorem for real values are treated in Chap. IV, while Taylor's series for complex values are treated in Chap. XIII. And the convergence of series will be found in Chap. IX.

EXERCISES I

1. Use the power series (7) to check the tabular values $e^{0.2} = 1.2214$ and $e^{-0.2} = 0.81873$.

2. Using the values found in Prob. 1, verify Eq. (10) for $z_1 = 0.2$ and $z_2 = -0.2$.

3. From Eqs. (21) and (24) deduce that $\dfrac{d}{dx}\left(\dfrac{e^{(a+bi)x}}{a+bi}\right) = e^{(a+bi)x}$, which implies that the indefinite integral $\displaystyle\int^x e^{(a+bi)x}dx = \dfrac{e^{(a+bi)x}}{a+bi}.$

4. Assuming a, b, and x real, evaluate the two indefinite integrals $\displaystyle\int^x e^{ax}\cos bx\, dx$ and $\displaystyle\int^x e^{ax}\sin bx\, dx$ by equating the real and imaginary parts of the last equation of Prob. 3.

Evaluate each of the following integrals after transforming the integrand to the second form by means of Eqs. (16), (17), (14), and (15):

5. $\displaystyle\int^x 8\sin^4 x\, dx = \int^x (\cos 4x - 4\cos 2x + 3)dx.$

6. $\displaystyle\int^x 8\sin^2 x\cos^2 x\, dx = \int^x (-\cos 4x + 1)dx.$

7. If n is any positive integer and z is any complex number, show that

$$e^{inz} = (\cos z + i\sin z)^n \qquad \text{and} \qquad e^{-inz} = (\cos z - i\sin z)^n.$$

8. From Prob. 7, deduce that

$$\cos nz = \cos^n z - \frac{n(n-1)}{2!}\cos^{n-2} z \sin^2 z$$
$$+ \frac{n(n-1)(n-2)(n-3)}{4!}\cos^{n-4} z \sin^4 z - \cdots.$$

The series terminates when terms are reached containing the factor $n - n = 0$. For example, $\cos 3z = \cos^3 z - 3 \cos z \sin^2 z$ and $\cos 4z = \cos^4 z - 6 \cos^2 z \sin^2 z + \sin^4 z$.

9. From Prob. 7, deduce that

$$\sin nz = n \cos^{n-1} z \sin z - \frac{n(n-1)(n-2)}{3!} \cos^{n-3} z \sin^3 z + \cdots.$$

The series terminates when terms are reached containing the factor $n - n = 0$. For example, $\sin 3z = 3 \cos^2 z \sin z - \sin^3 z$ and $\sin 4z = 4 \cos^3 z \sin z - 4 \cos z \sin^3 z$.

10. Verify that the sum of the geometric progression of exponentials $e^{iz} + e^{2iz} + \cdots + e^{niz}$ is $\dfrac{e^{(n+1)iz} - e^{iz}}{e^{iz} - 1} = \dfrac{e^{(n+\frac{1}{2})iz} - e^{iz/2}}{e^{iz/2} - e^{-iz/2}}$.

By expressing the trigonometric functions in terms of exponential functions and using the result of Prob. 10, show that

11. $\sin z + \sin 2z + \cdots + \sin nz = \dfrac{\cos \dfrac{z}{2} - \cos \left(n + \dfrac{1}{2}\right) z}{2 \sin \dfrac{z}{2}}$.

12. $\cos z + \cos 2z + \cdots + \cos nz = \dfrac{\sin \left(n + \dfrac{1}{2}\right) z - \sin \dfrac{z}{2}}{2 \sin \dfrac{z}{2}}$.

13. If a is any real number, prove that $|e^{ia}| = 1$.
14. For a and b real, prove that $|e^{a+bi}| = e^a$.

Express each of the following in the form $a + bi$, with a and b each real:

15. $e^{\pi i/4}$.   **16.** $e^{2\pi i}$.   **17.** $\cos 3i$.   **18.** $\sin(-1 + i)$.
19. $\cos(1 + 2i)$.   **20.** $\cosh 3i$.   **21.** $\sinh(2 - i)$.   **22.** $\cosh(1 + i)$.

Prove the following identities:

23. $1 - \tanh^2 x = \operatorname{sech}^2 x$.   **24.** $\coth^2 x - 1 = \operatorname{csch}^2 x$.
25. $\sinh 2x = 2 \sinh x \cosh x$.   **26.** $\cosh 2x = \cosh^2 x + \sinh^2 x$.
27. $\sinh ix = i \sin x$.   **28.** $\cosh ix = \cos x$.

29. If S is the sectorial area swept out by the radius vector r of Fig. 1, $dS = \frac{1}{2} r^2 d\theta$. Show that if x and y are given in terms of a parameter t, $dS = \frac{1}{2}(x \, dy - y \, dx)$. HINT: From $x = r \cos \theta$ and $y = r \sin \theta$, deduce $x' = r' \cos \theta - r \sin \theta \, \theta'$ and $y' = r' \sin \theta + r \cos \theta \, \theta'$, and hence $xy' - yx' = r^2\theta'$.

30. For the unit circle $x^2 + y^2 = 1$, we may put $x = \cos t$, $y = \sin t$, and deduce from Prob. 29 that $dS = \frac{1}{2} dt$. Similarly for the unit rectangular hyperbola $x^2 - y^2 = 1$, we may put $x = \cosh t$, $y = \sinh t$, and deduce that $dS = \tfrac{1}{2} dt$. It follows that in Fig. 8, with AB an arc of $x^2 + y^2 = 1$ and the shaded area equal to $t/2$, we shall have $OC = \cos t$, $CB = \sin t$, and $AD = \tan t$. Similarly, in Fig. 9, with AB an arc of $x^2 - y^2 = 1$ and the shaded area equal to $t/2$, we shall have $OC = \cosh t$, $CB = \sinh t$, and $AD = \tanh t$. This analogy between circular and hyperbolic functions is the reason for the designation of the latter as hyperbolic.

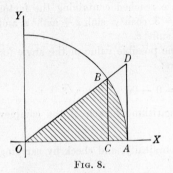

FIG. 8.   FIG. 9.

31. If u is any real number, the function Gudermannian of u, $\phi = \text{gd } u$, is defined as the value between $-\pi/2$ and $\pi/2$ which satisfies the relation $\phi = 2 \tan^{-1} e^u - \pi/2$. Show that $u = \log \tan (\pi/4 + \phi/2)$.

32. With the notation of Prob. 31, show that

$$\sinh u = \tan \phi, \qquad \cosh u = \sec \phi, \qquad \tanh u = \sin \phi,$$
$$\operatorname{csch} u = \cot \phi, \qquad \operatorname{sech} u = \cos \phi, \qquad \text{and} \ \coth u = \csc \phi.$$

33. If $u = 1$, compute ϕ from the defining relation of Prob. 31. Also verify that the value of the functions of u and ϕ taken from the tables satisfy the first three relations of Prob. 32.

34. Check the tabular values $\sinh 0.2 = 0.2013$ and $\cosh 0.2 = 1.0201$ (a) by using the power series (45) and (46), and (b) by using Eq. (34) and the result of Prob. 2.

35. If n is any positive integer and z is any complex number, show that

$$e^{nz} = (\cosh z + \sinh z)^n \qquad \text{and} \qquad e^{-nz} = (\cosh z - \sinh z)^n.$$

36. From Prob. 35, deduce that

$$\cosh nz = \cosh^n z + \frac{n(n-1)}{2!} \cosh^{n-2} z \sinh^2 z$$
$$+ \frac{n(n-1)(n-2)(n-3)}{4!} \cosh^{n-4} z \sinh^4 z + \cdots$$

The series terminates when terms are reached containing the factor

$n - n = 0$. For example, $\cosh 3z = \cosh^3 z + 3 \cosh z \sinh^2 z$ and $\cosh 4z = \cosh^4 z + 6 \cosh^2 z \sinh^2 z + \sinh^4 z$.

37. From Prob. 35, deduce that

$$\sinh nz = n \cosh^{n-1} z \sinh z$$
$$+ \frac{n(n-1)(n-2)}{3!} \cosh^{n-3} z \sinh^3 z + \cdots .$$

The series terminates when terms are reached containing the factor $n - n = 0$. For example, $\sinh 3z = 3 \cosh^2 z \sinh z + \sinh^3 z$ and $\sinh 4z = 4 \cosh^3 z \sinh z + 4 \cosh z \sinh^3 z$.

38. Find the absolute value and one possible value of the angle for each of the following complex numbers:

$$(a)\ 4 = 4 + 0i; \qquad (b)\ -9i = 0 - 9i; \qquad (c)\ \sqrt{3} + i.$$

39. Calculate one value of the logarithm of each of the complex numbers of Prob. 38.

Evaluate each of the following algebraically, and check by carrying out a graphical construction:

40. $(4 - 6i) + (-8 + 5i)$. **41.** $(-6 + 3i) - (2 + 5i)$.

42. $(8 + 3i)(-4 - 5i)$. **43.** $(3 - i)^2$.

44. $\dfrac{6 + 4i}{1 - i}$. **45.** $\dfrac{3 - 2i}{-2 - 3i}$.

46. Find the two square roots of each of the complex numbers of Prob. 38.

Find all the values of each of the following indicated roots:

47. $\sqrt[3]{8}$. **48.** $\sqrt[4]{-16}$. **49.** $\sqrt[5]{32i}$. **50.** $\sqrt[6]{1}$.

51. Show that all of the values of i^i are real and that one of them is $e^{-\pi/2}$.

52. It is found in elementary calculus that

$$\int^x \frac{dx}{a^2 + x^2} = \frac{1}{a} \tan^{-1} \frac{x}{a} \qquad \text{and} \qquad \int^x \frac{dx}{a^2 - x^2} = \frac{1}{2a} \log \frac{a + x}{a - x}.$$

Show that the second integral may be written in a form analogous to that for the first, with $\tan^{-1}$ replaced by $\tanh^{-1}$.

53. It is found in elementary calculus that

$$\int^x \frac{dx}{\sqrt{a^2 - x^2}} = \sin^{-1} \frac{x}{a} \qquad \text{and}$$

$$\int^x \frac{dx}{\sqrt{a^2 + x^2}} = \log (x + \sqrt{a^2 + x^2}).$$

Show that the second integral may be written in a form analogous to that for the first, with $\sin^{-1}$ replaced by $\sinh^{-1}$.

54. Prove the theorem of the mean for integrals:

$$\int_a^b F(x)dx = (b - a)F(\xi) \text{ for a suitable } \xi \text{ with } a < \xi < b.$$

HINT: Put $F(x) = f'(x)$ and use the mean value theorem (100).

55. By integrating the appropriate series termwise, verify that

$$\tanh^{-1} x = x + \frac{x^3}{3} + \frac{x^5}{5} + \frac{x^7}{7} + \cdots, \qquad |x| < 1.$$

56. Check the tabular value $\tanh^{-1} 0.5 = 0.5493$ (a) by using the series of Prob. 55; (b) by using Eq. (94).

57. Verify the expansion for the hyperbolic tangent in an infinite series $\tanh x = x - \frac{1}{3}x^3 + \frac{2}{15}x^5 - \frac{17}{315}x^7 + \cdots$ (a) by division of the series for $\sinh x$ by that for $\cosh x$; (b) by using the method of undetermined coefficients or Eq. (182) to find the series for the function inverse to the series of Prob. 55.

58. Check the tabular value $\tanh 0.2 = 0.1974$ (a) by using the series of Prob. 57; (b) by using the values found in Prob. 34.

59. By integrating the appropriate series termwise, verify that

$$\sinh^{-1} x = x - \frac{1}{2}\frac{x^3}{3} + \frac{1 \cdot 3}{2 \cdot 4}\frac{x^5}{5} - \frac{1 \cdot 3 \cdot 5}{2 \cdot 4 \cdot 6}\frac{x^7}{7} + \cdots, \qquad |x| < 1.$$

60. Check the tabular value $\sinh^{-1} 0.1 = 0.0998$ (a) by using the series of Prob. 59; (b) by using Eq. (92).

61. Check the tabular value $\cosh^{-1} 1.025 = 0.2231$ (a) by deducing from Eq. (40) that $\cosh^{-1} 1.025 = \sinh^{-1} 0.225$, and then using the series of Prob. 59; (b) by using Eq. (93).

62. Check the tabular values $\sin 11° = 0.1908$ and $\cos 11° = 0.9816$ by using series (8) and (9). Note that $11° = 11 \cdot \pi/180$ radian or $11(0.01745) = 0.1920$.

63. Check the tabular values $\sin 41° = 0.6561$ and $\cos 41° = 0.7547$ (a) by using the Taylor's series about the value $\pi/6$ and the known values of the sine and cosine of $\pi/6$ radian or $30°$; (b) by using the known values of the sine and cosine of $30°$, the values of the sine and cosine of $11°$ found in Prob. 62, and the addition theorems (11) and (12).

64. From Eq. (126) deduce the expansion

$$\log \frac{1 + x}{1 - x} = 2\left(x + \frac{x^3}{3} + \frac{x^5}{5} + \frac{x^7}{7} + \cdots\right), \qquad |x| < 1.$$

65. Show that the left member of the equation in Prob. 64 will reduce to $\log(m + 1) - \log m$ if $x = 1/(2m + 1)$. Using this result and the series of Prob. 64, check the tabular difference from a table of natural logarithms: log 11 − log 10 = 0.0953.

Derive the following series expansions by any convenient method:

66. $e^{\sin x} = 1 + x + \dfrac{x^2}{2} - \dfrac{x^4}{8} - \dfrac{x^5}{15} - \cdots .$

67. $e^{\tan^{-1} x} = 1 + x + \dfrac{x^2}{2} - \dfrac{x^3}{6} - \dfrac{7x^4}{24} - \cdots , \qquad |x| < 1.$

68. $\displaystyle\int_0^x e^{-x^2} dx = x - \dfrac{x^3}{3} + \dfrac{1}{2!}\dfrac{x^5}{5} - \dfrac{1}{3!}\dfrac{x^7}{7} + \cdots .$

69. $\displaystyle\int_0^x \cos x^2 dx = x - \dfrac{1}{2!}\dfrac{x^5}{5} + \dfrac{1}{4!}\dfrac{x^9}{9} - \dfrac{1}{6!}\dfrac{x^{13}}{13} + \cdots .$

70. $\displaystyle\int_0^x \sin x^2 dx = \dfrac{x^3}{3} - \dfrac{1}{3!}\dfrac{x^7}{7} + \dfrac{1}{5!}\dfrac{x^{11}}{11} - \dfrac{1}{7!}\dfrac{x^{15}}{15} + \cdots .$

71. $\displaystyle\int_0^x \dfrac{x^2}{1 + x^3} dx = \dfrac{x^3}{3} - \dfrac{x^6}{6} + \dfrac{x^9}{9} - \dfrac{x^{12}}{12} + \cdots , \qquad |x| < 1.$

72. Evaluate $\displaystyle\int_0^1 e^{-x^2} dx$ by using the result of Prob. 68.

73. Evaluate $\displaystyle\int_0^1 \sin x^2 dx$ by using the series of Prob. 70.

74. Evaluate $\displaystyle\int_0^1 \cosh x^2 dx$ by using a power series expansion.

75. Evaluate $\displaystyle\int_0^{0.5} \dfrac{\sin x}{x} dx$ by using a power series expansion.

Each of the following equations has a real root between the indicated limits. Compute this root to at least three significant figures.

76. $x^3 - 5x^2 + 6x - 1 = 0, \qquad 0.1 < x < 0.2.$
77. $x^5 + 3x^3 - 2x^2 + x + 1 = 0, \qquad -1 < x < 0.$
78. $e^x = 4x, \qquad 0.3 < x < 0.4.$ **79.** $\cos x = x, \qquad 0.7 < x < 0.8.$
80. $\tan x = 2x, \qquad 1 < x < 2.$ **81.** $2 \sin x = x, \qquad 1 < x < 2.$

Use l'Hospital's rule [Eq. (198)] to evaluate the following limits:

82. $\displaystyle\lim_{x \to 1} \dfrac{x^n - 1}{x - 1}.$ **83.** $\displaystyle\lim_{x \to 0} \dfrac{e^x - 1}{x}.$

84. $\displaystyle\lim_{x \to 0} \dfrac{\log (1 + x)}{x}.$ **85.** $\displaystyle\lim_{x \to -1} \dfrac{\sin \pi x}{1 + x}.$

86. $\displaystyle\lim_{x \to \pi/4} \dfrac{\tan x - 1}{x - \pi/4}.$ **87.** $\displaystyle\lim_{x \to \pi/3} \dfrac{\cos x - \frac{1}{2}}{x - \pi/3}.$

88. Show that each of the limits in Probs. 82 to 87 may be evaluated by a direct application of the definition of a derivative, namely,

$$\lim_{x \to a} \frac{f(x) - f(a)}{x - a} = f'(a).$$

Evaluate the following limits by any convenient method:

89. $\lim\limits_{x \to 0} \dfrac{a^x - b^x}{x}$.

90. $\lim\limits_{x \to 0} \dfrac{x - \tan^{-1} x}{\sin^{-1} x - x}$.

91. $\lim\limits_{x \to 0} \dfrac{\tan x - x}{x - \sin x}$.

92. $\lim\limits_{x \to 0} \dfrac{1 - \cos x}{\tan^2 x}$.

93. $\lim\limits_{x \to \infty} \dfrac{\cot^{-1} x}{\csc^{-1} x}$.

94. $\lim\limits_{x \to \pi/2} \dfrac{\csc 2x}{\csc 4x}$.

95. $\lim\limits_{x \to 0+} x^5 (\log x)^7$.

96. $\lim\limits_{x \to 0+} x^x$.

97. $\lim\limits_{x \to \pi/2} (\sin x)^{\tan x}$.

98. $\lim\limits_{x \to 2\pi} \left(\dfrac{1}{x - 2\pi} - \cot x \right)$.

99. $\lim\limits_{x \to 0} (1 - 3x)^{4/x}$.

100. $\lim\limits_{x \to +\infty} x^5 e^{-2^x} (\log x)^4$.

101. $\lim\limits_{x \to +\infty} \dfrac{1 - \log x}{\sqrt{1 + x^2}}$.   HINT: Use the form $\dfrac{\log x}{x} \dfrac{-1 + 1/\log x}{\sqrt{1 + 1/x^2}}$.

The following values are too small to be accurately computed by a direct use of four-place tables. Using power series, compute each value to at least three significant figures:

102. $2e^x - 2 - 2x - x^2$, when $x = 0.1$.

103. $\tan x + \tan^{-1} x - 2x$, when $x = 0.2$.

104. $2 \cosh x - 2 - x^2$, when $x = 0.2$.

105. $\tanh x + \tan x - \sinh x - \sin x$, when $x = 0.1$.

106. Evaluate $\lim\limits_{x \to 1} \dfrac{x^2 - 3x + 2}{x - 1}$ and $\lim\limits_{x \to 1} \dfrac{x^2 - 3x + 5}{x - 2}$, noting that in the second case Eq. (203) is not satisfied.

CHAPTER II

PARTIAL DIFFERENTIATION
AND IMPLICIT FUNCTIONS

In many situations we must consider a physical quantity as depending on more than one independent variable. For such cases the notion of an ordinary derivative and the methods of the differential calculus for functions of one variable must be generalized so as to apply to functions of several variables. This extension constitutes the subject of partial differentiation, to which we devote this chapter. We define partial derivatives and total differentials and study their fundamental properties. We discuss how the partial derivatives are transformed when we change from one set of variables or coordinates to another. The special case of inverse transformations leads to the subject of implicit functions and Jacobian determinants. In this connection a brief treatment of determinants is given. Finally, we state Taylor's theorem and solve some problems in maxima and minima for functions of more than one variable, using Lagrange's multipliers as well as direct methods.

21. Partial Derivatives and Total Differentials. Let u be a function of the two real variables x and y, so that

$$u = f(x,y). \tag{1}$$

Then for each fixed value of y, u is a function of x. If this is a differentiable function, we may apply the ordinary process of differentiation to it. The result is indicated by $\partial u/\partial x$, u_x, or $f_x(x,y)$, and is called the *partial derivative* of $f(x,y)$ with respect to x. Thus

$$\frac{\partial u}{\partial x} = u_x = f_x(x,y) = \lim_{h \to 0} \frac{f(x + h,y) - f(x,y)}{h}. \tag{2}$$

Similarly, if we keep x fixed, we may obtain a partial derivative with respect to y denoted by $\partial u/\partial y$, u_y or $f_y(x,y)$, with

$$\frac{\partial u}{\partial y} = u_y = f_y(x,y) = \lim_{k \to 0} \frac{f(x,y + k) - f(x,y)}{k}. \tag{3}$$

If we apply the law of finite increments [Eq. (105) of Sec. 10] to $f(x,y)$, considered as a function of x only with y fixed, we find

$$f(x + h,y) - f(x,y) = hf_x(x + \theta_1 h,y), \qquad (4)$$

for some suitable value of θ_1 with $0 < \theta_1 < 1$. Similarly, we may apply the law of finite increments to $f(x + h,y)$ considered as a function of y only by keeping $x + h$ fixed. The result is

$$f(x + h, y + k) - f(x + h,y) = kf_y(x + h, y + \theta_2 k), \qquad (5)$$

for some suitable value of θ_2 with $0 < \theta_2 < 1$.

Let Δu denote the increment of u when x and y both vary, so that

$$\Delta u = f(x + h, y + k) - f(x,y). \qquad (6)$$

Then it follows from Eqs. (4), (5), and (6) that

$$\Delta u = hf_x(x + \theta_1 h,y) + kf_y(x + h, y + \theta_2 k). \qquad (7)$$

When h and k are small, $\theta_1 h$ and $\theta_2 k$ will also be small. Thus in a plane with x and y as rectangular coordinates, the points

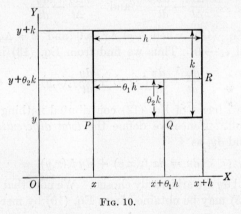

Fig. 10.

$Q = (x + \theta_1 h,y)$ and $R = (x + h, y + \theta_2 h)$ will each be near the point $P = (x,y)$. Let us assume that the partial derivatives $f_x(x,y)$ and $f_y(x,y)$ are continuous. Then $f_x(x + \theta_1 h,y)$ will be nearly equal to $f_x(x,y)$ and $f_y(x + h, y + \theta_2 k)$ will be nearly equal to $f_y(x,y)$. Consequently, if we write

$$f_x(x + \theta_1 h,y) - f_x(x,y) = \epsilon_1, \qquad (8)$$
$$f_y(x + h, y + \theta_2 k) - f_y(x,y) = \epsilon_2, \qquad (9)$$

the quantities ϵ_1 and ϵ_2 will each be numerically small when h

and k are small. Hence ϵ_1 and ϵ_2 will each approach zero when h and k approach zero. We may deduce from Eqs. (7), (8), and (9) that

$$\Delta u = h f_x(x,y) + k f_y(x,y) + \epsilon_1 h + \epsilon_2 k, \tag{10}$$

where

$$\epsilon_1 \rightarrow 0 \quad \text{and} \quad \epsilon_2 \rightarrow 0 \quad \text{when } (h,k) \rightarrow (0,0). \tag{11}$$

Since h and k are the increments of x and y, we replace them by Δx and Δy and write

$$\Delta u = \Delta x\, f_x(x,y) + \Delta y\, f_y(x,y) + \epsilon_1 \Delta x + \epsilon_2 \Delta y. \tag{12}$$

Suppose next that x and y are each functions of a new variable t. This makes $u(x,y)$ a function of t. We may then compute the derivative du/dt from

$$\frac{\Delta u}{\Delta t} = \frac{\Delta x}{\Delta t} f_x(x,y) + \frac{\Delta y}{\Delta t} f_y(x,y) + \epsilon_1 \frac{\Delta x}{\Delta t} + \epsilon_2 \frac{\Delta y}{\Delta t}. \tag{13}$$

When $\Delta t \rightarrow 0$; $\Delta x \rightarrow 0$ and $\Delta y \rightarrow 0$; also

$$\frac{\Delta x}{\Delta t} \rightarrow \frac{dx}{dt} \quad \text{and} \quad \frac{\Delta y}{\Delta t} \rightarrow \frac{dy}{dt}. \tag{14}$$

But, by Eq. (11), when $h = \Delta x \rightarrow 0$ and $k = \Delta y \rightarrow 0$, then $\epsilon_1 \rightarrow 0$, and $\epsilon_2 \rightarrow 0$. Thus we find from Eq. (13) in the limit,

$$\frac{du}{dt} = \frac{dx}{dt} f_x(x,y) + \frac{dy}{dt} f_y(x,y). \tag{15}$$

The last two terms of Eq. (12) contributed nothing to the preceding result. Hence we define the *total differential* of u, for given dx and dy, as

$$du = dx\, f_x(x,y) + dy\, f_y(x,y). \tag{16}$$

Here dx and dy are arbitrarily chosen. We note that the limiting relation (15) may be obtained from Eq. (16) by merely dividing by dt.

Equation (16) is consistent with the definition of a differential for a function of one variable, since, if y does not appear in the function $f(x,y)$, we shall have

$$f(x,y) = f(x); \quad f_x(x,y) = f'(x) \quad \text{and} \quad f_y(x,y) = 0.$$

Hence in this case Eq. (16) becomes

$$du = f'(x)dx, \quad \text{where } f'(x) = \frac{du}{dx}, \text{ and } dx \text{ is arbitrary.} \tag{17}$$

With another notation for the partial derivatives, Eq. (16) may be written·

$$du = \frac{\partial u}{\partial x} dx + \frac{\partial u}{\partial y} dy. \tag{18}$$

If x and y were each functions of the two new variables s and t, for s fixed they would be functions of t alone. In this case, when we divide Eq. (16) by dt we obtain partial derivatives. Hence we write the result as

$$\frac{\partial u}{\partial t} = \frac{\partial u}{\partial x} \frac{\partial x}{\partial t} + \frac{\partial u}{\partial y} \frac{\partial y}{\partial t}. \tag{19}$$

Similarly, by keeping t fixed, we find

$$\frac{\partial u}{\partial s} = \frac{\partial u}{\partial x} \frac{\partial x}{\partial s} + \frac{\partial u}{\partial y} \frac{\partial y}{\partial s}. \tag{20}$$

If we apply the relation (18) to x and y regarded as functions of the independent variables s and t, we find

$$dx = \frac{\partial x}{\partial s} ds + \frac{\partial x}{\partial t} dt \quad \text{and} \quad dy = \frac{\partial y}{\partial s} ds + \frac{\partial y}{\partial t} dt. \tag{21}$$

We may now deduce from Eqs. (19), (20), and (21) that

$$\frac{\partial u}{\partial x} dx + \frac{\partial u}{\partial y} dy = \frac{\partial u}{\partial x} \left(\frac{\partial x}{\partial s} ds + \frac{\partial x}{\partial t} dt \right) + \frac{\partial u}{\partial y} \left(\frac{\partial y}{\partial s} ds + \frac{\partial y}{\partial t} dt \right)$$
$$= \frac{\partial u}{\partial s} ds + \frac{\partial u}{\partial t} dt. \tag{22}$$

But the left member defines du when x and y are the independent variables, while the right member defines du when s and t are the independent variables. Since the two are equal, it follows that the value of du obtained from an equation of the form (18) does not depend on the choice of independent variables.

Similar definitions and results apply to functions of more than two variables. For example, if $u = f(x,y,z)$, the partial derivative

$$\frac{\partial u}{\partial x} = u_x = f_x(x,y,z) = \lim_{h \to 0} \frac{f(x + h,y,z) - f(x,y,z)}{h}. \tag{23}$$

The total differential is

$$du = \frac{\partial u}{\partial x} dx + \frac{\partial u}{\partial y} dy + \frac{\partial u}{\partial z} dz. \tag{24}$$

If x, y, and z are functions of one variable t, we may deduce from Eq. (24) that the total derivative of $u = f(x,y,z)$ is

$$\frac{du}{dt} = \frac{\partial u}{\partial x}\frac{dx}{dt} + \frac{\partial u}{\partial y}\frac{dy}{dt} + \frac{\partial u}{\partial z}\frac{dz}{dt}. \tag{25}$$

And, if x, y, and z are functions of several new variables, of which t is one, we may deduce that the partial derivative is

$$\frac{\partial u}{\partial t} = \frac{\partial u}{\partial x}\frac{\partial x}{\partial t} + \frac{\partial u}{\partial y}\frac{\partial y}{\partial t} + \frac{\partial u}{\partial z}\frac{\partial z}{\partial t}. \tag{26}$$

22. Alternative Notation. In Eqs. (19) and (20), y is held fast when we differentiate with respect to x. Also x is held fast when we differentiate with respect to y. Similarly t is held fast when we differentiate with respect to s while s is held fast when we differentiate with respect to t. In case any confusion on this point is likely to occur, we use parentheses with the fixed variables added as subscripts. Thus we write Eq. (20) as

$$\left(\frac{\partial u}{\partial s}\right)_t = \left(\frac{\partial u}{\partial x}\right)_y\left(\frac{\partial x}{\partial s}\right)_t + \left(\frac{\partial u}{\partial y}\right)_x\left(\frac{\partial y}{\partial s}\right)_t. \tag{27}$$

We give an example which shows why this more explicit notation is sometimes desirable. Let u be a function of the temperature T and pressure p of a gas, so that $u = u(T,p)$. Suppose next that, by means of the known relation between p, v, and T for the gas, we express T in terms of pressure and volume, $T(p,v)$. Then we shall have

$$\left(\frac{\partial u}{\partial v}\right)_p = \left(\frac{\partial u}{\partial T}\right)_p\left(\frac{\partial T}{\partial v}\right)_p + \left(\frac{\partial u}{\partial p}\right)_T\left(\frac{\partial p}{\partial v}\right)_p, \tag{28}$$

$$\left(\frac{\partial u}{\partial p}\right)_v = \left(\frac{\partial u}{\partial T}\right)_p\left(\frac{\partial T}{\partial p}\right)_v + \left(\frac{\partial u}{\partial p}\right)_T\left(\frac{\partial p}{\partial p}\right)_v. \tag{29}$$

When p is held fast, p does not change so that

$$\left(\frac{\partial p}{\partial v}\right)_p = 0. \tag{30}$$

Furthermore,

$$\left(\frac{\partial p}{\partial p}\right)_v = 1. \tag{31}$$

Consequently Eqs. (28) and (29) simplify to

$$\left(\frac{\partial u}{\partial v}\right)_p = \left(\frac{\partial u}{\partial T}\right)_p \left(\frac{\partial T}{\partial v}\right)_p \quad \text{and} \quad \left(\frac{\partial u}{\partial p}\right)_v = \left(\frac{\partial u}{\partial T}\right)_p \left(\frac{\partial T}{\partial p}\right)_v + \left(\frac{\partial u}{\partial p}\right)_T.$$
(32)

Note that in the last equation the use of the subscripts is essential, since without them we could not tell whether $\partial u/\partial p$ meant $(\partial u/\partial p)_T$, obtained from $u(T,p)$ with T held fast, or whether it meant $(\partial u/\partial p)_v$, obtained from $u[T(p,v), p]$ with v held fast.

23. Higher Partial Derivatives. The first partial derivatives of the first partial derivatives give the second partial derivatives. Thus,

$$\frac{\partial}{\partial x}\left(\frac{\partial u}{\partial x}\right) = \frac{\partial^2 u}{\partial x^2}, \qquad \frac{\partial}{\partial y}\left(\frac{\partial u}{\partial y}\right) = \frac{\partial^2 u}{\partial y^2}.$$
(33)

Now consider the expression

$$\Delta = f(x + h, y + k) - f(x + h, y) - f(x, y + k) + f(x,y).$$
(34)

We have

$$\lim_{k \to 0} \frac{\Delta}{hk} = \frac{1}{h}\left[f_y(x + h, y) - f_y(x,y)\right].$$
(35)

It follows that

$$\lim_{h \to 0}\lim_{k \to 0} \frac{\Delta}{hk} = [f_y(x,y)]_x = \frac{\partial}{\partial x}\left(\frac{\partial u}{\partial y}\right).$$
(36)

Similarly, we find

$$\lim_{k \to 0}\lim_{h \to 0} \frac{\Delta}{hk} = [f_x(x,y)]_y = \frac{\partial}{\partial y}\left(\frac{\partial u}{\partial x}\right).$$
(37)

We would expect that, under certain restrictions, the repeated limit in Eq. (36) would equal that in Eq. (37), which differs from it in the order in which the limits are taken. It would then follow that the partial derivatives on the right of these two equations are equal. In fact, it may be proved that, when all the partial derivatives that appear are continuous functions, then

$$\frac{\partial}{\partial x}\left(\frac{\partial u}{\partial y}\right) = \frac{\partial}{\partial y}\left(\frac{\partial u}{\partial x}\right) \quad \text{or} \quad \frac{\partial^2 u}{\partial x \, \partial y} = \frac{\partial^2 u}{\partial y \, \partial x}.$$
(38)

More generally, with similar assumptions as to continuity, any higher partial derivative is independent of the order in which the differentiations are performed. For example,

$$\frac{\partial^3 u}{\partial x^2 \, \partial y} = \frac{\partial^3 u}{\partial y \, \partial x^2} = \frac{\partial^3 u}{\partial x \, \partial y \, \partial x}. \tag{39}$$

24. Change of Variables. The formulas for the change of independent variables may be derived by one or more applications of equations similar in form to (18) and (24). Let us first consider the case of two variables x and y which are each functions of s and t. Thus, we have the relations

$$x = f(s,t), \qquad y = g(s,t), \tag{40}$$

which determine the partial derivatives

$$\frac{\partial x}{\partial s}, \frac{\partial x}{\partial t} \qquad \text{and} \qquad \frac{\partial y}{\partial s}, \frac{\partial y}{\partial t}. \tag{41}$$

Then, if U is any function of x and y, we shall have

$$U = F(x,y) = F[f(s,t), g(s,t)] = G(s,t). \tag{42}$$

Thus

$$\frac{\partial U}{\partial x} = F_x(x,y); \qquad \frac{\partial U}{\partial y} = F_y(x,y). \tag{43}$$

The derivatives

$$\frac{\partial U}{\partial s} = G_s(s,t) \qquad \text{and} \qquad \frac{\partial U}{\partial t} = G_t(s,t) \tag{44}$$

could be obtained, at least theoretically, by actually forming the function $G(s,t)$ by the substitutions indicated in Eq. (42). However, it is generally more convenient to deduce from Eq. (18) that

$$\frac{\partial U}{\partial s} = \frac{\partial U}{\partial x} \frac{\partial x}{\partial s} + \frac{\partial U}{\partial y} \frac{\partial y}{\partial s}, \tag{45}$$

and

$$\frac{\partial U}{\partial t} = \frac{\partial U}{\partial x} \frac{\partial x}{\partial t} + \frac{\partial U}{\partial y} \frac{\partial y}{\partial t}. \tag{46}$$

The second derivatives can be found by a second application of Eq. (18). Thus

$$\frac{\partial^2 U}{\partial s^2} = \frac{\partial}{\partial s} \left(\frac{\partial U}{\partial x} \frac{\partial x}{\partial s} + \frac{\partial U}{\partial y} \frac{\partial y}{\partial s} \right). \tag{47}$$

But

$$\frac{\partial}{\partial s} \left(\frac{\partial U}{\partial x} \frac{\partial x}{\partial s} \right) = \frac{\partial}{\partial s} \left(\frac{\partial U}{\partial x} \right) \frac{\partial x}{\partial s} + \frac{\partial U}{\partial x} \frac{\partial^2 x}{\partial s^2}. \tag{48}$$

And, by Eq. (18),

$$\frac{\partial}{\partial s}\left(\frac{\partial U}{\partial x}\right) = \frac{\partial}{\partial x}\left(\frac{\partial U}{\partial x}\right)\frac{\partial x}{\partial s} + \frac{\partial}{\partial y}\left(\frac{\partial U}{\partial x}\right)\frac{\partial y}{\partial s}$$

$$= \frac{\partial^2 U}{\partial x^2}\frac{\partial x}{\partial s} + \frac{\partial^2 U}{\partial x\,\partial y}\frac{\partial y}{\partial s}. \tag{49}$$

We may treat the term in Eq. (47) which involves y similarly. If we do this and combine our results, we shall find

$$\frac{\partial^2 U}{\partial s^2} = \frac{\partial^2 U}{\partial x^2}\left(\frac{\partial x}{\partial s}\right)^2 + 2\frac{\partial^2 U}{\partial x\,\partial y}\frac{\partial x}{\partial s}\frac{\partial y}{\partial s}$$

$$+ \frac{\partial^2 U}{\partial y^2}\left(\frac{\partial y}{\partial s}\right)^2 + \frac{\partial U}{\partial x}\frac{\partial^2 x}{\partial s^2} + \frac{\partial U}{\partial y}\frac{\partial^2 y}{\partial s^2}. \tag{50}$$

The equation for $\partial^2 U/\partial t^2$ may be found from this by replacing s by t throughout. By the same procedure used to derive Eq. (50), we may show that

$$\frac{\partial^2 U}{\partial s\,\partial t} = \frac{\partial^2 U}{\partial x^2}\frac{\partial x}{\partial s}\frac{\partial x}{\partial t} + \frac{\partial^2 U}{\partial x\,\partial y}\left(\frac{\partial x}{\partial s}\frac{\partial y}{\partial t} + \frac{\partial y}{\partial s}\frac{\partial x}{\partial t}\right) + \frac{\partial^2 U}{\partial y^2}\frac{\partial y}{\partial s}\frac{\partial y}{\partial t}$$

$$+ \frac{\partial U}{\partial x}\frac{\partial^2 x}{\partial s\,\partial t} + \frac{\partial U}{\partial y}\frac{\partial^2 y}{\partial s\,\partial t}. \tag{51}$$

These equations may be applied with any change of letters, for example with x,y and s,t interchanged; or with s,t replaced by u,v in the original or interchanged form. To give one instance,

$$\frac{\partial^2 U}{\partial x\,\partial y} = \frac{\partial^2 U}{\partial u^2}\frac{\partial u}{\partial x}\frac{\partial u}{\partial y} + \frac{\partial^2 U}{\partial u\,\partial v}\left(\frac{\partial u}{\partial x}\frac{\partial v}{\partial y} + \frac{\partial v}{\partial x}\frac{\partial u}{\partial y}\right)$$

$$+ \frac{\partial^2 U}{\partial v^2}\frac{\partial v}{\partial x}\frac{\partial v}{\partial y} + \frac{\partial U}{\partial u}\frac{\partial^2 u}{\partial x\,\partial y} + \frac{\partial U}{\partial v}\frac{\partial^2 v}{\partial x\,\partial y}, \tag{52}$$

where $U = F(u,v)$ and $u = f(x,y)$, $v = g(x,y)$.

If one of the variables is missing from any functional relationship, the corresponding partial derivative is zero, while the other partial derivative becomes an ordinary derivative. For example, if

$$U = F(x) \qquad \text{and} \qquad x = f(s), \tag{53}$$

we have

$$\frac{dU}{ds} = \frac{dU}{dx}\frac{dx}{ds} \qquad \text{and} \qquad \frac{d^2U}{ds^2} = \frac{d^2U}{dx^2}\left(\frac{dx}{ds}\right)^2 + \frac{dU}{dx}\frac{d^2x}{ds^2}. \tag{54}$$

With a different notation, this may be written

$$y = f(u) \quad \text{and} \quad u = g(x), \tag{55}$$

$$\frac{dy}{dx} = \frac{dy}{du}\frac{du}{dx} = f'(u)\frac{du}{dx}, \tag{56}$$

$$\frac{d^2y}{dx^2} = \frac{d^2y}{du^2}\left(\frac{du}{dx}\right)^2 + \frac{dy}{du}\frac{d^2u}{dx^2} = f''(u)\left(\frac{du}{dx}\right)^2 + f'(u)\frac{d^2u}{dx^2}. \tag{57}$$

Again, suppose that $U = f(u)$ and $u = g(x,y)$.   Then

$$\frac{\partial U}{\partial x} = \frac{\partial u}{\partial x}f'(u) \quad \text{and} \quad \frac{\partial U}{\partial y} = \frac{\partial u}{\partial y}f'(u). \tag{58}$$

As an application, let us prove that for any function f,

$$U = f(bx - ay) \tag{59}$$

is a solution of the equation

$$a\frac{\partial U}{\partial x} + b\frac{\partial U}{\partial y} = 0. \tag{60}$$

We put $u = bx - ay$ and find from Eq. (58) that

$$\frac{\partial U}{\partial x} = bf'(u), \qquad \frac{\partial U}{\partial y} = -af'(u). \tag{61}$$

Consequently, Eq. (60) is satisfied.

25. Applications of the Total Differential.   Suppose that the total differential of a function $u(x,y)$ is known in the form

$$du = A\, dx + B\, dy. \tag{62}$$

Then

$$\frac{\partial u}{\partial s} = A\frac{\partial x}{\partial s} + B\frac{\partial y}{\partial s}. \tag{63}$$

If we take $s = x$, we find

$$\frac{\partial x}{\partial x} = 1 \quad \text{and} \quad \frac{\partial y}{\partial x} = 0, \tag{64}$$

since y is held fast in the second differentiation.   It follows that

$$\frac{\partial u}{\partial x} = A \cdot 1 + B \cdot 0 = A. \tag{65}$$

in a similar manner we may take $s = y$ and deduce that $\partial u/\partial y = B$.

That is, if u is a function of x and y, Eq. (62) implies that

$$A = \frac{\partial u}{\partial x} \qquad \text{and} \qquad B = \frac{\partial u}{\partial y}. \tag{66}$$

Use of this fact is often the simplest way to compute the partial derivatives of a function. For example, if

$$\theta = \tan^{-1}\left(\frac{y}{x}\right), \tag{67}$$

we have

$$d\theta = \frac{1}{1 + (y/x)^2} \cdot \frac{x\,dy - y\,dx}{x^2} = -\frac{y}{x^2 + y^2}dx + \frac{x}{x^2 + y^2}dy. \tag{68}$$

Since this is in the form (62), we may deduce from Eq. (66) that

$$\frac{\partial \theta}{\partial x} = -\frac{y}{x^2 + y^2} \qquad \text{and} \qquad \frac{\partial \theta}{\partial y} = \frac{x}{x^2 + y^2}. \tag{69}$$

Again, to compute the partial derivatives $\partial u/\partial x$ and $\partial u/\partial y$ from the relations

$$x = f(u,v), \qquad y = g(u,v), \tag{70}$$

we may proceed as follows. If we differentiate Eq. (70) partially with respect to x and simplify the derivatives on the left by Eq. (64), we find that

$$1 = \frac{\partial x}{\partial u}\frac{\partial u}{\partial x} + \frac{\partial x}{\partial v}\frac{\partial v}{\partial x} \qquad \text{and} \qquad 0 = \frac{\partial y}{\partial u}\frac{\partial u}{\partial x} + \frac{\partial y}{\partial v}\frac{\partial v}{\partial x}. \tag{71}$$

We may calculate the derivatives $\partial x/\partial u$, $\partial x/\partial v$, $\partial y/\partial u$, and $\partial y/\partial v$ from Eq. (70), substitute the values in Eq. (71), and thus obtain two first-degree equations in $\partial u/\partial x$ and $\partial v/\partial x$. By solving these equations as simultaneous, we shall find the derivatives sought.

To illustrate for a specific case, suppose that

$$x = r \cos \theta \qquad \text{and} \qquad y = r \sin \theta \tag{72}$$

and that we wish to find $\partial r/\partial x$ and $\partial \theta/\partial x$. Then the equations analogous to Eq. (71) are

$$1 = \cos \theta \frac{\partial r}{\partial x} - r \sin \theta \frac{\partial \theta}{\partial x}, \qquad 0 = \sin \theta \frac{\partial r}{\partial x} + r \cos \theta \frac{\partial \theta}{\partial x}. \tag{73}$$

The solution of these simultaneous equations is found to be

$$\frac{\partial r}{\partial x} = \cos \theta, \qquad \frac{\partial \theta}{\partial x} = -\frac{\sin \theta}{r}. \tag{74}$$

The calculations may be carried out in differential form as follows:

$$dx = \cos \theta \, dr - r \sin \theta \, d\theta, \qquad dy = \sin \theta \, dr + r \cos \theta \, d\theta. \tag{75}$$

By solving these equations for dr and $d\theta$, we find that

$$dr = \cos \theta \, dx + \sin \theta \, dy, \qquad d\theta = -\frac{\sin \theta}{r} \, dx + \frac{\cos \theta}{r} \, dy. \tag{76}$$

We now observe that these equations are in the form of (62), so that by the principle expressed in Eq. (66), we must have

$$\frac{\partial r}{\partial x} = \cos \theta, \qquad \frac{\partial r}{\partial y} = \sin \theta, \qquad \frac{\partial \theta}{\partial x} = -\frac{\sin \theta}{r}, \qquad \frac{\partial \theta}{\partial y} = \frac{\cos \theta}{r}. \tag{77}$$

We note that the last two of these are in agreement with Eq. (69), since

$$\left. \begin{aligned} -\frac{\sin \theta}{r} &= -\frac{r \sin \theta}{r^2} = -\frac{y}{x^2 + y^2}, \\ \frac{\cos \theta}{r} &= \frac{r \cos \theta}{r^2} = \frac{x}{x^2 + y^2}. \end{aligned} \right\} \tag{78}$$

Suppose that U is a function of x and y and Eqs. (72) hold, so that

$$U(x,y) = U(r \cos \theta, \, r \sin \theta). \tag{79}$$

Consider the problem of expressing $\partial^2 U/\partial x^2$ in terms of derivatives of U with respect to r and θ. We might replace s by x, x by r, and y by θ in Eq. (50). But this would involve the second derivatives of r and θ with respect to x. To avoid the necessity of computing these second derivatives, we solve our problem by a more direct method.

From Eqs. (79) and (77), we have

$$\frac{\partial U}{\partial x} = \frac{\partial U}{\partial r} \frac{\partial r}{\partial x} + \frac{\partial U}{\partial \theta} \frac{\partial \theta}{\partial x} = \cos \theta \frac{\partial U}{\partial r} - \frac{\sin \theta}{r} \frac{\partial U}{\partial \theta}. \tag{80}$$

We now replace U by $\partial U/\partial x$ in the relation (80) and obtain

$$\frac{\partial^2 U}{\partial x^2} = \frac{\partial}{\partial x}\left(\frac{\partial U}{\partial x}\right) = \cos \theta \frac{\partial}{\partial r}\left(\frac{\partial U}{\partial x}\right) - \frac{\sin \theta}{r} \frac{\partial}{\partial \theta}\left(\frac{\partial U}{\partial x}\right). \tag{81}$$

Next replace $\partial U / \partial x$ in the expression just written by the right member of Eq. (80). The result is

$$\cos \theta \, \frac{\partial}{\partial r} \left(\cos \theta \, \frac{\partial U}{\partial r} - \frac{\sin \theta}{r} \, \frac{\partial U}{\partial \theta} \right)$$
$$- \frac{\sin \theta}{r} \, \frac{\partial}{\partial \theta} \left(\cos \theta \, \frac{\partial U}{\partial r} - \frac{\sin \theta}{r} \, \frac{\partial U}{\partial \theta} \right). \quad (82)$$

Consequently,

$$\frac{\partial^2 U}{\partial x^2} = \cos^2 \theta \, \frac{\partial^2 U}{\partial r^2} - \frac{2 \cos \theta \sin \theta}{r} \, \frac{\partial^2 U}{\partial r \, \partial \theta} + \frac{\sin^2 \theta}{r^2} \, \frac{\partial^2 U}{\partial \theta^2}$$
$$+ \frac{2 \cos \theta \sin \theta}{r^2} \, \frac{\partial U}{\partial \theta} + \frac{\sin^2 \theta}{r} \, \frac{\partial U}{\partial r}. \quad (83)$$

Similarly, we may show that

$$\frac{\partial^2 U}{\partial y^2} = \sin^2 \theta \, \frac{\partial^2 U}{\partial r^2} + \frac{2 \cos \theta \sin \theta}{r} \, \frac{\partial^2 U}{\partial r \, \partial \theta} + \frac{\cos^2 \theta}{r^2} \, \frac{\partial^2 U}{\partial \theta^2}$$
$$- \frac{2 \cos \theta \sin \theta}{r^2} \, \frac{\partial U}{\partial \theta} + \frac{\cos^2 \theta}{r} \, \frac{\partial U}{\partial r}. \quad (84)$$

It follows from the two preceding equations that

$$\frac{\partial^2 U}{\partial x^2} + \frac{\partial^2 U}{\partial y^2} = \frac{\partial^2 U}{\partial r^2} + \frac{1}{r^2} \, \frac{\partial^2 U}{\partial \theta^2} + \frac{1}{r} \, \frac{\partial U}{\partial r}. \quad (85)$$

The expression on the left is called the *Laplacian* of U and occurs in many equations of mathematical physics. Thus Eq. (85) is often convenient when we wish to introduce polar coordinates.

26. Determinants. The solution of linear equations is greatly facilitated by the determinant notation, which we shall discuss briefly. We shall find later that the determinant notation simplifies many expressions that occur in solid geometry and mechanics.

A *determinant* is a square array of numbers, written between two vertical lines, whose value is defined by the following chain of relations. The determinant of the second order,

$$\begin{vmatrix} a_1 & b_1 \\ a_2 & b_2 \end{vmatrix} = a_1 b_2 - a_2 b_1. \quad (86)$$

The determinant of the third order,

$$\begin{vmatrix} a_1 & b_1 & c_1 \\ a_2 & b_2 & c_2 \\ a_3 & b_3 & c_3 \end{vmatrix} = a_1 \begin{vmatrix} b_2 & c_2 \\ b_3 & c_3 \end{vmatrix} - a_2 \begin{vmatrix} b_1 & c_1 \\ b_3 & c_3 \end{vmatrix} + a_3 \begin{vmatrix} b_1 & c_1 \\ b_2 & c_2 \end{vmatrix}. \quad (87)$$

The determinant of the fourth order,

$$\begin{vmatrix} a_1 & b_1 & c_1 & d_1 \\ a_2 & b_2 & c_2 & d_2 \\ a_3 & b_3 & c_3 & d_3 \\ a_4 & b_4 & c_4 & d_4 \end{vmatrix} = a_1 \begin{vmatrix} b_2 & c_2 & d_2 \\ b_3 & c_3 & d_3 \\ b_4 & c_4 & d_4 \end{vmatrix} - a_2 \begin{vmatrix} b_1 & c_1 & d_1 \\ b_3 & c_3 & d_3 \\ b_4 & c_4 & d_4 \end{vmatrix}$$

$$+ a_3 \begin{vmatrix} b_1 & c_1 & d_1 \\ b_2 & c_2 & d_2 \\ b_4 & c_4 & d_4 \end{vmatrix} - a_4 \begin{vmatrix} b_1 & c_1 & d_1 \\ b_2 & c_2 & d_2 \\ b_3 & c_3 & d_3 \end{vmatrix}. \quad (88)$$

And so on for determinants of higher orders.

We do not use the determinant notation for a single number, since it might be confused with the notation for the absolute value of a number. Nevertheless, we may think of a determinant of the first order consisting of one number and having as its value the number itself. This convention makes Eq. (86) of the same form as the later relations.

An easy way to evaluate determinants of the second and third orders is to draw diagonal lines as indicated below and to write positive products for those sloping downward and negative products for those sloping upward. Thus

$$\begin{vmatrix} a_1 & b_1 \\ a_2 & b_2 \end{vmatrix} = a_1 b_2 - a_2 b_1, \quad (89)$$

in agreement with Eq. (86). And

$$\begin{vmatrix} a_1 & b_1 & c_1 \\ a_2 & b_2 & c_2 \\ a_3 & b_3 & c_3 \end{vmatrix} \begin{matrix} a_1 & b_1 \\ a_2 & b_2 \\ a_3 & b_3 \end{matrix} = a_1 b_2 c_3 + a_3 b_1 c_2 + a_2 b_3 c_1 - a_3 b_2 c_1 - a_1 b_3 c_2 \\ - a_2 b_1 c_3. \quad (90)$$

This agrees with the result obtained by replacing the second-order determinants in Eq. (87) by their expansions. After a little practice the student will find it unnecessary to recopy the numbers a_1, b_1, etc., and actually to draw in the diagonal lines, but he will merely visualize these steps mentally and directly write down the six products that give the expansion.

We warn the student that there is no simple modification of this procedure that gives directly the expansion of determinants of higher order than the third. In particular, if we expand each of the third-order determinants of Eq. (88) into its six terms, we shall find the expansion of the fourth-order determinant into

24 terms. But no system of sloping straight lines leads to all these terms.

Most of the applications made in this text will involve determinants of the second and third orders only.

In a determinant, the numbers making up the square array are called *elements*. Those in horizontal lines make up the *rows*. Thus a_2, b_2, c_2 are the elements of the second row of the third-order determinant in Eq. (87). The elements of a vertical line make up a *column*. Thus in (87), c_1, c_2, c_3 are the elements of the third column.

We mention some elementary properties of determinants:

I. Interchanging the rows and columns of a determinant does not change its value. Thus

$$\begin{vmatrix} a_1 & a_2 & a_3 \\ b_1 & b_2 & b_3 \\ c_1 & c_2 & c_3 \end{vmatrix} = \begin{vmatrix} a_1 & b_1 & c_1 \\ a_2 & b_2 & c_2 \\ a_3 & b_3 & c_3 \end{vmatrix}. \tag{91}$$

II. Interchanging two rows of a determinant, or interchanging two columns, reverses the sign of its value. Thus

$$\begin{vmatrix} c_1 & b_1 & a_1 \\ c_2 & b_2 & a_2 \\ c_3 & b_3 & a_3 \end{vmatrix} = - \begin{vmatrix} a_1 & b_1 & c_1 \\ a_2 & b_2 & c_2 \\ a_3 & b_3 & c_3 \end{vmatrix}. \tag{92}$$

III. If all the elements of any one row, or of any one column, of a determinant are zero, the value of the determinant is zero. Thus the determinant in Eq. (87) is zero if $a_3 = b_3 = c_3 = 0$. Also it would equal zero if $c_1 = c_2 = c_3 = 0$.

IV. If a determinant has two of its rows, or two of its columns, identical, the value of the determinant is zero. Thus the determinant in Eq. (87) is zero if $a_1 = b_1$, $a_2 = b_2$, and $a_3 = b_3$.

These results are valid for determinants of any order. For determinants of the second and third orders they may be deduced from the expansions given in Eqs. (89) and (90) by a direct calculation.

27. Linear Equations. Let us consider the system of first-degree, or linear, equations:

$$\begin{aligned} a_1x + b_1y + c_1z &= d_1 \\ a_2x + b_2y + c_2z &= d_2. \\ a_3x + b_3y + c_3z &= d_3 \end{aligned} \tag{93}$$

Let us multiply these equations by

$$\begin{vmatrix} b_2 & c_2 \\ b_3 & c_3 \end{vmatrix}, \qquad - \begin{vmatrix} b_1 & c_1 \\ b_3 & c_3 \end{vmatrix}, \qquad \text{and} \qquad \begin{vmatrix} b_1 & c_1 \\ b_2 & c_2 \end{vmatrix}, \qquad (94)$$

respectively, and then add the resulting equations. We thus find

$$\begin{vmatrix} a_1 & b_1 & c_1 \\ a_2 & b_2 & c_2 \\ a_3 & b_3 & c_3 \end{vmatrix} x = \begin{vmatrix} d_1 & b_1 & c_1 \\ d_2 & b_2 & c_2 \\ d_3 & b_3 & c_3 \end{vmatrix}, \qquad (95)$$

since the coefficients of y and z may be written as determinants with two columns identical, and hence are zero by Property IV of Sec. 26. We may deduce similar equations in y and z. From these equations we may derive the equations,

$$x = \frac{\begin{vmatrix} d_1 & b_1 & c_1 \\ d_2 & b_2 & c_2 \\ d_3 & b_3 & c_3 \end{vmatrix}}{D}, \qquad y = \frac{\begin{vmatrix} a_1 & d_1 & c_1 \\ a_2 & d_2 & c_2 \\ a_3 & d_3 & c_3 \end{vmatrix}}{D}, \qquad z = \frac{\begin{vmatrix} a_1 & b_1 & d_1 \\ a_2 & b_2 & d_2 \\ a_3 & b_3 & d_3 \end{vmatrix}}{D}, \qquad (96)$$

provided that $D \neq 0$, where D, the determinant of the system (93), is

$$D = \begin{vmatrix} a_1 & b_1 & c_1 \\ a_2 & b_2 & c_2 \\ a_3 & b_3 & c_3 \end{vmatrix}. \qquad (97)$$

This proves that if the system (93) has a solution, it must be given by Eqs. (96). And, when $D \neq 0$, it may be proved by a direct substitution that (96) does provide a solution of Eqs. (93).

For any system of n linear equations, written in a form analogous to Eqs. (93), let us call the determinant of the nth order, whose elements are the coefficients of the left members, the determinant of the system and denote it by D. Then if $D \neq 0$, the system has just one solution. For each variable the solution equals the quotient of two determinants. That in the denominator is D, and that in the numerator is obtained by replacing, in D, that column formed of coefficients of the variable sought by the constants on the right.

The rule just stated may be applied to a system of two linear equations

$$\begin{aligned} a_1 x + b_1 y &= c_1, \\ a_2 x + b_2 y &= c_2. \end{aligned} \qquad (98)$$

In this case the solution is

$$x = \frac{\begin{vmatrix} c_1 & b_1 \\ c_2 & b_2 \end{vmatrix}}{D} \quad \text{and} \quad y = \frac{\begin{vmatrix} a_1 & c_1 \\ a_2 & c_2 \end{vmatrix}}{D}, \tag{99}$$

provided that

$$D = \begin{vmatrix} a_1 & b_1 \\ a_2 & b_2 \end{vmatrix} \neq 0. \tag{100}$$

28. Implicit Functions. Suppose that we are given three differentiable functions, each containing the six variables x, y, z, u, v, w. The system of equations obtained by equating each function to zero is

$$\begin{aligned} F(x,y,z,u,v,w) &= 0, \\ G(x,y,z,u,v,w) &= 0, \\ H(x,y,z,u,v,w) &= 0. \end{aligned} \tag{101}$$

If a particular set of values x_0, y_0, z_0, u_0, v_0, w_0 satisfies these equations, and for all values of u, v, w near u_0, v_0, w_0 the equations may be solved for x, y, and z to give the relations:

$$x = x(u,v,w), \qquad y = y(u,v,w), \qquad z = z(u,v,w), \tag{102}$$

then Eqs. (102) are said to be *implicitly* defined by the original system (101). When thought of as derived in this way, the right members of Eqs. (102) are referred to as *implicit functions*.

From the original system (101) we may deduce the differential relations:

$$\begin{aligned} F_x dx + F_y dy + F_z dz + F_u du + F_v dv + F_w dw &= 0, \\ G_x dx + G_y dy + G_z dz + G_u du + G_v dv + G_w dw &= 0, \\ H_x dx + H_y dy + H_z dz + H_u du + H_v dv + H_w dw &= 0. \end{aligned} \tag{103}$$

The partial derivatives of x, y, z with respect to u, v, w may be found by solving these equations. For example, by putting

$$dv = dw = 0 \tag{104}$$

and solving for dx, we find after division by du that

$$\frac{\partial x}{\partial u} = - \frac{\begin{vmatrix} F_u & F_y & F_z \\ G_u & G_y & G_z \\ H_u & H_y & H_z \end{vmatrix}}{\begin{vmatrix} F_x & F_y & F_z \\ G_x & G_y & G_z \\ H_x & H_y & H_z \end{vmatrix}} \quad \text{when} \quad \begin{vmatrix} F_x & F_y & F_z \\ G_x & G_y & G_z \\ H_x & H_y & H_z \end{vmatrix} \neq 0. \tag{105}$$

Whenever the last condition holds, the system (101) actually does define implicit functions $x(u,v,w)$, $y(u,v,w)$, $z(u,v,w)$ whose partial derivatives may be found from Eqs. (103) by the method just illustrated. Practically, we may compute the derivatives of the implicit functions directly. And this procedure can fail to be significant only if it leads to an indicated division by zero at some stage of the calculation.

In Eqs. (102) there are three independent variables u, v, w and three dependent variables x, y, z. The system (101) contained three functions F, G, H. Our procedure is fairly general, however, and may be applied to any similar case in which the number of dependent variables equals the number of functions or equations in the original system. For example, consider the system

$$F(x,y,s,t,u,v,w) = 0,$$
$$G(x,y,s,t,u,v,w) = 0 \tag{106}$$

with two equations, two dependent variables, x and y, and five independent variables s, t, u, v, w. To solve for x and y and then find $\partial x/\partial u$, we first form the total differential relations:

$$F_x dx + F_y dy + F_s ds + F_t dt + F_u du + F_v dv + F_w dw = 0,$$
$$G_x dx + G_y dy + G_s ds + G_t dt + G_u du + G_v dv + G_w dw = 0. \tag{107}$$

We then put $ds = dt = dv = dw = 0$, solve for dx, and divide by du to obtain

$$\frac{\partial x}{\partial u} = -\frac{\begin{vmatrix} F_u & F_y \\ G_u & G_y \end{vmatrix}}{\begin{vmatrix} F_x & F_y \\ G_x & G_y \end{vmatrix}} \quad \text{when } \begin{vmatrix} F_x & F_y \\ G_x & G_y \end{vmatrix} \neq 0. \tag{108}$$

29. Jacobian Determinants.

As Eqs. (105) and (108) illustrate, the determinants that appear in the expressions for the partial derivatives of implicit functions are all formed in the same manner. Each determinant with n^2 elements is formed from n functions in a given order and n variables in a given order. The partial derivatives of the first function with respect to the variables, taken in order, make up the first row, the derivatives of the second function make up the second row, and so on. Or, considered by columns, the partial derivatives with respect to the first variable of the functions, taken in order, make up the first column, the derivatives with respect to the second variable make up the second column, and so on.

Determinants of this kind are called *Jacobians*.   A convenient notation for them is

$$\frac{\partial(F_1, F_2, F_3)}{\partial(x_1, x_2, x_3)} = \begin{vmatrix} \dfrac{\partial F_1}{\partial x_1} & \dfrac{\partial F_1}{\partial x_2} & \dfrac{\partial F_1}{\partial x_3} \\ \dfrac{\partial F_2}{\partial x_1} & \dfrac{\partial F_2}{\partial x_2} & \dfrac{\partial F_2}{\partial x_3} \\ \dfrac{\partial F_3}{\partial x_1} & \dfrac{\partial F_3}{\partial x_2} & \dfrac{\partial F_3}{\partial x_3} \end{vmatrix}. \tag{109}$$

The symbol on the left is read "the Jacobian of the functions F_1, F_2, F_3 with respect to the variables x_1, x_2, x_3." The notation applies to any number of functions and variables.   For instance,

$$\frac{\partial(F_1, F_2)}{\partial(x_1, x_2)} = \begin{vmatrix} \dfrac{\partial F_1}{\partial x_1} & \dfrac{\partial F_1}{\partial x_2} \\ \dfrac{\partial F_2}{\partial x_1} & \dfrac{\partial F_2}{\partial x_2} \end{vmatrix}. \tag{110}$$

This notation enables us to write Eq. (105) in the abbreviated form:

$$\frac{\partial x}{\partial u} = - \frac{\dfrac{\partial(F, G, H)}{\partial(u, y, z)}}{\dfrac{\partial(F, G, H)}{\partial(x, y, z)}} \quad \text{when} \quad \frac{\partial(F, G, H)}{\partial(x, y, z)} \neq 0. \tag{111}$$

Similarly, Eq. (108) may be written in the form:

$$\frac{\partial x}{\partial u} = - \frac{\dfrac{\partial(F, G)}{\partial(u, y)}}{\dfrac{\partial(F, G)}{\partial(x, y)}} \quad \text{when} \quad \frac{\partial(F, G)}{\partial(x, y)} \neq 0. \tag{112}$$

Instead of using differentials as in the preceding section, we may solve the problem mentioned there by taking partial derivatives.   Thus by differentiating Eqs. (101) partially with respect to u, holding v and w fast, we find

$$F_x \frac{\partial x}{\partial u} + F_y \frac{\partial y}{\partial u} + F_z \frac{\partial z}{\partial u} + F_u = 0,$$

$$G_x \frac{\partial x}{\partial u} + G_y \frac{\partial y}{\partial u} + G_z \frac{\partial z}{\partial u} + G_u = 0, \tag{113}$$

$$H_x \frac{\partial x}{\partial u} + H_y \frac{\partial y}{\partial u} + H_z \frac{\partial z}{\partial u} + H_u = 0.$$

These equations may now be solved for $\partial x/\partial u$ to give Eq. (105) or (111). If several derivatives such as $\partial x/\partial u$, $\partial x/\partial v$, and $\partial x/\partial w$ were required, this method would involve more writing than the use of Eqs. (103).

The method of partial differentiation has the advantage of being easily applicable to the problem of finding higher derivatives. Suppose, for instance, that we desire $\partial^2 x/\partial u \, \partial v$. We differentiate Eqs. (113) partially with respect to v, holding u and w fast. The result is $F_{xv} \dfrac{\partial x}{\partial u} + F_{yv} \dfrac{\partial y}{\partial u} + F_{zv} \dfrac{\partial z}{\partial u} +$

$$F_x \frac{\partial^2 x}{\partial u \, \partial v} + F_y \frac{\partial^2 y}{\partial u \, \partial v} + F_z \frac{\partial^2 z}{\partial u \, \partial v} + \left(F_{xx} \frac{\partial x}{\partial v} + F_{xy} \frac{\partial y}{\partial v} + F_{xz} \frac{\partial z}{\partial v} \right) \frac{\partial x}{\partial u}$$

$$+ \left(F_{yx} \frac{\partial x}{\partial v} + F_{yy} \frac{\partial y}{\partial v} + F_{yz} \frac{\partial z}{\partial v} \right) \frac{\partial y}{\partial u} + \left(F_{zx} \frac{\partial x}{\partial v} + F_{zy} \frac{\partial y}{\partial v} + F_{zz} \frac{\partial z}{\partial v} \right) \frac{\partial z}{\partial u}$$

$$+ F_{ux} \frac{\partial x}{\partial v} + F_{uy} \frac{\partial y}{\partial v} + F_{uz} \frac{\partial z}{\partial v} + F_{uv} = 0, \quad (114)$$

and two similar equations with F replaced by G and H. We may regard this as a system of three linear simultaneous equations in the variables $\partial^2 x/\partial u \, \partial v$, $\partial^2 y/\partial u \, \partial v$, $\partial^2 z/\partial u \, \partial v$, and so solve for these in terms of the first partial derivatives. And we have already indicated methods of finding the first partial derivatives.

We note that the determinant of the system whose first equation is (114) is the same as that of the system (113), so that the new system may be solved whenever the inequality in (111) holds. In fact, implicit functions will be defined and their higher derivatives found as indicated whenever the Jacobian of the functions involved with respect to the dependent variables is different from zero.

30. Functional Dependence. Consider a pair of functions in two variables, $F(x,y)$ and $G(x,y)$. If these are so related that for all x and y the value of F depends only on the value of G, $F = f(G)$ and F is said to be *functionally dependent* on G. In this case we have

$$F(x,y) = f[G(x,y)]. \quad (115)$$

By partial differentiation similar to that of Eq. (58) we find

$$F_x = G_x f'(G) \quad \text{and} \quad F_y = G_y f'(G). \quad (116)$$

Consequently the Jacobian of the functions F and G with respect to x and y is

$$\frac{\partial(F,G)}{\partial(x,y)} = \begin{vmatrix} F_x & F_y \\ G_x & G_y \end{vmatrix} = \begin{vmatrix} G_x f'(G) & G_y f'(G) \\ G_x & G_y \end{vmatrix} = 0. \quad (117)$$

In general we may consider n functions of n variables. These are said to be *functionally dependent* if the value of some one of the functions depends only on the values of the remaining $n - 1$ functions. It is true in general that, whenever n functions of n variables are functionally dependent, then the Jacobian of the functions with respect to these variables is zero for all values of the variables. That is, it vanishes identically.

Conversely, when the partial derivatives are all continuous and the Jacobian vanishes identically, it may be proved that, in some suitably restricted range, some one of the functions is dependent on the rest.

31. Taylor's Theorem. We may deduce Taylor's theorem for functions of two real variables from that for one variable as follows: Write

$$x = a + ht, \qquad y = b + kt, \tag{118}$$

so that when a, b, h, and k are constant,

$$f(x,y) = f(a + ht, b + kt) = F(t). \tag{119}$$

Then by Eq. (117) of Sec. 10,

$$F(t) = F(0) + F'(0)t + F''(0)\frac{t^2}{2!} + \cdots + F^{(n)}(\theta t)\frac{t^n}{n!}, \tag{120}$$

for a suitable value of θ between 0 and 1.

But we have

$$F'(t) = \frac{df}{dt} = \frac{\partial f}{\partial x}\frac{dx}{dt} + \frac{\partial f}{\partial y}\frac{dy}{dt} = h\frac{\partial f}{\partial x} + k\frac{\partial f}{\partial y}$$
$$= \left(h\frac{\partial}{\partial x} + k\frac{\partial}{\partial y}\right)f. \tag{121}$$

Similarly,

$$F''(t) = \left(h\frac{\partial}{\partial x} + k\frac{\partial}{\partial y}\right)^2 f = h^2\frac{\partial^2 f}{\partial x^2} + 2hk\frac{\partial^2 f}{\partial x\,\partial y} + k^2\frac{\partial^2 f}{\partial y^2}, \tag{122}$$

$$F'''(t) = \left(h\frac{\partial}{\partial x} + k\frac{\partial}{\partial y}\right)^3 f, \tag{123}$$

and so on for the higher derivatives, since each application of the operator $(h\,\partial/\partial x + k\,\partial/\partial y)$ on any function of $x = a + ht$ and $y = b + kt$ is equivalent to differentiation with respect to t.

Let us next put $t = 1$ in Eq. (120) to obtain

$$F(1) = F(0) + F'(0) + F''(0) \frac{1}{2!} + \cdots + F^{(n)}(\theta) \frac{1}{n!}. \quad (124)$$

By using Eq. (119) and observing from Eq. (118) that when $t = 0$, $x = a$, and $y = b$ while when $t = 1$, $x = a + h$, and $y = b + k$, we may deduce from this that

$$f(a + h, b + k) = f(a,b) + \left(h \frac{\partial}{\partial x} + k \frac{\partial}{\partial y} \right) f(x,y) \Big|_{\substack{x=a \\ y=b}}$$

$$+ \frac{1}{2!} \left(h \frac{\partial}{\partial x} + k \frac{\partial}{\partial y} \right)^2 f(x,y) \Big|_{\substack{x=a \\ y=b}} + \cdots$$

$$+ \frac{1}{n!} \left(h \frac{\partial}{\partial x} + k \frac{\partial}{\partial y} \right)^n f(x,y) \Big|_{\substack{x=a+\theta h \\ y=b+\theta k}}. \quad (125)$$

The meaning of the bars and subscripts is that after the differentiations are carried out, we are to replace x,y by a,b in all terms but the last. In the last term we must put $x = a + \theta h$ and $y = b + \theta k$, with θ a suitably chosen number between 0 and 1.

If we denote the coefficient of $h^p k^q$ in (125) by A_{pq}, we find from expansions similar to (122) that

$$A_{pq} = \frac{1}{(p+q)!} {}^{p+q}C_p \frac{\partial^{p+q}f}{\partial x^p \partial y^q} \Big|_{\substack{x=a \\ y=b}} = \frac{1}{p!q!} \frac{\partial^{p+q}f}{\partial x^p \partial y^q} \Big|_{\substack{x=a \\ y=b}}. \quad (126)$$

If we now put

$$x = a + h, \qquad y = b + k \qquad \text{so that}$$
$$h = x - a, \qquad k = y - b \quad (127)$$

and write R_n for the last term, the expansion (125) takes the form:

$$f(x,y) = A_{00} + A_{10}(x - a) + A_{01}(y - b) + A_{20}(x - a)^2$$
$$+ A_{11}(x - a)(y - b) + A_{02}(y - b)^2 + \cdots + R_n. \quad (128)$$

32. Taylor's Series. By analogy with the discussion of Sec. 11, we are led to consider infinite series of the type,

$$A_{00} + A_{10}(x - a) + A_{01}(y - b) + A_{20}(x - a)^2 + \cdots$$
$$+ A_{pq}(x - a)^p(y - b)^q + \cdots, \quad (129)$$

and their relation to analytic functions of the two complex variables.

If $f(x,y)$ is a continuous function of the two complex variables x and y for all complex values near x_0 and y_0 and is an analytic function of x for each fixed y and an analytic function of y for each fixed x, then $f(x,y)$ is said to be *analytic* in both variables at x_0, y_0. Such a function will have partial derivatives of all orders at all points at which it is analytic.

Suppose next that $f(x,y)$ is analytic at a,b. Then for p and q, each either zero or a positive integer, a value of A_{pq} is defined by Eq. (126). The infinite series (129) which has these values as its coefficients is called the *Taylor's series* of $f(x,y)$ about a,b. It may be proved that, under these conditions, the infinite series will converge to the values of the function for some range of values of x and y near a and b.

Furthermore, if a series of the form (129) is given and known to converge for a particular pair of values x_1 and y_1, then the series will also converge for all x and y such that

$$|x - a| < |x_1 - a| \quad \text{and} \quad |y - b| < |y_1 - b|. \quad (130)$$

For values satisfying this relation, the sum of the series will be an analytic function of x and y, $f(x,y)$ which has the given series as its Taylor's series about a,b. That is, the coefficients of the series will be related to the derivatives of the function by Eq. (126).

Practically, the only series of this type that may readily be written explicitly are those obtained by combining elementary functions of one variable with other simple functions. For example,

$$\sin (x + y) = (x + y) - \frac{1}{3!} (x + y)^3$$

$$+ \frac{1}{5!} (x + y)^5 - \cdots. \quad (131)$$

In this and the preceding section we have stated several definitions and results concerning Taylor's theorem, Taylor's series, and analytic functions for the case of two variables. With minor modifications, all our results apply to functions of three or more variables.

33. Maxima and Minima. Suppose that a function of two real variables, $u(x,y)$, has a minimum value for $x = a$, $y = b$ at an interior point of a two-dimensional region throughout which it is differentiable. Then for y fixed and equal to b, the function of a single variable, $u(x,b)$ must have a minimum at x, a. Since this is not an end point of the region under consideration in finding the minimum, the derivative with respect to x must be zero. Thus,

$$\frac{d}{dx}[u(x,b)]\Big|_a = \frac{\partial u}{\partial x}\Big|_{a,b} = 0. \tag{132}$$

Similarly, we must have

$$\frac{d}{dy}[u(a,y)]\Big|_b = \frac{\partial u}{\partial y}\Big|_{a,b} = 0. \tag{133}$$

Since the total differential of u given by Eq. (18) is

$$du = \frac{\partial u}{\partial x}dx + \frac{\partial u}{\partial y}dy, \tag{134}$$

it follows that at a,b the total differential $du = 0$ for all values of dx and dy.

Similar considerations apply to a maximum, and also to a function of more than two variables, and lead us to a series of conditions. We state the condition for the case of three variables.

A necessary condition for a function $u(x,y,z)$ to have a maximum or a minimum for $x = a$, $y = b$, $z = c$ interior to a region of differentiability is that

$$\frac{\partial u}{\partial x} = 0, \qquad \frac{\partial u}{\partial y} = 0, \qquad \frac{\partial u}{\partial z} = 0, \qquad \text{or}$$

$$du = 0 \text{ for all } dx,\ dy,\ dz. \tag{135}$$

It is possible to deduce tests that show in certain cases that we actually have a maximum or minimum from a study of the Taylor's expansions. However, such tests are almost useless. Practically, we may usually decide such questions for a particular value of a and b by a direct consideration of

$$f(a + h,\ b + k) - f(a,b) \tag{136}$$

for small values of h and k.

For example, by setting the two partial derivatives equal to zero, we find $u(0,0) = 0$ as a possible maximum or minimum of each of the functions

$$x^2 + y^2, \qquad -x^2 - y^2, \qquad x^2 - y^2. \tag{137}$$

For values near, but not equal to 0,0, the first expression is always positive and so has a minimum. For similar values the second is always negative and so has a maximum. The third expression is positive for $y = 0$ and x near zero, but it is negative for $x = 0$ and y near zero. Consequently it has neither a maximum nor a minimum for $x,y = 0,0$.

34. Lagrange's Multipliers. Suppose we seek the minimum or maximum value of $f(x,y,z)$, subject to the condition

$$g(x,y,z) = 0. \tag{138}$$

A convenient method of practically detecting possible values is to solve the system of four equations in the four quantities x, y, z, and λ found by adjoining to (138) the equations

$$\frac{\partial f}{\partial x} = \lambda \frac{\partial g}{\partial x}, \qquad \frac{\partial f}{\partial y} = \lambda \frac{\partial g}{\partial y}, \qquad \frac{\partial f}{\partial z} = \lambda \frac{\partial g}{\partial z}. \tag{139}$$

The quantity λ is known as the *multiplier*, and the method is due to Lagrange. It is easily remembered by considering the system (139) as the condition for

$$f(x,y,z) - \lambda g(x,y,z) \tag{140}$$

to have a minimum or maximum when x, y, and z are unrestricted and λ is fixed. If x, y, and z satisfy (138), their differentials must be such that

$$\frac{\partial g}{\partial x} dx + \frac{\partial g}{\partial y} dy + \frac{\partial g}{\partial z} dz = 0. \tag{141}$$

Otherwise the differentials dx, dy, and dz are not restricted. But if $f(x,y,z)$ has a minimum for x, y, z subject to (138), its total differential must be zero subject to the latter relation, and

$$\frac{\partial f}{\partial x} dx + \frac{\partial f}{\partial y} dy + \frac{\partial f}{\partial z} dz = 0 \tag{142}$$

for all dx, dy, and dz satisfying (141).

Let us assume that $\partial g/\partial z \neq 0$, and calculate

$$\lambda = \frac{\partial f/\partial z}{\partial g/\partial z}. \tag{143}$$

Let us then add Eq. (141), multiplied by $-\lambda$, to Eq. (142). The result is

$$\left(\frac{\partial f}{\partial x} - \lambda \frac{\partial g}{\partial x}\right) dx + \left(\frac{\partial f}{\partial y} - \lambda \frac{\partial g}{\partial y}\right) dy = 0, \tag{144}$$

since by Eq. (143)

$$\frac{\partial f}{\partial z} - \lambda \frac{\partial g}{\partial z} = 0, \tag{145}$$

and the left member is the coefficient of dz.

Since we may satisfy Eq. (141) for arbitrary values of dx and dy by putting

$$dz = -\frac{\dfrac{\partial g}{\partial x}\, dx + \dfrac{\partial g}{\partial y}\, dy}{\dfrac{\partial g}{\partial z}}, \tag{146}$$

it follows that Eq. (144) must be true for all values of dx and dy. In particular, we may put $dx = 1$ and $dy = 0$, or $dx = 0$ and $dy = 1$. This shows that we must have

$$\frac{\partial f}{\partial x} - \lambda \frac{\partial g}{\partial x} = 0 \quad \text{and} \quad \frac{\partial f}{\partial y} - \lambda \frac{\partial g}{\partial y} = 0. \tag{147}$$

Since Eqs. (145) and (147) taken together are equivalent to the system (139), we have proved the validity of Lagrange's method for the particular case considered.

A similar process applies for any number of variables. For example, a necessary condition for $f(x,y,z)$ to have a minimum when x, y, z are subjected to the two conditions

$$g(x,y,z) = 0 \quad \text{and} \quad h(x,y,z) = 0 \tag{148}$$

may be found by adding to these last the conditions that

$$f(x,y,z) - \lambda g(x,y,z) - \mu h(x,y,z) \tag{149}$$

have a minimum when λ and μ are fixed and x, y, z are unrestricted.

If $U(x,y,z)$ denotes the potential energy in a force field, at a point where $dU = 0$ equilibrium can occur. If U has a minimum, the equilibrium is stable. If we put $U = f(x,y,z)$, condition (138) corresponds to constraining the particle considered to lie on a surface, while condition (148) corresponds to constraining the particle to lie on two surfaces, or on their curve of intersection.

As a specific example of the method of Lagrange, consider the following two-dimensional problem. Find the point on the curve

$$x^2 y = 2, \quad \text{or} \quad x^2 y - 2 = 0, \tag{150}$$

which is nearest to the origin. Here we must make the distance from the point x,y to the origin, or its square $x^2 + y^2$, a minimum subject to condition (150). Using the function

$$x^2 + y^2 - \lambda(x^2y - 2) \tag{151}$$

in place of expression (140) and equating its partial derivatives to zero, we find the equations

$$2x - \lambda 2xy = 0, \qquad 2y - \lambda x^2 = 0. \tag{152}$$

From these equations, combined with Eq. (150), we find that

$$\lambda = 1, \qquad x = \pm \sqrt{2}, \qquad y = 1, \tag{153}$$

so that the two points at minimum distance from the origin are $\sqrt{2},1$ and $-\sqrt{2},1$.

35. References. For a more complete introduction to the subject of determinants, the reader may consult H. B. Fine's *College Algebra*, pp. 492–519 or L. E. Dickson's *First Course in the Theory of Equations*, pp. 101–127. Either of these may be followed by the more advanced discussion given in M. Bôcher's *Introduction to Higher Algebra*, pp. 20–53 or in L. E. Dickson's *Modern Algebraic Theories*, pp. 39–63.

For proofs of the theorems on partial derivatives, the reader is referred to Chap. X and the end of Chap. XIII of the author's *Treatise on Advanced Calculus*.

EXERCISES II

In each case compute $\partial z/\partial x$ and $\partial z/\partial y$ from the first form and check by using the second form:

1. $z = \log \sqrt{x^2 - y^2} = \frac{1}{2} [\log (x - y) + \log (x + y)]$.

2. $z = e^x \cosh y + e^x \sinh y = e^{x+y}$.

3. $z = \sin^{-1} \dfrac{x}{\sqrt{x^2 + y^2}} = \tan^{-1} \dfrac{x}{y}$.

4. $z = \log \sqrt{\dfrac{(x - 2)^2 + y^2}{(x + 2)^2 + y^2}} = \dfrac{1}{2} \{\log [(x - 2)^2 + y^2] - \log [(x + 2)^2 + y^2]\}$.

5. $z = \dfrac{y}{x - y} = -1 + \dfrac{x}{x - y}$.

6. What is the size of the error in c as computed from $c = \dfrac{a \sin C}{\sin A}$, when $a = 100 \pm 2$ ft., $A = 60° \pm 1°$, and $C = 45° \pm 1°$? HINT: Approximate the error by $\left|\dfrac{\partial c}{\partial a} \Delta a\right| + \left|\dfrac{\partial c}{\partial A} \Delta A\right| + \left|\dfrac{\partial c}{\partial C} \Delta C\right|$, with $\Delta a = 2$, $\Delta A = \Delta C = 0.017$, since $1°$ equals 0.017 radian.

7. Let p denote the percentage error in F, as computed from $F = kx^a y^b z^c$, due to errors of p_1 per cent in x, p_2 per cent in y, and p_3 per cent in z. Show that $p = |a|p_1 + |b|p_2 + |c|p_3$. HINT: The total differential of $\log F$ is $\dfrac{dF}{F} = a\dfrac{dx}{x} + b\dfrac{dy}{y} + c\dfrac{dz}{z}$.

8. A square plate s ft. on a side is placed in a wind tunnel. When the air velocity is V ft./sec., the pressure on the plate in pounds is $P = 0.0015V^2 s^2$. What percentage error will result in the computed value of P if s is known to within 0.5 per cent, V is known to within 2 per cent, and the numerical coefficient may be in error by 4 per cent? HINT: Use Prob. 7.

9. What percentage error in T, as computed from $T = 2\pi \sqrt{I/mgL}$, results from errors of 1 per cent in I and of 0.5 per cent in each of the quantities m, g, and L? HINT: Use Prob. 7.

10. A function of any number of variables is *homogeneous* of the nth degree in these variables if, when the variables are each multiplied by a scale factor k, the function is multiplied by k^n, for Example, for three variables x, y, z: $f(kx,ky,kz) = k^n f(x,y,z)$. Show that $\partial f/\partial x$, $\partial f/\partial y$, $\partial f/\partial z$ are each homogeneous functions of the $(n-1)$st degree in x, y, z. HINT: Put $kx = u$ and differentiate with respect to x to obtain the relation: $kf_x(kx,ky,kz) = k^n f_x(x,y,z)$.

Illustrate Prob. 10 by verifying that each of the following functions is homogeneous of the degree n indicated and that it has a partial derivative with respect to x homogeneous of the $(n-1)$st degree.

11. $\sqrt{x^2 - y^2} \sin^{-1}\dfrac{y}{x}$, $\quad n = 1$, **12.** $z = \tan^{-1}\dfrac{y}{x}$, $\quad n = 0$.

13. $\log (x^2 + y^2 + z^2) - 2 \log x$, $\quad n = 0$.

14. xy, $\frac{1}{2}xy$, $\frac{1}{2}x(y + z)$, $\quad n = 2$. These formulas for the area of a rectangle, triangle, and trapezoid illustrate that all area formulas are homogeneous functions of the second degree in the lengths.

15. xyz, $\pi x^2 y$, $\frac{1}{3}\pi x^2 y$, $\quad n = 3$. These formulas for the volumes of a rectangular solid, cylinder, and cone illustrate that all volume formulas are homogeneous functions of the third degree in the lengths.

16. $ax^p y^q$, and hence any polynomial whose terms are all of this type with $p + q$ the same for each term, $\quad n = p + q$.

17. Show that the homogeneous function of the nth degree of Prob. 10 may be written $f(x,y,z) = x^n f(1, y/x, z/x)$. HINT: Put $k = 1/x$ in the equation of Prob. 10.

18. Illustrate Prob. 17 by expressing each of the functions of Probs. 11 to 16 in the form x^n times a function of ratios of the variables present.

Verify by direct calculation that $\dfrac{\partial}{\partial x}\left(\dfrac{\partial z}{\partial y}\right) = \dfrac{\partial}{\partial y}\left(\dfrac{\partial z}{\partial x}\right)$ in each of the following cases:

19. The functions $z(x,y)$ of Probs. 1 to 5.

20. $z = 6 \sin^3 x \cos^5 y$.

21. $z = ax^p y^q$, and hence $z = P(x,y)$ any polynomial in x and y.

22. $z = f(u)$ where $u = g(x,y)$, any function of x and y.

Prove the following statements:

23. If $z = f(x + \alpha, y + \beta)$, then $\partial z/\partial x = \partial z/\partial \alpha$ and $\partial z/\partial y = \partial z/\partial \beta$.

24. If $x = r \cosh \theta$, $y = r \sinh \theta$, then $(\partial x/\partial r)_\theta = (\partial r/\partial x)_y$ and $(\partial y/\partial r)_\theta = -(\partial r/\partial y)_x$.

25. If $x = r \cosh \theta$ and $y = r \sinh \theta$, then for any function $U(x,y)$,
$$\left(\frac{\partial U}{\partial x}\right)^2 - \left(\frac{\partial U}{\partial y}\right)^2 = \left(\frac{\partial U}{\partial r}\right)^2 - \frac{1}{r^2}\left(\frac{\partial U}{\partial \theta}\right)^2.$$

26. Prove Euler's theorem on homogeneous functions of the nth degree: $x\dfrac{\partial f}{\partial x} + y\dfrac{\partial f}{\partial y} + z\dfrac{\partial f}{\partial z} = nf$. HINT: In the first equation of Prob. 10, put $kx = u$, $ky = v$, $kz = w$. Then differentiate with respect to k to obtain $x\dfrac{\partial f}{\partial u} + y\dfrac{\partial f}{\partial v} + z\dfrac{\partial f}{\partial w} = nk^{n-1}f(x,y,z)$. Now let $k = 1$.

27. By a direct substitution show that each of the functions of Probs. 11 to 16 satisfies the equation of Euler's theorem, Prob. 26.

28. If $f(x,y,z)$ is homogeneous of the nth degree, show that
$\left(x\dfrac{\partial}{\partial x} + y\dfrac{\partial}{\partial y} + z\dfrac{\partial}{\partial z}\right)^2 f(x,y,z) = n^2 f(x,y,z)$; but that the expression
$\left(x\dfrac{\partial}{\partial u} + y\dfrac{\partial}{\partial v} + z\dfrac{\partial}{\partial w}\right)^2 f(u,v,w)\big|_{u=x,v=y,w=z} = n(n-1)f(x,y,z)$. HINT: Apply Prob. 26 twice and use the result of Prob. 10.

29. If $z = (x^2 + y^2) \sin (x^2 + y^2)$, show that $y\dfrac{\partial z}{\partial x} - x\dfrac{\partial z}{\partial y} = 0$.

30. Show that the equation of Prob. 29 is satisfied by $z = f(x^2 + y^2)$, where $f(u)$ is any function.

31. Show that the function $z = y^2 \sin (x/y)$ satisfies the equation $x\dfrac{\partial z}{\partial x} + y\dfrac{\partial z}{\partial y} = 2z$, either directly or by applying Prob. 26 to a homogeneous function of the second degree in x and y.

32. Show that if $z = f\left(\dfrac{y}{x}\right)$ then $x\dfrac{\partial z}{\partial x} + y\dfrac{\partial z}{\partial y} = 0$, either directly or by applying Prob. 26 to a homogeneous function of the zero-th degree in x and y.

33. If $z = \tan^{-1} xy$, then $x\dfrac{\partial z}{\partial x} - y\dfrac{\partial z}{\partial y} = 0$.

34. Show that the equation of Prob. 33 is satisfied by $z = f(xy)$, where $f(u)$ is any function.

35. If $z = xe^{1/y}$, then $x\dfrac{\partial z}{\partial x} + y^2\dfrac{\partial z}{\partial y} = 0$.

36. Show that the partial differential equation of Prob. 35 is satisfied by $z = f(\log x + 1/y)$, where $f(u)$ is any function.

37. If $z = f[F(x) + G(y)]$, then $G'(y) \dfrac{\partial z}{\partial x} - F'(x) \dfrac{\partial z}{\partial y} = 0$, where $f(u)$, $F(x)$, and $G(y)$ are any functions, and the primes denote derivatives. Show that Eqs. (59) and (60) of the text, as well as Probs. 29, 30, and 32 to 36 can all be considered as special cases of this result.

38. If $z = f\left(\dfrac{x^2 + y^2}{y^2}\right)$, show that $x \dfrac{\partial z}{\partial x} + y \dfrac{\partial z}{\partial y} = 0$, either directly or by using Prob. 32.

39. Let $u = \dfrac{y}{x}$, $v = \dfrac{z^m}{x}$, and $f(u,v) = 0$. Show that as a consequence $mx \dfrac{\partial z}{\partial x} + my \dfrac{\partial z}{\partial y} = z$, either directly or by applying Prob. 26 to a homogeneous function of the $(1/m)$th degree in x and y.

40. If $x = u^2$, $y = 4u + 5v$, compute the partial derivatives of u and v with respect to x and y by the method used in the text to find Eq. (74). Check by solving for u and v and then differentiating.

41. If $(1 - y^2) \dfrac{d^2y}{dx^2} + y \left(\dfrac{dy}{dx}\right)^2 + (1 - y^2)^{3/2} = 0$, and $y = \sin z$, find the differential equation satisfied by $z(x)$.

42. If $x^2 \dfrac{d^2y}{dx^2} + x \dfrac{dy}{dx} + (x^2 - n^2)y = 0$, and $y = x^n z$, find the differential equation satisfied by $z(x)$.

43. If the conditions of Prob. 42 hold and in addition $x = 2\sqrt{t}$, find the differential equation satisfied by $z(t)$.

44. If $(1 - x^2) \dfrac{d^2y}{dx^2} - 2x \dfrac{dy}{dx} + n(n + 1)y = 0$, and $x = \cos\theta$, find the differential equation satisfied by $y(\theta)$.

45. The curvature of a plane curve is $\dfrac{1}{\rho} = \dfrac{d^2y/dx^2}{[1 + (dy/dx)^2]^{3/2}}$. Show that if $x = f(t)$, $y = g(t)$ the transformed expression for the curvature is

$$\frac{1}{\rho} = \frac{\dfrac{dx}{dt}\dfrac{d^2y}{dt^2} - \dfrac{dy}{dt}\dfrac{d^2x}{dt^2}}{\left[\left(\dfrac{dx}{dt}\right)^2 + \left(\dfrac{dy}{dt}\right)^2\right]^{3/2}}.$$

46. By transforming the expression given in Prob. 45, show that in polar coordinates $\dfrac{1}{\rho} = \dfrac{r^2 + 2\left(\dfrac{dr}{d\theta}\right)^2 - r \dfrac{d^2r}{d\theta^2}}{\left[r^2 + \left(\dfrac{dr}{d\theta}\right)^2\right]^{3/2}}.$

47. Show that, if $x = r \cos \theta$ and $y = r \sin \theta$, $\dfrac{x \dfrac{dy}{dx} - y}{x + y \dfrac{dy}{dx}} = r \dfrac{d\theta}{dr}$, and

check by interpreting the right member as $\tan \psi$, and the left member as $\tan (\tau - \theta)$, where the meaning of ψ, τ, and θ is shown in Fig. 11.

48. If $f(x,y) = 0$, show that $\dfrac{dy}{dx}$ $= -\dfrac{f_x}{f_y}$, while the second derivative $\dfrac{d^2y}{dx^2} = -\dfrac{f_{xx}f_y{}^2 - 2f_{xy}f_xf_y + f_{yy}f_x{}^2}{f_y{}^3}$ where the subscripts denote partial differentiation.

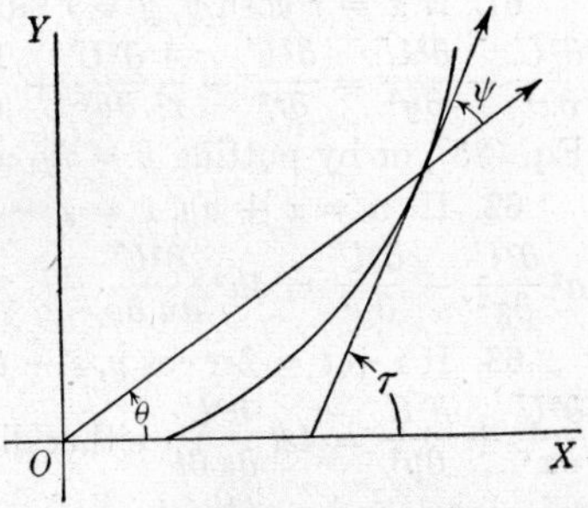

49. If $x^n + y^n = 1$, find dy/dx and d^2y/dx^2 by using Prob. 48, and check by means of the solved form $y = (1 - x^n)^{1/n}$.

50. If $x^3 + y^3 = xy$, find dy/dx by using Prob. 48.

Fig. 11.

51. By putting $y = tx$ in the equation of Prob. 50, show that $x = t/(1 + t^3)$, and hence $y = t^2/(1 + t^3)$. Find dx/dt and dy/dt and use these to check the result of Prob. 50.

52. If $u = f(x,y)$ and $y = F(x)$, compute d^2u/dx^2.

53. Show that $z = f\left(\dfrac{y}{x}\right) + xg\left(\dfrac{y}{x}\right)$ satisfies the partial differential equation $x^2 \dfrac{\partial^2 z}{\partial x^2} + 2xy \dfrac{\partial^2 z}{\partial x\, \partial y} + y^2 \dfrac{\partial^2 z}{\partial y^2} = 0$, either directly or by using the second result of Prob. 28.

54. If $U = \sin (x - ct) + \cos (x + ct)$, then $\dfrac{\partial^2 U}{\partial t^2} = c^2 \dfrac{\partial^2 U}{\partial x^2}$.

55. Show that the differential equation of Prob. 54 is satisfied by $U = f(x - ct) + g(x + ct)$, where $f(u)$ and $g(v)$ are any functions.

56. If $U = f(x + iy) + g(x - iy)$, prove $\partial^2 U/\partial x^2 + \partial^2 U/\partial y^2 = 0$.

57. Let $w = F(z)$ be any analytic function of the complex variable $z = x + iy$, and let $u(x,y)$ and $v(x,y)$ be two real functions such that $w = u(x,y) + iv(x,y)$. Show that $U = u(x,y)$ and $U = v(x,y)$ are each solutions of the equation of Prob. 56. HINT: In any power series for $F(z)$, replace i by $-i$ in $x + iy$ and the constants to define the function $G(x - iy) = u(x,y) - iv(x,y)$. Then $u = \frac{1}{2}[F(x + iy) + G(x - iy)]$, $v = i/2[-F(x + iy) + G(x - iy)]$. Now use Prob. 56.

58. Show that $U = \tan^{-1} \dfrac{y}{x}$ is a solution of $\dfrac{\partial^2 U}{\partial x^2} + \dfrac{\partial^2 U}{\partial y^2} = 0$, either directly or by using Prob. 57 with $F(z) = \log z$.

59. Show that $U = e^{a\theta} \cos (a \log r)$ is a solution of the equation $\dfrac{\partial^2 U}{\partial r^2} + \dfrac{1}{r^2} \dfrac{\partial^2 U}{\partial \theta^2} + \dfrac{1}{r} \dfrac{\partial U}{\partial r} = 0$, either directly or by using Prob. 57 with $F(z) = z^{-ia} = e^{-ia \log z} = e^{a\theta - ia \log r}$, and Eq. (85).

60. If $z = f(x,y)$ and $x = e^u$, $y = e^v$, verify that the differential equation $\dfrac{\partial^2 z}{\partial u^2} + \dfrac{\partial^2 z}{\partial v^2} = x^2 \dfrac{\partial^2 z}{\partial x^2} + y^2 \dfrac{\partial^2 z}{\partial y^2} + x \dfrac{\partial z}{\partial x} + y \dfrac{\partial z}{\partial y}$ is satisfied.

61. If $x = r \cosh \theta$, $y = r \sinh \theta$ show that for $U = f(x,y)$ satisfies: $\dfrac{\partial^2 U}{\partial x^2} - \dfrac{\partial^2 U}{\partial y^2} = \dfrac{\partial^2 U}{\partial r^2} - \dfrac{1}{r^2} \dfrac{\partial^2 U}{\partial \theta^2} + \dfrac{1}{r} \dfrac{\partial U}{\partial r}$, either by the method used to get Eq. (85), or by putting $y = iy_1$ and $\theta = i\theta_1$ in Eqs. (72) and (85).

62. If $u = x + ay$, $v = x - ay$, verify that $U = f(x,y)$ satisfies $a^2 \dfrac{\partial^2 U}{\partial x^2} - \dfrac{\partial^2 U}{\partial y^2} = 4a^2 \dfrac{\partial^2 U}{\partial u \, \partial v}$.

63. If $s + t = 2e^x \cos y$, $s - t = 2ie^x \sin y$, show that for $U = f(s,t)$: $\dfrac{\partial^2 U}{\partial x^2} + \dfrac{\partial^2 U}{\partial y^2} = 4st \dfrac{\partial^2 U}{\partial s \, \partial t}$, either directly or by using Prob. 62 with $a = i$, $u = \log s$, and $v = \log t$.

64. If $U = f(x,y)$ and $x = e^u \cos v$, $y = e^u \sin v$, verify the equations
$$\frac{\partial^2 U}{\partial u^2} = x^2 \frac{\partial^2 U}{\partial x^2} + 2xy \frac{\partial^2 U}{\partial x \, \partial y} + y^2 \frac{\partial^2 U}{\partial y^2} + x \frac{\partial U}{\partial x} + y \frac{\partial U}{\partial y} \text{ and}$$
$$\frac{\partial^2 U}{\partial v^2} = y^2 \frac{\partial^2 U}{\partial x^2} - 2xy \frac{\partial^2 U}{\partial x \, \partial y} + x^2 \frac{\partial^2 U}{\partial y^2} - x \frac{\partial U}{\partial x} - y \frac{\partial U}{\partial y}.$$

65. If the conditions of Prob. 64 hold, first derive the equation $\dfrac{\partial^2 U}{\partial u^2} + \dfrac{\partial^2 U}{\partial v^2} = (x^2 + y^2) \left(\dfrac{\partial^2 U}{\partial x^2} + \dfrac{\partial^2 U}{\partial y^2} \right)$, and deduce as a consequence $\dfrac{\partial^2 U}{\partial x^2} + \dfrac{\partial^2 U}{\partial y^2} = e^{-2u} \left(\dfrac{\partial^2 U}{\partial u^2} + \dfrac{\partial^2 U}{\partial v^2} \right)$.

66. If U is a function of $u(x,y)$ and $v(x,y)$, derive the relation $\dfrac{\partial^2 U}{\partial x^2} = \dfrac{\partial^2 U}{\partial u^2} \left(\dfrac{\partial u}{\partial x} \right)^2 + 2 \dfrac{\partial^2 U}{\partial u \, \partial v} \dfrac{\partial u}{\partial x} \dfrac{\partial v}{\partial x} + \dfrac{\partial^2 U}{\partial v^2} \left(\dfrac{\partial v}{\partial x} \right)^2 + \dfrac{\partial U}{\partial u} \dfrac{\partial^2 u}{\partial x^2} + \dfrac{\partial U}{\partial v} \dfrac{\partial^2 v}{\partial x^2}$, and show that $\partial^2 U / \partial y^2$ is a similar expression with x replaced by y.

67. If $u(x,y)$ and $v(x,y)$ satisfy the equations $\dfrac{\partial u}{\partial x} = \dfrac{\partial v}{\partial y}$, $\dfrac{\partial u}{\partial y} = -\dfrac{\partial v}{\partial x}$, show that $\dfrac{\partial^2 U}{\partial x^2} + \dfrac{\partial^2 U}{\partial y^2} = \left[\dfrac{\partial^2 U}{\partial u^2} + \dfrac{\partial^2 U}{\partial v^2} \right] \left[\left(\dfrac{\partial u}{\partial x} \right)^2 + \left(\dfrac{\partial u}{\partial y} \right)^2 \right]$.

68. By using the expressions in the hint to Prob. 57, show that the functions u and v of Prob. 57 satisfy the given conditions of Prob. 67. If $w = \log z$ in Prob. 57, $u = \log \sqrt{x^2 + y^2}$ and $v = \tan^{-1} \dfrac{y}{x}$. Also $z = e^w$ and $x = e^u \cos v$, $y = e^u \sin v$. Thus Prob. 65 is a special case of Prob. 67.

Evaluate each of the following determinants:

69. $\begin{vmatrix} 1 & 1 & 0 \\ 2 & -3 & 2 \\ -3 & 0 & 1 \end{vmatrix}$.   **70.** $\begin{vmatrix} 2 & -2 & 1 \\ -3 & 1 & 2 \\ 1 & 2 & 3 \end{vmatrix}$.   **71.** $\begin{vmatrix} 1 & 3 & 4 \\ 5 & 2 & 1 \\ -1 & 1 & -1 \end{vmatrix}$.

Using the method of determinants of Sec. 27, solve each of the following systems of linear equations:

72. $2x + 3y = 11,\ x - y = 3.$

73. $x - 3y + z = -6,\ 2x - y + z = 2,\ 3x - 4y + 3z = -3.$

74. $x + y - z = 0,\ x - y + z = 4,\ -x + y + z = 2.$

Let any number of variables be connected by a single equation of the form $f(x,y,z,u,v,\ \cdots\ ) = 0$. Prove the following relations between partial derivatives, each formed with all variables except the two directly involved held fast:

75. $\dfrac{\partial y}{\partial x} = -\dfrac{f_x}{f_y}.$ **76.** $\dfrac{\partial x}{\partial y}\dfrac{\partial y}{\partial x} = 1.$ **77.** $\dfrac{\partial x}{\partial y}\dfrac{\partial y}{\partial z}\dfrac{\partial z}{\partial x} = -1.$

78. $\dfrac{\partial x}{\partial y}\dfrac{\partial y}{\partial z}\dfrac{\partial z}{\partial u}\dfrac{\partial u}{\partial x} = 1.$ **79.** $\dfrac{\partial x}{\partial y}\dfrac{\partial y}{\partial z}\dfrac{\partial z}{\partial u}\dfrac{\partial u}{\partial v}\dfrac{\partial v}{\partial x} = -1.$

80. If $x^2 + 2y^2 + 4z^2 - u^2 - v^2 - w^2 = 0$, verify the equations of Probs. 76 to 79 after evaluating each of the partial derivatives.

81. If $f(v,p,T) = 0$, and $\alpha_p = \dfrac{1}{v}\left(\dfrac{\partial v}{\partial T}\right)_p$ while $E_T = -v\left(\dfrac{\partial p}{\partial v}\right)_T$, show that $\left(\dfrac{\partial p}{\partial T}\right)_v = \alpha_p E_T.$

82. If $u = f(x,y),\ v = g(x,y)$ may be solved for x and y, prove that the partial derivatives satisfy $\left(\dfrac{\partial u}{\partial x}\right)_y \left(\dfrac{\partial x}{\partial u}\right)_v + \left(\dfrac{\partial v}{\partial x}\right)_y \left(\dfrac{\partial x}{\partial v}\right)_u = 1$ and

$\left(\dfrac{\partial u}{\partial x}\right)_y \left(\dfrac{\partial y}{\partial u}\right)_v + \left(\dfrac{\partial v}{\partial x}\right)_y \left(\dfrac{\partial y}{\partial v}\right)_u = 0.$ HINT: The first expression is $(\partial x/\partial x)_y = 1$, and the second is $(\partial y/\partial x)_y = 0$.

83. If $u = e^x \cos y,\ v = e^x \sin y$, verify the equations of Prob. 82 after evaluating each of the partial derivatives.

84. If $F(x,y,z) = 0$ and $G(x,y,z) = 0$, we may consider any two of the variables x,y,z as a function of the third. Deduce the relations

$$\frac{dx}{\partial(F,G)/\partial(y,z)} = \frac{dy}{\partial(F,G)/\partial(z,x)} = \frac{dz}{\partial(F,G)/\partial(x,y)},$$ if no denominator is zero.

In Probs. 84 to 94 it is assumed that all Jacobians used as denominators are not zero for the values considered.

85. Use Prob. 84 to find the ratio of the differentials dx,dy,dz when $x^2 + y^2 + z^2 = 1$ and $x^2 + 2y^2 + 3z^2 = 2$.

86. If $x = f(u,v)$, $y = g(u,v)$, $z = h(u,v)$, we may consider z as a function of x and y. Show that $\left(\dfrac{\partial z}{\partial x}\right)_y = \dfrac{\partial(z,y)/\partial(u,v)}{\partial(x,y)/\partial(u,v)}$.

87. If $x = f(u,v,w)$, $y = g(u,v,w)$, $z = h(u,v,w)$, show that

$$\left(\frac{\partial x}{\partial u}\right)_{yz} = \frac{\partial(x,y,z)/\partial(u,v,w)}{\partial(y,z)/\partial(v,w)}.$$

88. If x,y,z,t are each functions of u and v, show that as a consequence $\dfrac{\partial(x,y)}{\partial(u,v)} \dfrac{\partial(z,t)}{\partial(u,v)} + \dfrac{\partial(y,z)}{\partial(u,v)} \dfrac{\partial(x,t)}{\partial(u,v)} + \dfrac{\partial(z,x)}{\partial(u,v)} \dfrac{\partial(y,t)}{\partial(u,v)} = 0$. HINT: Divide by the first term and use Prob. 86 to get $1 - \left(\dfrac{\partial z}{\partial x}\right)_y \left(\dfrac{\partial x}{\partial z}\right)_t - \left(\dfrac{\partial z}{\partial y}\right)_x \left(\dfrac{\partial y}{\partial z}\right)_t = 0$, or $\left(\dfrac{\partial z}{\partial z}\right)_t = 1$. Now reverse the steps.

89. If $f(x,y,u,v) = 0$ and $g(x,y,u,v) = 0$, show that

$$\left(\frac{\partial u}{\partial x}\right)_y = -\frac{\partial(f,g)/\partial(x,v)}{\partial(f,g)/\partial(u,v)}.$$

90. Use Prob. 89 to evaluate $(\partial u/\partial x)_y$ when $x + y + u + v - 4 = 0$ and $x^2 + y^2 + u^2 + v^2 - 4 = 0$.

91. If E is a function of S and v, and $dE = T\,dS - p\,dv$, show that $(\partial E/\partial S)_v = T$, $(\partial E/\partial v)_S = -p$, and hence $(\partial T/\partial v)_S = -(\partial p/\partial S)_v$.

92. If the quantities of Prob. 91 are all expressed as functions of any pair of variables α, β show that $\partial(T,S)/\partial(\alpha,\beta) = \partial(p,v)/\partial(\alpha,\beta)$. HINT: Express the derivatives in the last equation of Prob. 91 in terms of Jacobians with respect to α,β by applying Prob. 86 with suitably modified notation.

93. Prove that $\dfrac{\partial(x,y)}{\partial(u,v)} \dfrac{\partial(u,v)}{\partial(s,t)} = \dfrac{\partial(x,y)}{\partial(s,t)}$. A similar result holds for Jacobians of any order.

94. Show that $\dfrac{\partial(x,y)}{\partial(u,v)} = \dfrac{1}{\partial(u,v)/\partial(x,y)}$, either directly or as a special case of Prob. 93.

95. If $x = e^u \cos v$, $y = e^u \sin v$, verify the equation of Prob. 94 after evaluating each Jacobian.

96. If $u = \log x + \log y$ and $v = \cos xy$, verify that $\partial(u,v)/\partial(x,y)$ is identically zero. Also show directly that v is a function of u by eliminating x or y.

For each of the following functions, write the first few terms of the Taylor's series about $0,0$:

97. $\cos xy + xy \sin xy$.   **98.** $e^y \log (1 + x)$.

99. $e^x \cos y$. Check as the real part of the series for e^{x+iy}.

100. Find the value of x,y which makes the function of two variables $x^4 + y^4 - 4x - 32y + 2$ a minimum.

101. Find the point inside a triangle at which the sum of the squares of the distances to the vertices is a minimum.

102. A rectangular box, open at the top, is to hold 500 in.³ Find the dimensions for which the surface is a minimum.

103. A tank, open at the top, is in the form of an inverted cone surmounted by a cylinder. If the volume is given as 706.9 ft.³ (that is, 225π ft.³), find the dimensions for which the surface is least.

104. If $Ax^2 + 2Bxy + Cy^2 = 1$, where $AC > B^2$, then the maximum and minimum values of $u = x^2 + y^2$ are $\dfrac{A + C \pm \sqrt{(A - C)^2 + 4B^2}}{2(AC - B^2)}$.
Prove this statement.

105. Show that the area of the ellipse of Prob. 104 is expressible as $S = \pi/\sqrt{AC - B^2}$. HINT: $S = \pi ab$, where a and b are the semiaxes. And a^2 and b^2 are the maximum and minimum values of u found in Prob. 104.

106. Find the point in the plane $Ax + By + Cz = D$ which is nearest to the origin. HINT: Minimize $u = x^2 + y^2 + z^2$ subject to the condition $Ax + By + Cz - D = 0$.

107. Find the point in the surface $2xy^4z^4 = 1$ which is nearest to the origin. HINT: Minimize $u = x^2 + y^2 + z^2$ subject to the condition $\log x + 4 \log y + 4 \log z + \log 2 = 0$, for the case x, y, z positive.

108. Find the value of x,y,z which makes $x^2y^4z^6$ a maximum subject to the condition $x + y + z = 1$, if x,y,z are all positive.

109. Let S denote the area of a triangle whose sides are a, b, and c. From any point P inside the triangle draw perpendiculars to the sides and denote their lengths by u, v, and w. Show that these lengths may have any values that satisfy the condition $au + bv + cw = 2S$, and find the values of u, v, and w for which $u^2 + v^2 + w^2$ is a minimum.

CHAPTER III

VECTORS, CURVES, AND SURFACES IN SPACE

The main topic of this chapter is the differential geometry of twisted curves and surfaces in space. We begin with an introduction to solid analytic geometry. In this connection we present some elementary parts of vector analysis, the use of which greatly simplifies the entire discussion.

36. Coordinates in Space. We may locate points in three dimensions by using a coordinate system constructed as follows: Through any point O, selected as origin, we draw three mutually perpendicular lines, the x, y, and z axes. On each of these we take a positive direction, as indicated by the arrows in Fig. 12. We shall use right-handed systems. That is, we so choose the positive directions that a right-threaded screw along the z axis will advance in the positive direction when given the 90° turn which takes the positive x axis into the positive y axis.

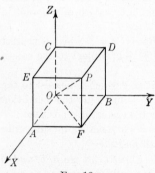

Fig. 12.

The coordinate axes determine three coordinate planes, the yz, zx, and xy planes. The signed distances of any point P from these planes are denoted by x, y, and z and are called the *coordinates* of P.

By drawing planes through P parallel to the coordinate planes, we may construct the rectangular parallelepiped shown in Fig. 12. The points D, E, F are the projections of P on the yz, zx, and xy planes. The points A, B, C are the projections of P on the x, y, and z axes.

$$x = DP = BF = CE = OA. \tag{1}$$

Thus x is the x coordinate of the projection F in the xy plane, or of the projection E in the zx plane. Also x is the distance from O to A, the projection on the x axis.

In the figure the signs of x, y, and z are all plus since the directions from D to P, E to P, and F to P are those taken as positive on the coordinate axes. But if P were behind the yz plane, x would be minus; if P were to the left of the zx plane, y would be minus; and if P were below the xy plane, z would be minus.

If a, b, c are given values of the coordinates, the point P may be constructed either by taking $OA = a$, $AF = b$, and $FP = c$; or by taking $OA = a$, $OB = b$, and $OC = c$ on the coordinate axes and thence determining the parallelepiped having P as the vertex opposite to O.

37. The Segment $\overline{OP}$. Let P be the point x,y,z and consider the directed line segment $\overline{OP}$. From the right triangles OFP

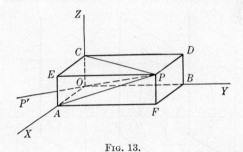

Fig. 13.

and OAF, we find

$$OP^2 = OF^2 + FP^2 \quad \text{and} \quad OF^2 = OA^2 + AF^2,$$

so that

$$OP^2 = OA^2 + AF^2 + FP^2 = x^2 + y^2 + z^2. \tag{2}$$

This determines OP, the length of $\overline{OP}$.

The direction of $\overline{OP}$ may be fixed by the cosines of the angles POX, POY, POZ which the segment makes with the positive coordinate axes. The cosines, which we denote by l,m,n are called the *direction cosines* of $\overline{OP}$. The angles themselves are called the *direction angles* of $\overline{OP}$. The direction angles, denoted by α,β,γ, may always be considered as having values in the range $0 \leqq \theta \leqq \pi$. (π radians = 180°.) From the right triangles OAP, OBP, OCP we find

$$l = \cos \alpha = \frac{OA}{OP} = \frac{x}{OP}. \qquad \text{Similarly, } m = \cos \beta = \frac{y}{OP},$$

$$n = \cos \gamma = \frac{z}{OP}. \quad (3)$$

From these relations and (2) we may deduce that

$$l^2 + m^2 + n^2 = \cos^2 \alpha + \cos^2 \beta + \cos^2 \gamma = 1. \qquad (4)$$

If we extend the line PO through O to a point P' such that $OP' = PO$, the segment $\overline{OP'}$ will have direction angles $\pi - \alpha$, $\pi - \beta$, $\pi - \gamma$ so that its direction cosines l', m', n' will be equal to $-l, -m, -n$.

38. Direction Ratios. Let L be any straight line. Draw the line through O parallel to L, and let $\overline{P'P}$ be a segment of this line bisected by O. Then l, m, n the direction cosines of OP, or

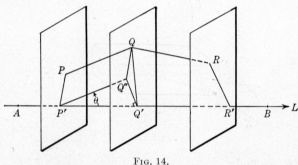

Fig. 14.

l', m', n' those of OP', are taken as the direction cosines of L. Any set of numbers a, b, c not all zero which are proportional to these cosines are called *direction ratios*. Except for the distinction between $\overline{OP}$ and $\overline{OP'}$, the cosines may be found from the ratios. For if

$$l = ka, \qquad m = kb, \qquad n = kc \qquad (5)$$

then

$$1 = l^2 + m^2 + n^2 = k^2(a^2 + b^2 + c^2)$$

and

$$k = \pm \frac{1}{\sqrt{a^2 + b^2 + c^2}}, \qquad (6)$$

one sign giving l, m, n and the other l', m', n'.

39. Projections of Line Segments. Let L be a line through the two points A and B. And, on L, choose the positive direction as that from A to B. Also let $\overline{PQ}$ be any directed line segment. The planes through P and Q perpendicular to L will determine points P' and Q' on L. The segment $\overline{P'Q'}$, or the signed distance from P' to Q', is called the *projection* of $\overline{PQ}$ on L or on $\overline{AB}$. We determine the angle θ, between L and $\overline{PQ}$ as follows: Draw a line segment parallel to $\overline{PQ}$ through any point of L, for example, $\overline{P'Q''}$ through P'. Then take θ as the angle in the range $0 \leqq \theta \leqq \pi$ made by this segment with the positive direction on L, that of $\overline{AB}$.

From the right triangle $P'Q'Q''$ we find

$$\text{Proj}_{AB}\ \overline{PQ} = P'Q' = P'Q'' \cos\theta = PQ \cos\theta. \tag{7}$$

Consequently,

$$\text{Proj}_{AB}\ \overline{QP} = Q'P' = -PQ \cos\theta. \tag{8}$$

For any three points P, Q, and R we see that

$$\text{Proj}_{AB}\ \overline{PR} = \text{Proj}_{AB}\ \overline{PQ} + \text{Proj}_{AB}\ \overline{QR}, \tag{9}$$

since this is equivalent to $P'R' = P'Q' + Q'R'$ where P', Q', R' are the projections of P, Q, R on AB.

40. The Segment $\overline{P'P''}$.
Consider a pair of points $P'(x',y',z')$ and $P''(x'',y'',z'')$. Let the segment $\overline{P'P''}$ have direction cosines l,m,n and a length s. Then the projections of the segment $\overline{P'P''}$ on the coordinate axes are

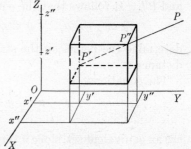

Fig. 15.

$$x'' - x' = sl,$$
$$y'' - y' = sm, \qquad\qquad z'' - z' = sn. \tag{10}$$

But by Eq. (4)

$$l^2 + m^2 + n^2 = 1. \tag{11}$$

Consequently,

$$(x'' - x')^2 + (y'' - y')^2 + (z'' - z')^2 = s^2(l^2 + m^2 + n^2) = s^2. \tag{12}$$

This determines the length s,

$$s = |P'P''| = \sqrt{(x'' - x')^2 + (y'' - y')^2 + (z'' - z')^2}. \tag{13}$$

And from Eq. (10),

$$l = \frac{x'' - x'}{s}, \qquad m = \frac{y'' - y'}{s}, \qquad n = \frac{z'' - z'}{s}. \qquad (14)$$

Equations (13) and (14) could also be deduced from the parallelepiped with edges parallel to the axes and diagonal $P'P''$ by reasoning similar to that of Sec. 37.

Equation (14) shows that we may take $x'' - x'$, $y'' - y'$, $z'' - z'$ as direction ratios for the straight line through the points P' and P''.

41. The Straight Line. Let us keep the point P' fixed and take $P(x,y,z)$ as any point on the straight line through $P'P''$. Then if t is the (variable) signed distance from P' to P, we shall have the relations

$$l = \frac{x - x'}{t}, \qquad m = \frac{y - y'}{t}, \qquad n = \frac{z - z'}{t}, \qquad (15)$$

analogous to Eqs. (14). Conversely, if these equations hold, the segment $\overline{P'P}$ (or $\overline{PP'}$ if t is negative) will have the same direction cosines as $\overline{P'P''}$, and P will be on the straight line through P' and P''. It follows that the equations

$$x = x' + lt, \qquad y = y' + mt, \qquad z = z' + nt \qquad (16)$$

determine the points on the straight line in terms of the signed distance t.

The equations

$$\frac{x - x'}{l} = \frac{y - y'}{m} = \frac{z - z'}{n} \qquad (17)$$

are an equivalent set, since if these hold we may take the common value of the ratio as the parameter t. Here, in place of the direction cosines l, m, n, we may use any direction ratios a, b, c proportional to them. We then write

$$\frac{x - x'}{a} = \frac{y - y'}{b} = \frac{z - z'}{c}. \qquad (18)$$

These equations hold if, and only if, the segment $\overline{P'P}$ has a fixed direction, and so are the equations of the straight line through P' with direction ratios a, b, c. In particular, we have

$$\frac{x - x'}{x'' - x'} = \frac{y - y'}{y'' - y'} = \frac{z - z'}{z'' - z'} \qquad (19)$$

as the equations of the straight line through the points P' and P''.

We continue to write equations of the form (17), (18), and (19) even when one or two of the three denominators are zero, interpreting them as meaning that the corresponding numerators are zero.

42. Vectors. In many geometrical and physical applications of mathematics we meet the concept of a *vector*, or directed magnitude. A vector is determined by its length and direction. It may be graphically represented by any line segment having this length and this direction. The position of the initial point is unessential, and any two segments $\overline{P'P''}$ having the same length and the same direction represent the same vector. We sometimes use a particular representative segment as $\overline{P'P''}$ to denote a vector but more often find a single letter convenient. In print, we use boldface type, as $\mathbf{a}$, to indicate a vector. In writing, a dash over the letter, as $\bar{a}$, may be used. The length of a vector may be denoted by the absolute value sign or simply by the letter in ordinary type or without the dash. Thus with the notation of Sec. 40, if

$$\mathbf{a} = \overline{P'P''}, \qquad |\mathbf{a}| \text{ or } a = |P'P''| = s. \tag{20}$$

We may think of a segment with coincident end points $\overline{P'P'}$ as representing a vector of zero length and undetermined direction. We call this the *null vector* but represent it by an ordinary zero in equations where its character may be inferred from the context.

For any real number C, by $C\mathbf{a}$ (or $\mathbf{a}C$) we mean the vector whose length is C times that of $\mathbf{a}$ and having the same direction as $\mathbf{a}$ if C is positive and the opposite direction if C is negative. If C is zero, $C\mathbf{a}$ is the null vector. In particular when C is -1, we write $-\mathbf{a}$ for $(-1)\mathbf{a}$ and if

$$\mathbf{a} = \overline{P'P''}, \qquad -\mathbf{a} = \overline{P''P'}. \tag{21}$$

The real numbers, or numbers represented by signed coordinates on a scale, are referred to as *scalars*. The operation that converts the vector $\mathbf{a}$ into $C\mathbf{a}$ is called *multiplication* of the vector $\mathbf{a}$ by the scalar C.

43. Addition and Subtraction of Vectors. Let $\overline{PQ}$ be a segment representing the vector $\mathbf{a}$ and $\overline{QR}$ be a segment representing the vector **b**, so that

$$\mathbf{a} = \overline{PQ}, \qquad \mathbf{b} = \overline{QR}. \qquad \text{Then } \mathbf{a} + \mathbf{b} = \overline{PR}. \qquad (22)$$

Also if S is on RQ produced so that $SQ = QR$,

$$\mathbf{b} = \overline{SQ}, \qquad -\mathbf{b} = \overline{QS}, \qquad \text{and} \qquad \mathbf{a} - \mathbf{b} = \overline{PS}. \qquad (23)$$

Thus vectors are added and subtracted by the parallelogram law.

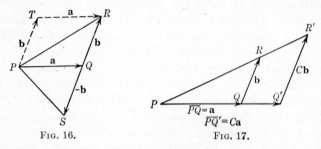

Fig. 16.   Fig. 17.

It follows at once from the definition that

$$\mathbf{a} + \mathbf{b} = \mathbf{b} + \mathbf{a}. \qquad (24)$$
$$C(\mathbf{a} + \mathbf{b}) = C\mathbf{a} + C\mathbf{b}. \qquad (25)$$
$$\mathbf{a} + (\mathbf{b} + \mathbf{c}) = (\mathbf{a} + \mathbf{b}) + \mathbf{c}. \qquad (26)$$

Also, if

$$\mathbf{a} + \mathbf{b} = \mathbf{c}, \qquad \text{then } \mathbf{c} - \mathbf{b} = \mathbf{a}. \qquad (27)$$

44. Components. By drawing $\overline{OP}$ equal in magnitude and direction to a given vector **r**, we obtain a representative segment

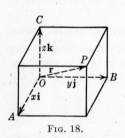

for **r** with initial point at the origin. Let the coordinates of P be x,y,z and construct the parallelepiped as in Sec. 36. If **i**, **j**, and **k** denote unit vectors along the positive x, y, and z axes, respectively, we shall have

Fig. 18.

$$\overline{OA} = x\mathbf{i},$$
$$\overline{OB} = y\mathbf{j}, \qquad (28)$$
$$\overline{OC} = z\mathbf{k}.$$

Consequently,

$$\mathbf{r} = x\mathbf{i} + y\mathbf{j} + z\mathbf{k}, \qquad (29)$$

and we have decomposed **r** into three component vectors, each parallel to a coordinate axis. We call the scalars x, y, z which multiply **i**, **j**, **k** the *components* of the vector. Thus the vector **r** has components x, y, and z if its component vectors are $x\mathbf{i}$, $y\mathbf{j}$, and $z\mathbf{k}$ and the relation (29) holds. The components may be obtained directly from the projections of any representative segment on the coordinate axes.

By the rules of Sec. 43, we may deduce from Eq. (29) that

$$C\mathbf{r} = Cx\mathbf{i} + Cy\mathbf{j} + Cz\mathbf{k}, \tag{30}$$

so that the components of $C\mathbf{r}$ are C times the components of $\mathbf{r}$.

Again, if

$$\mathbf{r}' = x'\mathbf{i} + y'\mathbf{j} + z'\mathbf{k}, \tag{31}$$

we find from this and Eq. (29) that

$$\mathbf{r} + \mathbf{r}' = (x + x')\mathbf{i} + (y + y')\mathbf{j} + (z + z')\mathbf{k}, \tag{32}$$

so that the components of $\mathbf{r} + \mathbf{r}'$ are formed by adding corresponding components.

In general, the operations of addition, subtraction, or multiplication by a scalar may be effected by applying these operations to the components of the vectors involved.

As an illustration, the two points $P'(x',y',z')$ and $P''(x'',y'',z'')$ determine vectors

$$\overline{OP'} = \mathbf{r}' = x'\mathbf{i} + y'\mathbf{j} + z'\mathbf{k}, \qquad \overline{OP''} = \mathbf{r}''$$
$$= x''\mathbf{i} + y''\mathbf{j} + z''\mathbf{k}. \tag{33}$$

The vector

$$\overline{P'P''} = \mathbf{r}'' - \mathbf{r}' = (x'' - x')\mathbf{i} + (y'' - y')\mathbf{j} + (z'' - z')\mathbf{k}. \tag{34}$$

This is in accord with Sec. 40.

If l, m, n are direction cosines, the vector

$$\mathbf{u} = l\mathbf{i} + m\mathbf{j} + n\mathbf{k} \tag{35}$$

is of unit length, since

$$|\mathbf{u}| = u = \sqrt{l^2 + m^2 + n^2} = 1. \tag{36}$$

For any vector $\mathbf{r}$ with length r and direction cosines l, m, n, we have

$$\mathbf{r} = r\mathbf{u} = rl\mathbf{i} + rm\mathbf{j} + rn\mathbf{k}. \tag{37}$$

Thus $\mathbf{r}$ has as its components rl, rm, rn and its direction cosines may be found by dividing its components by its length. Applied to the vector $\mathbf{r}'' - \mathbf{r}'$ of length s, this checks Eq. (14).

Similarly, Eq. (15) states that

$$\mathbf{r} - \mathbf{r}' = t\mathbf{u}, \quad \text{or} \quad \mathbf{r} = \mathbf{r}' + t\mathbf{u}, \tag{38}$$

in which t may be positive, negative, or zero.

45. The Scalar Product.   For any two vectors $\mathbf{a}$ and $\mathbf{b}$ we may calculate the expression $ab \cos \theta$, where θ is the angle $(0 \leqq \theta \leqq \pi)$ made by their positive directions as in Sec. 39, and a and b are their lengths.   We call this expression the *scalar* or *dot product* of the two vectors and write

$$\mathbf{a} \cdot \mathbf{b} = ab \cos \theta. \tag{39}$$

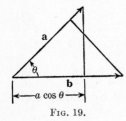

Fig. 19.

By Sec. 39 the projection of $\mathbf{a}$ on $\mathbf{b}$ is $a \cos \theta$, and the projection of $\mathbf{b}$ on $\mathbf{a}$ is $b \cos \theta$. Consequently, we have

$$\mathbf{a} \cdot \mathbf{b} = a \, \text{Proj}_a \, \mathbf{b} = b \, \text{Proj}_b \, \mathbf{a}. \tag{40}$$

It follows from the original definition that

$$\mathbf{a} \cdot \mathbf{b} = \mathbf{b} \cdot \mathbf{a}, \tag{41}$$

so that the scalar product is commutative, that is, does not depend on the order in which the two vectors are written.

Also, for any two scalars p and q,

$$(p\mathbf{a}) \cdot (q\mathbf{b}) = pqab \cos \theta = pq(\mathbf{a} \cdot \mathbf{b}). \tag{42}$$

Finally, by Eq. (9),

$$\text{Proj}_a \, \mathbf{b} + \text{Proj}_a \, \mathbf{c} = \text{Proj}_a \, (\mathbf{b} + \mathbf{c}). \tag{43}$$

If we multiply by a and use Eq. (40), we may deduce that

$$\mathbf{a} \cdot (\mathbf{b} + \mathbf{c}) = \mathbf{a} \cdot \mathbf{b} + \mathbf{a} \cdot \mathbf{c} \quad \text{or} \quad (\mathbf{b} + \mathbf{c}) \cdot \mathbf{a}$$
$$= \mathbf{b} \cdot \mathbf{a} + \mathbf{c} \cdot \mathbf{a}. \tag{44}$$

Thus the scalar product is distributive and we may expand products like

$$(\mathbf{a} + \mathbf{b}) \cdot (\mathbf{c} + \mathbf{d}) = \mathbf{a} \cdot \mathbf{c} + \mathbf{a} \cdot \mathbf{d} + \mathbf{b} \cdot \mathbf{c} + \mathbf{b} \cdot \mathbf{d} \tag{45}$$

as in ordinary algebra.

If the two vectors $\mathbf{a}$ and $\mathbf{b}$ have the same direction, they make a zero angle.   Thus $\theta = 0$ and $\cos \theta = 1$ in Eq. (39).   In particular,

$$\mathbf{a} \cdot \mathbf{a} = a^2, \tag{46}$$

and the scalar product of a vector by itself is the square of its length.

If the two vectors **a** and **b** are perpendicular, $\theta = 90°$ and $\cos \theta = 0$.   Hence,

if $\mathbf{a} \perp \mathbf{b}, \qquad \mathbf{a} \cdot \mathbf{b} = 0.$ (47)

These facts enable us to compute all the scalar products involving the three unit vectors **i**, **j**, **k**.   We have

$$\mathbf{i} \cdot \mathbf{i} = \mathbf{j} \cdot \mathbf{j} = \mathbf{k} \cdot \mathbf{k} = 1 \tag{48}$$

and

$$\mathbf{i} \cdot \mathbf{j} = \mathbf{j} \cdot \mathbf{i} = \mathbf{j} \cdot \mathbf{k} = \mathbf{k} \cdot \mathbf{j} = \mathbf{k} \cdot \mathbf{i} = \mathbf{i} \cdot \mathbf{k} = 0. \tag{49}$$

We may now express the scalar product of any two vectors in terms of their components.   Let **a** have components a_x, a_y, a_z and **b** have components b_x, b_y, b_z.   Then

$$\mathbf{a} = a_x\mathbf{i} + a_y\mathbf{j} + a_z\mathbf{k} \qquad \text{and} \qquad \mathbf{b} = b_x\mathbf{i} + b_y\mathbf{j} + b_z\mathbf{k}. \tag{50}$$

Thus

$$\mathbf{a} \cdot \mathbf{b} = (a_x\mathbf{i} + a_y\mathbf{j} + a_z\mathbf{k}) \cdot (b_x\mathbf{i} + b_y\mathbf{j} + b_z\mathbf{k}). \tag{51}$$

By the process used in Eqs. (44) and (45), this may be distributed into nine separate products.   We may then bring out the scalar factors, as in Eq. (42), and reduce the dot products which involve **i**, **j**, and **k** only by Eqs. (48) and (49).   The final result is

$$\mathbf{a} \cdot \mathbf{b} = a_x b_x + a_y b_y + a_z b_z. \tag{52}$$

In particular, by Eq. (46)

$$a^2 = \mathbf{a} \cdot \mathbf{a} = a_x{}^2 + a_y{}^2 + a_z{}^2, \tag{53}$$

and similarly

$$b^2 = \mathbf{b} \cdot \mathbf{b} = b_x{}^2 + b_y{}^2 + b_z{}^2. \tag{54}$$

Except for notation, these are equivalent to Eqs. (2) and (12).

Since

$$\mathbf{a} \cdot \mathbf{b} = ab \cos \theta, \qquad \text{or} \qquad \cos \theta = \frac{\mathbf{a} \cdot \mathbf{b}}{ab}, \tag{55}$$

we have by Eqs. (52), (53), and (54):

$$\cos \theta = \frac{a_x b_x + a_y b_y + a_z b_z}{\sqrt{a_x{}^2 + a_y{}^2 + a_z{}^2} \sqrt{b_x{}^2 + b_y{}^2 + b_z{}^2}}. \tag{56}$$

This determines the cosine of the angle between two vectors or segments in terms of their components.

If the two vectors are perpendicular, $\cos \theta = 0$, and

$$a_x b_x + a_y b_y + a_z b_z = 0. \tag{57}$$

Conversely, if this condition holds, by Eq. (52),

$$\mathbf{a} \cdot \mathbf{b} = ab \cos \theta = 0. \tag{58}$$

Hence, either $\cos \theta = 0$ and the vectors are perpendicular, or a or b is zero, and one of the vectors is a null vector. Thus, if neither vector is a null vector, condition (57) is a necessary and sufficient condition for perpendicularity.

Whereas scalar or dot multiplication of vectors may for the most part be treated by the familiar rules of algebra, there is one important exception. In ordinary algebra, if a product is zero, one of the factors must be zero. But if the scalar product of two vectors is zero, we have the alternative possibility of perpendicularity. For example, in ordinary algebra, if

$$a \neq 0, \qquad \text{and} \qquad ab = ac \qquad \text{or} \qquad a(b - c) = 0, \tag{59}$$

we may conclude that

$$b - c = 0 \qquad \text{and} \qquad b = c. \tag{60}$$

But if

$$\mathbf{a} \neq \mathbf{0}, \qquad \text{and} \qquad \mathbf{a} \cdot \mathbf{b} = \mathbf{a} \cdot \mathbf{c} \qquad \text{or} \qquad \mathbf{a} \cdot (\mathbf{b} - \mathbf{c}) = 0, \tag{61}$$

we may conclude only that

$$\text{either} \qquad \mathbf{b} - \mathbf{c} = 0, \qquad \text{or} \qquad (\mathbf{b} - \mathbf{c}) \perp \mathbf{a}. \tag{62}$$

46. Planes. Consider any equation of the first degree

$$Ax + By + Cz = D. \tag{63}$$

Then A, B, C cannot all be zero, since it is of the first degree. Let $P'(x',y',z')$ be one point whose coordinates satisfy the equation, so that

$$Ax' + By' + Cz' = D. \tag{64}$$

Then, if $P(x,y,z)$ is any point that satisfies (63), we may deduce by subtraction that

$$A(x - x') + B(y - y') + C(z - z') = 0. \tag{65}$$

By Eqs. (52) and (34) the left member may be considered as the scalar product of the vector $\overline{P'P}$ and a vector $\mathbf{a}$ with components A,B,C. Since $\mathbf{a} \neq 0$, either $\overline{P'P} = 0$ and P is P', or the vector $\overline{P'P}$ is perpendicular to the vector $\mathbf{a}$. In either case the point P lies in the plane through P' perpendicular to $\mathbf{a}$. Conversely, if P is in this plane, either $\overline{P'P} = 0$ or $\overline{P'P}$ is perpendicular to $\mathbf{a}$, and Eq. (65) will hold. But Eqs. (65) and (64) may be added to give Eq. (63). This proves that Eq. (63) is the equation of a plane.

Conversely, by taking A,B,C any set of direction ratios for the direction perpendicular, or normal, to a given plane, and x',y',z' as the coordinates of any point in the plane, we may write an equation of the type (65). If we define D by Eq. (64), this equation is reducible to the form (63). This proves

Every first-degree equation in x, y, and z represents a plane, and every plane is representable by some first-degree equation.

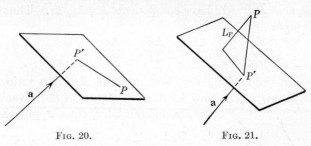

FIG. 20.   FIG. 21.

Consider next a point $P(x,y,z)$ *not* in the plane (63). Let $\mathbf{a}$ be a normal vector with components A,B,C. Denote by L_P the signed perpendicular distance from the plane to P, measured positive in the direction of $\mathbf{a}$. Then L_P equals the projection of $\overline{P'P}$ on the direction of $\mathbf{a}$, so that by Eq. (40),

$$aL_P = a \operatorname{Proj}_{\mathbf{a}} \overline{P'P} = \mathbf{a} \cdot \overline{P'P}$$
$$= A(x - x') + B(y - y') + C(z - z'). \qquad (66)$$

But

$$a = \sqrt{A^2 + B^2 + C^2}, \qquad (67)$$

so that

$$L_P = \frac{A(x - x') + B(y - y') + C(z - z')}{\sqrt{A^2 + B^2 + C^2}}$$
$$= \frac{Ax + By + Cz - D}{\sqrt{A^2 + B^2 + C^2}}. \qquad (68)$$

This determines the distance from the plane to P. The distance L_P is positive for x,y,z on the same side of the plane as $x' + A$, $y' + B$, $z' + C$, and negative for x,y,z on the same side of the plane as $x' - A$, $y' - B$, $z' - C$. When the point is in the plane, L_P is zero, and Eq. (63) holds, so that (68) still applies in this case.

47. Tangent Line to a Space Curve. The equations

$$x = f(t), \qquad y = g(t), \qquad z = h(t) \qquad (69)$$

determine a point $P(x,y,z)$ for each value of t. In general, this point will vary continuously with t and as t traces an interval, P will describe the arc of a curve in space. Let t_0 be a fixed value, which determines a fixed point $P_0(x_0,y_0,z_0)$. Then if $t_0 + \Delta t$ is a value near t_0, which determines $P'(x_0 + \Delta x, y_0 + \Delta y, z_0 + \Delta z)$, the segment $\overline{P_0P'}$ will have components Δx, Δy, Δz. Thus these numbers, or

$$\frac{\Delta x}{\Delta t}, \qquad \frac{\Delta y}{\Delta t}, \qquad \frac{\Delta z}{\Delta t}, \qquad (70)$$

which are proportional to them, are the direction ratios of a secant through P_0. Now let $\Delta t \to 0$. Then, if our given functions are differentiable, these approach

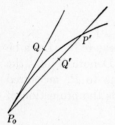

FIG. 22.

$$\frac{dx}{dt}\Big|_0 = f'(t_0), \qquad \frac{dy}{dt}\Big|_0 = g'(t_0),$$

$$\frac{dz}{dt}\Big|_0 = h'(t_0). \qquad (71)$$

Assume that these are not all zero, so that

$$f'(t_0)^2 + g'(t_0)^2 + h'(t_0)^2 > 0. \qquad (72)$$

Then the numbers in (71) may be taken as direction ratios of a line through P_0 and

$$Q[x_0 + f'(t_0),\ y_0 + g'(t_0),\ z_0 + h'(t_0)].$$

The equations of this line may be written

$$\frac{x - x_0}{f'(t_0)} = \frac{y - y_0}{g'(t_0)} = \frac{z - z_0}{h'(t_0)}. \qquad (73)$$

But the secant line through P_0 and P' has direction ratios (70) and therefore contains the point $Q'\left(x_0 + \frac{\Delta x}{\Delta t},\ y_0 + \frac{\Delta y}{\Delta t},\ z_0 + \frac{\Delta z}{\Delta t}\right)$. When $\Delta t \to 0$, $Q' \to Q$, so that the secant through $\overline{P_0Q'}$ approaches the line through $\overline{P_0Q}$. This limiting line is defined to be the tangent to the curve at P_0. Thus the equations of the tangent are given by (73) and may be written in the alternative forms:

$$\frac{x - x_0}{\dfrac{dx}{dt}\bigg|_0} = \frac{y - y_0}{\dfrac{dy}{dt}\bigg|_0} = \frac{z - z_0}{\dfrac{dz}{dt}\bigg|_0}, \tag{74}$$

or

$$\frac{x - f(t_0)}{f'(t_0)} = \frac{y - g(t_0)}{g'(t_0)} = \frac{z - h(t_0)}{h'(t_0)}. \tag{75}$$

The fact that the length of the chord P_0P' is

$$P_0P' = \sqrt{\Delta x^2 + \Delta y^2 + \Delta z^2} \tag{76}$$

suggests that a definition of length of arc based on inscribed polygons would make

$$\left(\frac{ds}{dt}\right)^2 = \left(\frac{dx}{dt}\right)^2 + \left(\frac{dy}{dt}\right)^2 + \left(\frac{dz}{dt}\right)^2, \tag{77}$$

and

$$s - s_0 = \int_{t_0}^{t} \sqrt{\left(\frac{dx}{dt}\right)^2 + \left(\frac{dy}{dt}\right)^2 + \left(\frac{dz}{dt}\right)^2}\, dt. \tag{78}$$

This is, in fact, the case and we shall accordingly use these relations as the fundamental ones for the arc length s.

48. Derivative of a Vector. If a vector has its components variable but functions of a parameter t, we may write

$$\mathbf{r}(t) = f(t)\mathbf{i} + g(t)\mathbf{j} + h(t)\mathbf{k}. \tag{79}$$

By the derivative of the vector $\mathbf{r}$ with respect to t we mean the vector

$$\mathbf{r}'(t) = \lim_{\Delta t \to 0} \frac{\mathbf{r}(t + \Delta t) - \mathbf{r}(t)}{\Delta t}. \tag{80}$$

By applying this definition to the form given in (79), we find

$$\mathbf{r}'(t) = f'(t)\mathbf{i} + g'(t)\mathbf{j} + h'(t)\mathbf{k}. \tag{81}$$

Thus to differentiate a vector, we need merely differentiate each component.

Let us take a point $P(x,y,z)$ such that

$$\overline{OP} = \mathbf{r}(t), \quad \text{and} \quad x = f(t), \quad y = g(t), \quad z = h(t). \tag{82}$$

Then, when t varies, the end point P will describe a space curve as in the last section.   The vector $\mathbf{r}'(t)$ is parallel to the tangent to this curve.   And the length of $\mathbf{r}'(t)$ is

$$|\mathbf{r}'| = \sqrt{\mathbf{r}' \cdot \mathbf{r}'} = \sqrt{f'(t)^2 + g'(t^2) + h'(t)^2} = \frac{ds}{dt}, \qquad (83)$$

the derivative of the arc length with respect to the parameter.

When t is the time, $\mathbf{r}'(t)$ has a length equal to the speed in the path, and components equal to the velocities of x, y, and z along the axes.   Thus it is the velocity vector of the moving point P.

Similarly, $\mathbf{r}''(t)$ with components d^2x/dt^2, d^2y/dt^2, d^2z/dt^2, or

$$\mathbf{r}''(t) = f''(t)\mathbf{i} + g''(t)\mathbf{j} + h''(t)\mathbf{k} \qquad (84)$$

is the time derivative of the velocity vector or the acceleration vector of the moving point P.

49. Surfaces.   The equation

$$z = f_1(x,y) \qquad (85)$$

determines a single point P for each value of x and y.   In general, when x and y vary continuously over some two-dimensional region, the point P will vary continuously over the portion of a surface in space.   Similar remarks apply to $x = f_2(y,z)$ and to $y = f_3(z,x)$.   A more general equation is

$$F(x,y,z) = 0. \qquad (86)$$

If F_x, F_y, F_z are not all zero, this may be solved in some restricted region for one of the variables in terms of the other two and so represents a surface.

Let $x = x(t)$, $y = y(t)$, $z = z(t)$ be the equations of any curve lying in the surface (86), so that

$$F[x(t),y(t),z(t)] = 0 \qquad (87)$$

for all values of t.   Then, by differentiation with respect to t,

$$F_x \frac{dx}{dt} + F_y \frac{dy}{dt} + F_z \frac{dz}{dt} = 0. \qquad (88)$$

We assume that the parameter t has been so selected that $[x'(t)]^2 + [y'(t)]^2 + [z'(t)]^2 > 0$.   For example, we may take $t = s$, the arc length.   By Eq. (52) the left member of (88) may be considered as the scalar product of the two vectors:

$$\mathbf{N} = F_x\mathbf{i} + F_y\mathbf{j} + F_z\mathbf{k} \qquad (89)$$

and

$$\mathbf{T} = x'(t)\mathbf{i} + y'(t)\mathbf{j} + z'(t)\mathbf{k}. \qquad (90)$$

As neither of these vectors is zero and $\mathbf{N} \cdot \mathbf{T} = 0$, they must be perpendicular. Thus a plane through the point $P(x,y,z)$ perpendicular to $\mathbf{N}$ will contain all the tangent lines drawn to curves on the surface passing through P. We call this plane the *tangent plane* to the surface at P. The direction of $\mathbf{N}$, which is perpendicular or normal to this plane, is called the *normal* to the surface at P.

The equation of the tangent plane to the surface at $P_0(x_0,y_0,z_0)$ is found by Eq. (65) to be

$$F_x(x_0,y_0,z_0)(x - x_0) + F_y(x_0,y_0,z_0)(y - y_0) + F_z(x_0,y_0,z_0)(z - z_0) = 0. \quad (91)$$

If the equation of the surface is given in the form

$$z = f(x,y), \qquad (92)$$

we may put $F(x,y,z) = z - f(x,y)$ and write the equation of the tangent plane at $P_0(x_0,y_0,z_0)$ in the form

$$z - z_0 = \left.\frac{\partial f}{\partial x}\right|_0 (x - x_0) + \left.\frac{\partial f}{\partial y}\right|_0 (y - y_0). \qquad (93)$$

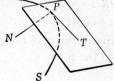

Fig. 23.

50. Surface near a Tangent Plane. We wish to investigate the form of a surface S near a given point. Let $z = f(x,y)$ be the equation of S, so that $z_0 = f(x_0,y_0)$. Consider the Taylor's expansion of $f(x,y)$ about x_0,y_0, namely,

$$z = f(x_0,y_0) + \left.\frac{\partial f}{\partial x}\right|_0 (x - x_0) + \left.\frac{\partial f}{\partial y}\right|_0 (y - y_0)$$
$$+ \frac{1}{2}\left.\frac{\partial^2 f}{\partial x^2}\right|_0 (x - x_0)^2 + \left.\frac{\partial^2 f}{\partial x\,\partial y}\right|_0 (x - x_0)(y - y_0)$$
$$+ \frac{1}{2}\left.\frac{\partial^2 f}{\partial y^2}\right|_0 (y - y_0)^2 + \cdots. \qquad (94)$$

We note that since $z_0 = f(x_0,y_0)$, this expansion reduces to Eq. (93) of the tangent plane at P_0 if we omit all terms containing powers of degree greater than one in $(x - x_0)$ and $(y - y_0)$.

Let us next take new coordinate axes x',y',z' with the $x'y'$ plane coinciding with the tangent plane to the surface at x_0,y_0,z_0.

Then the new equation of the tangent plane will be $z' = 0$, so that the constant term and first-order terms will not appear. We also take the new origin at the point P_0. Then the new coordinates of P_0 are

$$x_0', \ y_0', \ z_0' = 0, \ 0, \ 0. \qquad (95)$$

Consequently the expansion (94) takes the form

$$z' = \tfrac{1}{2}(Ax'^2 + 2Bx'y' + Cy'^2) + \cdots , \qquad (96)$$

where

$$A = \left.\frac{\partial^2 f'}{\partial x'^2}\right|_0, \qquad B = \left.\frac{\partial^2 f'}{\partial x' \, \partial y'}\right|_0, \qquad C = \left.\frac{\partial^2 f'}{\partial y'^2}\right|_0. \qquad (97)$$

For the new axes the equation of the surface is $z' = f'(x',y')$, and

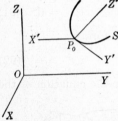

the second derivatives are evaluated at the origin.

Up to terms of the third order, the surface is approximated by the second-degree surface:

$$z' = \tfrac{1}{2}(Ax'^2 + 2Bx'y' + Cy'^2). \qquad (98)$$

This is called the *osculating paraboloid.*

Fig. 24.

By a suitable rotation of the axes in the $x'y'$ plane, the term $Bx'y'$ may be made to disappear, and the equation of the osculating paraboloid reduced to the form

$$z'' = \tfrac{1}{2}(ax''^2 + by''^2). \qquad (99)$$

In this equation the z'' axis is along $\mathbf{N}$, the normal to the surface

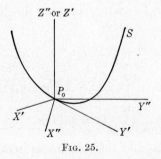

Fig. 25.

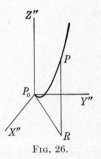

Fig. 26.

at P_0, and the x'' and y'' axes are suitably chosen in the tangent plane to the given surface S at P_0.

The curves in which S is cut by planes through the normal $\mathbf{N}$ are called the *normal sections* of S at P_0. Suppose that a normal section C is cut out by a plane making an angle θ with the $x''z''$ plane. Let P be any point of C near P_0, and R the projection of P on the $x''y''$ plane. Then if $P_0R = r$, we have from Fig. 27,

$$x'' = r \cos \theta, \qquad y'' = r \sin \theta. \quad (100)$$

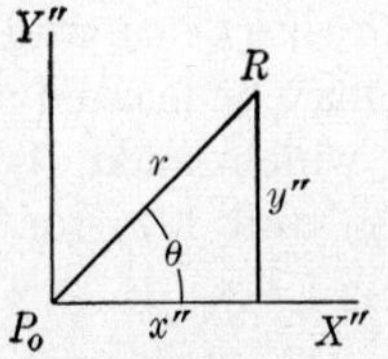

FIG. 27.

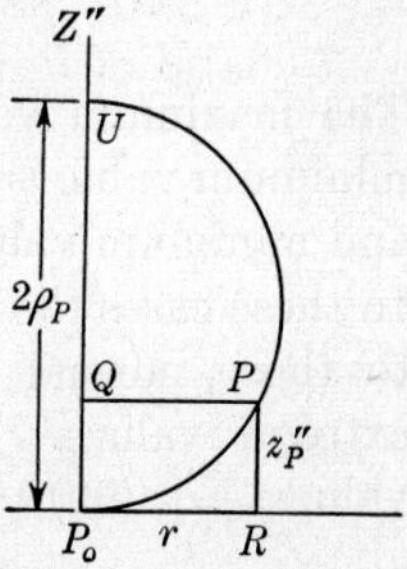

FIG. 28.

Next draw a circle through P tangent to P_0R at P_0. Then, if ρ_P is the radius of this circle and $z_P'' = RP$, we have from Fig. 28,

$$QP^2 = UQ \cdot QP_0 \qquad \text{or} \qquad r^2 = (2\rho_P - z_P'')z_P'', \quad (101)$$

and

$$\rho_P = \frac{r^2 - z_1''^2}{2z_1''} \qquad \text{or} \qquad \frac{1}{\rho_P} = \frac{2z_P''}{r^2 + z_P''^2}. \quad (102)$$

But, since Eq. (99) was obtained by dropping higher powers, for a point x'', y'', z_P'' on S we may write

$$2z_P'' = (ax''^2 + by''^2) + O(r^3) = r^2(a \cos^2 \theta + b \sin^2 \theta) + O(r^3). \quad (103)$$

Here $O(r^3)$ stands for terms whose degree in x'' and y'' is at least three. Hence, when transformed by Eq. (100), they contain a factor r^3 and so are of the third order in r.

It follows from Eqs. (102) and (103) that

$$\frac{1}{\rho_P} = \frac{a \cos^2 \theta + b \sin^2 \theta + O(r)}{1 + O(r^2)}, \quad (104)$$

where the terms $O(r)$ contain a factor r and the terms $O(r^2)$ contain a factor r^2. Hence these terms approach zero when $r \to 0$. If we denote the limit of ρ_P when $r \to 0$ by ρ, we have

$$\frac{1}{\rho} = a \cos^2 \theta + b \sin^2 \theta. \quad (105)$$

This is Euler's form for the curvature of any normal section.

Since $\sin^2 \theta + \cos^2 \theta = 1$,

$$\frac{1}{\rho} = a + (b - a) \sin^2 \theta. \tag{106}$$

The maximum value of $\sin^2 \theta$ is 1 for $\theta = 90°$ or $270°$. The minimum value is zero for $\theta = 0°$ or $180°$. Hence the maximum and minimum values of $1/\rho$ are b,a (if $b > a$), and a,b (if $a > b$). In these cases the x'' and y'' axes may be located as the tangents to those normal sections at P_0 which make $1/\rho$ take on its extreme values. If we write $1/\rho_1$ and $1/\rho_2$ for these extreme values, Eq. (99) takes the form

$$z'' = \frac{1}{2}\left(\frac{x''^2}{\rho_1} + \frac{y''^2}{\rho_2}\right). \tag{107}$$

The numbers ρ_1 and ρ_2 are called the *principal radii of curvature* of the surface S at P_0. The product $1/(\rho_1\rho_2)$ is called the *total curvature*.

The sections of the surface S parallel to the tangent plane are found by placing $z_P = k$ in Eq. (103). The result may be written

$$2k = \frac{x''^2}{\rho_1} + \frac{y''^2}{\rho_2} + O(r^3). \tag{108}$$

Hence, to within terms of the third order these curves are conics similar to the curves found by putting

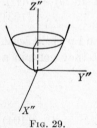

FIG. 29.

$z'' = \pm 1$ in (107), or

$$\pm 1 = \frac{1}{2}\left(\frac{x''^2}{\rho_1} + \frac{y''^2}{\rho_2}\right). \tag{109}$$

This is called the equation of the *indicatrix* of the surface S at P_0. When ρ_1 and ρ_2 have the same sign, the indicatrix is an ellipse for one of the signs and is an imaginary ellipse for the other sign. Hence the sections of the surface are approximately ellipses on one side of the tangent plane. Near P_0 the surface lies entirely on this side. Such a point is called an *elliptic point* or point of positive total curvature, since $1/(\rho_1\rho_2)$ is positive. When ρ_1 and ρ_2 have opposite signs, the indicatrix is a hyperbola with asymptotes given by

$$\frac{x''^2}{\rho_1} + \frac{y''^2}{\rho_2} = 0, \qquad z'' = 0. \tag{110}$$

In this case, near P_0, the surface will lie on one side of the tangent plane in one set of opposite regions between these lines, and on the opposite side in the other pair of opposite regions. The surface S near P_0 will cut the tangent plane in curves tangent to the asymptotes (110). Such a point is a *hyperbolic point*, or point of negative total curvature, since $1/(\rho_1\rho_2)$ is negative.

If one coefficient $1/\rho_1$ or $1/\rho_2$ is zero, the indicatrix (109) represents a pair of (real or imaginary) parallel lines. In this case Eq. (107) represents a parabolic cylinder, and the point is called a *parabolic point*, or point of zero total curvature, since

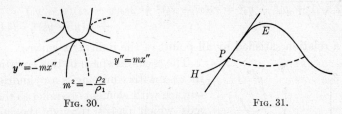

$$y'' = -mx'' \qquad y'' = mx''$$
$$m^2 = -\frac{\rho_2}{\rho_1}$$

FIG. 30.   FIG. 31.

$1/(\rho_1\rho_2) = 0$. In this case the osculating paraboloid (here a parabolic cylinder) lies on one side of the tangent plane and is tangent to it along the x'' or y'' axis. The surface S, near P_0, will also touch or cut the tangent plane in a curve tangent to this axis, but in general it will lie on both sides of the tangent plane near P_0.

The bell-shaped solid of revolution, shown in Fig. 31, illustrates all three types of points. There is a circle of parabolic points. All points above this are elliptic, and all below this are hyperbolic.

Let us return to the original axes, in which S had the equation $z = f(x,y)$, and introduce the abbreviations

$$\frac{\partial z}{\partial x} = p, \qquad \frac{\partial z}{\partial y} = q, \qquad \frac{\partial^2 z}{\partial x^2} = r, \qquad \frac{\partial^2 z}{\partial x\,\partial y} = s, \qquad \frac{\partial^2 z}{\partial y^2} = t. \quad (111)$$

We indicate that these derivatives are to be evaluated at P_0 by appending a subscript zero. Then Eq. (93) for the tangent plane at P_0 may be written

$$z - z_0 = p_0(x - x_0) + q_0(y - y_0). \qquad (112)$$

And the equation of the osculating paraboloid at P_0 is

$$z = z_0 + p_0(x - x_0) + q_0(y - y_0) + \tfrac{1}{2}r_0(x - x_0)^2 \\ + s_0(x - x_0)(y - y_0) + \tfrac{1}{2}t_0(y - y_0)^2, \quad (113)$$

since this approximates the expansion (94) up to terms of the third order. The points on this paraboloid whose perpendicular distance from the tangent plane (112) is ± 1 will make up the indicatrix of Eq. (109). By Eq. (68), such points $P(x,y,z)$ will satisfy the relation

$$\frac{z - z_0 - p_0(x - x_0) - q_0(y - y_0)}{\sqrt{1 + p_0{}^2 + q_0{}^2}} = \pm 1. \tag{114}$$

If we solve this equation for z and substitute in Eq. (113), we obtain

$$\pm 2\sqrt{1 + p_0{}^2 + q_0{}^2} = r_0(x - x_0)^2 + 2s_0(x - x_0)(y - y_0) \\ + t_0(y - y_0)^2, \tag{115}$$

as a relation satisfied by all points of the indicatrix curves.

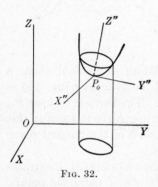

Fig. 32.

The locus in space of this equation in x,y,z with z missing is a cylindrical surface with elements parallel to the z axis which passes through the indicatrix curves. In the xy plane the locus of this equation in x and y is the orthogonal projection of the indicatrix. The point P_0 on the surface S will be elliptic, hyperbolic, or parabolic according as the indicatrix curves and hence their orthogonal projections are ellipses, hyperbolas, or pairs of parallel straight lines.

When Eqs. (115) represent hyperbolas, the asymptotes are given by the equation

$$r_0(x - x_0)^2 + 2s_0(x - x_0)(y - y_0) + t_0(y - y_0)^2 = 0. \tag{116}$$

If we divide this equation by $(x - x_0)^2$ and set the slope

$$\frac{y - y_0}{x - x_0} = \lambda, \tag{117}$$

we obtain the quadratic equation

$$t_0\lambda^2 + 2s_0\lambda + r_0 = 0, \tag{118}$$

whose roots are the slopes of the asymptotes. Hence the roots are real, and the discriminant of the quadratic equation (118), or

$$(2s_0)^2 - 4t_0r_0 = 4(s_0{}^2 - r_0t_0), \tag{119}$$

must be positive. Conversely, if

$$s_0{}^2 - r_0 t_0 > 0, \tag{120}$$

Eqs. (115) will represent hyperbolas.

If

$$s_0{}^2 - r_0 t_0 = 0, \tag{121}$$

the roots of Eq. (118) will be equal. Hence the left member of Eq. (118), as well as of (116), will be a square. In this case Eqs. (115) will represent pairs of parallel lines.

If

$$s_0{}^2 - r_0 t_0 < 0, \tag{122}$$

the roots of Eq. (118) will be imaginary. Hence the left member of Eq. (118), as well as of (116), will be a sum of two squares. In this case Eqs. (115) will represent ellipses.

The discussion just given leads to the following conclusions:

The point $P(x,y,z)$ of the surface $z = f(x,y)$ will be

$$
\begin{aligned}
\text{Elliptic,} \quad &\text{if} \quad \left(\frac{\partial^2 f}{\partial x\, \partial y}\right)^2 - \frac{\partial^2 f}{\partial x^2}\frac{\partial^2 f}{\partial y^2} < 0, \\[2mm]
\text{Parabolic,} \quad &\text{if} \quad \left(\frac{\partial^2 f}{\partial x\, \partial y}\right)^2 - \frac{\partial^2 f}{\partial x^2}\frac{\partial^2 f}{\partial y^2} = 0, \\[2mm]
\text{Hyperbolic,} \quad &\text{if} \quad \left(\frac{\partial^2 f}{\partial x\, \partial y}\right)^2 - \frac{\partial^2 f}{\partial x^2}\frac{\partial^2 f}{\partial y^2} > 0,
\end{aligned}
\tag{123}
$$

where all the derivatives are evaluated at $P(x,y,z)$.

51. The Vector Product. For any two vectors **a** and **b**, *taken in this order*, we may form a new vector by the following geometric construction: (1) Represent the vectors by two segments OA and OB having the same initial point O. (2) Determine the angle θ, $0 < \theta < \pi$, from **a** to **b**, and compute the value $n = ab \sin \theta$. Since $\theta = \angle AOB$, n equals the area of the parallelogram $OAPB$. (3) Draw ON of length n, perpendicular to plane OAB and in such a direction that a right-threaded screw along ON will advance when turned from OA to OB through the angle θ. Then the segment ON represents the new vector **n** to be constructed.

We call the vector **n** the *vector product*, or cross product, of **a** and **b** in this order, and denote it by $\mathbf{a} \times \mathbf{b}$. Thus in Fig. 33,

$$\mathbf{n} = \overline{ON} = \mathbf{a} \times \mathbf{b} = \overline{OA} \times \overline{OB}. \tag{124}$$

To construct the vector product $\mathbf{b} \times \mathbf{a}$, we compute

$$n' = ba \sin \theta = n,$$

as before.   However, since we now rotate the screw from OB to OA through the angle θ, we must draw ON' in the opposite

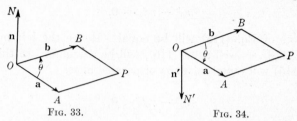

FIG. 33.   FIG. 34.

direction to that previously used.   Thus the direction of a vector product is reversed if we interchange the order of the factors, and

$$\mathbf{b} \times \mathbf{a} = -\mathbf{a} \times \mathbf{b}. \tag{125}$$

Hence vector products are *not* commutative, and we must note the order of the factors.   The property expressed in Eq. (125)

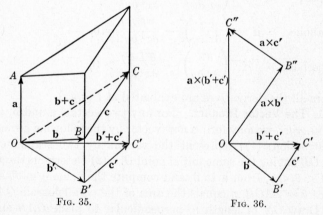

FIG. 35.   FIG. 36.

merits careful attention, since it makes vector products unlike the products used in arithmetic and algebra.

However, vector products are distributive.   That is,

$$\mathbf{a} \times (\mathbf{b} + \mathbf{c}) = \mathbf{a} \times \mathbf{b} + \mathbf{a} \times \mathbf{c}. \tag{126}$$

This may be seen from Figs. 35 and 36.   In Fig. 35, $OB = \mathbf{b}$ and $BC = \mathbf{c}$, so that $OC = \mathbf{b} + \mathbf{c}$.   Also $OA = \mathbf{a}$, and a triangular prism is constructed with OA as one edge and OBC as the base. Then a right section $OB'C'$ is formed by a plane through O perpendicular to **a**. Call $OB' = \mathbf{b}'$, $B'C' = \mathbf{c}'$, and $OC' = \mathbf{b}' + \mathbf{c}'$. Then the parallelogram formed on OA and OB has the same area as the rectangle formed on OA and OB', so that

$$\mathbf{a} \times \mathbf{b} = \mathbf{a} \times \mathbf{b}'. \tag{127}$$

Similarly,

$$\mathbf{a} \times \mathbf{c} = \mathbf{a} \times \mathbf{c}' \quad \text{and} \quad \mathbf{a} \times (\mathbf{b} + \mathbf{c}) = \mathbf{a} \times (\mathbf{b}' + \mathbf{c}'). \tag{128}$$

In Fig. 36, triangle $OB'C'$ is shown in its true shape, and triangle $OB''C''$ is formed from it by multiplying each of its sides by a and rotating the triangle through 90°. OA is not shown in this figure but would be represented by a vector coming forward perpendicular to the page. It follows that

$$\overline{OB''} = \mathbf{a} \times \mathbf{b}', \quad \overline{B''C''} = \mathbf{a} \times \mathbf{c}', \quad \overline{OC''} = \mathbf{a} \times (\mathbf{b}' + \mathbf{c}'). \tag{129}$$

This shows that

$$\mathbf{a} \times (\mathbf{b}' + \mathbf{c}') = \overline{OC''} = \overline{OB''} + \overline{B''C''} = \mathbf{a} \times \mathbf{b}' + \mathbf{a} \times \mathbf{c}', \tag{130}$$

or by Eqs. (127) and (128)

$$\mathbf{a} \times (\mathbf{b} + \mathbf{c}) = \mathbf{a} \times \mathbf{b} + \mathbf{a} \times \mathbf{c}, \tag{131}$$

which is the distributive law we wished to prove.

By multiplying Eq. (131) by -1 and using Eq. (125), we may deduce that

$$(\mathbf{b} + \mathbf{c}) \times \mathbf{a} = \mathbf{b} \times \mathbf{a} + \mathbf{c} \times \mathbf{a}. \tag{132}$$

For any two scalars p and q, it follows directly from the definition of the cross product that

$$(p\mathbf{a}) \times (q\mathbf{b}) = pq(\mathbf{a} \times \mathbf{b}). \tag{133}$$

If the two vectors **a** and **b** are parallel or lie on the same straight line, they make a zero angle. Thus $\theta = 0$ and $\sin \theta = 0$. Consequently $n = ab \sin \theta = 0$ and $n = 0$. In particular,

$$\mathbf{a} \times \mathbf{a} = 0, \quad \text{and} \quad (p\mathbf{a}) \times (q\mathbf{a}) = 0. \tag{134}$$

If the two vectors **a** and **b** are perpendicular, $\theta = 90°$ and $\sin \theta = 1$. Consequently, $n = ab \sin \theta = ab$, and,

if $$\mathbf{a} \perp \mathbf{b}, \quad |\mathbf{a} \times \mathbf{b}| = ab. \tag{135}$$

Equations (134) and (135) are easily remembered by noting that the parallelogram $OAPB$ degenerates in the first case and is a rectangle in the second case. And its area is $n = |\mathbf{a} \times \mathbf{b}|$.

Using Eq. (134), we find for the three unit vectors

$$\mathbf{i} \times \mathbf{i} = 0, \qquad \mathbf{j} \times \mathbf{j} = 0, \qquad \mathbf{k} \times \mathbf{k} = 0. \tag{136}$$

And, by a direct application of the definition

$$\mathbf{j} \times \mathbf{k} = \mathbf{i}, \qquad \mathbf{k} \times \mathbf{i} = \mathbf{j}, \qquad \mathbf{i} \times \mathbf{j} = \mathbf{k}, \tag{137}$$

while

$$\mathbf{k} \times \mathbf{j} = -\mathbf{i}, \qquad \mathbf{i} \times \mathbf{k} = -\mathbf{j}, \qquad \mathbf{j} \times \mathbf{i} = -\mathbf{k}. \tag{138}$$

That the product has length unity is in accord with Eq. (135). Also the relation of Eq. (138) to (137) is in accord with Eq. (125).

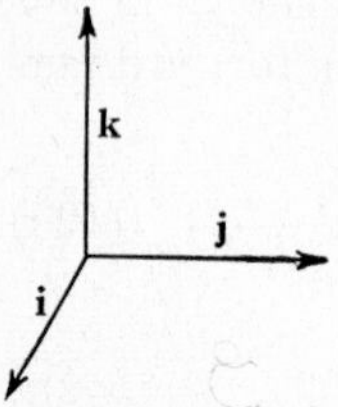

We may now express the vector product of two vectors $\mathbf{a}$ and $\mathbf{b}$ in terms of their components. Let

$$\mathbf{a} = a_x\mathbf{i} + a_y\mathbf{j} + a_z\mathbf{k}, \tag{139}$$

and

$$\mathbf{b} = b_x\mathbf{i} + b_y\mathbf{j} + b_z\mathbf{k}. \tag{140}$$

Fig. 37.

Then

$$\mathbf{a} \times \mathbf{b} = (a_x\mathbf{i} + a_y\mathbf{j} + a_z\mathbf{k}) \times (b_x\mathbf{i} + b_y\mathbf{j} + b_z\mathbf{k}). \tag{141}$$

This may be distributed into nine separate products, by Eqs. (131) and (132). We may then bring out the scalar factors by Eq. (133). Practically this is essentially the method of expanding a product in algebra, except that here in each final term we must write the unit vector which came from the first parenthesis in (141) before that which came from the second parenthesis. Finally, we may evaluate the cross products involving $\mathbf{i}$, $\mathbf{j}$, and $\mathbf{k}$ only by using Eqs. (136), (137), and (138). The result is

$$\mathbf{a} \times \mathbf{b} = \mathbf{i}(a_yb_z - a_zb_y) + \mathbf{j}(a_zb_x - a_xb_z) + \mathbf{k}(a_xb_y - a_yb_x). \tag{142}$$

This is easily kept in mind if written as a determinant:

$$\mathbf{a} \times \mathbf{b} = \begin{vmatrix} \mathbf{i} & \mathbf{j} & \mathbf{k} \\ a_x & a_y & a_z \\ b_x & b_y & b_z \end{vmatrix} = \mathbf{i}\begin{vmatrix} a_y & a_z \\ b_y & b_z \end{vmatrix} + \mathbf{j}\begin{vmatrix} a_z & a_x \\ b_z & b_x \end{vmatrix} + \mathbf{k}\begin{vmatrix} a_x & a_y \\ b_x & b_y \end{vmatrix}. \tag{143}$$

The form (142) may be obtained from this by expanding the determinants by the methods of Sec. 26.

The fact that $\mathbf{b} \times \mathbf{a}$ is $-\mathbf{a} \times \mathbf{b}$ corresponds to the fact that interchanging two rows of the determinant reverses its sign. In writing the determinant for a cross product we must be careful to put the components of the first factor in the middle row.

Let us project the vectors $\overline{OA} = \mathbf{a}$ and $\overline{OB} = \mathbf{b}$ on the yz plane, to obtain $\overline{OA'} = \mathbf{a}'$ and $\overline{OB'} = \mathbf{b}'$. Then

$$\mathbf{a}' = a_y\mathbf{j} + a_z\mathbf{k} \qquad \text{and} \qquad \mathbf{b}' = b_y\mathbf{j} + b_z\mathbf{k}. \tag{144}$$

By putting $a_x = b_x = 0$ in Eq. (143) we find that

$$\mathbf{a}' \times \mathbf{b}' = \mathbf{i}\begin{vmatrix} a_y & a_z \\ b_y & b_z \end{vmatrix} = \mathbf{i}(a_yb_z - a_zb_y). \tag{145}$$

This shows that the vector product of the projections of $\mathbf{a}$ and of $\mathbf{b}$ on a plane perpendicular to the x axis is equal to the vector component of $\mathbf{a} \times \mathbf{b}$ on the x axis. Hence the length of this component equals the area of the parallelogram $OA'P'B'$, the projection of $OAPB$ on the yz plane. Similar statements hold for the components on the y and z axes and for projections on planes perpendicular to them.

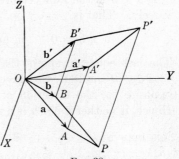

FIG. 38.

We may find the length of $\mathbf{a} \times \mathbf{b}$ by using Eqs. (53) and (143) to obtain

$$|\mathbf{a} \times \mathbf{b}|^2 = (\mathbf{a} \times \mathbf{b}) \cdot (\mathbf{a} \times \mathbf{b}) = \begin{vmatrix} a_y & a_z \\ b_y & b_z \end{vmatrix}^2 + \begin{vmatrix} a_z & a_x \\ b_z & b_x \end{vmatrix}^2 + \begin{vmatrix} a_x & a_y \\ b_x & b_y \end{vmatrix}^2. \tag{146}$$

But, since $|\mathbf{a} \times \mathbf{b}| = ab \sin \theta$,

$$\begin{aligned} |\mathbf{a} \times \mathbf{b}|^2 &= a^2b^2 \sin^2 \theta = a^2b^2(1 - \cos^2 \theta) \\ &= \begin{vmatrix} a^2 & ab \cos \theta \\ ab \cos \theta & b^2 \end{vmatrix} = \begin{vmatrix} \mathbf{a} \cdot \mathbf{a} & \mathbf{a} \cdot \mathbf{b} \\ \mathbf{a} \cdot \mathbf{b} & \mathbf{b} \cdot \mathbf{b} \end{vmatrix}. \end{aligned} \tag{147}$$

A comparison of Eqs. (147) and (146) establishes the Lagrangian identity:

$$\begin{vmatrix} \mathbf{a} \cdot \mathbf{a} & \mathbf{a} \cdot \mathbf{b} \\ \mathbf{a} \cdot \mathbf{b} & \mathbf{b} \cdot \mathbf{b} \end{vmatrix} = (\mathbf{a} \times \mathbf{b}) \cdot (\mathbf{a} \times \mathbf{b}). \tag{148}$$

Written in terms of the components, the identity is:

$$\begin{vmatrix} a_x{}^2 + a_y{}^2 + a_z{}^2 & a_xb_x + a_yb_y + a_zb_z \\ a_xb_x + a_yb_y + a_zb_z & b_x{}^2 + b_y{}^2 + b_z{}^2 \end{vmatrix}$$
$$= \begin{vmatrix} a_y & a_z \\ b_y & b_z \end{vmatrix}^2 + \begin{vmatrix} a_z & a_x \\ b_z & b_x \end{vmatrix}^2 + \begin{vmatrix} a_x & a_y \\ b_x & b_y \end{vmatrix}^2. \quad (149)$$

We may determine $\sin \theta$ by noting that

$$\sin^2 \theta = \frac{(ab \sin \theta)^2}{a^2b^2} = \frac{(\mathbf{a} \times \mathbf{b}) \cdot (\mathbf{a} \times \mathbf{b})}{(\mathbf{a} \cdot \mathbf{a})(\mathbf{b} \cdot \mathbf{b})}. \quad (150)$$

The expression for the numerator in terms of components is the right member of (149), while the denominator is

$$(\mathbf{a} \cdot \mathbf{a})(\mathbf{b} \cdot \mathbf{b}) = (a_x{}^2 + a_y{}^2 + a_z{}^2)(b_x{}^2 + b_y{}^2 + b_z{}^2). \quad (151)$$

If $\mathbf{a} \times \mathbf{b}$ is the null vector, it will have zero length and conversely. That is,

$$\mathbf{a} \times \mathbf{b} = 0 \quad \text{if, and only if, } ab \sin \theta = 0. \quad (152)$$

The last equation shows that a, b, or $\sin \theta = 0$. In the last case $\theta = 0°$ or $180°$, the direction of $\mathbf{a}$ is either the same as, or opposite to, the direction of $\mathbf{b}$, and the vectors are parallel. Hence, if neither $\mathbf{a}$ nor $\mathbf{b}$ is a null vector, the equation

$$\mathbf{a} \times \mathbf{b} = 0, \quad (153)$$

is a necessary and sufficient condition for parallelism.

Again, from the relation between three vectors

$$\mathbf{a} \times \mathbf{b} = \mathbf{a} \times \mathbf{c} \quad \text{or} \quad \mathbf{a} \times (\mathbf{b} - \mathbf{c}) = 0, \quad (154)$$

we may conclude only that either

$$\mathbf{a} = 0, \quad \mathbf{b} = \mathbf{c}, \quad \text{or } \mathbf{b} - \mathbf{c} \text{ is parallel to } \mathbf{a}. \quad (155)$$

52. Angular Rotation. Suppose that a rigid body is rotating about an axis OQ with angular velocity ω radians/sec. Let $\mathbf{a}$ be any vector of length ω drawn along the axis in the direction in which a right-threaded screw would be advanced by the rotation. Let P be any point of the body and O any point on the axis. Denote the vector $\overline{OP}$ by $\mathbf{b}$. Also draw PQ, the perpendicular from P to the axis. Let q denote the length of QP. Then the rotation causes P to move in a circle of radius q, with a velocity of ωq. This velocity is perpendicular to QP and OP, and hence in the direction of $\mathbf{a} \times \mathbf{b}$. Again,

$$a = \omega \qquad \text{and} \qquad q = QP = b \sin \theta, \qquad (156)$$

so that the length of $\mathbf{a} \times \mathbf{b}$ is

$$|\mathbf{a} \times \mathbf{b}| = ab \sin \theta = \omega q = v.$$

Consequently, $\mathbf{v}$, the induced velocity at P is given by
$$\mathbf{v} = \mathbf{a} \times \mathbf{b}. \qquad (157)$$

If we call $\mathbf{a}$ the vector angular velocity, this may be written

Induced velocity at $P = $ (vector angular velocity) $\times (\overline{OP})$,   (158)

where O is any point on the axis of rotation.

The relation (158) shows that angular velocities may not only be represented by vectors but may be added vectorially, provided their axes intersect. For, let OQ_1 and OQ_2 be two intersecting axes of rotation, and let the vector $\mathbf{a}_1$ of length ω_1 on $\overline{OQ_1}$ and the vector $\mathbf{a}_2$ of length ω_2 on $\overline{OQ_2}$ represent velocities. Then the induced velocities at P are

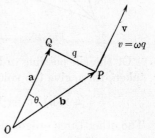

$$\mathbf{v}_1 = \mathbf{a}_1 \times \overline{OP}$$
and $\qquad\qquad (159)$
$$\mathbf{v}_2 = \mathbf{a}_2 \times \overline{OP}.$$

Fig. 39.

It follows by Eq. (132) that

$$\mathbf{v}_1 + \mathbf{v}_2 = (\mathbf{a}_1 + \mathbf{a}_2) \times \overline{OP}. \qquad (160)$$

That is, if the rotations $\mathbf{a}_1$ and $\mathbf{a}_2$ act simultaneously, the sum of the velocities induced by them is the velocity induced at P by the rotation about an axis through O whose angular velocity vector is $\mathbf{a}_1 + \mathbf{a}_2$. Under these conditions it is usually most convenient to represent the vectors $\mathbf{a}_1$, $\mathbf{a}_2$, and $\mathbf{a}_1 + \mathbf{a}_2$ by segments having O as their initial point. Such as OQ_1, OQ_2, and OQ in Fig. 40.

53. The Triple Scalar Product. If $\mathbf{a}$, $\mathbf{b}$, $\mathbf{c}$, are three vectors taken in such an order that $\mathbf{a} \times \mathbf{b}$ makes an acute angle with $\mathbf{c}$, the triple product $(\mathbf{a} \times \mathbf{b}) \cdot \mathbf{c}$ is a scalar quantity equal to the volume of the parallelepiped having $\mathbf{a}$, $\mathbf{b}$, $\mathbf{c}$ as three of its edges.

For let the segment ON represent $\mathbf{n} = \mathbf{a} \times \mathbf{b}$, and let C' be the projection of C on the line ON. Then if $OC' = h$,

$$(\mathbf{a} \times \mathbf{b}) \cdot \mathbf{c} = \mathbf{n} \cdot \mathbf{c} = \mathbf{n} \text{ Proj}_\mathbf{n} c = nh. \qquad (161)$$

But n is the area of $OAPB$, the base of the parallelepiped, and since ON is perpendicular to this base, or the parallel base $CA'P'B'$, OC' or h is the height of the parallelepiped. Hence the right member of Eq. (161) is the base times the altitude. This is the volume as we stated.

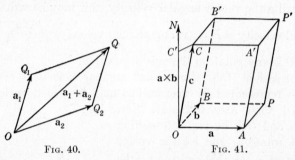

FIG. 40.　　　　　　　FIG. 41.

Of the six possible orders in which the vectors $\mathbf{a}, \mathbf{b}, \mathbf{c}$ may be taken, three give the volume of the parallelepiped $V = nh$:

$$(\mathbf{a} \times \mathbf{b}) \cdot \mathbf{c} = (\mathbf{b} \times \mathbf{c}) \cdot \mathbf{a} = (\mathbf{c} \times \mathbf{a}) \cdot \mathbf{b} = V. \qquad (162)$$

The other three orders give the negative of the volume

$$(\mathbf{b} \times \mathbf{a}) \cdot \mathbf{c} = (\mathbf{c} \times \mathbf{b}) \cdot \mathbf{a} = (\mathbf{a} \times \mathbf{c}) \cdot \mathbf{b} = -V. \qquad (163)$$

Since the *dot* product is commutative, we also have

$$\mathbf{c} \cdot (\mathbf{a} \times \mathbf{b}) = \mathbf{a} \cdot (\mathbf{b} \times \mathbf{c}) = \mathbf{b} \cdot (\mathbf{c} \times \mathbf{a}) = V. \qquad (164)$$

Let us express the middle one of these in terms of components. By Eq. (143) we have

$$\mathbf{b} \times \mathbf{c} = \begin{vmatrix} \mathbf{i} & \mathbf{j} & \mathbf{k} \\ b_x & b_y & b_z \\ c_x & c_y & c_z \end{vmatrix} = \mathbf{i} \begin{vmatrix} b_y & b_z \\ c_y & c_z \end{vmatrix} + \mathbf{j} \begin{vmatrix} b_z & b_x \\ c_z & c_x \end{vmatrix} + \mathbf{k} \begin{vmatrix} b_x & b_y \\ c_x & c_y \end{vmatrix}. \qquad (165)$$

From this and Eq. (52)

$$\mathbf{a} \cdot (\mathbf{b} \times \mathbf{c}) = a_x \begin{vmatrix} b_y & b_z \\ c_y & c_z \end{vmatrix} + a_y \begin{vmatrix} b_z & b_x \\ c_z & c_x \end{vmatrix} + a_z \begin{vmatrix} b_x & b_y \\ c_x & c_y \end{vmatrix} = \begin{vmatrix} a_x & a_y & a_z \\ b_x & b_y & b_z \\ c_x & c_y & c_z \end{vmatrix}. \qquad (166)$$

If $h = 0$, $OC' = 0$, and C is in plane OAB. If $n = 0$, $OB = 0$, $OA = 0$, or B is on the line OA. In any of these cases, the points O, A, B, C are all in the same plane. And these are the only cases in which $V = nh = 0$. Hence a necessary and sufficient condition that the vectors **a**, **b**, and **c** are all parallel to the same plane is

$$\mathbf{a} \cdot (\mathbf{b} \times \mathbf{c}) = 0. \tag{167}$$

54. Frenet Formulas for Twisted Curves. Let $P(x,y,z)$ be any point on a curve in space, and let us take s, the arc length from some fixed point of the curve to P, as the parameter. Then if $\mathbf{r} = \overline{OP}$, the vector from the origin of coordinates to P, we shall have

$$\mathbf{r}(s) = x(s)\mathbf{i} + y(s)\mathbf{j} + z(s)\mathbf{k}. \tag{168}$$

By Sec. 48, the vector

$$\frac{d\mathbf{r}}{ds} = \mathbf{r}'(s) = x'(s)\mathbf{i} + y'(s)\mathbf{j} + z'(s)\mathbf{k} \tag{169}$$

is directed along the tangent to the curve, in the direction of increasing s. Its length is unity, since s here plays the role of the parameter t in Eq. (83). This also follows from Eq. (77), or

$$ds^2 = dx^2 + dy^2 + dz^2, \tag{170}$$

which implies that

$$1 = \left(\frac{dx}{ds}\right)^2 + \left(\frac{dy}{ds}\right)^2 + \left(\frac{dz}{ds}\right)^2 = x'^2 + y'^2 + z'^2. \tag{171}$$

Let **t** denote the unit vector along the tangent line, $\mathbf{r}'(s)$. Then

$$\mathbf{t} = \frac{d\mathbf{r}}{ds}. \tag{172}$$

By Eq. (169), $x'(s)$, $y'(s)$, $z'(s)$ are direction ratios for $\mathbf{r}'(s)$ or **t**. And by Eq. (171) they are the direction cosines themselves. We denote them by l_t, m_t, n_t, so that

$$l_t = \frac{dx}{ds}, \qquad m_t = \frac{dy}{ds}, \qquad n_t = \frac{dz}{ds}. \tag{173}$$

And

$$\mathbf{t} = l_t\mathbf{i} + m_t\mathbf{j} + n_t\mathbf{k}. \tag{174}$$

By differentiating $\mathbf{t}(s)$, we obtain a new vector $\mathbf{t}'(s)$. The line through P in the direction of $\mathbf{t}'(s)$ is called the *principal normal* of the twisted curve at P. Denote a unit vector along $\mathbf{t}'(s)$ by $\mathbf{p}$, and let C be the length of $\mathbf{t}'(s)$. Then

$$\frac{d\mathbf{t}}{ds} = \mathbf{t}'(s) = C\mathbf{p}. \tag{175}$$

And if l_p, m_p, n_p are the direction cosines of the principal normal, that is, of $\mathbf{t}'(s)$ or of $\mathbf{p}$, we have, as in Eq. (35),

$$\mathbf{p} = l_p\mathbf{i} + m_p\mathbf{j} + n_p\mathbf{k}. \tag{176}$$

The curvature of the given curve in space is the rate of turning of its tangent line as determined by the following construction. For each value of s, represent the vector $\mathbf{t}(s)$ by a segment with initial point at the origin, $\overline{OQ}$. Since $\mathbf{t}(s)$ is a unit vector, Q will

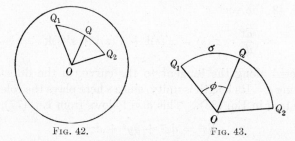

Fig. 42.   Fig. 43.

lie on a sphere of unit radius with center at O. As s varies, the end point Q will trace a space curve Q_1QQ_2 on the sphere. And the segment OQ will trace out a conical surface, which may be developed on a plane into a sector of a unit circle. Let σ denote the length of arc on the spherical curve from some fixed point Q_1 to any point Q. Then σ equals arc Q_1Q on the sphere, and hence equals arc Q_1Q on the plane development. Let the angle at the vertex Q_1OQ in the plane development be called ϕ. Then the rate of change of ϕ with respect to s is defined to be the curvature of the given curve in space. Its reciprocal is called the *radius of curvature* and is denoted by ρ. Thus

$$\frac{1}{\rho} = \lim_{\Delta s \to 0} \frac{\Delta\phi}{\Delta s} = \frac{d\phi}{ds}. \tag{177}$$

On the unit circle,

$$\phi = \angle Q_1OQ = Q_1Q = \sigma.$$

And we may apply Eq. (83) to the curve Q_1QQ_2 on the sphere by replacing $\mathbf{r}$, s, and t by $OQ = \mathbf{t}$, σ, and s. The result is

$$\frac{d\sigma}{ds} = \left| \frac{d\mathbf{t}}{ds} \right| = \sqrt{\frac{d\mathbf{t}}{ds} \cdot \frac{d\mathbf{t}}{ds}}, \quad \text{or} \quad C\sqrt{\mathbf{p} \cdot \mathbf{p}} = C, \quad (178)$$

by Eq. (175). It follows that

$$\frac{1}{\rho} = \frac{d\phi}{ds} = \frac{d\sigma}{ds} = C. \quad (179)$$

Hence the factor C in Eq. (175) is the curvature, as we anticipated by our notation. We may rewrite Eq. (175) as

$$\frac{d\mathbf{t}}{ds} = \frac{1}{\rho}\mathbf{p}, \quad \text{or} \quad \mathbf{p} = \rho\frac{d\mathbf{t}}{ds}. \quad (180)$$

It follows from this and Eqs. (174) and (176) that

$$l_p = \rho\frac{dl_t}{ds}, \quad m_p = \rho\frac{dm_t}{ds}, \quad n_p = \rho\frac{dn_t}{ds}. \quad (181)$$

Since $\mathbf{t}$ is a unit vector, we may write

$$\mathbf{t} \cdot \mathbf{t} = 1. \quad (182)$$

The familiar rule for differentiating products applies without change to scalar products. That is,

$$\frac{d}{dt}(\mathbf{U} \cdot \mathbf{V}) = \frac{d\mathbf{U}}{dt} \cdot \mathbf{V} + \mathbf{U} \cdot \frac{d\mathbf{V}}{dt}$$

and

$$\frac{d}{dt}(\mathbf{U} \cdot \mathbf{U}) = 2\mathbf{U} \cdot \frac{d\mathbf{U}}{dt}. \quad (183)$$

By differentiating Eq. (182) we find

$$2\mathbf{t} \cdot \frac{d\mathbf{t}}{ds} = 0. \quad (184)$$

This shows that either $\mathbf{t}'(s)$ is a null vector, or $\mathbf{t}'(s)$ is perpendicular to $\mathbf{t}$. If $\mathbf{t}'(s) = 0$, it has no direction, and Eq. (175) is true with $C = 0$ and any unit vector $\mathbf{p}$. However, in this case we take $\mathbf{p}$ any unit vector perpendicular to $\mathbf{t}$, so that in all cases

$$\mathbf{t} \cdot \mathbf{p} = 0, \quad \text{and} \quad \mathbf{t} \perp \mathbf{p}. \quad (185)$$

As we consider the curve to have the same direction as its tangent, all lines through P perpendicular to the tangent are normal to the curve. Thus Eq. (185) justifies the designation of **p** as the principal normal.

Let us next consider the vector **b** defined by the relation:

$$\mathbf{b} = \mathbf{t} \times \mathbf{p}. \qquad (186)$$

Since **t** and **p** are each of unit length and are perpendicular, the vector **b** is of unit length. And **t**, **p**, and **b** are three mutually perpendicular unit vectors which form a right-hand trihedral like that formed by **i**, **j**, and **k**. The line through P in the direction of **b** is called the *binormal* of the twisted curve at P, since it is a second special direction normal to the curve. If l_b, m_b, n_b are the direction cosines of the binormal, we may write

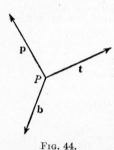

FIG. 44.

$$\mathbf{b} = l_b\mathbf{i} + m_b\mathbf{j} + n_b\mathbf{k}. \qquad (187)$$

The familiar rule for differentiating products applies to vector products, provided we preserve the order of the factors. That is,

$$\frac{d}{dt}(\mathbf{U} \times \mathbf{V}) = \frac{d\mathbf{U}}{dt} \times \mathbf{V} + \mathbf{U} \times \frac{d\mathbf{V}}{dt}. \qquad (188)$$

By differentiating Eq. (186) we find

$$\frac{d\mathbf{b}}{ds} = \frac{d\mathbf{t}}{ds} \times \mathbf{p} + \mathbf{t} \times \frac{d\mathbf{p}}{ds}. \qquad (189)$$

The first term is zero, by Eqs. (175) and (134). Hence

$$\frac{d\mathbf{b}}{ds} = \mathbf{t} \times \frac{d\mathbf{p}}{ds}, \qquad (190)$$

and the vector $d\mathbf{b}/ds$ is perpendicular to **t**.

But **b** is a unit vector, so that we may write

$$\mathbf{b} \cdot \mathbf{b} = 1, \qquad (191)$$

and deduce by differentiation the equation analogous to (184):

$$2\mathbf{b} \cdot \frac{d\mathbf{b}}{ds} = 0. \qquad (192)$$

This shows that either $d\mathbf{b}/ds = 0$, or it is perpendicular to **b**.

In any case we may write

$$\frac{d\mathbf{b}}{ds} = -T\mathbf{p},\tag{193}$$

since $d\mathbf{b}/ds$ must be parallel to $\mathbf{p}$ by reason of its perpendicularity to $\mathbf{t}$ and $\mathbf{b}$ unless $d\mathbf{b}/ds = 0$, in which case (193) holds with $T = 0$.

Let us next construct an angle θ related to $\mathbf{b}$ and Eq. (193) in the same way that the angle ϕ was related to $\mathbf{t}$ and Eq. (175). That is, we represent the unit vector $\mathbf{b}$ by a segment with initial

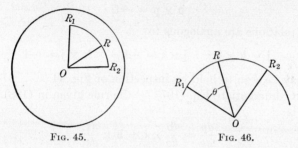

Fig. 45.   Fig. 46.

point at the origin, $\overline{OR}$. Then as s varies, $\overline{OR} = \mathbf{b}(s)$ traces out a conical surface bounded by the curve R_1RR_2 on the unit sphere. This conical surface may be developed on a plane into a sector of a unit circle. And, if R_1 is a fixed point and R a variable point on the spherical curve or on its plane development, we define

$$\theta = \angle R_1OR = R_1R.\tag{194}$$

We then have, analogous to Eqs. (178) and (179),

$$\frac{d\theta}{ds} = \left|\frac{d\mathbf{b}}{ds}\right| = \sqrt{\frac{d\mathbf{b}}{ds} \cdot \frac{d\mathbf{b}}{ds}} = T.\tag{195}$$

This equation shows that T measures the rate of turning of the binormal, with respect to s. We call T the *torsion*, and its reciprocal, $\tau = 1/T$, the *radius of torsion*. The direction of turning of $\mathbf{b}$ may be associated with the direction of the tangent to the arc R_1RR_2 in Fig. 45 for increasing s, that is, the direction of $\mathbf{b}'(s)$. And, by Eq. (193), the sign of T or of τ determines whether this last direction is negatively or positively directed along $\mathbf{p}$.

We may rewrite Eq. (193) as

$$\frac{d\mathbf{b}}{ds} = -\frac{1}{\tau}\mathbf{p}, \quad \text{or} \quad \mathbf{p} = -\tau\frac{d\mathbf{b}}{ds}. \tag{196}$$

We wish next to find a simple expression for $d\mathbf{p}/ds$, similar to that for $d\mathbf{t}/ds$ in Eq. (180) and that for $d\mathbf{b}/ds$ in Eq. (196). We begin by noting that

$$\mathbf{p} = \mathbf{b} \times \mathbf{t}, \tag{197}$$

and

$$\mathbf{p} \times \mathbf{t} = -\mathbf{b}, \tag{198}$$
$$\mathbf{b} \times \mathbf{p} = -\mathbf{t}. \tag{199}$$

These relations are analogous to

$$\mathbf{j} = \mathbf{k} \times \mathbf{i}, \quad \mathbf{j} \times \mathbf{i} = -\mathbf{k}, \quad \mathbf{k} \times \mathbf{j} = -\mathbf{i} \tag{200}$$

and may be seen to hold by inspection of Fig. 44.

Next, differentiate Eq. (197) by the rule given in (188). The result is

$$\frac{d\mathbf{p}}{ds} = \frac{d\mathbf{b}}{ds} \times \mathbf{t} + \mathbf{b} \times \frac{d\mathbf{t}}{ds}. \tag{201}$$

On substituting the expressions given in Eqs. (196) and (180) for the derivatives on the right, we find

$$\frac{d\mathbf{p}}{ds} = -\frac{1}{\tau}\mathbf{p} \times \mathbf{t} + \frac{1}{\rho}\mathbf{b} \times \mathbf{p}. \tag{202}$$

Finally, we may replace the cross products by their values as given in Eqs. (198) and (199), and so find

$$\frac{d\mathbf{p}}{ds} = \frac{1}{\tau}\mathbf{b} - \frac{1}{\rho}\mathbf{t}. \tag{203}$$

This is the expression that we were seeking.

Equations (180), (196), and (203), or

$$\frac{d\mathbf{t}}{ds} = \frac{1}{\rho}\mathbf{p}, \quad \frac{d\mathbf{b}}{ds} = -\frac{1}{\tau}\mathbf{p}, \quad \frac{d\mathbf{p}}{ds} = \frac{1}{\tau}\mathbf{b} - \frac{1}{\rho}\mathbf{t}, \tag{204}$$

are collectively known as the *Frenet formulas* for curves in space.

We obtain a simple interpretation of these equations if we think in terms of motion. Let us allow a point to move along the given curve with unit velocity, so that the elapsed time is measured by s. And let the moving point P be one vertex of a rigid body in the form of a cube, one unit on a side, which moves so that at each instant three of its edges $\overline{PT'}$, $\overline{PP'}$, $\overline{PB'}$ coincide with **t**, **p**, **b** for the point P. The instantaneous motion of the cube will be a translation of P along the curve with unit speed, combined with a rotation about some axis through P. The rotation will be the same as that of the cube with one vertex at O, and having three of its edges $\overline{OT''}$, $\overline{OP''}$, $\overline{OB''}$ parallel to $\overline{PT'}$, $\overline{PP'}$, $\overline{PB'}$ or **t**, **p**, **b**.

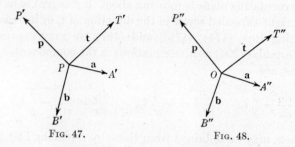

FIG. 47.   FIG. 48.

Now suppose that this second cube were rotating with vector angular velocity, as defined in Sec. 52, $\overline{OA''} = \mathbf{a}$, where

$$\mathbf{a} = \frac{1}{\tau}\mathbf{t} + \frac{1}{\rho}\mathbf{b}. \tag{205}$$

Then by Eq. (157) the induced velocity at T'' would be

$$\mathbf{v}_t = \mathbf{a} \times (\overline{OT''}) = \left(\frac{1}{\tau}\mathbf{t} + \frac{1}{\rho}\mathbf{b}\right) \times \mathbf{t} = \frac{1}{\rho}\mathbf{p}. \tag{206}$$

Similarly the induced velocity at P'' would be

$$\mathbf{v}_p = \mathbf{a} \times (\overline{OP''}) = \left(\frac{1}{\tau}\mathbf{t} + \frac{1}{\rho}\mathbf{b}\right) \times \mathbf{p} = \frac{1}{\tau}\mathbf{b} - \frac{1}{\rho}\mathbf{t}, \tag{207}$$

and that at B'' would be

$$\mathbf{v}_b = \mathbf{a} \times (\overline{OB''}) = \left(\frac{1}{\tau}\mathbf{t} + \frac{1}{\rho}\mathbf{b}\right) \times \mathbf{b} = -\frac{1}{\tau}\mathbf{p}. \tag{208}$$

The right members of the last three equations are the same as the right members of (204). And, since s measures the time, the left members of (204) may be thought of as velocities. Hence, with our hypothetical rotation, three of the edges, and hence all points of the cube, would have precisely the velocities needed to keep the cube in Fig. 48 parallel to that in Fig. 47.

This shows that the instantaneous motion of the cube on the trihedral **t**, **p**, **b** in Fig. 47 is a unit translation along **t** combined with a rotation whose angular velocity vector is $\overline{PA'} = $ **a**. And the Frenet formulas (204) state that **a** is given by Eq. (205). That is, **a** is perpendicular to the principal normal, has a component $1/\rho$ along the binormal, and has a component $1/\tau$ along the tangent. The plane through P, **t** and **p**, or $PT'P'$ is called the *osculating plane* of the given curve at P. When τ is positive, the osculating plane is rotating about the tangent so as to advance a right-threaded screw in the direction of **t**, or increasing s.

By using Eqs. (174), (176), and (187) we may express the Frenet formulas (204) as nine equations in the components. The first three are

$$\frac{dl_t}{ds} = \frac{1}{\rho}\, l_p, \qquad \frac{dl_b}{ds} = -\frac{1}{\tau}\, l_p, \qquad \frac{dl_p}{ds} = \frac{1}{\tau}\, l_b - \frac{1}{\rho}\, l_t. \qquad (209)$$

The others may be obtained from these by replacing l by m and then by n.

By starting with Eq. (172) and using the Frenet formulas (204), we may establish the following series of equations:

$$\frac{d\mathbf{r}}{ds} = \mathbf{t}, \qquad \frac{d^2\mathbf{r}}{ds^2} = \frac{d\mathbf{t}}{ds} = \frac{\mathbf{p}}{\rho},$$

$$\frac{d^3\mathbf{r}}{ds^3} = \frac{d}{ds}\left(\frac{\mathbf{p}}{\rho}\right) = \mathbf{p}\frac{d}{ds}\left(\frac{1}{\rho}\right) + \frac{1}{\rho}\frac{d\mathbf{p}}{ds} = -\frac{\rho'}{\rho^2}\mathbf{p} + \frac{1}{\rho\tau}\mathbf{b} - \frac{1}{\rho^2}\mathbf{t}. \qquad (210)$$

These may be used to study the behavior of a space curve near a particular point P_0. To do this, let us measure s from this point and take a set of axes with this point as origin, and the x, y, and z axes along the tangent principal normal and binormal, respectively. Then we may write the vector Maclaurin's series:

$$\mathbf{r} = \left(\frac{d\mathbf{r}}{ds}\right)_0 s + \frac{1}{2!}\left(\frac{d^2\mathbf{r}}{ds^2}\right)_0 s^2 + \frac{1}{3!}\left(\frac{d^3\mathbf{r}}{ds^3}\right)_0 s^3 + \cdots, \qquad (211)$$

for

$$\mathbf{r} = x\mathbf{i} + y\mathbf{j} + z\mathbf{k}, \qquad (212)$$

since the components of the right member of (211) are the ordinary Maclaurin's series for the components of the left member. The subscripts zero mean that the derivatives are to be evaluated at the new origin, $P_0 = 0$, and the first term is absent since $\mathbf{r} = 0$ when $s = 0$. If we evaluate the derivatives in Eq. (211) by using Eq. (210) and noting that for our special coordinate system,

$$\mathbf{t}_0 = \mathbf{i}, \qquad \mathbf{p}_0 = \mathbf{j}, \qquad \mathbf{b}_0 = \mathbf{k}, \qquad (213)$$

we find that

$$\mathbf{r} = s\mathbf{i} + \frac{s^2}{2\rho_0}\mathbf{j} + \frac{s^3}{6}\left(-\frac{1}{\rho_0{}^2}\mathbf{i} - \frac{\rho_0'}{\rho_0{}^2}\mathbf{j} + \frac{1}{\rho_0\tau_0}\mathbf{k}\right) + \cdots. \quad (214)$$

The components of this equation are

$$x = s \quad * \quad - \frac{s^3}{6\rho_0{}^2} + \cdots,$$

$$y = * \quad \frac{s^2}{2\rho_0} - \frac{\rho_0's^3}{6\rho_0{}^2} + \cdots, \qquad (215)$$

$$z = * \quad * \quad \frac{s^3}{6\rho_0\tau_0} + \cdots.$$

These expansions show that the tangent line ($y = 0$, $z = 0$) approximates the curve to terms of the first order in s. And the parabola in the osculating plane ($z = 0$) whose equation is $2\rho_0 y = x^2$ approximates the curve to terms of the second order in s. In place of the parabola we could use the circle of curvature given by

$$z = 0, \qquad 2\rho_0 y = x^2 + y^2. \quad (216)$$

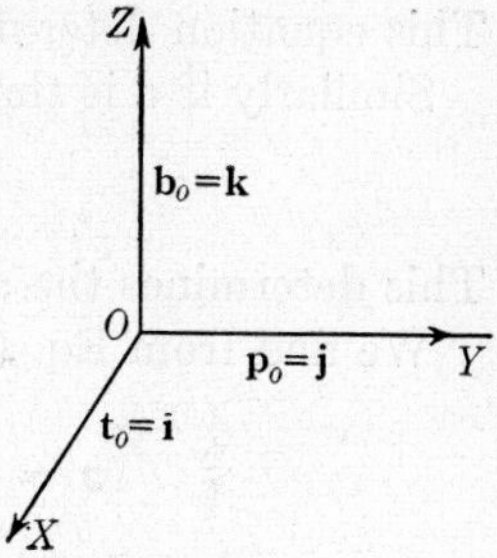

To approximate the curve to terms of the third order in s, we must use a twisted curve and could use the third-order curve given by

$$y = \frac{x^2}{2\rho_0} - \frac{\rho_0'x^3}{6\rho_0{}^2} \quad \text{and} \quad z = \frac{x^3}{6\rho_0\tau_0}. \quad (217)$$

Fig. 49.

Any curve with the same position of $\mathbf{t}_0$, $\mathbf{p}_0$, and $\mathbf{b}_0$ and the same values of ρ_0 and τ_0 will have the same leading terms in the expansions (215) and may be used in place of (217). In particular, we may find a suitable circular helix. This is called the *osculating helix* of the given space curve at P_0 and will be right-threaded if the torsion is positive and left-threaded if the torsion is negative.

55. Curves with Parameter *t*. Let the variable point P on a space curve be expressed in terms of the parameter t. We may think of P as a moving point with t the time.   As in mechanics, we use dots over the letters for differentiation with respect to t, the time.   Then

$$\mathbf{r}(t) = x(t)\mathbf{i} + y(t)\mathbf{j} + z(t)\mathbf{k}, \qquad (218)$$

and, as in Sec. 48, the velocity vector

$$\mathbf{v} = \dot{\mathbf{r}} = \dot{x}\mathbf{i} + \dot{y}\mathbf{j} + \dot{z}\mathbf{k}, \qquad (219)$$

while the acceleration vector

$$\mathbf{a} = \dot{\mathbf{v}} = \ddot{\mathbf{r}} = \ddot{x}\mathbf{i} + \ddot{y}\mathbf{j} + \ddot{z}\mathbf{k}. \qquad (220)$$

If we denote the speed in the path, $\dot{s}$ by v, and recall (172), we find

$$\mathbf{v} = \frac{d\mathbf{r}}{dt} = \frac{d\mathbf{r}}{ds}\frac{ds}{dt} = \mathbf{t}v. \qquad (221)$$

Since $\mathbf{t}$ is a unit vector,* v is the length of $\mathbf{v}$ and

$$v^2 = \dot{x}^2 + \dot{y}^2 + \dot{z}^2. \qquad (222)$$

This equation determines the speed v in terms of the time t.
    Similarly if a is the length of $\mathbf{a}$,

$$a^2 = \ddot{x}^2 + \ddot{y}^2 + \ddot{z}^2. \qquad (223)$$

This determines the acceleration in the path.
    We find from Eq. (221) that

$$\mathbf{a} = \frac{d\mathbf{v}}{dt} = \frac{d}{dt}(\mathbf{t}v) = \mathbf{t}\frac{dv}{dt} + v\frac{d\mathbf{t}}{dt}. \qquad (224)$$

But, by Eq. (180),

$$\frac{d\mathbf{t}}{dt} = \frac{d\mathbf{t}}{ds}\frac{ds}{dt} = \frac{1}{\rho}\mathbf{p}v = \frac{v}{\rho}\mathbf{p}. \qquad (225)$$

It follows that

$$\mathbf{a} = \dot{v}\mathbf{t} + \frac{v^2}{\rho}\mathbf{p}. \qquad (226)$$

This equation shows that the acceleration vector lies in the osculating plane and has components

$\dot{v} = dv/dt$ along the tangent and v^2/ρ along the principal normal.
$$(227)$$

This fact is of importance in mechanics and shows that the

---
* In this section t always means the time, or parameter, and *not* $|\mathbf{t}| = 1$.

accelerations for the motion in a space curve are the same as they would be if the point moved along the circle of curvature (216) with the same value of v and dv/dt.

We may determine one expression for ρ as follows. From Eq. (226) and the fact that $\mathbf{t}$ and $\mathbf{p}$ are perpendicular unit vectors, we find

$$a^2 = \mathbf{a} \cdot \mathbf{a} = \dot{v}^2 + \frac{v^4}{\rho^2}. \tag{228}$$

Consequently,

$$\rho^2 = \frac{v^4}{a^2 - \dot{v}^2} \quad \text{and} \quad \rho = \frac{v^2}{\sqrt{a^2 - \dot{v}^2}}. \tag{229}$$

We use the positive square root, since ρ is positive.

Again, from Eqs. (221) and (226),

$$\mathbf{v} \times \mathbf{a} = (t v) \times \left(\dot{v} \mathbf{t} + \frac{v^2}{\rho} \mathbf{p} \right) = \frac{v^3}{\rho} \mathbf{b}, \tag{230}$$

since from Fig. 44,

$$\mathbf{t} \times \mathbf{t} = 0 \quad \text{and} \quad \mathbf{t} \times \mathbf{p} = \mathbf{b}. \tag{231}$$

But by Eqs. (219), (220), and (143),

$$\mathbf{v} \times \mathbf{a} = \begin{vmatrix} \mathbf{i} & \mathbf{j} & \mathbf{k} \\ \dot{x} & \dot{y} & \dot{z} \\ \ddot{x} & \ddot{y} & \ddot{z} \end{vmatrix} = \begin{vmatrix} \dot{y} & \dot{z} \\ \ddot{y} & \ddot{z} \end{vmatrix} \mathbf{i} + \begin{vmatrix} \dot{z} & \dot{x} \\ \ddot{z} & \ddot{x} \end{vmatrix} \mathbf{j} + \begin{vmatrix} \dot{x} & \dot{y} \\ \ddot{x} & \ddot{y} \end{vmatrix} \mathbf{k}. \tag{232}$$

Since $\mathbf{b}$ is a unit vector, Eq. (230) shows that the length of $\mathbf{v} \times \mathbf{a}$ is v^3/ρ. Hence we may equate v^6/ρ^2 to the square of the length of $\mathbf{v} \times \mathbf{a}$, as found from the right member of (232), and

$$\frac{v^6}{\rho^2} = \begin{vmatrix} \dot{y} & \dot{z} \\ \ddot{y} & \ddot{z} \end{vmatrix}^2 + \begin{vmatrix} \dot{z} & \dot{x} \\ \ddot{z} & \ddot{x} \end{vmatrix}^2 + \begin{vmatrix} \dot{x} & \dot{y} \\ \ddot{x} & \ddot{y} \end{vmatrix}^2. \tag{233}$$

This leads to an alternative expression for

$$\rho = \frac{v^3}{\sqrt{\begin{vmatrix} \dot{y} & \dot{z} \\ \ddot{y} & \ddot{z} \end{vmatrix}^2 + \begin{vmatrix} \dot{z} & \dot{x} \\ \ddot{z} & \ddot{x} \end{vmatrix}^2 + \begin{vmatrix} \dot{x} & \dot{y} \\ \ddot{x} & \ddot{y} \end{vmatrix}^2}}. \tag{234}$$

We note that by the Lagrangian identity, (148) and (149), the right member of (233) is equal to

$$\begin{vmatrix} \dot{x}^2 + \dot{y}^2 + \dot{z}^2 & \dot{x}\ddot{x} + \dot{y}\ddot{y} + \dot{z}\ddot{z} \\ \dot{x}\ddot{x} + \dot{y}\ddot{y} + \dot{z}\ddot{z} & \ddot{x}^2 + \ddot{y}^2 + \ddot{z}^2 \end{vmatrix} = \begin{vmatrix} v^2 & v\dot{v} \\ v\dot{v} & a^2 \end{vmatrix}. \tag{235}$$

Consequently,

$$\frac{v^6}{\rho^2} = v^2 a^2 - (v\dot{v})(v\dot{v}) = v^2(a^2 - \dot{v}^2), \tag{236}$$

which is equivalent to the relation (229).

Since $\mathbf{v} = \mathbf{t}v$, the direction of $\mathbf{t}$ is the same as that of $\mathbf{v}$, whose components are given in (219). And the direction of $\mathbf{b}$ is the same as that of $\mathbf{v} \times \mathbf{a}$, by (230), of which the components are given in (232). To find the components of a vector in the direction of $\mathbf{p}$, we proceed as follows. From Eq. (226),

$$\frac{v^2}{\rho}\mathbf{p} = \mathbf{a} - \dot{v}\mathbf{t}, \qquad \text{and} \qquad \frac{v^4}{\rho}\mathbf{p} = v^2\mathbf{a} - v\dot{v}\mathbf{v}. \tag{237}$$

We may express this in terms of x, y, z, and their derivatives by using Eqs. (219), (220), (222) and

$$v\dot{v} = \dot{x}\ddot{x} + \dot{y}\ddot{y} + \dot{z}\ddot{z}, \tag{238}$$

which is obtained by differentiation from Eq. (222). The result is

$$\frac{v^4}{\rho}\mathbf{p} = [(\dot{y}^2 + \dot{z}^2)\ddot{x} - (\dot{y}\ddot{y} + \dot{z}\ddot{z})\dot{x}]\mathbf{i} + [(\dot{x}^2 + \dot{z}^2)\ddot{y} - (\dot{x}\ddot{x} + \dot{z}\ddot{z})\dot{y}]\mathbf{j}$$
$$[(\dot{x}^2 + \dot{y}^2)\ddot{z} - (\dot{x}\ddot{x} + \dot{y}\ddot{y})\dot{z}]\mathbf{k}. \tag{239}$$

This same equation might have been obtained from

$$\frac{v^4}{\rho}\mathbf{p} = \left(\frac{v^3}{\rho}\right)v\mathbf{b} \times \mathbf{t} = \left(\frac{v^3}{\rho}\mathbf{b}\right) \times (v\mathbf{t}) = (\mathbf{v} \times \mathbf{a}) \times \mathbf{v}, \tag{240}$$

expressed in terms of components by the use of (219) and (232).

To obtain an expression containing τ, we differentiate Eq. (226):

$$\dot{\mathbf{a}} = \frac{d}{dt}\left(\dot{v}\mathbf{t} + \frac{v^2}{\rho}\mathbf{p}\right) = \frac{d\dot{v}}{dt}\mathbf{t} + \dot{v}\frac{d\mathbf{t}}{dt} + \frac{d}{dt}\left(\frac{v^2}{\rho}\right)\mathbf{p} + \frac{v^2}{\rho}\frac{d\mathbf{p}}{dt}. \tag{241}$$

But, by Eq. (203),

$$\frac{d\mathbf{p}}{dt} = \frac{d\mathbf{p}}{ds}\frac{ds}{dt} = \left(\frac{1}{\tau}\mathbf{b} - \frac{1}{\rho}\mathbf{t}\right)v = \frac{v}{\tau}\mathbf{b} - \frac{v}{\rho}\mathbf{t}. \tag{242}$$

Using this and (225), we may deduce from Eq. (241) that

$$\dot{\mathbf{a}} = \left(\ddot{v} - \frac{v^3}{\rho^2}\right)\mathbf{t} + \left[\frac{v\dot{v}}{\rho} + \frac{d}{dt}\left(\frac{v^2}{\rho}\right)\right]\mathbf{p} + \frac{v^3}{\rho\tau}\mathbf{b}. \tag{243}$$

It follows from this and the relations

$$\mathbf{b} \cdot \mathbf{t} = 0, \qquad \mathbf{b} \cdot \mathbf{p} = 0, \qquad \mathbf{b} \cdot \mathbf{b} = 1, \tag{244}$$

that

$$\mathbf{b} \cdot \dot{\mathbf{a}} = \frac{v^3}{\rho\tau}. \tag{245}$$

From Eqs. (245) and (230),

$$(\mathbf{v} \times \mathbf{a}) \cdot \dot{\mathbf{a}} = \frac{v^3}{\rho} \mathbf{b} \cdot \dot{\mathbf{a}} = \frac{v^6}{\rho^2\tau}. \tag{246}$$

The components of $\mathbf{v}$ are given in Eq. (219), those of $\mathbf{a}$ in Eq. (220), while those of $\dot{\mathbf{a}}$ are given in the equation

$$\dot{\mathbf{a}} = \dddot{x}\mathbf{i} + \dddot{y}\mathbf{j} + \dddot{z}\mathbf{k}, \tag{247}$$

found by differentiation from (220). Using these, Eq. (166), and the discussion in Sec. 53 which precedes it, we find

$$(\mathbf{v} \times \mathbf{a}) \cdot \dot{\mathbf{a}} = \mathbf{v} \cdot (\mathbf{a} \times \dot{\mathbf{a}}) = \begin{vmatrix} \dot{x} & \dot{y} & \dot{z} \\ \ddot{x} & \ddot{y} & \ddot{z} \\ \dddot{x} & \dddot{y} & \dddot{z} \end{vmatrix}. \tag{248}$$

We may deduce from Eq. (246) that

$$\frac{1}{\tau} = \frac{(\mathbf{v} \times \mathbf{a}) \cdot \dot{\mathbf{a}}}{v^6/\rho^2}, \tag{249}$$

or by Eqs. (233) and (248):

$$\frac{1}{\tau} = \frac{\begin{vmatrix} \dot{x} & \dot{y} & \dot{z} \\ \ddot{x} & \ddot{y} & \ddot{z} \\ \dddot{x} & \dddot{y} & \dddot{z} \end{vmatrix}}{\begin{vmatrix} \dot{y} & \dot{z} \\ \ddot{y} & \ddot{z} \end{vmatrix}^2 + \begin{vmatrix} \dot{z} & \dot{x} \\ \ddot{z} & \ddot{x} \end{vmatrix}^2 + \begin{vmatrix} \dot{x} & \dot{y} \\ \ddot{x} & \ddot{y} \end{vmatrix}^2}. \tag{250}$$

We note here the corresponding formula for $1/\rho$,

$$\frac{1}{\rho} = \frac{\sqrt{\begin{vmatrix} \dot{y} & \dot{z} \\ \ddot{y} & \ddot{z} \end{vmatrix}^2 + \begin{vmatrix} \dot{z} & \dot{x} \\ \ddot{z} & \ddot{x} \end{vmatrix}^2 + \begin{vmatrix} \dot{x} & \dot{y} \\ \ddot{x} & \ddot{y} \end{vmatrix}^2}}{(\dot{x}^2 + \dot{y}^2 + \dot{z}^2)^{3/2}}, \tag{251}$$

deduced from Eqs. (233) and (222).

It is easy to compute all the quantities mentioned in this section for a specific curve for which we are given the coordinates as definite particular functions of t. We differentiate each coordinate three times and calculate the values of

$$\dot{x},\ \dot{y},\ \dot{z};\qquad \begin{vmatrix}\dot{y} & \dot{z}\\ \ddot{y} & \ddot{z}\end{vmatrix},\ \begin{vmatrix}\dot{z} & \dot{x}\\ \ddot{z} & \ddot{x}\end{vmatrix},\ \begin{vmatrix}\dot{x} & \dot{y}\\ \ddot{x} & \ddot{y}\end{vmatrix};\qquad \begin{vmatrix}\dot{x} & \dot{y} & \dot{z}\\ \ddot{x} & \ddot{y} & \ddot{z}\\ \dddot{x} & \dddot{y} & \dddot{z}\end{vmatrix}.\qquad(252)$$

Then the first triplet determine the direction of the tangent **t**. The second triplet determine the direction of the binormal **b**. And since $\mathbf{p} = \mathbf{b} \times \mathbf{t}$, the direction of the principal normal may be found from the cross product of any vector along the binormal by any vector along the tangent. And from the quantities (252), the curvature may be found from Eq. (251) and the torsion from Eq. (250).

56. Curvilinear Coordinates on a Surface. Just as the coordinates of a point on a space curve may be expressed in terms of one parameter, so the coordinates of a point on a surface may be expressed in terms of two parameters. In fact the equations

$$x = f(u,v), \qquad y = g(u,v), \qquad z = h(u,v) \qquad (253)$$

in general determine a surface. For, if the Jacobian

$$\frac{\partial(x,y)}{\partial(u,v)} \neq 0, \qquad (254)$$

we may solve the first pair of equations for u and v in terms of x and y. And then, by substitution in the last equation, obtain an equation of the form.

$$z = F(x,y). \qquad (255)$$

For any particular value of v, v_0, Eqs. (253) represent a space curve in terms of the parameter u. Similarly, for any particular u, u_0, the equations represent a space curve given in terms of the parameter v. These curves form a curvilinear coordinate system on the surface.

As an illustration, suppose that

$$x = a \cos v \cos u, \qquad y = a \cos v \sin u, \qquad z = a \sin v. \quad (256)$$

From the first two equations,

$$x^2 + y^2 = a^2 \cos^2 v,$$

so that

$$x^2 + y^2 + z^2 = a^2. \qquad (257)$$

Hence in this case the surface is a sphere of radius a with center at the origin. For $v = v_0$, z is constant and the resulting curves are parallels of latitude on the sphere. For $u = u_0$, $y = x \tan u_0$ and the resulting curves are meridians.

A curve on the surface (253) may be defined by two equations

$$u = u(t), \qquad v = v(t). \tag{258}$$

For these, combined with (253) determine x, y, and z in terms of t. For such a curve we have

$$\frac{dx}{dt} = \frac{\partial x}{\partial u}\frac{du}{dt} + \frac{\partial x}{\partial v}\frac{dv}{dt}. \tag{259}$$

Using dots for t differentiation and subscripts for partial deriva-

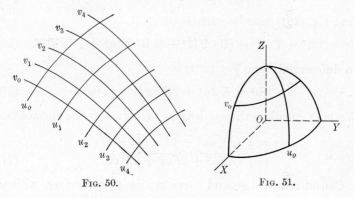

FIG. 50.   FIG. 51.

tives, we may rewrite this equation as

$$\dot{x} = x_u \dot{u} + x_v \dot{v}. \tag{260}$$

Similarly, we have

$$\dot{y} = y_u \dot{u} + y_v \dot{v} \qquad \text{and} \qquad \dot{z} = z_u \dot{u} + z_v \dot{v}. \tag{261}$$

If we substitute these expressions in the equation

$$\dot{s}^2 = \dot{x}^2 + \dot{y}^2 + \dot{z}^2, \tag{262}$$

obtained from Eq. (77), and introduce the abbreviations

$$E = x_u{}^2 + y_u{}^2 + z_u{}^2, \qquad F = x_u x_v + y_u y_v + z_u z_v,$$
$$G = x_v{}^2 + y_v{}^2 + z_v{}^2, \tag{263}$$

we find that

$$\dot{s}^2 = E\dot{u}^2 + 2F\dot{u}\dot{v} + G\dot{v}^2. \tag{264}$$

Let us introduce the vector $\mathbf{U}$, tangent to the curves $v = $ constant, defined by

$$\mathbf{U} = x_u\mathbf{i} + y_u\mathbf{j} + z_u\mathbf{k}, \tag{265}$$

and the vector $\mathbf{V}$, tangent to the curves $u = $ constant, defined by

$$\mathbf{V} = x_v\mathbf{i} + y_v\mathbf{j} + z_v\mathbf{k}. \tag{266}$$

Also let us denote by $\mathbf{T}$ the vector tangent to the curve with parameter t, defined by

$$\mathbf{T} = \dot{x}\mathbf{i} + \dot{y}\mathbf{j} + \dot{z}\mathbf{k}. \tag{267}$$

Then we may abbreviate Eqs. (260) and (261) as

$$\mathbf{T} = \mathbf{U}\dot{u} + \mathbf{V}\dot{v}. \tag{268}$$

And Eq. (264) may be written

$$\dot{s}^2 = \mathbf{T} \cdot \mathbf{T} = (\mathbf{U} \cdot \mathbf{U})\dot{u}^2 + 2(\mathbf{U} \cdot \mathbf{V})\dot{u}\dot{v} + (\mathbf{V} \cdot \mathbf{V})\dot{v}^2. \tag{269}$$

In differential form, Eq. (264) is

$$ds^2 = E\,du^2 + 2F\,du\,dv + G\,dv^2. \tag{270}$$

We may calculate the arc lengths of curves in the surface from

$$\begin{aligned} s &= \int \sqrt{E\,du^2 + 2F\,du\,dv + G\,dv^2} \\ &= \int \sqrt{E\dot{u}^2 + 2F\dot{u}\dot{v} + G\dot{v}^2}\,dt. \end{aligned} \tag{271}$$

Consider next a second curve on the same surface, with parameter t_1. Let us use primes to denote differentiation with respect to t_1 and introduce the vector $\mathbf{T}_1$, tangent to the second curve, defined by

$$\mathbf{T}_1 = x'\mathbf{i} + y'\mathbf{j} + z'\mathbf{k}. \tag{272}$$

Then for the arc length of the second curve s_1, we have

$$s_1'^2 = \mathbf{T}_1 \cdot \mathbf{T}_1 = x'^2 + y'^2 + z'^2. \tag{273}$$

Suppose that the two curves intersect and that the angle between the curves, defined as the angle between their tangent lines, is θ. Then

$$\mathbf{T} \cdot \mathbf{T}_1 = \dot{s}s_1' \cos\theta = \dot{x}x' + \dot{y}y' + \dot{z}z', \tag{274}$$

and

$$\cos\theta = \frac{\dot{x}x' + \dot{y}y' + \dot{z}z'}{\sqrt{\dot{x}^2 + \dot{y}^2 + \dot{z}^2}\,\sqrt{x'^2 + y'^2 + z'^2}}. \tag{275}$$

Let us apply this to the two coordinate curves through a given point v constant with tangent **U** and u constant with tangent **V**. Here Eqs. (265) and (266) replace (267) and (272), and u and v are the parameters in place of t and t_1. We call the angle between the coordinate curves ω. Then we have

$$
\begin{aligned}
\cos \omega &= \frac{\mathbf{U} \cdot \mathbf{V}}{\sqrt{\mathbf{U} \cdot \mathbf{U}}\sqrt{\mathbf{V} \cdot \mathbf{V}}} \\
&= \frac{x_u x_v + y_u y_v + z_u z_v}{\sqrt{x_u{}^2 + y_u{}^2 + z_u{}^2}\sqrt{x_v{}^2 + y_v{}^2 + z_v{}^2}} = \frac{F}{\sqrt{EG}},
\end{aligned}
\tag{276}
$$

where the last term follows from Eq. (263).

This shows that $F = 0$ is a necessary and sufficient condition for the parametric curves to cut at right angles, or orthogonally. The meridians and parallels on the sphere given by Eq. (256) are an illustration, since for these equations we have

$$
ds^2 = a^2(\cos^2 v \, du^2 + dv^2),
\tag{277}
$$

so that $F = 0$.

Let **A** denote the vector product $\mathbf{U} \times \mathbf{V}$, having a length A and components J_1, J_2, J_3. Then

$$
\mathbf{A} = \mathbf{U} \times \mathbf{V} = J_1\mathbf{i} + J_2\mathbf{j} + J_3\mathbf{k}.
\tag{278}
$$

But by Eqs. (265), (266) and (143),

$$
\mathbf{U} \times \mathbf{V} = \begin{vmatrix} \mathbf{i} & \mathbf{j} & \mathbf{k} \\ x_u & y_u & z_u \\ x_v & y_v & z_v \end{vmatrix} = \begin{vmatrix} y_u & z_u \\ y_v & z_v \end{vmatrix}\mathbf{i} + \begin{vmatrix} z_u & x_u \\ z_v & x_v \end{vmatrix}\mathbf{j} + \begin{vmatrix} x_u & y_u \\ x_v & y_v \end{vmatrix}\mathbf{k}.
\tag{279}
$$

Hence,

$$
J_1 = \frac{\partial(y,z)}{\partial(u,v)}, \qquad J_2 = \frac{\partial(z,x)}{\partial(u,v)}, \qquad J_3 = \frac{\partial(x,y)}{\partial(u,v)},
\tag{280}
$$

and each of J_1, J_2, J_3 is the Jacobian determinant of a pair of coordinates with respect to the parameters. By Eq. (145) and the conclusions drawn from it, each of the components J_1, J_2, J_3 may be interpreted geometrically as the signed area of the parallelogram obtained by projecting the parallelogram on **U** and **V** on one of the coordinate planes.

The area of the parallelogram on **U** and **V** is A. By Eq. (278) we have

$$
A^2 = J_1{}^2 + J_2{}^2 + J_3{}^2.
\tag{281}
$$

A second expression for A may be found by applying the Lagrangian identity, (148), to

$$A^2 = (\mathbf{U} \times \mathbf{V}) \cdot (\mathbf{U} \times \mathbf{V}) = \begin{vmatrix} \mathbf{U} \cdot \mathbf{U} & \mathbf{U} \cdot \mathbf{V} \\ \mathbf{U} \cdot \mathbf{V} & \mathbf{V} \cdot \mathbf{V} \end{vmatrix}. \quad (282)$$

A comparison of Eqs. (269) and (264) shows that the determinant in the right member is

$$\begin{vmatrix} E & F \\ F & G \end{vmatrix} = EG - F^2, \quad \text{and} \quad A^2 = EG - F^2 \quad (283)$$

For a small value of the differential du, the arc of the curve $v = $ constant, for values of u between u and $u + du$, is approximated by the differential tangent vector

$$\mathbf{U}\,du = x_u du\,\mathbf{i} + y_u du\,\mathbf{j} + z_u du\,\mathbf{k}. \quad (284)$$

Similarly, for a small value of the differential dv, the arc of the curve $u = $ constant, for values of v between v and $v + dv$, is approximated by the differential tangent vector

$$\mathbf{V}\,dv = x_v dv\,\mathbf{i} + y_v dv\,\mathbf{j} + z_v dv\,\mathbf{k}. \quad (285)$$

57. Area of a Curved Surface. A definition of the area of a curved surface may be based on the principle that the area of a small part of the surface is approximated by the area of the projection of this part on the tangent plane to the surface at any point of the small part. This principle suggests that the area of the curvilinear quadrilateral PS' made up of points on the surface for which u is between u and $u + du$, and v is between v and $v + dv$ may be approximated by the area of the parallelogram PT' in the tangent plane and having the vectors $\mathbf{U}\,du$ and $\mathbf{V}\,dv$ as two of its sides. But the area of PT' is the length of the vector:

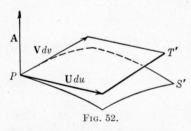

Fig. 52.

$$(\mathbf{U}\,du) \times (\mathbf{V}\,dv) = du\,dv(\mathbf{U} \times \mathbf{V}) = du\,dv\,\mathbf{A}. \quad (286)$$

Hence by Eq. (283)

$$(\text{area } PT') = A\,du\,dv = \sqrt{EG - F^2}\,du\,dv. \quad (287)$$

If we denote the area of the curved surface by S, the approximation of curved area PS' by plane area PT' and Eq. (287) makes plausible the differential relation:

$$dS = A \, du \, dv = \sqrt{EG - F^2} \, du \, dv, \qquad (288)$$

an abbreviation for the fact that the curved area S of the portion of the surface made up of points for which $u_1 < u < u_2$, $v_1(u) < v < v_2(u)$, is given by

$$S = \int_{u_1}^{u_2} du \int_{v_1(u)}^{v_2(u)} \sqrt{EG - F^2} \, dv. \qquad (289)$$

The two preceding equations are, in fact, consequences of the definition and we shall accordingly take them as the fundamental relations for surface area.

We note that since the vectors $\mathbf{U}$ and $\mathbf{V}$ are in the tangent plane to the surface at P, the vector $\mathbf{A} = \mathbf{U} \times \mathbf{V}$ is normal to the surface at P. Hence, by Eqs. (278) and (281) the direction cosines of this normal direction will be

$$\cos \alpha = l = \frac{J_1}{A}, \qquad \cos \beta = m = \frac{J_2}{A}, \qquad \cos \gamma = n = \frac{J_3}{A}. \qquad (290)$$

From the last of these relations,

$$A = \frac{J_3}{\cos \gamma} = \sec \gamma \, J_3. \qquad (291)$$

Suppose that the equation of the surface is given in the form

$$z = f(x,y). \qquad (292)$$

This is equivalent to the relations

$$x = u, \qquad y = v, \qquad z = f(u,v). \qquad (293)$$

Consequently, we have for the partial derivatives

$$x_u = 1, x_v = 0; \qquad y_u = 0, y_v = 1; \qquad z_u = f_x, z_v = f_y. \qquad (294)$$

Since $x = u$ and $y = v$, we may replace u,v by x,y and write f_x and f_y in place of f_u and f_v as we have done in evaluating z_u and z_v.

From the values in (294), by Eq. (263),

$$E = 1 + f_x{}^2, \qquad F = f_x f_y, \qquad G = 1 + f_y{}^2. \qquad (295)$$

Accordingly, by Eq. (270),

$$ds^2 = (1 + f_x{}^2)dx^2 + 2f_x f_y dx\, dy + (1 + f_y{}^2)dy^2. \quad (296)$$

Again, from the values in (294) and Eq. (280),

$$J_1 = -f_x, \qquad J_2 = -f_y, \qquad J_3 = 1. \quad (297)$$

Accordingly, by Eq. (281),

$$A^2 = f_x{}^2 + f_y{}^2 + 1. \quad (298)$$

This may be checked by using Eqs. (283) and (295).

Another expression for A follows from Eqs. (291) and (297):

$$A = \sec \gamma. \quad (299)$$

The result of substituting the values of A from Eqs. (298) and (299) in Eq. (288) and replacing u,v by x,y is

$$dS = A\, dx\, dy = \sqrt{f_x{}^2 + f_y{}^2 + 1}\; dx\, dy = \sec \gamma\, dx\, dy. \quad (300)$$

The equation corresponding to (289) for the area S of the portion of the surface (292) made up of points for which $x_1 < x < x_2$, $y_1(x) < y < y_2(x)$, is

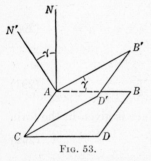

Fig. 53.

$$S = \int_{x_1}^{x_2} dx \int_{y_1(x)}^{y_2(x)} \sqrt{f_x{}^2 + f_y{}^2 + 1}\; dy. \quad (301)$$

We may interpret the expression for dS involving $\sec \gamma$ if we recall the following geometrical facts about the projections of plane areas. Let AN be normal to plane AD, and AN' be normal to plane AD', and let AC be on the line of intersection of the two planes. Consider a rectangle $ACD'B'$ in AD' and its orthogonal projection on AD, $ACDB$. If angle $NAN' = \gamma$, angle BAB' also $= \gamma$, and

$$\text{Area } ACDB = (AB)(BD) = (AB' \cos \gamma)(B'D')$$
$$= \cos \gamma\, (AB')(B'D') = \cos \gamma\, (\text{area } ACD'B'). \quad (302)$$

A similar relation holds between the area of any rectangle with one side parallel to the line of intersection and its projection on the other plane. And as any area (Fig. 54) in one plane is the limit of the sum of areas of rectangles of this type, we have

$$(\text{Area in } AD) = \cos \gamma\, (\text{related area on } AD'). \quad (303)$$

Now let P be any point on the surface (292) and Q the projection of P on the xy plane. Construct QR, a rectangle in the xy plane with one vertex at Q and with sides dx parallel to the

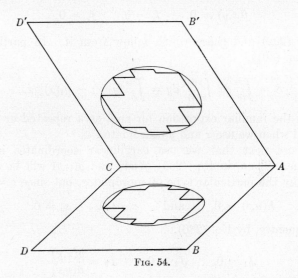

FIG. 54.

x axis and dy parallel to the y axis. Then, if the rectangular prism with edges parallel to the z axis and having the rectangle QR as base cuts the tangent plane to the surface at P in the parallelogram PT', QR will be the orthogonal projection of PT' on the xy plane. And, since the z axis is normal to the xy plane, the angle between the normals to the planes of QR and PT' will be the angle γ as defined in (290). Consequently, by Eq. (303).

(Area QR) = $\cos \gamma$ (area PT')
so that
(area PT') = $\sec \gamma$ (area QR).   (304)

Since the area of QR is $dx\,dy$, this may be written

(Area PT') = $\sec \gamma\,dx\,dy$.   (305)

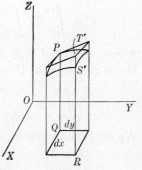

FIG. 55.

This helps one to recollect Eq. (300), which bears the same relation to (305) that Eq. (288) does to (287).

58. Plane Areas and Curvilinear Coordinates. Let us apply our formulas to plane areas in the xy plane itself. Since one form of the equation for the xy plane is $z = 0$, we may take

$$f(x,y) = 0, \qquad f_x = 0, \qquad f_y = 0, \tag{306}$$

in Eq. (292) and those which follow from it. In particular, from Eq. (301),

$$S = \int_{x_1}^{x_2} dx \int_{y_1(x)}^{y_2(x)} dy = \int_{x_1}^{x_2} [y_2(x) - y_1(x)]dx. \tag{307}$$

This is the familiar expression for area as a repeated or single integral when we use x and y coordinates.

Suppose next that we use curvilinear coordinates in the xy plane. Then, in Eq. (253), $f(u,v)$ and $g(u,v)$ will be determined by the particular type of coordinates, but since $z = 0$,

$$h(u,v) = 0, \qquad \text{and} \qquad z_u = 0, \qquad z_v = 0. \tag{308}$$

Consequently, by Eq. (280),

$$J_1 = 0, \qquad J_2 = 0, \qquad J_3 = \frac{\partial(x,y)}{\partial(u,v)}. \tag{309}$$

And it follows from Eq. (281) that

$$A^2 = J_3{}^2, \qquad \text{and} \qquad A = J_3 = \frac{\partial(x,y)}{\partial(u,v)}, \qquad \text{if } J_3 > 0. \tag{310}$$

Hence,

$$S = \int_{u_1}^{u_2} du \int_{v_1(u)}^{v_2(u)} A \, dv = \int_{u_1}^{u_2} du \int_{v_1(u)}^{v_2(u)} \frac{\partial(x,y)}{\partial(u,v)} \, dv. \tag{311}$$

A comparison of Eqs. (307) and (311) shows that if the limits are so related that they correspond to the same areas,

$$\int_{x_1}^{x_2} dx \int_{y_1(x)}^{y_2(x)} dy = \int_{u_1}^{u_2} du \int_{v_1(u)}^{v_2(u)} \frac{\partial(x,y)}{\partial(u,v)} \, dv. \tag{312}$$

We abbreviate this by writing,

$$dx \, dy = \frac{\partial(x,y)}{\partial(u,v)} \, du \, dv. \tag{313}$$

The two preceding equations suggest that if the limits are related as they are for Eq. (312),

$$\int_{x_1}^{x_2} dx \int_{y_1(x)}^{y_2(x)} F(x,y)dy$$

$$= \int_{u_1}^{u_2} du \int_{v_1(u)}^{v_2(u)} F[x(u,v),y(u,v)] \frac{\partial(x,y)}{\partial(u,v)} dv, \quad (314)$$

for any function $F(x,y)$ and this is the case.

By Eqs. (278) and (309), for the z plane as given by (308),

$$\mathbf{U} \times \mathbf{V} = J_3 \mathbf{k}. \tag{315}$$

Consequently, to make $J_3 > 0$, as required to give the positive square root for A in Eq. (310), we must so choose the parametric curves that $\mathbf{U} \times \mathbf{V}$ is in the direction of the positive z axis.

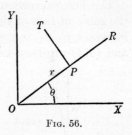

For example, if we use polar coordinates in a plane, the tangent vectors in the directions of increasing r and of increasing θ have the directions of PR and PT. Since $\overline{PT} \times \overline{PR}$ has the direction of the negative z axis, while $\overline{PR} \times \overline{PT}$ has the direction of

Fig. 56.

the positive z axis, we consider r, θ as in the order u, v. Then from

$$x = r \cos \theta, \qquad y = r \sin \theta, \tag{316}$$

we may deduce that

$$\frac{\partial(x,y)}{\partial(r,\theta)} = r. \tag{317}$$

Then we have as equations analogous to (313) and (312),

$$dx \, dy = r \, dr \, d\theta, \tag{318}$$

and

$$S = \int_{x_1}^{x_2} dx \int_{y_1(x)}^{y_2(x)} dy = \int_{r_1}^{r_2} dr \int_{\theta_1(r)}^{\theta_2(r)} r \, d\theta. \tag{319}$$

If we calculate the repeated integral of the differential (318) in the other order and suitably modify the notation for the limits, we find

$$S = \int_{\theta_1}^{\theta_2} d\theta \int_{r_1(\theta)}^{r_2(\theta)} r \, dr = \tfrac{1}{2} \int_{\theta_1}^{\theta_2} \{[r_2(\theta)]^2 - [r_1(\theta)]^2\} d\theta. \tag{320}$$

This is a familiar formula of elementary calculus.

Equations (312) to (314) may be given a more general interpretation. We may think of the element of area as a signed quantity, whose algebraic sign at each point is defined to be the sign of J_3 at that point. Geometrically, the sign is that of the z component or only nonzero component of $\mathbf{U} \times \mathbf{V}$, by Eq. (315). Or, by the remark after Eq. (280), the signed element of area and the signed area of the parallelogram on the vectors $\mathbf{U}$ and $\mathbf{V}$ have the same algebraic sign. Thus the sign depends on which set of parametric curves we take first, and which direction on each curve we consider as that for which the parameter increases, since these conditions determine the direction and order of the vectors $\mathbf{U}$ and $\mathbf{V}$.

The last expression in Eq. (312) will represent the area, in the sense of sum of signed differential elements traced out as u_1 increases to u_2 and $v_1(u)$ increases to $v_2(u)$. And Eqs. (312) and (314) are then valid even when $J_3 < 0$, provided that the limits are so selected that one (or three) of the variables x, y, u, and v decreases if J_3 is negative.

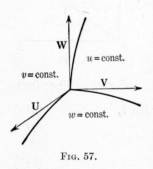

Fig. 57.

59. Volumes and Curvilinear Coordinates. Relations similar to Eqs. (312), (313), and (314) hold for repeated integrals of any order. For the third order we may make such equations plausible by the following considerations. Let the equations that define the three Cartesian coordinates x, y, z in terms of three curvilinear coordinates u, v, w be

$$x = x(u,v,w), \qquad y = y(u,v,w), \qquad z = z(u,v,w). \quad (321)$$

By putting one of the variables u, v, or w constant, we obtain three parametric surfaces. And by putting two of the variables constant, we obtain three parametric curves. These are the curves of intersection of pairs of parametric surfaces. If v and w are constant, u alone varies, and we may define a vector tangent to the resulting curve by the equation,

$$\mathbf{U} = x_u\mathbf{i} + y_u\mathbf{j} + z_u\mathbf{k}. \quad (322)$$

Similarly, we may define vectors tangent to the other parametric curves by the equations

$$\mathbf{V} = x_v\mathbf{i} + y_v\mathbf{j} + z_v\mathbf{k} \qquad \text{and} \qquad \mathbf{W} = x_w\mathbf{i} + y_w\mathbf{j} + z_w\mathbf{k}. \quad (323)$$

It follows from Eq. (166) that

$$\mathbf{U} \cdot (\mathbf{V} \times \mathbf{W}) = \begin{vmatrix} x_u & y_u & z_u \\ x_v & y_v & z_v \\ x_w & y_w & z_w \end{vmatrix} = \frac{\partial(x,y,z)}{\partial(u,v,w)}. \tag{324}$$

By the discussion in Sec. 53, this will represent the volume of the parallelepiped formed on the three vectors $\mathbf{U}$, $\mathbf{V}$, $\mathbf{W}$ if these are taken in the proper order. For any order we may consider each expression in (324) as equal to the signed volume on $\mathbf{U}$, $\mathbf{V}$, $\mathbf{W}$.

For small values of the differentials, the tangent vector $\mathbf{U}\,du$ will approximate the arc of the first parametric curve whose points have values of u between u and $u + du$. Similar remarks apply to the vectors $\mathbf{V}\,dv$ and $\mathbf{W}\,dw$. This suggests the following facts. The volume corresponding to points with u between u and $u + du$, v between v

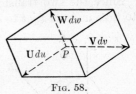

Fig. 58.

and $v + dv$, and w between w and $w + dw$ is approximated by the volume of the parallelepiped on the vectors $\mathbf{U}\,du$, $\mathbf{V}\,dv$, and $\mathbf{W}\,dw$ or

$$dV = (\mathbf{U}\,du) \cdot [(\mathbf{V}\,dv) \times (\mathbf{W}\,dw)] = \mathbf{U} \cdot (\mathbf{V} \times \mathbf{W})\,du\,dv\,dw$$

$$= \frac{\partial(x,y,z)}{\partial(u,v,w)}\,du\,dv\,dw. \tag{325}$$

With suitably related limits,

$$V = \int dx \int dy \int dz = \int du \int dv \int \frac{\partial(x,y,z)}{\partial(u,v,w)}\,dw. \tag{326}$$

Also, if $F[x(u,v,w),y(u,v,w),z(u,v,w)] = G(u,v,w)$, then for suitably related limits,

$$\int dx \int dy \int F(x,y,z)dz$$

$$= \int du \int dv \int G(u,v,w)\,\frac{\partial(x,y,z)}{\partial(u,v,w)}\,dw. \tag{327}$$

The two preceding equations, as well as others similar to them but with the triply repeated integrals taken in other orders, may be easily recollected from the differential relation

$$dx\,dy\,dz = \frac{\partial(x,y,z)}{\partial(u,v,w)}\,du\,dv\,dw. \tag{328}$$

Equations (326) and (327) are valid for signed elements and negative values of the Jacobian, if we make proper conventions as to the choice of limits.

If we change variables from x,y,z to p,q,r

$$dx\ dy\ dz = \frac{\partial(x,y,z)}{\partial(p,q,r)}\ dp\ dq\ dr, \tag{329}$$

while if we change variables from p,q,r to u,v,w

$$dp\ dq\ dr = \frac{\partial(p,q,r)}{\partial(u,v,w)}\ du\ dv\ dw. \tag{330}$$

Since the two transformations just mentioned must combine to take us from x,y,z to u,v,w, Eqs. (329) and (330) must together be equivalent to Eq. (328) and

$$\frac{\partial(x,y,z)}{\partial(u,v,w)} = \frac{\partial(x,y,z)}{\partial(p,q,r)} \cdot \frac{\partial(p,q,r)}{\partial(u,v,w)}. \tag{331}$$

Jacobians of any order satisfy relations of this type.

Let us illustrate (328) for the spherical polar coordinates r, ϕ, θ of Fig. 59. From

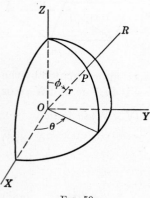

Fig. 59.

$$x = r \cos \theta \sin \phi,$$
$$y = r \sin \theta \sin \phi, \tag{332}$$
$$z = r \cos \phi,$$

we may deduce that

$$\frac{\partial(x,y,z)}{\partial(r,\phi,\theta)} = r^2 \sin \phi. \tag{333}$$

so that

$$dx\ dy\ dz = r^2 \sin \phi\ dr\ d\phi d\theta, \tag{334}$$

and the volume in spherical polar coordinates may be computed from

$$V = \int d\theta \int \sin \phi\ d\phi \int r^2 dr. \tag{335}$$

60. References. For a more complete introduction to the subject of solid analytic geometry, the reader may consult *Coordinate Geometry*, by H. B. Fine and H. Thompson. A more elaborate account of the elements of vector analysis will be found in the first four chapters of J. G. Coffin's *Vector Analysis*. The properties of curves and surfaces are more fully discussed in W. C. Graustein's *Elementary Differential Geometry*, which uses a vector notation different from that of this text, and in L. P. Eisenhart's *Differential Geometry* which uses no vector notation.

The reader interested in a detailed derivation of the fundamental formulas for arc length and surface area from satisfactory definitions is referred to Chaps. VIII and XI of the author's *Treatise on Advanced Calculus*.

EXERCISES III

1. A cube 12 units on a side has its edges parallel to the coordinate axes, and its center at the origin. Write the coordinates of each of its vertices.

Find the length and direction cosines of the segment OP if

2. $P = (1,2,3)$.   **3.** $P = (-2,-4,1)$.   **4.** $P = (2,-3,-5)$.

5. Find the length of each side of the triangle whose vertices are the points of Probs. 2, 3, and 4.

6. Write equations for three indefinite straight lines, each of which lines contains one side of the triangle of Prob. 5.

7. A segment has direction angles α, β, and γ. If $\alpha = 70°$. $\beta = 50°$, and γ is an acute angle, find γ.

8. The vectors **a**, **b**, and **c** are defined by

$$\mathbf{a} = 5\mathbf{i} - 4\mathbf{j} + 2\mathbf{k}, \qquad \mathbf{b} = 2\mathbf{i} + 3\mathbf{j} - 4\mathbf{k}, \qquad \mathbf{c} = -\mathbf{i} -\mathbf{j} -\mathbf{k}.$$

Find the length of each of these three vectors.

Using the values of **a**, **b**, and **c** given in Prob. 8, express each of the following vectors in terms of **i**, **j**, and **k** and find its length.

9. $-\mathbf{a}$.   **10.** $2\mathbf{b}$.   **11.** $5\mathbf{c}$.   **12.** $\mathbf{a} + \mathbf{b}$.
13. $\mathbf{a} - \mathbf{b}$.   **14.** $2\mathbf{a} + 3\mathbf{c}$.   **15.** $2\mathbf{a} + \mathbf{b} + 5\mathbf{c}$.

Using the values of **a**, **b**, and **c** given in Prob. 8, evaluate each of the following scalar products:

16. $\mathbf{a} \cdot \mathbf{a}$.   **17.** $\mathbf{a} \cdot \mathbf{b}$.   **18.** $\mathbf{a} \cdot \mathbf{c}$.   **19.** $\mathbf{b} \cdot \mathbf{c}$.   **20.** $\mathbf{c} \cdot \mathbf{c}$.

21. $(2\mathbf{a} + 3\mathbf{c}) \cdot (2\mathbf{a} + \mathbf{b} + 5\mathbf{c})$. First use the result of Probs. 14 and 15. Then check by distributing the product and using the results of Probs. 16 to 20.

22. Find $\cos \theta$, where θ is the angle between the vectors **a** and **b** of Prob. 8.

23. Let P be the center of gravity of two masses m_1 at P_1 and m_2 at P_2. If $\overline{OP}_1 = \mathbf{r}_1$, $\overline{OP}_2 = \mathbf{r}_2$, and $\overline{OP} = \mathbf{r}$, show that $\mathbf{r} = \dfrac{m_1\mathbf{r}_1 + m_2\mathbf{r}_2}{m_1 + m_2}$. HINT: $m_1\overline{P_1P} = m_2\overline{PP}_2$ or $m_1(\mathbf{r}_1 - \mathbf{r}) = m_2(\mathbf{r} - \mathbf{r}_2)$.

24. Show that the projection of the vector $x\mathbf{i} + y\mathbf{j} + z\mathbf{k}$ on the segment whose direction cosines are l, m, n is $lx + my + nz$.

25. Write the equation of a plane through the point $2,-1,3$ perpendicular to a line with direction ratios $4,-1,-1$.

26. Find the length of the perpendicular drawn from the point $1,1,-1$ to the plane of Prob. 25.

27. If the segment drawn from O perpendicular to a plane represents the vector $p\mathbf{u}$, where $\mathbf{u} = l\mathbf{i} + m\mathbf{j} + n\mathbf{k}$ is a unit vector, show that the equation of the plane may be written $lx + my + nz = p$. HINT: For P in the plane and $\mathbf{r} = \overline{OP}$, $\mathbf{u} \cdot (\mathbf{r} - p\mathbf{u}) = 0$ or $\mathbf{u} \cdot \mathbf{r} = p$.

28. Show that the perpendicular distance measured in the direction of $\mathbf{u}$ from the plane of Prob. 27 to the point x',y',z' is given by the relations $L_p = \mathbf{u} \cdot (\mathbf{r}' - p\mathbf{u}) = lx + my + nz - p$.

29. A space curve is defined by $x = t$, $y = t^3$, $z = t^5$. Write equations for the line tangent to this curve at the point where $t = 2$.

30. Show that the length of arc of the curve $x = 2t$, $y = t^2$, $z = \log t$ measured from the point P_0 where $t = 1$ to any point is given by $s = t^2 - 1 + \log t$.

31. Write equations for the line tangent to the curve of Prob. 30 at the point where $t = 1$.

32. The point P moves in such a way that at time t, the segment $\overline{OP} = \mathbf{r} = t \cos t\,\mathbf{i} + t \sin t\,\mathbf{j} + 2t\mathbf{k}$. Find the velocity and acceleration vector of P at time t. Show that for $t = 0$, $\mathbf{v} = \mathbf{i} + 2\mathbf{k}$, $\mathbf{a} = 2\mathbf{j}$.

Write an equation for the plane tangent to

33. The sphere $x^2 + y^2 + z^2 = 9$, at the point $2,1,2$.

34. The paraboloid $4z = x^2 + y^2$, at the point $2,4,5$.

35. The torus $(\sqrt{x^2 + y^2} - 4)^2 + z^2 = 4$, at the point $4,3,\sqrt{3}$.

36. Show that the ellipsoid $x^2 + 4y^2 + 9z^2 = 26$ and the hyperboloid $x^2 + y^2 - z^2 = 4$ intersect at the point $1,2,1$. Find their angle of intersection (that is, the angle between their tangent planes) at this point.

37. Show that $z + z_0 = y_0 x + x_0 y$ is the equation of the plane tangent to $z = xy$ at (x_0,y_0,z_0) if $z_0 = x_0 y_0$.

38. Show that $Ax_0 x + By_0 y + Cz_0 z = D$ is the equation of the plane tangent to $Ax^2 + By^2 + Cz^2 = D$ at (x_0,y_0,z_0) if this point is on the surface, that is, $Ax_0^2 + By_0^2 + Cz_0^2 = D$.

39. Let $Q(x,y,z)$ be a second-degree polynomial and $Q(x,y,z) = 0$ be the equation of a quadric surface. If $Q(x_0,y_0,z_0) = 0$, show that the equation of the plane tangent to the quadric at (x_0,y_0,z_0) may be obtained from the equation $Q(x,y,z) = 0$ by putting x_0x in place of x^2, $(y_0x + x_0y)/2$ in place of xy, $(x + x_0)/2$ in place of x and putting corresponding expressions in place of y^2, z^2, yz, xz, y, and z obtained from those just written by permuting the letters. Problems 37 and 38 are special cases of this.

40. Two surfaces are said to cut orthogonally at a point P if they intersect at P and have their tangent planes perpendicular there. Show that the condition for this is that the coordinates of P satisfy the equations of the surfaces $F(x,y,z) = 0$, $G(x,y,z) = 0$, and the orthogonal relation $F_x(x,y,z)G_x(x,y,z) + F_y(x,y,z)G_y(x,y,z) + F_z(x,y,z)G_z(x,y,z) = 0$.

41. Using Prob. 40, show that as a special case the surfaces $xyz = 2$ and $x^2 + y^2 - 2z^2 = 3$ cut orthogonally at all points on their curve of intersection, and in particular at $(2,1,1)$.

Using the test relations (123), show that

42. Every point of the surface $z = xy$ is a hyperbolic point.

43. Every point of the surface $z = x^2$ is a parabolic point.

44. Every point of the surface $z = 2x^2 + 4y^2$ is an elliptic point.

The vectors $\mathbf{a}$, $\mathbf{b}$, $\mathbf{c}$ and $\mathbf{d}$ are defined by

$$\mathbf{a} = 2\mathbf{i} + 3\mathbf{k}, \qquad \mathbf{b} = -\mathbf{j} - 2\mathbf{k}, \qquad \mathbf{c} = 2\mathbf{i} - 2\mathbf{j} + 2\mathbf{k}, \qquad \mathbf{d} = 3\mathbf{i} - \mathbf{j} - \mathbf{k}.$$

Express each of the following vector products in terms of $\mathbf{i}$, $\mathbf{j}$, and $\mathbf{k}$:

45. $\mathbf{a} \times \mathbf{b}$.   **46.** $\mathbf{b} \times \mathbf{c}$.   **47.** $\mathbf{c} \times \mathbf{d}$.
48. $\mathbf{d} \times \mathbf{a}$.   **49.** $(\mathbf{a} - \mathbf{c}) \times (\mathbf{b} - \mathbf{d})$.

50. Verify that the vectors $\mathbf{a} = \mathbf{i} - 2\mathbf{j} + 3\mathbf{k}$ and $\mathbf{b} = -2\mathbf{i} - 2\mathbf{j} + \mathbf{k}$ satisfy the Lagrangian identity (148) by directly calculating each member of Eq. (149).

51. The vectors $\mathbf{a} = \cos A\,\mathbf{i} + \sin A\,\mathbf{j}$ and $\mathbf{b} = \cos B\,\mathbf{i} - \sin B\,\mathbf{j}$ are two unit vectors in the xy plane, making angles A and $-B$ with the x axis. Deduce the formula for $\cos(A + B)$ from $\mathbf{a} \cdot \mathbf{b}$, and the formula for $\sin(A + B)$ from $\mathbf{b} \times \mathbf{a}$.

52. If $\mathbf{c} = \mathbf{a} - \mathbf{b}$, the vectors $\mathbf{a}$, $\mathbf{b}$, and $\mathbf{c}$ form a triangle. Deduce the law of cosines $c^2 = a^2 + b^2 - 2\,ab\cos C$ from the identical relation $\mathbf{c} \cdot \mathbf{c} = (\mathbf{a} - \mathbf{b}) \cdot (\mathbf{a} - \mathbf{b})$. Also deduce the law of sines $a\sin B = b\sin A$ from $\mathbf{c} \times \mathbf{c} = \mathbf{c} \times (\mathbf{a} - \mathbf{b})$.

53. Show that, for any two vectors $\mathbf{a}$ and $\mathbf{b}$,

$$(\mathbf{a} + \mathbf{b}) \cdot (\mathbf{a} - \mathbf{b}) = \mathbf{a} \cdot \mathbf{a} - \mathbf{b} \cdot \mathbf{b}, \qquad \text{but}$$
$$(\mathbf{a} + \mathbf{b}) \times (\mathbf{a} - \mathbf{b}) = \mathbf{a} \times \mathbf{a} - \mathbf{b} \times \mathbf{b} - 2\mathbf{a} \times \mathbf{b}.$$

Also, $(\mathbf{a} + \mathbf{b}) \cdot (\mathbf{a} + \mathbf{b}) = \mathbf{a} \cdot \mathbf{a} + 2\mathbf{a} \cdot \mathbf{b} + \mathbf{b} \cdot \mathbf{b}$, but
$$(\mathbf{a} + \mathbf{b}) \times (\mathbf{a} + \mathbf{b}) = 0.$$

54. The quantities $\begin{vmatrix} B & C \\ B' & C' \end{vmatrix}$, $\begin{vmatrix} C & A \\ C' & A' \end{vmatrix}$, $\begin{vmatrix} A & B \\ A' & B' \end{vmatrix}$, are possible direction ratios for the line of intersection of the planes $Ax + By + Cz = D$ and $A'x + B'y + C'z = D'$. Prove this. HINT: Consider the vector product $(A\mathbf{i} + B\mathbf{j} + C\mathbf{k}) \times (A'\mathbf{i} + B'\mathbf{j} + C'\mathbf{k})$.

55. The Jacobians $\dfrac{\partial(F,G)}{\partial(y,z)}$, $\dfrac{\partial(F,G)}{\partial(z,x)}$, $\dfrac{\partial(F,G)}{\partial(x,y)}$ are possible direction ratios for the line tangent at x,y,z to the curve of intersection of the surfaces $F(x,y,z) = 0$ and $G(x,y,z) = 0$. Prove this statement. HINT: Consider the expression $(F_x\mathbf{i} + F_y\mathbf{j} + F_z\mathbf{k}) \times (G_x\mathbf{i} + G_y\mathbf{j} + G_z\mathbf{k})$.

56. Using Prob. 55, write equations for the line tangent at 1,1,1 to the curve of intersection of the cylinders $z^3 - x = 0$, $x^2 - y = 0$. Check by using the form $x = t^3$, $y = t^6$, $z = t$.

57. Let $\dfrac{x - x'}{A'} = \dfrac{y - y'}{B'} = \dfrac{z - z'}{C'}$ and $\dfrac{x - x''}{A''} = \dfrac{y - y''}{B''} = \dfrac{z - z''}{C''}$ be the equations of two straight lines L' and L''. Show that the distance from L' to L'', measured along their common perpendicular in the direction of $\mathbf{a}' \times \mathbf{a}''$ is $\dfrac{(\mathbf{r}'' - \mathbf{r}') \cdot (\mathbf{a}' \times \mathbf{a}'')}{|\mathbf{a}' \times \mathbf{a}''|}$, where we have assumed $\mathbf{a}' = A'\mathbf{i} + B'\mathbf{j} + C'\mathbf{k}$, $\mathbf{r}' = x'\mathbf{i} + y'\mathbf{j} + z'\mathbf{k}$, and similar equations for $\mathbf{a}''$ and $\mathbf{r}''$.

58. Prove the identity $\mathbf{a} \times (\mathbf{b} \times \mathbf{c}) = (\mathbf{a} \cdot \mathbf{c})\mathbf{b} - (\mathbf{a} \cdot \mathbf{b})\mathbf{c}$, by finding the components of both sides.

59. Show that $\mathbf{a} \times (\mathbf{b} \times \mathbf{c}) \neq (\mathbf{a} \times \mathbf{b}) \times \mathbf{c}$, unless $\mathbf{a}$ and $\mathbf{c}$ are parallel, $\mathbf{b}$ is perpendicular to $\mathbf{a}$ and $\mathbf{c}$, or one of the vectors has zero length. HINT: By changing letters in Prob. 58, deduce the equation $\mathbf{c} \times (\mathbf{a} \times \mathbf{b}) = (\mathbf{c} \cdot \mathbf{b})\mathbf{a} - (\mathbf{c} \cdot \mathbf{a})\mathbf{b}$. Hence by combining with Prob. 58 deduce $\mathbf{a} \times (\mathbf{b} \times \mathbf{c}) - (\mathbf{a} \times \mathbf{b}) \times \mathbf{c} = (\mathbf{c} \cdot \mathbf{b})\mathbf{a} - (\mathbf{a} \cdot \mathbf{b})\mathbf{c}$.

60. A rectangular block 2 by 4 by 8 in. is rotating about a diagonal joining O and Q, two opposite vertices, with an angular velocity of 3 radians/sec. We refer points of the block to axes along three of its edges in such a way that the edges represent $2\mathbf{i}_1$, $4\mathbf{j}_1$, and $8\mathbf{k}_1$, and $\overline{OQ} = 2\mathbf{i}_1 + 4\mathbf{j}_1 + 8\mathbf{k}_1$. We write $\mathbf{i}_1$, $\mathbf{j}_1$, $\mathbf{k}_1$ to remind us that the axes are rotating with the block. Express the velocity at $P(x,y,z)$, that is, where $\overline{OP} = x\mathbf{i}_1 + y\mathbf{j}_1 + z\mathbf{k}_1$, induced by the rotation about $\overline{OQ}$, in terms of $\mathbf{i}_1$, $\mathbf{j}_1$, $\mathbf{k}_1$.

61. Any motion of a rigid body with one of its points fixed at O may be considered at any instant as a rotation about some instantaneous axis OQ. That is, if the instantaneous angular velocity vector is $\mathbf{a}$ at time t, the velocity of the point P of the body will be $\mathbf{v}_b = \mathbf{a} \times \overline{OP}$. We may refer any moving point to a frame of reference attached to the rigid body by means of three mutually perpendicular unit vectors $\mathbf{i}_1, \mathbf{j}_1, \mathbf{k}_1$ drawn through O in the rigid body, as in Prob. 60. If the vector

$\overline{OP} = x(t)\mathbf{i}_1 + y(t)\mathbf{j}_1 + z(t)\mathbf{k}_1$, show that $\mathbf{v}_r = x'(t)\mathbf{i}_1 + y'(t)\mathbf{j}_1 + z'(t)\mathbf{k}_1$ is the velocity relative to the moving frame, and the absolute velocity of P with respect to fixed axes is $\mathbf{v}_a = \mathbf{v}_r + \mathbf{v}_b = \mathbf{v}_r + \mathbf{a} \times \overline{OP}$.

62. Let the polar coordinates of a point moving in the xy plane be $r(t)$ and $\theta(t)$. For any position of the point P, draw unit vectors $\mathbf{i}_1 = \overline{OR}$ along $\overline{OP}$, $\mathbf{j}_1$ in the direction of increasing θ perpendicular to $\mathbf{i}_1$ at O in the xy plane, and $\mathbf{k}_1 = \mathbf{k}$ from O along the z axis. These may be used as the $\mathbf{i}_1$, $\mathbf{j}_1$, $\mathbf{k}_1$ of Prob. 61. Here $\mathbf{a} = \dot{\theta}\mathbf{k}_1$. And $\overline{OP} = r\mathbf{i}_1$. From Prob. 61 deduce that $\mathbf{v}_a = \dot{r}\mathbf{i}_1 + r\dot{\theta}\mathbf{j}_1$. The absolute acceleration of P, $\mathbf{a}_a$, is the absolute velocity of a point V such that $\overline{OV} = \dot{r}\mathbf{i}_1 + r\dot{\theta}\mathbf{j}_1$. Deduce from this that $\mathbf{a}_a = (\ddot{r} - r\dot{\theta}^2)\mathbf{i}_1 + (r\ddot{\theta} + 2\dot{r}\dot{\theta})\mathbf{j}_1$.

63. Find the volume of the parallelepiped three of whose edges are $\mathbf{a} = 4\mathbf{i} - \mathbf{j} + \mathbf{k}$, $\mathbf{b} = \mathbf{i} + 5\mathbf{j} - \mathbf{k}$, $\mathbf{c} = -\mathbf{i} - \mathbf{j} + 6\mathbf{k}$.

Use the components to prove the following rules for differentiating products involving the scalar function $f(t)$ and the vector functions $\mathbf{U}(t)$ and $\mathbf{V}(t)$:

64. $\dfrac{d}{dt}(f\mathbf{U}) = \dfrac{df}{dt}\mathbf{U} + f\dfrac{d\mathbf{U}}{dt}.$

65. $\dfrac{d}{dt}(\mathbf{U} \cdot \mathbf{V}) = \dfrac{d\mathbf{U}}{dt} \cdot \mathbf{V} + \mathbf{U} \cdot \dfrac{d\mathbf{V}}{dt} = \mathbf{U} \cdot \dfrac{d\mathbf{V}}{dt} + \mathbf{V} \cdot \dfrac{d\mathbf{U}}{dt}.$

66. $\dfrac{d}{dt}(\mathbf{U} \times \mathbf{V}) = \dfrac{d\mathbf{U}}{dt} \times \mathbf{V} + \mathbf{U} \times \dfrac{d\mathbf{V}}{dt} = \mathbf{U} \times \dfrac{d\mathbf{V}}{dt} - \mathbf{V} \times \dfrac{d\mathbf{U}}{dt}.$

For the curve $x = 3t$, $y = 3t^2$, $z = 2t^3$ and the point P_1 where $t = 1$:
67. Find the direction cosines of the tangent, principal normal, and binormal at P_1.
68. Write an equation for the plane normal to the curve at P_1.
69. Write an equation for the osculating plane at P_1.
70. Write equations for the tangent line at P_1.
71. Calculate the curvature at P_1.
72. Calculate the torsion at P_1.
73. Calculate the arc length from P_0 where $t = 0$ to P_1.

For the curve of intersection of the cylinders $z = y^2$, $x = z^2$ and the point P_2 where $y = 1$. (HINT: If $y = t$; $x = t^4$, $y = t$, $z = t^2$.)
74. Find the direction cosines of the tangent, principal normal, and binormal at P_2.
75. Write an equation for the plane normal to the curve at P_2.
76. Write an equation for the osculating plane at P_2.
77. Write equations for the tangent line at P_2.
78. Calculate the curvature at P_2.
79. Calculate the torsion at P_2.

For the curve $x = e^t \sin 2t$, $y = e^t \cos 2t$, $z = 2e^t$, and the point P_0 where $t = 0$:

80. Find the direction cosines of the tangent, principal normal, and binormal at P_0.

81. Write an equation for the plane normal to the curve at P_0.

82. Write an equation for the osculating plane at P_0.

83. Write equations for the tangent line at P_0.

84. Calculate the curvature at P_0.

85. Calculate the torsion at P_0.

86. Find the arc length from P_0 to P_1 where $t = 1$.

87. Show that the curve $x = e^{at} \sin bt$, $y = e^{at} \cos bt$, $z = ce^{at}$ lies on the cone $z^2 = c^2(x^2 + y^2)$ and cuts all the elements of the cone at the same angle. The curve of Probs. 80 to 86 is an example.

88. Show that the curve $x = a \cos t$, $y = a \sin t$, $z = a (\tan \alpha)t$ lies on the cylinder $x^2 + y^2 = a^2$ and cuts all the elements of the cylinder at the same angle. It is the circular helix or screw curve.

89. Prove that the principal normal to the helix of Prob. 88 at any point coincides with the line normal to the cylinder $x^2 + y^2 = a^2$ at the same point.

For the helix of Prob. 88 and the point P_t for any value of t:

90. Find the direction cosines of the tangent, principal normal, and binormal at P_t.

91. Write an equation for the plane normal to the curve at P_t.

92. Write an equation for the osculating plane at P_t.

93. Write equations for the tangent line at P_t.

94. Show that the curvature is the same for all points, $\dfrac{1}{\rho} = \dfrac{\cos^2 \alpha}{a}$.

95. Show that the torsion is the same for all points, $\dfrac{1}{\tau} = \dfrac{\sin \alpha \cos \alpha}{a}$.

96. Show that the arc length from P_0 where $t = 0$ is $s = a \sec \alpha\, t$.

97. Show that if the arc length of Prob. 96 is the parameter, the equations of the helix become $x = a \cos \left(\dfrac{\cos \alpha}{a} s\right)$, $y = a \sin \left(\dfrac{\cos \alpha}{a} s\right)$, and $z = (\sin \alpha)\, s$. Also express the direction cosines of Prob. 90 in terms of s.

98. Verify directly that the values of $\mathbf{t}$, $\mathbf{b}$, $\mathbf{p}$, ρ, and τ found in Probs. 97, 94, and 95 satisfy the Frenet formulas (204) or (209).

99. For a curve in the xy plane, $z = 0$. Show that in this case the formula (251) for the curvature reduces to that found in Prob. 45 of Exercises II (page 72) if t is the parameter. Also that if $x = t$, the formula reduces further to the elementary one quoted in the same problem.

Verify that each of the following surfaces of revolution is represented by the parametric equations as given. Also show that the curves $u =$ constant are meridians, or sections by planes through the z axis, and that the curves $v =$ constant are the parallels, or circles cut out by planes parallel to the xy plane. And find the element of arc and of area in terms of u and v.

100. The cylinder $x^2 + y^2 = a^2$; $x = a \cos u, y = a \sin u, z = v$.

101. The cone $a^2z^2 = x^2 + y^2$; $x = av \cos u, y = av \sin u, z = v$.

102. The paraboloid $a^2z = c(x^2 + y^2)$; $x = av \, \cos u, \ y = av \, \sin u,$ $z = cv^2$.

103. The ellipsoid $\dfrac{x^2}{a^2} + \dfrac{y^2}{a^2} + \dfrac{z^2}{c^2} = 1$; $x = a \cos u \cos v, y = a \sin u \cos v,$ $z = c \sin v$.

104. The hyperboloid $\dfrac{x^2}{a^2} + \dfrac{y^2}{a^2} - \dfrac{z^2}{c^2} = 1$, for which $x = a \cos u \cosh v,$ $y = a \sin u \cosh v, z = c \sinh v$.

105. The surface of revolution $F(x^2 + y^2, z) = 0$; $x = f(v) \cos u,$ $y = f(v) \sin u, z = g(v)$, where $F[f(v)^2, g(v)] = 0$. Special cases are given in Probs. 100 to 104.

Find the element of arc and of area in terms of u and v for each of the following surfaces. These surfaces may be obtained from those of Probs. 100 to 105 by contracting all lengths parallel to the y axis in the ratio of b to a. Here the curves $u =$ constant are sections by planes through the z axis, and the curves $v =$ constant are similar ellipses cut out by planes parallel to the xy plane.

106. The cylinder $\dfrac{x^2}{a^2} + \dfrac{y^2}{b^2} = 1$; $x = a \cos u, y = b \sin u, z = v$.

107. The cone $z^2 = \dfrac{x^2}{a^2} + \dfrac{y^2}{b^2}$; $x = av \cos u, y = bv \sin u, z = v$.

108. The paraboloid $\dfrac{z}{c} = \dfrac{x^2}{a^2} + \dfrac{y^2}{b^2}$; $x = av \cos u, y = bv \sin u, z = cv^2$.

109. The ellipsoid $\dfrac{x^2}{a^2} + \dfrac{y^2}{b^2} + \dfrac{z^2}{c^2} = 1$, for which $x = a \, \cos u \, \cos v,$ $y = b \sin u \cos v, z = c \sin v$.

110. The hyperboloid $\dfrac{x^2}{a^2} + \dfrac{y^2}{b^2} - \dfrac{z^2}{c^2} = 1$, for which $x = a \cos u \cosh v,$ $y = b \sin u \cosh v, z = c \sinh v$.

111. The surface $G \left(\dfrac{x^2}{a^2} + \dfrac{y^2}{b^2}, \ z \right) = 0$; $x = af(v) \cos u, y = bf(v) \sin u,$ $z = g(v)$ where $G[f(v)^2, g(v)] = 0$.

112. Show that in Prob. 105, and hence in Probs. 100 to 104, the parametric curves cut at right angles.

113. The parametric equations $x = v \cos u$, $y = v \sin u$, $z = ku$ represent a warped helicoid (square thread screw surface). Find the element of arc and of area in terms of u and v.

114. If the hyperboloid of Prob. 110 is represented by $x = av$, $y = b(\cosh u + v \sinh u)$, $z = c(\sinh u + v \cosh u)$, the $u = $ constant curves are straight lines. Find the element of arc in terms of du and dv at the point for which $u = 0$ and $v = 0$, and hence find the cosine of the angle at which the parametric curves through this point intersect.

115. If θ is the angle between two curves on a surface as in Eq. (275), show that $\cos \theta = \dfrac{E\dot{u}\dot{u}' + F(\dot{u}\dot{v}' + \dot{v}\dot{u}') + G\dot{v}\dot{v}'}{\sqrt{E\dot{u}^2 + 2F\dot{u}\dot{v} + G\dot{v}^2}\ \sqrt{Eu'^2 + 2Fu'v' + Gv'^2}}.$

116. Let $P_1(u,v)$ be any point on a surface S_1 given by equations of the form (253). Then any set of equations of this form for a second surface S_2 determines a mapping of S_1 on S_2, by which $P_1(u,v)$ is mapped on $P_2(u,v)$. By Eq. (270), applied to S_1 at $P_1(u,v)$ and to S_2 at $P_2(u,v)$, the relation $ds_2 = M(u,v)ds_1$ will hold if the proportionality condition $E_2/E_1 = F_2/F_1 = G_2/G_1$ is satisfied, with $[M(u,v)]^2$ the common value of the ratios. Hence, by the mapping, all differential lengths at P_1 will be multiplied by $M(u,v)$. Show that in this case, if $M \neq 0$, the mapping preserves angles, in the sense that the angle between C_1 and C_1', two curves through P_1 on S_1, is the same as that of the transformed curves C_2 and C_2' through P_2 on S_2. A mapping of this type is said to be conformal. HINT: Let $\dot{u}$, $\dot{v}$ determine the directions tangent to C_1 and C_2, and u',v' determine the directions tangent to C_1' and C_2'. Use the result of Prob. 115.

By a mere change of scale, the surface of the earth may be mapped on S_1, a sphere of radius a, given by Eqs. (256), with v the latitude and u the longitude. Any pair of functions $x(u,v)$, $y(u,v)$; or $r(u,v)$, $\theta(u,v)$ for polar coordinates; will then determine a map of the earth's surface on the xy plane. On the sphere $ds_1{}^2 = a^2(\cos^2 v\, du^2 + dv^2)$ while on the plane $ds_2{}^2 = dx^2 + dy^2 = dr^2 + r^2\, d\theta^2$.

117. The stereographic projection of the earth's surface is obtained by projecting the points of S_1 on to the xy plane by straight lines through $(0,0,1)$, the north pole of S_1. In this case the mapping functions are $x = a \tan (v/2 + \pi/4) \cos u$, $y = a \tan (v/2 + \pi/4) \sin u$, equivalent to $r = a \tan (v/2 + \pi/4)$, $\theta = u$. Show that the differentials satisfy $dr^2 + r^2 d\theta^2 = (a^2/4) \sec^4 (v/2 + \pi/4) (\cos^2 v\, du^2 + dv^2)$, so that we have $ds_2 = \frac{1}{2} \sec^2 (v/2 + \pi/4)ds_1$. Hence by Prob. 116 the mapping is conformal, angles are preserves, and lengths are multiplied by a factor depending on the latitude.

118. If $x = au$, $y = af(v)$, the meridians and parallels on the earth, or on S_1 of Prob. 116, will be mapped on the coordinate lines in the xy plane. The equator will map on the x axis if $f(0) = 0$. To make a rhumb line on the sphere which cuts all the meridians at the same angle α go into a straight line in the plane cutting the lines $x =$ constant at the same angle α, we must have $\cot \alpha = \dfrac{dv}{\cos v \, du} = \dfrac{dy}{dx} = \dfrac{f'(v)dv}{du}$. From these conditions, deduce that $f(v) = \displaystyle\int_0^v \sec v \, dv = \log \tan (v/2 + \pi/4)$. The resulting mapping is called *Mercator's projection*.

119. For the Mercator projection of Prob. 118, given by $x = au$, $y = a \log \tan (v/2 + \pi/4)$, show that the expression for the arc length $dx^2 + dy^2 = a^2 \sec^2 v \, (\cos^2 v \, du^2 + dv^2)$, so that $ds_2 = \sec v \, ds_1$. Hence by Prob. 116 the mapping is conformal, angles are preserved, and lengths are multiplied by a factor depending on the latitude.

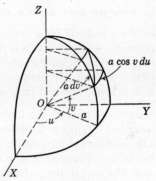

Fig. 60.

120. Using Probs. 31 and 32 of Exercises I (page 39), show that the Mercator projection of the two preceding problems may be defined by $x = au$, $y = a \, \mathrm{gd}^{-1}v$, and that we may use $y = a \sinh^{-1} (\tan v)$, $y = a \cosh^{-1} (\sec v)$, $y = a \tanh^{-1} (\sin v)$ in place of the second equation

121. Show that under the stereographic projection of Prob. 117, the images of the circles on the sphere S_1 are the circles and straight lines of the xy plane S_2. HINT: From $A(x^2 + y^2) + Bx + Cy + D = 0$ in S_2, deduce

$$Aa^2 \tan^2 (v/2 + \pi/4) + (B \cos u + C \sin u)a \tan (v/2 + \pi/4)$$
$$+ D + 0,$$

and hence by (256), if the point $P(x,y,z)$ is on S_1, the sphere of radius a, $aBx + aCy + (a^2A - D)z + a(a^2A + D) = 0$. This represents a plane. This plane cuts the sphere S_1 in a circle, and the steps may be reversed.

122. Let u and v be rectangular coordinates in a first plane S_1, so that $ds_1{}^2 = du^2 + dv^2$. And let the points of the xy plane S_2 be expressed in terms of curvilinear coordinates by the equations $x = x(u,v)$, $y = y(u,v)$, and $z = 0$. Then we may map S_1 on S_2 as in Prob. 116. Express $ds_2{}^2 = dx^2 + dy^2$ in terms of du and dv and show that the condition of Prob. 116 for the map to be conformal will hold if $\dfrac{\partial x}{\partial u} = \dfrac{\partial y}{\partial v}$, $\dfrac{\partial x}{\partial v} = -\dfrac{\partial y}{\partial u}$, and $M^2 = \left(\dfrac{\partial x}{\partial u}\right)^2 + \left(\dfrac{\partial y}{\partial u}\right)^2 \neq 0$.

123. Let $u = u(x,y)$, $v = v(x,y)$ be the solution of the equations $x = x(u,v)$ and $y = y(u,v)$ of Prob. 122. Show that the map will be conformal if $\dfrac{\partial u}{\partial x} = \dfrac{\partial v}{\partial y}$, $\dfrac{\partial u}{\partial y} = -\dfrac{\partial v}{\partial x}$ and $M^{-2} = \left(\dfrac{\partial u}{\partial x}\right)^2 + \left(\dfrac{\partial u}{\partial y}\right)^2 \neq 0$.

For the relation to analytic functions of a complex variable, see Probs. 57, 67, and 68 of Exercises II (page 73).

124. By Prob. 68 of Exercises II (page 74) the mapping equations $u = \log \sqrt{x^2 + y^2}$ and $v = \tan^{-1} \frac{y}{x}$ satisfy the condition of Prob. 123 and so determine a conformal mapping of a uv plane on an xy plane. With a change of scale and notation, $x_m = av$, $y_m = au$, $x_s = ax$, $y_s = ay$ we have $x_m = a \tan^{-1} \frac{y_s}{x_s}$, $y_m = a \log \sqrt{x_s^2 + y_s^2} - a \log a$ as the equations for a conformal map of an $x_m y_m$ plane M on an $x_s y_s$ plane S. Show that this is the same mapping that would be obtained by projecting P_1 on the sphere S_1 on P_s in S by the stereographic projection of Prob. 117; projecting P_1 on P_m in M by the Mercator projection of Prob. 119; and then making $P_s(x_s, y_s)$ the image of $P_m(x_m, y_m)$.

Find the area of the limited portion of a curved surface which is described by each of the following statements:

125. The part of the cylinder $z = x^2$ whose projection on the xy plane is the triangle bounded by $y = 0$, $y = x$, $x = 1$.

126. The part of the surface $z = xy$ cut out by the cylinder $x^2 + y^2 = 1$. HINT: $dS = \sqrt{1 + x^2 + y^2}\, dx\, dy = \sqrt{1 + r^2}\, r\, dr\, d\theta$.

127. The part of the cylinder $z^2 + y^2 = 1$ above the xy plane cut out by the cylinder $x^2 + y^2 = 1$.

128. The part of the sphere $x^2 + y^2 + z^2 = 1$ above the xy plane cut out by the cylinder $x^2 + y^2 = x$. HINT: The differential of area is $dS = (1 - x^2 - y^2)^{-\frac{1}{2}} dx\, dy = (1 - r^2)^{-\frac{1}{2}} r\, dr\, d\theta$, and the area integral is
$$S = 2 \int_0^{\pi/2} d\theta \int_0^{\cos\theta} (1 - r^2)^{-\frac{1}{2}} r\, dr.$$

129. The part of the sphere $x^2 + y^2 + z^2 = 1$ above the xy plane whose projection on the xy plane is inside the first half loop of the curve whose polar equation is $r = \cos n\theta$. HINT: See hint to Prob. 128.

130. The part of the cylinder $z^2 + y^2 = y$ above the xy plane which is cut out by the sphere $x^2 + y^2 + z^2 = 1$.

131. The part of the surface $z = xy$ whose projection on the xy plane is inside the first half loop of the curve whose polar equation is $r^2 = \cos 2n\theta$. HINT: See hint to Prob. 126 for dS and note that the inner integral is $\int_0^{\sqrt{\cos 2n\theta}} \sqrt{1 + r^2}\, r\, dr = \frac{1}{3}(2\sqrt{2} \cos^3 n\theta - 1)$, since we may write $1 + \cos 2n\theta = 2 \cos^2 n\theta$.

132. The area generated by revolving an arc of the curve $y = f(x)$ about the x axis is $2\pi \int y\, ds = 2\pi \int_{x_1}^{x_2} f(x) \sqrt{1 + f'(x)^2}\, dx$. Check this formula by using the parametric equations for the surface of revolution: $x = u$, $y = f(u) \cos v$, $z = f(u) \sin v$.

133. Find the expression for the element of volume in terms of u, v, and w if $x = u(1 - v)$, $y = uv(1 - w)$, $z = uvw$.

134. Using Prob. 133, show that the volume of the tetrahedron three of whose edges are $\overline{OA} = \mathbf{i}$, $\overline{OB} = \mathbf{j}$, $\overline{OZ} = \mathbf{k}$ may be expressed as

$$\int_0^1 dx \int_0^{1-x} dy \int_0^{1-x-y} dz = \int_0^1 dw \int_0^1 v\, dv \int_0^1 u^2\, du.$$

Also show by direct calculation that either member equals $\frac{1}{6}$.

CHAPTER IV

INTEGRATION. THE DEFINITE INTEGRAL. MULTIPLE INTEGRALS

Our discussion of integration begins with the fundamental properties of the definite integral. We then describe methods of integrating certain general classes of functions. We consider improper integrals, multiple integrals, integrals containing a parameter, as well as the problem of differentiating and integrating such integrals. We also show how some definite integrals that cannot be easily evaluated may be treated by series, numerical methods, or other special devices.

61. The Indefinite Integral. Let $f(x)$ be a given function. Then any function $F(x)$ such that

$$\frac{dF}{dx} = F'(x) = f(x), \tag{1}$$

is called an *indefinite integral*, or antiderivative of $f(x)$. If one function $F(x)$ is known, any function

$$G(x) = F(x) + C, \tag{2}$$

where C is a constant, is also an indefinite integral of $f(x)$, since

$$G'(x) = F'(x) = f(x). \tag{3}$$

Moreover, every indefinite integral of $f(x)$ is given by (2) with a suitable C. For, let $I(x)$ be any one such indefinite integral and set $H(x) = I(x) - F(x)$. Then $I'(x) = f(x)$, so that

$$H'(x) = I'(x) - F'(x) = 0. \tag{4}$$

Since its derivative is zero, $H(x)$ must equal a constant. If we call this constant C, we have

$$I(x) - F(x) = H(x) = C \qquad \text{and} \qquad I(x) = F(x) + C. \tag{5}$$

This shows that $I(x)$ is given by (2), as we stated.

144

62. The Definite Integral. For any function $f(x)$ given on an interval a,b we may make the following construction. Divide the interval a,b into n parts by points

$$a = x_0 < x_1 < x_2 < \cdots < x_{n-1} < x_n = b. \qquad (6)$$

Then select a point ξ_i in each interval,

$$x_0 \leqq \xi_1 \leqq x_1 \cdots x_{i-1} \leqq \xi_i \leqq x_i \cdots x_{n-1} \leqq \xi_n \leqq x_n, \qquad (7)$$

and form the sum

$$S_n = f(\xi_1)(x_1 - x_0) + f(\xi_2)(x_2 - x_1) + \cdots \\ + f(\xi_n)(x_n - x_{n-1}). \qquad (8)$$

We assume that $f(x)$ is of simple type, for example, an elementary function, so that the curve $y = f(x)$ has a continuous graph like that shown in Fig. 61. [A continuous graph is one without breaks, so that as

$$x \to a, \; f(x) \to f(a).]$$

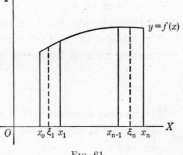

We also suppose that each of the intervals $\Delta x_i = x_i - x_{i-1}$ is small. Then, if $f(x) > 0$, S_n represents the sum of the areas of certain rectangles which ap-

Fig. 61.

proximate the area under the curve. This suggests that certain sequences of sums S_n will approach a limit equal to the area under the curve. Let us abbreviate Eq. (8) by

$$S_n = \sum_{i=1}^{n} f(\xi_i)(x_i - x_{i-1}) = \sum_{i=1}^{n} f(\xi_i)\Delta x_i, \qquad (9)$$

and denote the area under the curve by A. Then it is in fact the case that

$$A = \lim_{n \to \infty} \sum_{i=1}^{n} f(\xi_i)\Delta x_i, \qquad \text{if } \lim_{n \to \infty} d_n = 0, \qquad (10)$$

where for each n, d_n is the largest value of Δx_i or $(x_i - x_{i-1})$ used in forming the sum S_n.

The limit on the right of Eq. (10), which exists even when $f(x)$ is sometimes negative or zero, is called the *definite integral* of $f(x)$ from a to b.   And, with the usual notation,

$$\int_a^b f(x)dx = \lim_{n \to \infty} \sum_{i=1}^n f(\xi_i)\Delta x_i, \qquad \text{if } \lim_{n \to \infty} d_n = 0. \qquad (11)$$

If $g(x)$ is a second continuous function, it is also true that

$$\int_a^b f(x)g(x)dx = \lim_{n \to \infty} \sum_{i=1}^n f(\xi_i)g(\xi_i')\Delta x_i, \qquad \text{if } \lim_{n \to \infty} d_n = 0. \qquad (12)$$

Here the ξ_i', like the ξ_i, are any points in the interval x_{i-1},x_i.

In this result the product fg may be replaced by $F(f,g)$, any continuous function of f and g, to obtain

$$\int_a^b F[f(x),g(x)]dx = \lim_{n \to \infty} \sum_{i=1}^n F[f(\xi_i),g(\xi_i')]\Delta x_i, \qquad \text{if } \lim_{n \to \infty} d_n = 0.$$
$$(13)$$

Similar results also hold for more than two functions.

Equations (10) and (11) lead to the fundamental relation for evaluating an area by means of a definite integral,

$$A = \int_a^b f(x)dx. \qquad (14)$$

Let us next consider a thin rod with one end at $x = a$ and the other at $x = b$, and having at each point a density $\rho(x)$.   For a

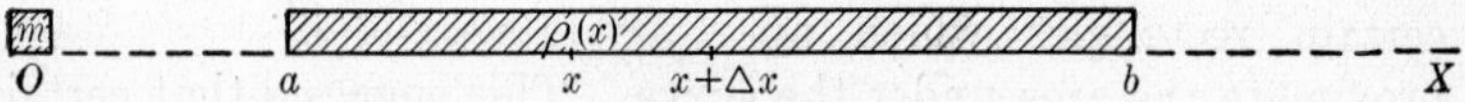

FIG. 62.

part of the rod between x and $x + \Delta x$, with Δx small, we would expect $\rho(\xi)\Delta x$ to equal the weight of the part, for a suitable ξ between x and $x + \Delta x$.   Also we would expect the attraction of the part by a mass m at the origin to be the same as if the part of the rod were all at a suitable distance ξ' in the interval, $x \leqq \xi' \leqq x + \Delta x$.   This suggests

$$\Delta F = \frac{km}{\xi'^2} \rho(\xi)\Delta x \qquad (15)$$

as the attraction of the part of length Δx, and

$$\sum_{i=1}^n \frac{km}{\xi_i'^2} \rho(\xi_i)\Delta x_i \qquad (16)$$

as the attraction of the whole rod.   Equation (12) then leads to
the evaluation of the attraction of the rod by m in terms of a
definite integral,

$$F = \int_a^b \frac{km}{x^2}\, \rho(x)dx. \tag{17}$$

Equations of the type of (12) or (13) are frequently the guide to
the appropriate method of evaluating other geometrical or
physical concepts by definite integrals.

63. Properties of the Definite Integral.   The variable x in
the notation for a definite integral may be replaced by any other
letter without altering its value.   Thus

$$\int_a^b f(x)dx = \int_a^b f(t)dt. \tag{18}$$

For if we plotted $y = f(t)$, we could regard the values x_i as points
of subdivision on the t axis, and ξ_i as values in the intervals
from x_{i-1} to x_i.   Thus the limit on the right of Eq. (11) would
define the right member of Eq. (18) equally as well as it defines
the left member of that equation.

So far, we have assumed $a < b$.   The symbol for a definite
integral in other cases is defined by the relations

$$\int_a^a f(x)dx = 0, \qquad \int_b^a f(x)dx = -\int_a^b f(x)dx. \tag{19}$$

These definitions make the equations

$$\int_a^b f(x)dx + \int_b^c f(x)dx + \int_c^a f(x)dx = 0 \tag{20}$$

and

$$\int_a^b f(x)dx + \int_b^c f(x)dx = \int_a^c f(x)dx \tag{21}$$

true for all values of a, b, and c.

Equation (21) shows that, if they have the same function or
integrand, integrals may be added like the signed intervals over
which they are taken.

It is also true that, for the same interval, integrals may be
added like the functions involved.   That is,

$$\int_a^b f(x)dx + \int_a^b g(x)dx = \int_a^b [f(x) + g(x)]dx. \tag{22}$$

Again, for any constant k,

$$\int_a^b kf(x)dx = k \int_a^b f(x)dx. \tag{23}$$

The two preceding results are immediate consequences of Eq. (11).

Suppose that the curve in Fig. 63 has its maximum at M, for $x = x_2$, and its minimum at m, for $x = x_1$. Then the area under the curve will be less than that of the rectangle on a,b under the line through M, and greater than that of the rectangle on a,b under the line through m. Hence, for some point R between m and M, the area of the rectangle under the line through R will equal the area under the curve. If $x = \xi$ at R, the height of this rectangle will be $f(\xi)$. And, since ξ is between x_1 and x_2, it will be between a and b. This suggests the mean value theorem for integrals,

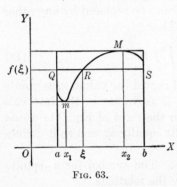

FIG. 63.

$$\int_a^b f(x)dx = (b - a)f(\xi), \tag{24}$$

for a suitably chosen value of ξ between a and b.

The mean value theorem holds whenever $f(x)$ is *continuous*, even when $f(x)$ is not positive, and $b < a$ or $b = a$.

64. Calculation from the Indefinite Integral. Let us consider the definite integral of $f(x)$ from a fixed point a to a variable point x:

$$I(x) = \int_a^x f(x)dx = \int_a^x f(t)dt. \tag{25}$$

The second expression follows from Eq. (18) and avoids the possibility of confusing x, the variable of integration, with x, the variable limit. To find the derivative of $I(x)$, $I'(x)$, we must first calculate the difference quotient,

$$\frac{\Delta I}{\Delta x} = \frac{I(x + h) - I(x)}{h}. \tag{26}$$

It follows from Eq. (25) that the numerator is

$$I(x + h) - I(x) = \int_a^{x+h} f(t)dt - \int_a^x f(t)dt = \int_x^{x+h} f(t)dt, \tag{27}$$

by Eq. (21). And, from the mean value theorem (24),

$$\int_{x}^{x+h} f(t)dt = hf(\xi) \tag{28}$$

for a suitably chosen value of ξ between x and $x + h$. We may conclude from the three preceding equations that

$$\frac{\Delta I}{\Delta x} = f(\xi). \tag{29}$$

When $h \to 0$, $x + h \to x$, and since ξ is between x and $x + h$, $\xi \to x$. Consequently, when $f(x)$ is continuous, $f(\xi)$ will approach $f(x)$, and

$$\lim_{h \to 0} \frac{\Delta I}{\Delta x} = \lim_{h \to 0} f(\xi) = f(x). \tag{30}$$

This proves that

$$\frac{dI}{dx} = I'(x) = f(x). \tag{31}$$

This shows that $I(x)$ is an indefinite integral of $f(x)$ as defined in Sec. 61. Hence, by Eq. (5), if $F(x)$ is any known indefinite integral of $f(x)$,

$$I(x) = F(x) + C. \tag{32}$$

Let us put $x = a$ in this equation to obtain

$$I(a) = F(a) + C, \tag{33}$$

and eliminate the constant by subtraction. The result is

$$I(x) - I(a) = F(x) - F(a). \tag{34}$$

But from Eqs. (25) and (19),

$$I(a) = \int_{a}^{a} f(x)dx = 0. \tag{35}$$

Thus $I(a)$ may be omitted from (34) and, if we replace $I(x)$ by its value from (25), we find

$$\int_{a}^{x} f(x)dx = F(x) - F(a) = F(x) \Big|_{a}^{x}. \tag{36}$$

This expression is defined to mean the difference that precedes it.

In particular, when the upper limit is b, we have

$$\int_{a}^{b} f(x)dx = F(x) \Big|_{a}^{b} = F(b) - F(a). \tag{37}$$

This is the familiar formula that enables us to calculate the definite integral of any integrand for which some indefinite integral is known.

65. Differentiation of Integrals. Since

$$I = \int_a^b f(x)dx = F(b) - F(a), \qquad \text{where } F'(x) = f(x), \quad (38)$$

we find

$$\frac{\partial I}{\partial b} = F'(b) = f(b) \tag{39}$$

and

$$\frac{\partial I}{\partial a} = -F'(a) = -f(a). \tag{40}$$

That is, the derivative of a definite integral with respect to an upper limit of integration equals the integrand evaluated at the upper limit. For a lower limit of integration the derivative equals the negative of the integrand evaluated at the lower limit.

Suppose that the integrand contains a parameter u, so that

$$I(u) = \int_a^b f(x,u)dx. \tag{41}$$

In this case we may wish to find the derivative of I with respect to u when a and b are kept constant. We have for the difference quotient

$$\frac{I(u + \Delta u) - I(u)}{\Delta u} = \int_a^b \frac{f(x,u + \Delta u) - f(x,u)}{\Delta u} \, dx, \tag{42}$$

by the properties expressed in Eqs. (22) and (23), since Δu is constant during the integration on x. When $\Delta u \to 0$,

$$\frac{I(u + \Delta u) - I(u)}{\Delta u} \to \frac{dI}{du}, \qquad \text{and} \qquad \frac{f(x,u + \Delta u) - f(x,u)}{\Delta u} \to \frac{\partial f}{\partial u}. \tag{43}$$

This suggests that

$$\frac{dI}{du} = \int_a^b \frac{\partial f}{\partial u} \, dx. \tag{44}$$

When a and b are finite and $\partial f/\partial u$ is continuous in both variables, this is a correct result. If these conditions are not met, for example, if b is ∞ or if $\partial f/\partial u \to \infty$ as $x \to b$, there are three possibilities. (1) The right member of Eq. (44) may not be a convergent integral in the sense of Sec. 71, in which case the equation is meaningless. (2) The right member may converge, but fail to represent the derivative dI/du. (3) The equation may be true. The student of applied mathematics is unlikely to encounter the second possibility and, in practice, may assume that Eq. (44) holds whenever the right member converges.

By the rule of total differentiation of Sec. 21, for any function of three variables $I(u,a,b)$:

$$dI = \frac{\partial I}{\partial u}\,du + \frac{\partial I}{\partial a}\,da + \frac{\partial I}{\partial b}\,db. \tag{45}$$

If we use the values of the derivatives of

$$I(u,a,b) = \int_a^b f(x,u)dx, \tag{46}$$

given by Eqs. (44), (40), and (39), we find for this function

$$dI = \left[\int_a^b f_u(x,u)dx\right]du - f(a,u)da + f(b,u)db. \tag{47}$$

It follows that, if a and b are each functions of u,

$$\frac{dI}{du} = \int_a^b f_u(x,u)dx - f(a,u)\frac{da}{du} + f(b,u)\frac{db}{du}. \tag{48}$$

As a simple illustration of this formula, consider

$$I(u) = \int_{2u}^{3u} (x-u)^2 dx. \tag{49}$$

Then, for this function we find from Eq. (48)

$$I'(u) = \int_{2u}^{3u} (-2)(x-u)dx - u^2(2) + 4u^2(3). \tag{50}$$

The reader may check this by showing that the integral on the right in (49) equals $7u^3/3$ and that the expression on the right in (50) equals $7u^2$.

66. General Reductions. We recall a few general methods of reducing integrals to those of simpler types. In this section u and v denote functions of x. The linear relation

$$\int_a^b (Au + Bv)dx = A\int_a^b u\,dx + B\int_a^b v\,dx \tag{51}$$

enables us to decompose sums and factor out constants.

The rule of integration by parts

$$\int_a^b u \frac{dv}{dx} dx = uv \Big|_a^b - \int_a^b v \frac{du}{dx} dx \qquad (52)$$

will reduce an integral with u a simple inverse function (for example, $\log x$ or $\sin^{-1} x$) and v an algebraic function to an integral with $v \, du/dx$ an algebraic integrand. Also, if $u = x^n$, with n a positive integer and v is of exponential type, that is, e^x, $\sin x$, $\cos x$, the new integrand will contain the factor x^{n-1}. Thus n reductions of this type will lead to an integrand free of x.

Finally, the rule of substitution

$$\int_a^b f(x)dx = \int_A^B f[g(t)]g'(t)dt, \qquad (53)$$

if $g'(t) \neq 0$ for $A < t < B$ and $a = g(A)$, $b = g(B)$, may be used to simplify some integrals.

Equations (51), (52), and (53) may all be verified by noting that both sides equal zero for $b = a$ and have their derivatives with respect to b, as obtained from Eq. (39), equal for all values of b.

67. Rational Integrands. We recall the method used to integrate rational functions. A rational function may always be reduced to the quotient of two polynomials. If the degree of the numerator $P_1(x)$ is the same or greater than the degree of the denominator $D(x)$, we may by division find polynomials $Q(x)$ and $P(x)$ such that

$$\frac{P_1(x)}{D(x)} = Q(x) + \frac{P(x)}{D(x)} \qquad (54)$$

and the fraction on the right is a proper fraction, that is, has its numerator $P(x)$ of lower degree than that of its denominator $D(x)$.

The polynomial $Q(x)$ is easily integrated. Let us next consider the integration of the proper fraction $P(x)/D(x)$.

Suppose first that the roots of $D(x) = 0$ are all distinct. Let $D(x)$ be of the nth degree and call the roots $r_1, r_2, \cdots, r_n$. Then constants $A_1, A_2, \cdots, A_n$ may be found to satisfy the relation

$$\frac{P(x)}{D(x)} = \frac{A_1}{x - r_1} + \frac{A_2}{x - r_2} + \cdots + \frac{A_n}{x - r_n}. \qquad (55)$$

The A_n could be evaluated by clearing of fractions, equating coefficients of corresponding powers of x, and solving the set of n linear equations that result. However, when the roots are all distinct, the following method is simpler.

Let us multiply both sides of Eq. (55) by $x - r_1$, and then let $x \to r_1$. The first term on the right is A_1, and the other terms contain the factor $x - r_1$, and so approach 0 when $x \to r_1$. Since $D(r_1) = 0$, we may deduce from l'Hospital's rule of Sec. 15 that

$$\lim_{x \to r_1} \frac{(x - r_1)P(x)}{D(x)} = \frac{P(x) + (x - r_1)P'(x)}{D'(x)} \bigg|_{x = r_1} = \frac{P(r_1)}{D'(r_1)}. \quad (56)$$

This is the limit on the left and so equals A_1. Thus

$$A_1 = \frac{P(r_1)}{D'(r_1)}, \quad \text{and} \quad A_2 = \frac{P(r_2)}{D'(r_2)}, \cdots, A_n = \frac{P(r_n)}{D'(r_n)}, \quad (57)$$

as a similar argument shows. This may be used as a formula to compute the coefficients in Eq. (55).

We assume that the polynomials $P(x)$ and $D(x)$ have real coefficients. Then either r and A are both real, and

$$\int \frac{A}{x - r}\, dx = A \log |x - r|, \quad (58)$$

or the complex roots occur in conjugate pairs, and we use

$$2\mathbf{R} \int \frac{A + Bi}{x - a - bi}\, dx$$
$$= A \log [(x - a)^2 + b^2] - 2B \tan^{-1} \frac{x - a}{b}. \quad (59)$$

Here $\mathbf{R}$ denotes the real part of a complex number. Thus

$$(x + iy) + (x - iy) = 2\mathbf{R}(x + iy), \quad (60)$$

and the left member of Eq. (59) is

$$2\mathbf{R} \int \frac{A + Bi}{x - a - bi}\, dx = \int \frac{A + Bi}{x - a - bi}\, dx$$
$$+ \int \frac{A - Bi}{x - a + bi}\, dx. \quad (61)$$

As an illustration, consider

$$I_1 = \int \frac{(2x + 3)dx}{x^3 + x^2 - 2x}. \quad (62)$$

Here the three values of r are 0, 1, -2, since

$$D(x) = x^3 + x^2 - 2x = x(x - 1)(x + 2). \qquad (63)$$

And, by Eq. (57), for each r the value of A is

$$A = \frac{P(r)}{D'(r)} = \frac{2r + 3}{3r^2 + 2r - 2}, \qquad (64)$$

so that the three values of A are $-\frac{3}{2}$, $\frac{5}{3}$, $-\frac{1}{6}$. Hence, by Eq. (58), the value of I_1 is found to be

$$I_1 = -\tfrac{3}{2} \log x + \tfrac{5}{3} \log |x - 1| - \tfrac{1}{6} \log |x + 2|. \qquad (65)$$

As a second illustration, consider

$$I_2 = \int \frac{dx}{x^3 + 8}.$$

Here the three values of r are -2, $1 + \sqrt{3}\,i$, and $1 - \sqrt{3}\,i$. And, by Eq. (57), for each r the value of A is

$$A = \frac{P(r)}{D'(r)} = \frac{1}{3r^2} \quad \text{or} \quad \frac{-r}{24}, \quad \text{since } r^3 = -8. \quad (66)$$

Thus the three values of A are $\frac{1}{12}$, $-(1 + \sqrt{3}\,i)/24$, $-(1 - \sqrt{3}\,i)/24$. Using Eq. (58) with $A = \frac{1}{12}$, $r = -2$, and Eq. (59) with $a = 1$, $b = \sqrt{3}$, $A = -1/24$, $B = -\sqrt{3}/24$, the value of I_2 is found to be

$$I_2 = \frac{1}{12} \log |x + 2| - \frac{1}{24} \log (x^2 - 2x + 4)$$

$$+ \frac{\sqrt{3}}{12} \tan^{-1} \frac{x - 1}{\sqrt{3}}. \quad (67)$$

If the Eq. $D(x) = 0$ has multiple roots, each factor $(x - r)^m$ in $D(x)$ will lead to a series of fractions

$$\frac{A'}{(x - r)} + \frac{A''}{(x - r)^2} + \cdots + \frac{A^{(m)}}{(x - r)^m}. \qquad (68)$$

These could be integrated by using

$$\int \frac{A}{(x - r)^k} \, dx = A \frac{(x - r)^{-k+1}}{-k + 1}. \qquad (69)$$

For real values of r, the coefficients A are real. For two conjugate imaginary roots $a + bi$ and $a - bi$, the corresponding A will be conjugate and each pair of corresponding terms on the right of (69) will give a real result.

When multiple roots are present, a method of calculating the integral, due to Hermite, is preferable to the one just outlined. We shall now present this simpler method. Let the denominator be written with highest coefficient unity, so that

$$D(x) = (x - r_1)^{m_1}(x - r_2)^{m_2} \cdots (x - r_k)^{m_k}. \tag{70}$$

Put

$$S(x) = (x - r_1)(x - r_2) \cdots (x - r_k), \tag{71}$$
$$T(x) = (x - r_1)^{m_1-1}(x - r_2)^{m_2-1} \cdots (x - r_k)^{m_k-1}. \tag{72}$$

Thus

$$D(x) = S(x)T(x). \tag{73}$$

We note that $T(x)$, and hence $S(x)$, may be found by elementary algebra without solving the equation $D(x) = 0$, since $T(x)$ is the highest common factor of $D(x)$ and $D'(x)$.

Then, for the integral of the proper fraction $P(x)/D(x)$, we may write

$$\int \frac{P(x)}{D(x)} \, dx = \int \frac{S_1(x)}{S(x)} \, dx + \frac{T_1(x)}{T(x)}, \tag{74}$$

where $S_1(x)$ is a polynomial of degree one less than that of $S(x)$, and $T_1(x)$ is a polynomial of degree one less than that of $T(x)$, in general. We use letters for the, at present, undetermined coefficients of $S_1(x)$ and $T_1(x)$. In exceptional cases some of the leading coefficients may later turn out to be zero, in which case the degrees will be less than those stated.

It follows from Eq. (74) by differentiation that

$$\frac{P(x)}{D(x)} = \frac{S_1(x)}{S(x)} + \frac{d}{dx}\left[\frac{T_1(x)}{T(x)}\right]. \tag{75}$$

If this is cleared of fractions and coefficients of corresponding powers of x are equated, a set of linear equations will result that may be solved for the coefficients of $S_1(x)$ and $T_1(x)$.

As an example, consider

$$I_3 = \int \frac{x^2 - 4x + 7}{(x - 1)^2(x^2 + 1)} \, dx$$

$$= \int \frac{Ax^2 + Bx + C}{(x - 1)(x^2 + 1)} \, dx + \frac{D}{x - 1}. \tag{76}$$

The result of differentiating and clearing of fractions is

$$x^2 - 4x + 7 = (Ax^2 + Bx + C)(x - 1) - D(x^2 + 1)$$
$$= Ax^3 + (B - A - D)x^2 + (-B + C)x$$
$$+ (-C - D). \quad (77)$$

This leads to the equations

$$A = 0, \quad B - A - D = 1, \quad -B + C = -4,$$
$$-C - D = 7, \quad (78)$$

whose solution is

$$A = 0, \quad B = -1, \quad C = -5, \quad D = -2. \quad (79)$$

Thus the integrand in Eq. (76) is

$$\frac{Ax^2 + Bx + C}{(x - 1)(x^2 + 1)} = \frac{-x - 5}{(x - 1)(x - i)(x + i)}$$
$$= \frac{-3}{x - 1} + 2\mathbf{R}\,\frac{3/2 - i}{x - i}. \quad (80)$$

The simple fractions on the right are found by applying Eqs. (55) and (57) with $P(x) = -x - 5$ and

$$D(x) = (x - 1)(x^2 + 1) = x^3 - x^2 + x - 1,$$
$$D'(x) = 3x^2 - 2x + 1, \quad (81)$$

so that

$$\frac{P(1)}{D'(1)} = \frac{-6}{2} = -3, \qquad \frac{P(i)}{D'(i)} = \frac{-i - 5}{-2 - 2i} = \frac{(5 + i)(1 - i)}{2(1 + i)(1 - i)}$$
$$= \frac{6 - 4i}{4} = \frac{3}{2} - i. \quad (82)$$

It follows from Eqs. (80), (58), and (59) that

$$\int \frac{Ax^2 + Bx + C}{(x - 1)(x^2 + 1)}\, dx = -3 \log |x - 1| + \frac{3}{2} \log (x^2 + 1)$$
$$+ 2 \tan^{-1} x. \quad (83)$$

Finally, from Eqs. (76), (79), and (83) we have

$$I_3 = -3 \log |x - 1| + \frac{3}{2} \log (x^2 + 1) + 2 \tan^{-1} x - \frac{2}{x - 1}. \quad (84)$$

68. Algebraic Integrands. We next describe a few general classes of integrals of algebraic functions which may be reduced to integrals of rational functions by suitable substitutions. Throughout this section, $R(u,v)$ denotes any rational function of the two variables u and v. And we assume that the letters a, b, etc. denote real numbers.

For the integrand $R[x, (ax + b)^{p/q}]$, p and q any integers and $a \neq 0$, the substitution

$$t = (ax + b)^{1/q}, \tag{85}$$

rationalizes the integral, since it makes

$$\int R[x, (ax + b)^{p/q}]dx = \int R\left[\frac{t^q - b}{a}, t^p\right]\frac{qt^{q-1}}{a} dt. \tag{86}$$

The special case where $p = 1$, $q = 2$,

$$\int R(x, \sqrt{ax + b})dx = \int R\left(\frac{t^2 - b}{a}, t\right)\frac{2t}{a} dt, \tag{87}$$

is the one most frequently encountered in practice.

Another example of this type of integral is

$$\int(ax + b)^r x^s dx \qquad \text{with } r \text{ and } s \text{ rational fractions and } r, s,$$
$$\text{or } r + s \text{ an integer.} \tag{88}$$

If s is an integer and $r = p/q$, the integrand is $R[x, (ax + b)^{p/q}]$. If r is an integer and $s = p/q$, the integrand is $R(x, x^{p/q})$. And if $r + s$ is an integer, we may put $t = a + b/x$ and

$$\int(ax + b)^r x^s dx = -b^{r+s+1}\int t^r(t - a)^{-r-s-2}dt. \tag{89}$$

Since $r + s$ is an integer, the exponent of $(t - a)$ is integral. Hence if $r = p/q$, the last integrand is of the type $R(t, t^{p/q})$.

For the integrand $R(x, \sqrt{ax^2 + bx + c})$ there are three cases. If the roots of $ax^2 + bx + c = 0$ are h and k, real and unequal, we may write

$$ax^2 + bx + c = a(x - h)(x - k). \tag{90}$$

Then the relation

$$\sqrt{ax^2 + bx + c} = t(x - k), \qquad \text{or} \qquad a(x - h) = t^2(x - k) \tag{91}$$

determines x as a rational function of t, say $f(t)$. Thus

$$x = f(t) = \frac{ah - kt^2}{a - t^2} \qquad \text{and} \qquad \frac{dx}{dt} = f'(t) = \frac{2a(h - k)t}{(a - t^2)^2}. \tag{92}$$

Consequently, we have

$$\int R(x, \sqrt{ax^2 + bx + c})dx = \int R\{f(t), t[f(t) - k]\}f'(t)dt, \quad (93)$$

and the new integrand is a rational function of t.

If the roots of $ax^2 + bx + c$ are equal, $h = k$ and Eq. (90) becomes

$$ax^2 + bx + c = a(x - k)^2. \quad (94)$$

Consequently, in this case

$$\int R(x, \sqrt{ax^2 + bx + c})dx = \int R[x, \sqrt{a}\,(x - k)]dx, \quad (95)$$

so that the integrand is a rational function of x.

Finally, let us suppose that the roots of $ax^2 + bx + c = 0$ are conjugate complex numbers $m + in$ and $m - in$. Then

$$ax^2 + bx + c = a(x - m - in)(x - m + in)$$
$$= a[(x - m)^2 + n^2]. \quad (96)$$

To make the radical real, a must be positive. Here we put

$$(x - m)^2 + n^2 = (x - m + t)^2, \quad \text{or} \quad n^2 = 2t(x - m) + t^2. \quad (97)$$

This again determines x as a rational function of t, say $g(t)$. Thus

$$x = g(t) = \frac{n^2 + 2mt - t^2}{2t} \quad \text{and} \quad \frac{dx}{dt} = g'(t) = \frac{-n^2 - t^2}{2t^2}. \quad (98)$$

Consequently, we have

$$\int R(x, \sqrt{ax^2 + bx + c})dx$$
$$= \int R\{g(t), \sqrt{a}\,[g(t) - m + t]\}g'(t)dt, \quad (99)$$

and the new integrand is a rational function of t.

The foregoing discussion shows that if X is a polynomial in x of the second degree, the integral of $R(x, \sqrt{X})$ can be found in terms of elementary functions. In simple cases, the value will be found listed in tables of integrals. In more complicated cases, the practical procedure is as follows. As $R(x, \sqrt{X})$ is the quotient of two polynomials in x and $\sqrt{X}$, it may be expressed in the form

$$R(x, \sqrt{X}) = \frac{K + L\sqrt{X}}{M + N\sqrt{X}}, \quad (100)$$

where K, L, M, N are all polynomials in x. For we may use the identities

$$(\sqrt{X})^{2n} = X^n \quad \text{and} \quad (\sqrt{X})^{2n+1} = X^n \sqrt{X} \quad (101)$$

to eliminate the higher powers of $\sqrt{X}$.

Next rationalize the denominator,

$$\frac{K + L \sqrt{X}}{M + N \sqrt{X}} = \frac{K + L \sqrt{X}}{M + N \sqrt{X}} \frac{M - N \sqrt{X}}{M - N \sqrt{X}}$$

$$= \frac{(KM - LNX) + (LM - KN) \sqrt{X}}{M^2 - N^2 X} = U + V \sqrt{X}, \quad (102)$$

where U and V are each rational functions of x. The rational function U may be integrated by the methods of Sec. 67. For the remaining part of the integrand, write

$$V \sqrt{X} = \frac{VX}{\sqrt{X}} \quad (103)$$

and decompose the rational function VX into a polynomial, the $Q(x)$ of Eq. (54), and a sum of partial fractions of the type found in Eqs. (55) and (68). This reduces our problem to the integration of terms of the type,

$$\frac{x^n}{\sqrt{X}}, \qquad \frac{1}{(x - r)^k \sqrt{X}}. \quad (104)$$

For terms of the first type, with $n > 0$, we use the reduction formula which follows. Here $X = ax^2 + bx + c$, with $a \neq 0$.

$$\int \frac{x^n}{\sqrt{X}} dx = \frac{x^{n-1} \sqrt{X}}{an} - \frac{b(2n - 1)}{2an} \int \frac{x^{n-1}}{\sqrt{X}} dx$$

$$- \frac{c(n - 1)}{an} \int \frac{x^{n-2}}{\sqrt{X}} dx. \quad (105)$$

This enables us to reduce the integral of the term of the first type with largest value of n to integrals with smaller exponents. Thus a repeated application of the process will reduce the integrals of terms of the first type to an integral with $n = 0$. We note that, for $n = 1$, the last term in (105) is zero.

For terms of the second type in (104) we may use the following reduction formulas:

Let $X = ax^2 + bx + c$, $S = ar^2 + br + c$,   and

$$T = 2ar + b. \quad (106)$$

Then, when $S \neq 0$,

$$\int \frac{dx}{(x-r)^k \sqrt{X}} = -\frac{1}{(k-1)S} \frac{\sqrt{X}}{(x-r)^{k-1}}$$
$$-\frac{(2k-3)T}{2(k-1)S} \int \frac{dx}{(x-r)^{k-1} \sqrt{X}}$$
$$-\frac{a(k-2)}{(k-1)S} \int \frac{dx}{(x-r)^{k-2} \sqrt{X}}. \quad (107)$$

And, when $S = 0$,

$$\int \frac{dx}{(x-r)^k \sqrt{X}} = -\frac{2}{(2k-1)T} \frac{\sqrt{X}}{(x-r)^k}$$
$$-\frac{2a(k-1)}{(2k-1)T} \int \frac{dx}{(x-r)^{k-1} \sqrt{X}}. \quad (108)$$

This enables us to reduce the integral of the term of the second type with largest value of k to integrals with smaller exponents if $k \geqq 2$. Thus a repeated application of the process will reduce the integrals of terms of the second type to integrals with $k = 1$ or $k = 0$.

This reduces the problem of integrating $R(x, \sqrt{X})$ to integrals of one of the two types,

$$\frac{dx}{\sqrt{X}} \quad \text{and} \quad \frac{dx}{(x-r)\sqrt{X}}. \quad (109)$$

These may be found from the tables. See also Probs. 26 to 33 of Exercises IV (page 187).

69. Integrands Involving Trigonometric or Exponential Functions. Any rational function of trigonometric functions of x may be written in the form $R(\sin x, \cos x)$, since all the other trigonometric functions are expressible rationally in terms of the sine and cosine. But the substitution

$$t = \tan \frac{x}{2} \quad (110)$$

makes

$$\int R(\sin x, \cos x) dx = \int R\left(\frac{2t}{1+t^2}, \frac{1-t^2}{1+t^2}\right) \frac{2dt}{1+t^2}, \quad (111)$$

and the new integrand is a rational function of t.

Similarly the substitution

$$t = \tanh \frac{x}{2} \tag{112}$$

rationalizes the integral of any rational function of hyperbolic functions of x, since

$$\int R(\sinh x, \cosh x)dx = \int R\left(\frac{2t}{1-t^2}, \frac{1+t^2}{1-t^2}\right) \frac{2dt}{1-t^2}. \tag{113}$$

If $R(u)$ denotes any rational function of a single variable u, the integrand $R(e^{ax})$ is rationalizable. For, if $t = e^{ax}$,

$$\int R(e^{ax})dx = \int R(t) \frac{dt}{at}. \tag{114}$$

This method is applicable to the integral of $R(\sinh x, \cosh x)$, with $a = 1$, and to the particular case $R(\tanh x)$ with $a = 2$, since

$$\tanh x = \frac{e^x - e^{-x}}{e^x + e^{-x}} = \frac{e^{2x} - 1}{e^{2x} + 1}. \tag{115}$$

Similarly the method applies to the integral of $R(\sin x, \cos x)$ with $a = i$ and to the particular case $R(\tan x)$ with $a = 2i$. This procedure is sometimes preferable to that indicated in Eqs. (111) and (113).

70. Other Elementary Integrals. Consider an integrand that is algebraic except for a single inverse function, which enters as a factor. Its integration may be reduced to that of an algebraic integrand by an integration by parts, as illustrated in connection with Eq. (52). The algebraic integrand may be rational, or of one of the types described in Sec. 68. For example, if $P(x)$ is any polynomial and n is any integer,

$$\int x^n \log P(x)dx = \frac{x^{n+1}}{n+1} \log P(x) - \int \frac{x^{n+1}}{n+1} \frac{P'(x)}{P(x)} dx, \tag{116}$$

$$\int x^n \tan^{-1} P(x)dx = \frac{x^{n+1}}{n+1} \tan^{-1} P(x)$$
$$- \int \frac{x^{n+1}}{n+1} \frac{P'(x)dx}{1 + [P(x)]^2}. \tag{117}$$

In each of these cases the last integrand is rational. Again,

$$\int x^n \sin^{-1}(ax + b) = \frac{x^{n+1}}{n + 1} \sin^{-1}(ax + b)$$
$$- \int \frac{x^{n+1}}{n + 1} \frac{a\,dx}{\sqrt{1 - (ax + b)^2}}, \quad (118)$$

and the last integral is rationalizable.

The integral of any polynomial in any number of variables each of which is either x, e^{kx}, $\sin ax$, $\cos bx$, $\sinh cx$, $\cosh dx$, with any values of the constants, may be evaluated. If we express functions of the last four types in terms of (complex or real) exponentials and multiply out, the integral becomes a sum of multiples of terms of the type

$$\int x^n e^{px} dx. \quad (119)$$

These may be evaluated by integrating by parts repeatedly, as remarked after Eq. (52). Another convenient method of evaluating the integral (119) is to predict the form of the result as a polynomial of the nth degree times e^{px} and use the method of undetermined coefficients.

For example, if $\mathbf{I}$ denotes the imaginary part of a complex number, so that $\mathbf{I}(a + bi) = b$, then

$$\int xe^x \sin 2x\,dx = \tfrac{1}{2}\mathbf{I}\int xe^{(1+2i)x}dx$$
$$= (Ax + B)\cos 2x\,e^x + (Cx + D)\sin 2x\,e^x. \quad (120)$$

By equating the derivatives of the two sides, we find that

$$xe^x \sin 2x = (Ax + B + A + 2Cx + 2D)\cos 2x\,e^x$$
$$+ (Cx + D + C - 2Ax - 2B)\sin 2x\,e^x. \quad (121)$$

This will hold if

$$A + 2C = 0, \quad C - 2A = 1, \quad B + A + 2D = 0,$$
$$D + C - 2B = 0. \quad (122)$$

The solution of these equations is

$$A = -\tfrac{2}{5}, \quad B = \tfrac{4}{25}, \quad C = \tfrac{1}{5}, \quad D = \tfrac{3}{25}. \quad (123)$$

Hence, by Eq. (120),

$$\int xe^x \sin 2x\,dx = \frac{e^x}{25}[(-10x + 4)\cos 2x + (5x + 3)\sin 2x].$$
$$(124)$$

71. Improper Integrals. If $f(x)$ is continuous throughout the interval a,b, any indefinite integral $F(x)$ will have a derivative $F'(x) = f(x)$ for $a \leqq x \leqq b$. Hence $F(x)$ will be continuous for such values of x. Consequently

$$\lim_{x \to b} F(x) = F(b), \qquad \text{and} \qquad \lim_{x \to b} [F(x) - F(a)] = F(b) - F(a).$$
$$(125)$$

This shows that under the conditions stated

$$\lim_{x \to b} \int_a^x f(x)dx = \int_a^b f(x)dx. \qquad (126)$$

In case $f(x)$ is continuous for all values of x with $a \leqq x < b$, but $f(x)$ is discontinuous at b, the definite integral is defined by Eq. (126) if the limit on the left is finite. In this case the integral is *convergent*. If the

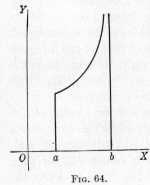

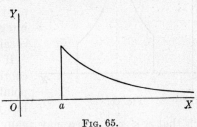

FIG. 64.   FIG. 65.

expression on the left of Eq. (126) does not define a finite limit, the integral on the right is said to be *divergent*, and no meaning is assigned to it.

Similarly, if $f(x)$ is continuous for all values of x with $a < x \leqq b$, we use

$$\lim_{x \to a} \int_x^b f(x)dx = \int_a^b f(x)dx \qquad (127)$$

as the definition of the right member.

And a similar equation is used if one of the limits is infinite. Thus,

$$\lim_{x \to \infty} \int_a^x f(x)dx = \int_a^\infty f(x)dx, \qquad (128)$$

and

$$\lim_{x \to -\infty} \int_x^b f(x)dx = \int_{-\infty}^b f(x)dx. \qquad (129)$$

In the defining equations (126) through (129) we have assumed that the upper limit is greater than the lower limit. However, similar definitions apply if this is not the case. These are such that Eq. (19) holds for the new type of integral.

Let us next consider a function $f(x)$ which is continuous throughout the interval a,b except for the value c, that is, for $a \leqq x < c$ and $c < x \leqq b$. Then we define

$$\int_a^b f(x)dx = \int_a^c f(x)dx + \int_c^b f(x)dx. \qquad (130)$$

If both the integrals on the right of this equation are convergent

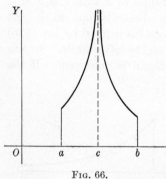

when defined by relations similar in form to Eqs. (126) and (127), then the integral on the left of Eq. (130) is said to be *convergent*. If either or both of the integrals on the right diverge, then the integral on the left of Eq. (130) is said to be *divergent*.

If a is $- \infty$ or a point of discontinuity of $f(x)$ and b is ∞ or a point of discontinuity of $f(x)$, but $f(x)$ is continuous for all x

Fig. 66.

such that $a < x < b$, we may again use Eq. (130) to define the integral on the left in terms of those on the right. And a similar decomposition may be used to define the integral when $f(x)$ has several points of discontinuity.

Definite integrals that may be defined in terms of $f(x)$ by the single limiting process given in Eq. (11) are called *proper* integrals. In contradistinction, the integrals of this section that are defined in terms of the limits of proper integrals are called *improper* integrals.

The properties expressed in Eqs. (20) through (23) all hold for convergent improper integrals. And Eq. (37) may still be used to evaluate such integrals, provided that

$$\frac{dF}{dx} = F'(x) \text{ is finite and } = f(x) \qquad \text{for } a < x < b, \quad (131)$$

and $F(x)$ approaches finite limits as $x \to a$ and $x \to b$.

As examples of integrals with one or both limits infinite, we have

$$\int_{-\infty}^{-1} \frac{dx}{x^3} = \frac{x^{-2}}{-2}\Big|_{-\infty}^{-1} = -\frac{1}{2}. \tag{132}$$

$$\int_{0}^{\infty} e^{-x}dx = -e^{-x}\Big|_{0}^{\infty} = 1. \tag{133}$$

$$\int_{-\infty}^{\infty} \frac{dx}{1+x^2} = \tan^{-1} x\Big|_{-\infty}^{\infty} = \pi. \tag{134}$$

As examples of integrands discontinuous at one limit, we have

$$\int_{0}^{2} \frac{dx}{\sqrt{x}} = 2\sqrt{x}\Big|_{0}^{2} = 2\sqrt{2}, \tag{135}$$

in which the integrand becomes infinite at the lower limit zero, and

$$\int_{0}^{2/\pi} \left(2x\sin\frac{1}{x} - \cos\frac{1}{x}\right) dx = x^2\sin\frac{1}{x}\Big|_{0}^{2/\pi} = \frac{4}{\pi^2}, \tag{136}$$

in which the integrand oscillates as x approaches the lower limit zero.

And, as examples of integrands that become infinite at both limits, we have

$$\int_{1}^{2} \frac{dx}{\sqrt{(x-1)(2-x)}} = \sin^{-1}(2x-3)\Big|_{1}^{2} = \pi. \tag{137}$$

$$\int_{-2}^{2} \frac{x^2dx}{\sqrt{4-x^2}} = -\frac{x}{2}\sqrt{4-x^2} + 2\sin^{-1}\frac{x}{2}\Big|_{-2}^{2} = 2\pi. \tag{138}$$

If condition (131) holds but $F(x)$ fails to approach a finite limit as $x \to a$ or as $x \to b$, the integral diverges. Thus

$$\int_{1}^{\infty} \frac{dx}{\sqrt{x}} = 2\sqrt{x}\Big|_{1}^{\infty} \text{ diverges,} \tag{139}$$

since $2\sqrt{x} \to \infty$ as $x \to \infty$.

$$\int_{-\infty}^{0} \cos x\, dx = \sin x\Big|_{-\infty}^{0} \text{ diverges,} \tag{140}$$

since $\cos x$ oscillates as $x \to -\infty$.

$$\int_{1}^{2} \frac{dx}{(x-1)(2-x)} = \log\frac{x-1}{2-x}\Big|_{1}^{2} \text{ diverges,} \tag{141}$$

since the logarithm becomes infinite at either limit.

It is sometimes convenient to apply the reductions of Sec. 66 to convergent improper integrals. In particular, Eqs. (51), (52), and (53) will hold whenever all the improper integrals involved are convergent. For example, the expression

$$4 \int_0^a \frac{a\,dx}{\sqrt{a^2 - x^2}} = 4a \, \sin^{-1} \frac{x}{a} \Big|_0^a = 2\pi a \qquad (142)$$

involves an improper integral, since the integrand becomes infinite at the upper limit. It could be evaluated by the substitution $x = a \cos t$, which makes

$$4 \int_0^a \frac{a\,dx}{\sqrt{a^2 - x^2}} = -4 \int_{\pi/2}^0 a\,dt = 4a \int_0^{\pi/2} dt = 2\pi a. \quad (143)$$

We note that the expression in x is that obtained for the length of the circumference of the circle $x^2 + y^2 = a^2$, in terms of x. And the expression in t could be obtained directly by using the parametric equations of the circle, $x = a \cos t$, $y = a \sin t$. This illustrates that when the calculation of a geometrical or physical quantity leads to a convergent improper integral, the value of the quantity is correctly given by using the definitions of this section.

72. Tests for Convergence. For many improper integrals it is inconvenient or impossible to find a simple indefinite integral $F(x)$ satisfying the conditions (131). Consequently we cannot decide whether the improper integral converges by a direct use of the method of Sec. 71. However, we can frequently settle the question by the following considerations.

We first define the phrase "$f(x)$ behaves like $g(x)$ as $x \to b$," to mean the two functions $f(x)$ and $g(x)$ are such that

$$\lim_{x \to b} \frac{f(x)}{g(x)} = k \neq 0. \qquad (144)$$

The following statements illustrate this definition:

$$\sin x \text{ behaves like } x \text{ as } x \to 0. \qquad (145)$$

$$\cosh x = \frac{e^x + e^{-x}}{2} \text{ behaves like } e^x \text{ as } x \to \infty,$$
$$\text{and behaves like } e^{-x} \text{ as } x \to -\infty. \qquad (146)$$

$$\frac{1}{1 + x^2} \text{ behaves like } x^{-2} \text{ as } x \to \infty, \text{ or } x \to -\infty. \quad (147)$$

$$\frac{a}{\sqrt{a^2 - x^2}} \text{ behaves like } (a - x)^{-\frac{1}{2}} \text{ as } x \to a. \qquad (148)$$

$$\frac{x^2}{\sqrt{4 - x^2}} \text{ behaves like } (2 - x)^{-\frac{1}{2}} \text{ as } x \to 2,$$
$$\text{and behaves like } (2 + x)^{-\frac{1}{2}} \text{ as } x \to -2. \qquad (149)$$

$$\frac{1}{(x - 1)(2 - x)} \text{ behaves like } (x - 1)^{-1} \text{ as } x \to 1,$$
$$\text{and behaves like } (x - 2)^{-1} \text{ as } x \to 2. \qquad (150)$$

$$\frac{1}{\sqrt{(x - 1)(2 - x)}} \text{ behaves like } (x - 1)^{-\frac{1}{2}} \text{ as } x \to 1,$$
$$\text{and behaves like } (2 - x)^{-\frac{1}{2}} \text{ as } x \to 2. \qquad (151)$$

Now consider the integral of $f(x)$ from a to b. *Suppose that $f(x)$ is continuous for all x such that $a < x < b$ and behaves like $g(x)$ as $x \to b$. Then if $g(x)$ is continuous and of fixed algebraic sign for all x such that $a < x < b$, the improper integrals*

$$\int_a^b f(x)dx \qquad and \qquad \int_a^b g(x)dx \qquad (152)$$

will both diverge or both converge.

A similar statement may be made if the only discontinuity is at a, the lower limit, or if one of the limits is infinite.

A simple calculation shows that the integrals

$$\int_a^c (c - x)^{-1+p}dx \qquad and \qquad \int_c^b (x - c)^{-1+p}dx \qquad (153)$$

are convergent if p is any positive number, $p > 0$. Similarly

$$\int_a^\infty x^{-1-p}dx \qquad and \qquad \int_{-\infty}^b (-x)^{-1-p}dx \qquad (154)$$

are convergent if $p > 0$. Hence the behavior of an integrand like $|x - c|^{-1+p}$ as $x \to c$, or like $|x|^{-1-p}$ as $x \to \infty$ or $-\infty$, where $p > 0$, does not, of itself, spoil the convergence of the integral.

On the other hand, if we replace p by $-q$, where q is positive or zero, the integrals (153) and (154) will diverge. Thus the behavior of an integrand like $|x - c|^{-1-q}$ as $x \to c$, or like x^{-1+q}, where $q > 0$, makes the integral diverge.

The examples of Sec. 71 illustrate the statements just made. Example (132) with $p = 2$, $-1 - p = -3$; (135) with $c = 0$, $p = \frac{1}{2}$ and $-1 + p = -\frac{1}{2}$; (139) with $q = \frac{1}{2}$, $-1 + q = -\frac{1}{2}$ are essentially test integrals as they stand. The convergence of the integrals (134), (137), (138), and (142) might have been predicted from the behavior of their integrands as described in (147), (151), (149), and (148). Similarly the divergence of the integral (141) could have been predicted from the behavior of its integrand as stated in (150).

As a further illustration we note that the elliptic integrals

$$\int_{-1}^{1} \frac{dx}{\sqrt{(1-x^2)(4-x^2)}}, \qquad \int_{1}^{2} \frac{dx}{\sqrt{(x^2-1)(4-x^2)}},$$

$$\int_{2}^{\infty} \frac{dx}{\sqrt{(x^2-1)(x^2-4)}} \qquad (155)$$

are all convergent. For the first integral behaves like $(x+1)^{-\frac{1}{2}}$ as $x \to -1$ and like $(1-x)^{-\frac{1}{2}}$ as $x \to 1$; the second behaves like $(x-1)^{-\frac{1}{2}}$ as $x \to 1$, and like $(2-x)^{-\frac{1}{2}}$ as $x \to 2$; the third behaves like $(x-2)^{-\frac{1}{2}}$ as $x \to 2$ and like x^{-2} as $x \to \infty$.

There are separate comparison tests for convergence and for divergence which are more general than that just given. First suppose that for all x such that $a < x < b$, $f(x)$ is continuous, $g(x)$ is continuous and of *fixed* algebraic *sign*, and near b

$$\left| \frac{f(x)}{g(x)} \right| < M, \qquad \text{some fixed number.} \qquad (156)$$

Then

$$\int_{a}^{b} f(x)dx \text{ converges if } \int_{a}^{b} g(x)dx \text{ converges.} \qquad (157)$$

The condition (156) will automatically follow if

$$\lim_{x \to b} \frac{f(x)}{g(x)} = k \neq 0 \text{ or if } \lim_{x \to b} \frac{f(x)}{g(x)} = 0. \qquad (158)$$

In view of the identity

$$f(x) = \frac{f(x)}{g(x)} g(x), \qquad (159)$$

the test just described shows that the convergence of an integral whose integrand $g(x)$ is of fixed sign is not disturbed by the introduction of any bounded factor. For example, the integrals

$$\int_{-\infty}^{\infty} \frac{\sin x}{1+x^2} dx \qquad (160)$$

and

$$\int_{1}^{2} \frac{\sin (x-1)^{-1} \cos (2-x)^{-1}}{\sqrt{(x-1)(2-x)}} dx \qquad (161)$$

both converge, even though they contain factors that change
sign infinitely often in the interval of integration. For they
may be obtained from the convergent integrals (134) and (137)
by multiplying in factors that are always at most one in numerical
value.

The comparison test could also be applied directly, using x^{-2} as
the function $g(x)$ near both limits for the first integral (160), and
for the second integral (161) by using $(x - 1)^{-\frac{1}{2}}$ near 1 and
$(2 - x)^{-\frac{1}{2}}$ near 2 as the comparison function $g(x)$. However, it
is a little simpler to think of each integrand as a bounded factor
times an integrand behaving like these comparison functions.

As an example where the ratio of (158) approaches zero, we
consider

$$\lim_{x \to \infty} \frac{e^{-x}}{x^{-2}} = \lim_{x \to \infty} \frac{x^2}{e^x} = 0, \tag{162}$$

where the second limit is evaluated by Eq. (224) of Sec. 17.
We chose the exponent in the denominator as -2 because, by
(154), with $p = 1$,

$$\int_1^\infty x^{-2}dx \text{ converges.} \tag{163}$$

Thus, we may conclude that

$$\int_1^\infty e^{-x}dx \qquad \text{and hence} \qquad \int_0^\infty e^{-x}dx \text{ converges,} \tag{164}$$

as we showed directly in (133).

A similar argument, or a direct calculation, shows that

$$\int_a^\infty e^{-px}dx \text{ converges for } p > 0 \text{ and } a \text{ finite.} \tag{165}$$

Hence e^{-px} may be used as the function $g(x)$ of either test. For
example, from

$$\lim_{x \to \infty} \frac{e^{-x^2}}{e^{-x}} = \lim_{x \to \infty} \frac{1}{e^{x^2-x}} = 0, \tag{166}$$

we may conclude that the integral

$$\int_0^\infty e^{-x^2}dx \text{ converges.} \tag{167}$$

And from

$$\lim_{x \to \infty} \frac{x^3e^{-x}}{e^{-\frac{1}{2}x}} = \lim_{x \to \infty} \frac{x^3}{e^{\frac{1}{2}x}} = 0, \tag{168}$$

we may conclude that

$$\int_0^\infty x^3 e^{-x} dx \text{ converges.} \tag{169}$$

We shall next formulate the corresponding comparison test for divergence. Suppose that for all x such that $a < x < b$, $f(x)$ and $g(x)$ are *both* continuous and of *fixed* algebraic *sign*. And, near b, let

$$\left| \frac{f(x)}{g(x)} \right| > M, \qquad \text{some fixed number.} \tag{170}$$

Then

$$\int_a^b f(x)dx \text{ diverges if } \int_a^b g(x)dx \text{ diverges.} \tag{171}$$

The condition (170) will automatically follow if

$$\lim_{x \to b} \frac{f(x)}{g(x)} = k \neq 0, \text{ or if } \lim_{x \to b} \frac{f(x)}{g(x)} = \infty \text{ or } = -\infty. \tag{172}$$

And here the introduction of a bounded factor in the denominator will not disturb the divergence of an integral, if the old and the new integrand are both of fixed sign. For example, from

$$\lim_{x \to \infty} \frac{e^{x^2}}{e^x} = \lim_{x \to \infty} e^{x^2 - x} = \infty, \tag{173}$$

and the fact that

$$\int_0^\infty e^x dx = e^x \Big|_0^\infty \text{ diverges,} \tag{174}$$

we may conclude that

$$\int_0^\infty e^{x^2} dx \text{ diverges.} \tag{175}$$

Again, the divergence of

$$\int_1^2 \frac{dx}{2 (\sin x)(x - 1)(2 - x)} \tag{176}$$

follows from (141) and the fact that for x near 2

$$\frac{1}{2 \sin x} > \frac{1}{2}. \tag{177}$$

We state without proof or motivation Abel's test, which is applicable to certain integrands that are not of fixed sign. The integrand must be the product of two functions $f(x)$ and $p(x)$, each of special type.   The test states that

$$\int_a^\infty f(x)p(x)dx \text{ converges} \tag{178}$$

if $p(x)$ is positive and steadily decreases to zero as x increases to infinity and $f(x)$ is a function such that for some finite value M,

$$\left|\int_a^x f(x)dx\right| < M \quad \text{for all } x > a. \tag{179}$$

For example, for all $x > 1$,

$$\int_1^x \sin x \, dx = -\cos x \Big|_1^x = -\cos x + \cos 1, \tag{180}$$

and, since the numerical value of $\cos x$ never exceeds 1,

$$\left|\int_1^x \sin x \, dx\right| < 2. \tag{181}$$

Also, for $p > 0$ and $x > 1$, the function x^{-p} is positive and decreasing, with $x^{-p} \to 0$ as $x \to \infty$.   Thus by Abel's test,

$$\int_1^\infty \frac{\sin x}{x^p} \, dx \text{ converges if } p > 0. \tag{182}$$

Similar reasoning shows that

$$\int_1^\infty \frac{\cos x}{x^p} \, dx \text{ converges if } p > 0. \tag{183}$$

More generally, since

$$\int_1^x x^{m-1} \sin x^m dx = -\frac{1}{m} \cos x^m \Big|_1^x, \tag{184}$$

the integral

$$\int_1^\infty \frac{\sin x^m}{x^{p+1-m}} \, dx \text{ converges if } p > 0. \tag{185}$$

And similar reasoning shows that

$$\int_1^\infty \frac{\cos x^m}{x^{p+1-m}} \, dx \text{ converges if } p > 0. \tag{186}$$

If $p > 2$ in the integrals (182) and (183), or if $p + 1 - m > 2$ in the integrals (185) and (186), the convergence follows from the comparison test described in connection with Eq. (159). But the convergence of such special cases as

$$\int_1^\infty \frac{\sin x}{x}\, dx \qquad (p = 1), \qquad \int_1^\infty \frac{\cos x}{\sqrt{x}}\, dx \qquad (p = \tfrac{1}{2}), \quad (187)$$

or

$$\int_1^\infty \sin (x^2)dx \qquad (p = 1,\ m = 2),$$

$$\int_1^\infty \sqrt{x} \cos (x^2)dx \qquad (p = \tfrac{1}{2},\ m = 2), \qquad (188)$$

could not be established by the earlier tests.

73. Multiple Integrals. Let $f(x,y)$ be a function of x and y and R a two-dimensional region of the xy plane. For any point $P = (x,y)$ we define the symbol $f(P)$ by the equation

$$f(P) = f(x,y). \qquad (189)$$

Then we may make a two-dimensional construction similar to that made on the interval in Sec. 62. We subdivide R into n small subregions. These may be of any shape but must completely fill R. We let d_n denote the length of the largest interval having its end points on the boundary of any one of the small subregions. Let ΔR_i denote the ith region or its area. Select some point P_i in each subregion R_i and form the sum

$$S_n = \sum_{i=1}^n f(P_i)\Delta R_i. \qquad (190)$$

Then for simple types of regions R, subregions ΔR_i, and functions $f(x,y)$, any sequence of sums S_n such that $d_n \to 0$ as $n \to \infty$ will approach a limit. This limit is called the *double integral* of $f(P)$, or $f(x,y)$, over R. And we write

$$\int_R f(P)dR = \lim_{n\to\infty} \sum_{i=1}^n f(P_i)\Delta R_i \qquad \text{if } \lim_{n\to\infty} d_n = 0. \quad (191)$$

The double integral represents the area of R if $f(x,y) = 1$. It represents the volume of the right cylinder whose base is R and whose height at x,y is $f(x,y)$, shown in Fig. 68. And, if $f(x,y)$ is equal to sec γ for a surface, the double integral represents the area of the part of the surface whose projection on the

xy plane is R, by Eq. (301) of Sec. 57. The double integral also represents the mass of a plate covering R whose density at x,y is $f(x,y)$. Furthermore, certain other physical quantities of plates such as moments or moments of inertia are expressible as double integrals. See Probs. 38 to 48, Exercises IV (page 189).

The triple integral is similarly defined by starting with a region R in three dimensions and a function of three variables $f(x,y,z)$. If when $P = (x,y,z)$, $f(P) = f(x,y,z)$, the defining relation is again (191), in which the elements ΔR_i like the region R are now three-dimensional.

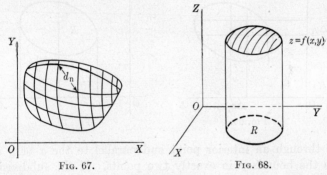

FIG. 67.   FIG. 68.

With $f(x,y,z) = 1$, the triple integral represents the volume of R. As it stands the triple integral represents the mass of a solid covering R whose density at x,y,z is $f(x,y,z)$. And certain other physical quantities of solids such as moments and moments of inertia are expressible as triple integrals. See Probs. 49 to 54.

We may encounter multiple integrals with more than three variables. For example, the component of gravitational attraction of a solid A' by a solid A, along the x axis, would be the sextuple integral,

$$F_x = \int_{A,A'} X(P)dR, \tag{192}$$

where

$$P = (x,y,z,x',y',z'), \qquad dR = dx\,dy\,dz\,dx'dy'dz', \tag{193}$$

and

$$X(P) = \frac{\rho(x,y,z)\rho'(x',y',z')(x - x')}{[(x - x')^2 + (y - y')^2 + (z - z')^2]^{3/2}}. \tag{194}$$

An equation similar to (44) applies to multiple integrals whose integrands contain one or more parameters. For example, let

$$I = \int_R f(P,u,v)dR, \tag{195}$$

where P is a point and R a region in two (or three) dimensions. Then if the region R does not depend on the parameters u and v,

$$\frac{\partial I}{\partial u} = \int_R \frac{\partial f}{\partial u} \, dR. \tag{196}$$

74. Iterated Integrals. Consider the double integral over a region R, like that in Fig. 69, which is such that every straight

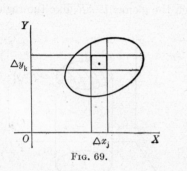

FIG. 69.

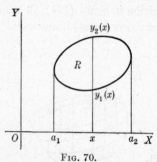

FIG. 70.

line through an interior point and parallel to the x or y axis cuts the boundary in exactly two points. If the subdivisions ΔR_i of Eq. (190) are rectangles formed by drawing lines parallel to the coordinate axes, we shall have for the area of the ith

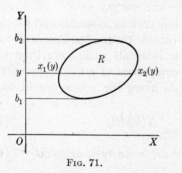

FIG. 71.

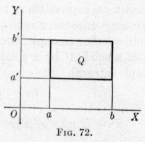

FIG. 72.

subdivision $\Delta R_i = \Delta x_j \Delta y_k$. For some rectangles cut by the boundary of R, only a part is a subregion of R. However, we still use the whole rectangle, as this simplifies the discussion and does not change the limit in Eq. (191). We may now select ξ_j in Δx_j and η_k in Δy_k, and take $P_i = (\xi_j, \eta_k)$. Then

$$\sum f(P_i)\Delta R_i = \sum_{j,k} f(\xi_j, \eta_k)\Delta x_j \Delta y_k$$

$$= \sum_j \Delta x_j \sum_k f(\xi_j, \eta_k)\Delta y_k$$

$$= \sum_k \Delta y_k \sum_j f(\xi_j, \eta_k)\Delta x_j. \qquad (197)$$

In view of Eqs. (11) and (191), this suggests that

$$\int_R f(P)dR = \int_{a_1}^{a_2} dx \int_{y_1(x)}^{y_2(x)} f(x,y)dy = \int_{b_1}^{b_2} dy \int_{x_1(y)}^{x_2(y)} f(x,y)dx. \quad (198)$$

The functions and constants used as limits are so chosen that the region R is made up of those points (Fig. 70) for which

$$a_1 < x < a_2 \qquad \text{and} \qquad y_1(x) < y < y_2(x), \qquad (199)$$

or of those points (Fig. 71) for which

$$b_1 < y < b_2 \qquad \text{and} \qquad x_1(y) < x < x_2(y). \qquad (200)$$

In particular, if the region R is Q, a rectangle consisting of those points for which (Fig. 72)

$$a < x < b \qquad \text{and} \qquad a' < y < b', \qquad (201)$$

the relation just written reduces to

$$\int_Q f(P)dR = \int_a^b dx \int_{a'}^{b'} f(x,y)dy = \int_{a'}^{b'} dy \int_a^b f(x,y)dx. \quad (202)$$

The relations (198) and (202) always hold when $f(x,y)$ is continuous in both variables. When $f(x,y)$ has points, or curves, of discontinuity or where some of the single integrals have infinite limits, some or all of the expressions in Eq. (198) may be meaningless. However, if either of the expressions on the right involves only convergent improper integrals, it will give the value of the geometrical or physical quantity represented by the double integral on the left.

The repeated simple integrals that constitute the right members of Eqs. (198) and (202) are called *iterated* integrals.

Suppose that the region R of a double integral is such that some lines through interior points cut the boundary in more than two points. In some cases we may still use one of the iterated integrals of Eq. (198). Thus the first one, whose limits are given by Eq. (199), is valid for the region of Fig. 73. And the second one, whose limits are given by Eq. (200), is valid for the region of Fig. 74. In other cases (Fig. 75) it is usually possible to decompose the region into parts for each of which one of the iterated integrals is valid.

A discussion similar to that just given for double integrals could be made for multiple integrals in three or more variables. This would show that such integrals can be expressed in terms of iterated integrals involving three or more single integrations.

The expression of double and triple integrals by repeated or iterated integrals in curvilinear coordinates, and the method of changing from one set of curvilinear coordinates to another have already been given in Secs. 58 and 59.

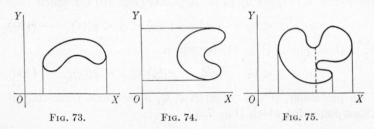

FIG. 73.   FIG. 74.   FIG. 75.

75. Integrals Containing a Parameter. Suppose that the integrand of a definite integral contains a parameter, as in Eq. (41), so that

$$I(u) = \int_a^b f(x,u)dx. \qquad (203)$$

Then the integral of $I(u)$ with respect to u from a' to b' is

$$\int_{a'}^{b'} I(u)du = \int_{a'}^{b'} du \int_a^b f(x,u)dx. \qquad (204)$$

By Eq. (202), this equals

$$\int_a^b dx \int_{a'}^{b'} f(x,u)du, \qquad (205)$$

and the integrations with respect to x and u may be performed in either order.

The inversion of the order of integration sometimes leads to the evaluation of a particular definite integral. To illustrate this, consider

$$\int_0^\infty e^{-ux}dx = \frac{e^{-ux}}{-u}\Big|_0^\infty = \frac{1}{u}, \qquad \text{if } u > 0. \qquad (206)$$

By integrating both sides of this equation with respect to u from a to b, we find

$$\int_0^\infty \frac{e^{-ax} - e^{-bx}}{x} \, dx = \log \frac{b}{a}, \quad b > a > 0. \tag{207}$$

We may also use the process of differentiation with respect to a parameter [Eq. (44)] to evaluate integrals. For example, if we differentiate both sides of Eq. (206) with respect to u and reverse the signs, we find

$$\int_0^\infty x e^{-ux} dx = \frac{1}{u^2}, \quad \text{if } u > 0. \tag{208}$$

A similar procedure is applicable to indefinite integrals. For, let $F(x,u)$ be any indefinite integral with respect to x of $f(x,u)$. Then we have

$$\int_a^x f(x,u)dx = F(x,u) - F(a,u). \tag{209}$$

By differentiation with respect to u, it follows that

$$\int_a^x f_u(x,u)dx = F_u(x,u) - F_u(a,u), \tag{210}$$

where the subscripts denote partial derivatives. The last equation shows that $F_u(x,u)$ is an indefinite integral with respect to x of $f_u(x,u)$.

For example, from

$$\int^x \frac{dx}{x^2 + a^2} = \frac{1}{a} \tan^{-1} \frac{x}{a}, \tag{211}$$

we may obtain

$$\int^x \frac{dx}{(x^2 + a^2)^2} = \frac{1}{2a^3} \tan^{-1} \frac{x}{a} + \frac{x}{2a^2(x^2 + a^2)}, \tag{212}$$

by differentiation with respect to a, followed by division by $-2a$. And the integrals with higher powers in the denominators could be found by a repetition of the process.

Similarly, by differentiation, from

$$\int^x \sin ax \, dx = -\frac{1}{a} \cos ax, \quad \text{and} \quad \int^x \cos ax \, dx = \frac{1}{a} \sin ax, \tag{213}$$

we may obtain

$$\int^x x \cos ax \, dx = \frac{\cos ax}{a^2} + \frac{x \sin ax}{a}, \qquad (214)$$

and, with reversal of sign,

$$\int^x x \sin ax \, dx = \frac{\sin ax}{a^2} - \frac{x \cos ax}{a}. \qquad (215)$$

And the integrals with higher powers of x could be found by repeated differentiation.

The procedure just illustrated simplifies the systematic construction or checking of a table of integrals.

76. Series Methods. Definite integrals of functions for which no indefinite integral can be found can sometimes be calculated by the use of infinite series.

One method is to expand the integrand in a power series, or power series combined with other terms easy to integrate. Thus from

$$e^{-x} = 1 - x + \frac{x^2}{2!} - \frac{x^3}{3!} + \cdots, \qquad (216)$$

we may obtain the expansion

$$\frac{e^{-x}}{x} = \frac{1}{x} - 1 + \frac{x}{2!} - \frac{x^2}{3!} + \cdots \qquad (217)$$

From this, we find by termwise integration that

$$\int_{x_0}^x \frac{e^{-x}}{x} \, dx = \left(\log x - x + \frac{x^2}{2 \cdot 2!} - \frac{x^3}{3 \cdot 3!} + \cdots \right)\Big|_{x_0}^x. \qquad (218)$$

This method has been illustrated in Probs. 68 to 75 of Exercises I (page 42).

Some integrals may be computed by using a series expansion in powers of a parameter. For example, consider the expansion

$$(e^{2x} + a^2 e^{-2x})^{-\frac{1}{2}} = e^{-x} - \tfrac{1}{2}a^2 e^{-5x} + \tfrac{3}{8}a^4 e^{-9x} + \cdots. \qquad (219)$$

From this, we find by termwise integration, that

$$\int_{x_0}^x \frac{dx}{(e^{2x} + a^2 e^{-2x})^{\frac{1}{2}}} = \left(-e^{-x} + \frac{1}{10} a^2 e^{-5x} - \frac{1}{24} a^4 e^{-9x} + \cdots \right)\Big|_{x_0}^x. \qquad (220)$$

This is valid if $ae^{-4x} < 1$ at both limits and converges rapidly if ae^{-4x} is small compared with unity.

Repeated integration by parts will sometimes lead to a series expansion of an integral. For example,

$$\int^x \frac{e^{-x}}{x}\,dx = -\frac{e^{-x}}{x} - \int^x \frac{e^{-x}}{x^2}\,dx, \qquad (221)$$

$$\int^x \frac{e^{-x}}{x^2}\,dx = -\frac{e^{-x}}{x^2} - 2!\int^x \frac{e^{-x}}{x^3}\,dx, \qquad (222)$$

and so on. This suggests that the expansion

$$\int_{x_0}^x \frac{e^{-x}}{x}\,dx = e^{-x}\left(-\frac{1}{x} + \frac{1}{x^2} - \frac{2!}{x^3} + \frac{3!}{x^4} - \cdots\right)\Bigg|_{x_0}^x \qquad (223)$$

may be used to compute the value of the integral on the left. Owing to the factorials in the numerators, for any value of x the terms ultimately increase indefinitely, and the infinite series diverges. However, the error made by stopping at any point is of the order of magnitude of the first term omitted. Consequently, for large values of x, the first few terms will give a good approximation to the function expanded. Divergent expansions with properties like those just described are known as *asymptotic* series. If x_0 and x are both large compared with unity, the use of the asymptotic series (223) involves less computation than the use of the convergent series (218). If we wished to compute the integral from 1 to 100, a practical procedure would be to use (218) for the interval 1 to 10 and (223) for the interval 10 to 100.

77. Graphical Integration. Suppose that the values of the integrand $f(x)$ can be found numerically. For example, $f(x)$ may be given by a simple function with all parameters specified so that its values can be calculated. Or $f(x)$ may be known directly from a series of tabulated values, or from a graph. Under any of these conditions a graph showing the values of $f(x)$ for $a < x < b$ is either at hand or may be constructed. Then the integral of $f(x)$ from a to b is represented by the area A bounded by the curve, the x axis, and the extreme ordinates. Since it is usually desirable to take different units on the x and y axes, the numerical value of the area must be figured with due regard for the scales used. We proceed to describe several methods of finding the area A, and hence an approximate value of the integral by means of the relation

$$\int_a^b f(x)dx = A. \tag{224}$$

We shall illustrate these methods for an integral whose value is known,

$$I = \int_0^{\frac{1}{2}} 10 \sin \pi x \, dx = \frac{10}{\pi} = 3.18310. \tag{225}$$

The graph of $y = f(x) = 10 \sin \pi x$ between the limits $x = a = 0$ and $x = b = \frac{1}{2}$ is shown in Fig. 76.

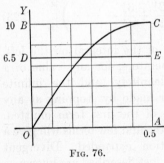

Fig. 76.

By sliding a transparent straightedge over the graph parallel to the x axis until the right position, as estimated by eye, is reached, we may rule a straight line parallel to the x axis such that the part of A above this line has the same area as the part below. If the ordinate of this line is $\bar{f}$,

$$\int_a^b f(x)dx = (b - a)\bar{f}, \tag{226}$$

where $\bar{f}$ is read in the units of the y scale. In Fig. 76 we have ruled in the line DE, whose ordinate $\bar{f} = OD = 6.5$. Thus

$$I = (b - a)\bar{f} = (\tfrac{1}{2})(6.5) = 3.3 \text{ approximately.} \tag{227}$$

A second method is to estimate the number of coordinate squares in A. Thus, in Fig. 76, A contains 14 whole squares, and parts of squares that aggregate about 5 squares. One way to account for the scales used on the x and y axes is to use the squares to find the ratio of A to some rectangle. For example, in the figure the rectangle $OACB$ contains 30 squares and, with the scales used, has an area figured as $10(\frac{1}{2}) = 5$. Thus

$$I = A = \tfrac{19}{30}(5) = 3.2 \text{ approximately.} \tag{228}$$

Or we may use a planimeter to find the ratio of A to some rectangle. For the theory of the simplest type of planimeter, see Prob. 115 of Exercises IV (page 197).

Results such as we have obtained, which are accurate to within a few per cent, are often useful as checks and are sufficiently accurate for some purposes. The planimeter method, or a refinement of the square counting in which the unit is a square centimeter and fractions are estimated with the help of millimeter rulings, may be made to give slide-rule accuracy or an error less than one-half of 1 per cent. For greater accuracy we may use an arithmetic method such as Simpson's rule, which is described in the next section.

78. Numerical Integration. We shall next consider methods of computing the integral of $f(x)$ based on a table of numerical values of the function. Let the interval from a to b be divided into n equal parts, each of length

$$h = \frac{b - a}{n}. \qquad (229)$$

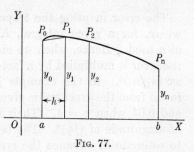

FIG. 77.

Call the ordinates of $y = f(x)$ at the end points and points of subdivision $y_0, y_1, y_2, \cdots, y_n$. If these meet the curve $y = f(x)$ at $P_0, P_1, P_2, \cdots, P_n$, the area under the curve may be approximated by that under the polygonal line whose vertices are at these points. But this area is made up of trapezoids with areas

$$\frac{h}{2}(y_0 + y_1), \qquad \frac{h}{2}(y_1 + y_2), \qquad \cdots, \qquad \frac{h}{2}(y_{n-1} + y_n). \quad (230)$$

Hence the approximating area is

$$A_t = h\left(\frac{y_0}{2} + y_1 + y_2 + \cdots + y_{n-1} + \frac{y_n}{2}\right). \quad (231)$$

This formula for an approximate value of the integral of $f(x)$ from a to b [Eq. (224)] is known as the *trapezoidal rule*.

Let us compute the integral (225), using the trapezoidal rule with $n = 2$ and also with $n = 4$. Here $f(x) = 10 \sin \pi x$. And, since $a = 0$, $b = \frac{1}{2}$, by (229) $h = \frac{1}{4}$ when $n = 2$ and $h = \frac{1}{8}$ when $n = 4$. Using M to denote the multiplier of y_i in (231), we construct the following table.

x	$10 \sin \pi x = y$	$n = 2, h = \frac{1}{4}$		$n = 4, h = \frac{1}{8}$	
		M	My	M	My
0	0	$\frac{1}{2}$	0	$\frac{1}{2}$	0
0.125	3.827			1	3.827
0.25	7.701	1	7.071	1	7.071
0.375	9.239			1	9.239
0.5	10	$\frac{1}{2}$	5	$\frac{1}{2}$	5
			$4\overline{|12.071}$		$8\overline{|25.137}$
			3.018		3.142

The error in using the trapezoidal rule is of the form Kh^2, where, for a given integral, K changes slowly with the value of n used. Hence, when we change from n_1 to n_2 subdivisions, the error is multiplied by a factor that may be roughly estimated as $(n_1/n_2)^2$. In the example just worked out, the errors are found from the exact value given in (225) to be 0.16 when $n = 2$, and 0.04 when $n = 4$. Their ratio is $\frac{1}{4}$ which is of the order of magnitude of $(\frac{1}{2})^2$. The behavior of the error may be used to estimate in advance the error of successive approximations. Thus, suppose we did not know the exact value of the integral in (225) but found as above the values of A_t as 3.018 for $n = 2$ and 3.142 for $n = 4$. If the second value is an improvement on the first, the first has the units figure correct and is in error in the tenths figure. And, if the error of the second is about $(\frac{1}{2})^2$ times that of the first, its error must be in the hundredths place. Thus the correct value is within some hundredths of 3.14 and we should expect a result correct to three figures would result from taking $n = 8$. It is simpler to take $n = 10$, and for this we find $A_t = 3.177$, for which the error is less than one in the hundredths place. The last value could be improved by noting that if 3.177 is relatively correct, the error of 3.142 is 0.035. Thus, the estimated error of the result for $n = 10$ is $(0.035)(\frac{4}{10})^2 = 0.006$. This leads to the improved value $3.177 + 0.006 = 3.183$.

If the number of subdivisions n is *even*, we may approximate the curve $y = f(x)$ of Fig. 77 for each pair of intervals, as $P_0 P_1 P_2$, by a parabolic arc passing through the three points. The area under this parabolic arc, shown in Fig. 78, may be thought of as a trapezoid under the chord P_0P_2 plus the parabolic segment between the parabolic arc and the chord. The area of the trapezoid is

$$Q_0Q_2\tfrac{1}{2}(Q_0P_0 + Q_2P_2) = 2h\tfrac{1}{2}(y_0 + y_2) = h(y_0 + y_2). \quad (232)$$

The area of the parabolic segment is $\tfrac{2}{3}$ the area of the circumscribing parallelogram $P_0P_0'P_2'P_2$ or

$$\frac{2}{3}\,Q_0Q_2 \cdot P_1'P_1 = \frac{2}{3}\,(2h)\left(y_1 - \frac{y_0 + y_2}{2}\right) = \frac{h}{3}\,(4y_1 - 2y_0 - 2y_2),$$
$$(233)$$

since

$$P_1'P_1 = Q_1P_1 - Q_1P_1' = y_1 - \frac{y_0 + y_2}{2}. \quad (234)$$

By adding the right members of Eqs. (232) and (233), we find that the area under the parabolic arc $P_0P_1P_2$ is

$$\frac{h}{3}\,(y_0 + 4y_1 + y_2). \quad (235)$$

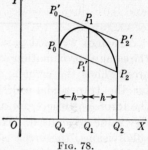

In Fig. 78 the areas of the trapezoid and parabolic segment were positive and were to be added. However, in all cases the correct algebraic area under arc $P_0P_1P_2$ is given by (235).

We may write similar expressions for the areas under parabolic arcs through $P_2P_3P_4$, $P_4P_5P_6$, $\cdots$, $P_{n-2}P_{n-1}P_n$, namely,

$$\frac{h}{3}\,(y_2 + 4y_3 + y_4), \qquad \frac{h}{3}\,(y_4 + 4y_5 + y_6), \qquad \cdots,$$
$$\frac{h}{3}\,(y_{n-2} + 4y_{n-1} + y_n). \quad (236)$$

If we add all the expressions in (235) and (236), we find

$$A_s = \frac{h}{3}\,(y_0 + 4y_1 + 2y_2 + 4y_3 + 2y_4 + \cdots$$
$$+ 2y_{n-2} + 4y_{n-1} + y_n), \quad (237)$$

since each y_i with i odd is a middle ordinate and, except for y_0 and y_n, each y_i with i even is an end ordinate twice. Formula (237) for an approximate value of the integral of $f(x)$ from a to b [Eq. (224)], in which n is necessarily *even*, is known as *Simpson's rule*.

Let us apply Simpson's rule to the integral (225), again taking $n = 2$ and $n = 4$ as we did when illustrating the trapezoidal rule. Here we construct the table:

x	$10 \sin \pi x = y$	$n = 2, h = \frac{1}{4}$		$n = 4, h = \frac{1}{8}$	
		M	My	M	My
0	0	1	0	1	0
0.125	3.8268			4	15.3072
0.25	7.0711	4	28.2844	2	14.1422
0.375	9.2388			4	36.9552
0.5	10	1	10	1	10
		12	38.2844	24	76.4046
			3.1904		3.1835

Although we used parabolic arcs in deriving Simpson's rule, the same approximation would have been obtained by using cubic arcs. Thus the error is of an order in h two higher than that for the trapezoidal rule. For Simpson's rule the error is of the form Kh^4 where, for a given integral, K changes slowly with the value of n used. Hence, when we change from n_1 to n_2 subdivisions, the error is multiplied by a factor that may be roughly estimated as $(n_1/n_2)^4$. In the example just worked out, the errors are found from the exact value given in (225) to be -0.0073 when $n = 2$, and -0.0004 when $n = 4$. Their ratio is $\frac{1}{18}$ which is of the order of magnitude of $(\frac{1}{2})^4$. The behavior of the error may be used to estimate in advance the error of successive approximations. Thus, suppose we did not know the exact value of the integral (225) but found as above the values of A_s as 3.1904 for $n = 2$ and 3.1835 for $n = 4$. If the second value is an improvement on the first, the first has only a slight error in the hundredths figure. And, if the error of the second is about $(\frac{1}{2})^4$ times that of the first, its error must be in excess and either in the last figure, or a small error in the one before the last. Thus the correct value is within 0.001

of 3.183. We could improve this by assuming 3.1835 as relatively correct and so calculating the error of 3.1904 as -0.0069. From this we estimate the error for $n = 4$ as

$$(\tfrac{1}{2})^4(-0.0069) = -0.0004,$$

which added to 3.1835 gives 3.1831 as probably correct to within 1 in the last place. With $n = 8$, we should expect to get directly a result correct to four decimal places. It is simpler to take $n = 10$, and for this we find $A_s = 3.18312$. This has a last figure only 2 in excess of the correct value, which is not surprising, since we would have estimated the error in advance as

$$(\tfrac{4}{10})^4(-0.0004) = -0.00001.$$

With the same number of subdivisions, Simpson's rule is always more accurate than the trapezoidal rule, and the advantage is greater the smaller the value of h used. Thus Simpson's rule is preferable whenever great accuracy is needed. The trapezoidal rule is chiefly used when the sum of the ordinates has already been calculated for some other purpose. If the ordinates are tabulated for an odd number of intervals, say $2m = 1$, each of length H, we may use Simpson's rule for the first $2m$ intervals with $n = 2m$ and $h = H$. And for the last interval from y_{2m} to y_{2m+1}, we may either use the trapezoidal rule or interpolate one more value $y_{2m+\frac{1}{2}}$ and use Simpson's rule with $n = 2$, $h = H/2$. In interpolating for $y_{2m+\frac{1}{2}}$ we must either use higher differences or graphical methods, since linear interpolation would lead to the same result as using a single trapezoid.

79. References. Throughout this chapter we have frequently referred to tables of integrals. Besides the tables of this type to be found in most handbooks and many elementary texts on calculus, we may in particular recommend B. O. Peirce's *Short Table of Integrals* and H. B. Dwight's *Tables of Integrals and Other Mathematical Data* as being especially comprehensive.

The reader interested in theoretical questions connected with the material of this chapter is referred to the author's *Treatise on Advanced Calculus*, where he will find proper integrals discussed in Chaps. VI, VII, and XI, and improper integrals and convergence questions discussed in Chaps. VIII, IX, and XII.

EXERCISES IV

1. Show that $\int_0^a f(x)dx = \int_0^a f(a-x)dx$. And in particular $\int_0^{\pi/2} F(\sin x)dx = \int_0^{\pi/2} F(\cos x)dx$, $\int_0^\pi F(\cos x)dx = \int_0^\pi F(-\cos x)dx$.

2. If $f(x) = f(-x)$, $f(x)$ is called an *even* function. Show that for an even function $\int_{-a}^0 f(x)dx = \int_0^a f(x)dx = \frac{1}{2}\int_{-a}^a f(x)dx$.

3. If $f(x) = x^4 + 3x^2 + 1$ and $a = 2$, verify the relations of Prob. 2 by calculating each integral directly.

4. If $F(u)$ is any single-valued function of u, show that each of the functions $F(x^2)$, $F(\cos x)$, and $F(\sin^2 x)$ is an even function of x.

5. If $f(x) = -f(-x)$, $f(x)$ is called an *odd* function. Show that for an odd function $\int_{-a}^0 f(x)dx = -\int_0^a f(x)dx$ and $\int_{-a}^a f(x)dx = 0$.

6. If $f(x) = x^3 - 2x$ and $a = 2$, verify the relations of Prob. 5 by calculating each integral directly.

7. If $F(u)$ is any single-valued function of u, show that each of the functions $xF(x^2)$, $\sin x\, F(\cos x)$, and $\tan x\, F(\sin^2 x)$ is an odd function of x.

8. If $f(x + T) = f(x)$, $f(x)$ is called a *periodic* function having T as a period. Show that for any such function and any positive integer n $\int_a^{a+T} f(x)dx = \int_0^T f(x)dx$ for an interval of one complete period, while $\int_a^{a+nT} f(x)dx = \int_0^{nT} f(x)dx = n\int_0^T f(x)dx$, for n periods.

9. If $f(x) = \sin x$, $a = 2$, $T = 2\pi$, and $n = 7$, verify the relations of Prob. 8 by calculating each integral directly.

10. If $F(u)$ is any single-valued function of u, show that $F(\sin x)$ and $F(\cos x)$ each have the period 2π. And if $F(u)$ is an even function, $F(\sin x)$ and $F(\cos x)$ each have the period π.

Find dI/du, using Eq. (48) and check by integrating first:

11. $\int_{u^2}^{3u^2} (x^2 + u^4)dx$.   **12.** $\int_0^{\sqrt{u}} (x + \sqrt{u})dx$.

13. If $I(c) = \int_{a/c}^{b/c} \dfrac{f(cx)}{x}\, dx$, where a and b are independent of c, show that $dI/dc = 0$. HINT: Use Eq. (48) or make the substitution $cx = t$.

14. Find dI/dc if $I(c) = \int_{\pi/(2c)}^{\pi/c} \dfrac{\sin cx}{x}\, dx$. See hint to Prob. 13.

15. If $I(a) = \int_0^x f(ax)dx$, show that $\dfrac{dI}{da} = \dfrac{xf(ax) - I(a)}{a}$. HINT: Use Eq. (44) and then integrate by parts, or else make the substitution $ax = t$ in the integral before using (44).

As illustrations of Prob. 15, find dI/da if

16. $I(a) = \int_0^x \tan^{-1} ax \, dx.$ **17.** $I(a) = \int_0^x \sin^{-1} ax \, dx.$

Evaluate each of the following indefinite integrals:

18. $\int \dfrac{6 \, dx}{x^3 - x}.$ **19.** $\int \dfrac{x \, dx}{(x^2 + 1)(x - 1)}.$ **20.** $\int \dfrac{4 \, dx}{x^4 + x^2}.$

21. $\int \dfrac{x^2 + 1}{(x - 1)^4} \, dx.$ **22.** $\int \dfrac{x^3 dx}{(x^2 + 4)(x - 1)^2}.$

Derive each of the following integration formulas:

23. $\int \dfrac{(cx + d)dx}{(x - a)(x - b)} = \dfrac{ac + d}{a - b} \log |x - a| + \dfrac{bc + d}{b - a} \log |x - b|,$ $a \neq b.$

24. $\int \dfrac{(cx + d)dx}{(x - a)^2} = -\dfrac{ac + d}{x - a} + c \log |x - a|.$

25. $\int \dfrac{(cx + d)dx}{(x - a)^2 + b^2} = \dfrac{c}{2} \log [(x - a)^2 + b^2]$

$$+ \dfrac{ac + d}{b} \tan^{-1} \dfrac{x - a}{b},\qquad b \neq 0.$$

In Probs. 26 to 33, $X = ax^2 + bx + c$ with $a \neq 0$.

26. $\int \dfrac{dx}{\sqrt{X}} = \dfrac{-1}{\sqrt{-a}} \sin^{-1} \dfrac{2ax + b}{\sqrt{b^2 - 4ac}},$ $a < 0.$

27. $\int \dfrac{dx}{\sqrt{X}} = \dfrac{1}{\sqrt{a}} \log \left| ax + \dfrac{b}{2} + \sqrt{aX} \right|,$ $a > 0.$

28. Deduce the formula of Prob. 26 from that of Prob. 27 by writing $a = -q^2$, $\sqrt{a} = iq$, omitting the absolute value signs and interpreting the logarithm of a complex quantity as in Sec. 5.

29. Show that when r is real the problem of evaluating $\dfrac{dx}{(x - r)\sqrt{X}}$ may be reduced to an integral in t of the type of Probs. 26 and 27 by the substitution $x = r + 1/t$. Hence deduce the result stated in Prob. 30.

30. With $S = ar^2 + br + c$, $T = 2ar + b$, $U = br + 2c$, show that

$$\int \dfrac{dx}{(x - r)\sqrt{X}} = \dfrac{1}{\sqrt{-S}} \sin^{-1} \dfrac{Tx + U}{(x - r)\sqrt{b^2 - 4ac}},\qquad S < 0,$$

and

$$\int \dfrac{dx}{(x - r)\sqrt{X}} = \dfrac{1}{\sqrt{S}} \log \left| \dfrac{Tx + U - 2\sqrt{SX}}{(x - r)} \right|,\qquad S > 0.$$

HINT: Use Prob. 29, and note that $T^2 - 4aS = b^2 - 4ac.$

31. Show that, if r is complex, the sum of the conjugate complex terms

$$k \int \dfrac{dx}{(x - r)\sqrt{X}} + \bar{k} \int \dfrac{dx}{(x - \bar{r})\sqrt{X}} = 2\mathbf{R}k \int \dfrac{dx}{(x - r)\sqrt{X}} \text{ is a real}$$

quantity which may be found by using the last formula of Prob. 30, omitting the absolute value signs, and interpreting the logarithm as in Sec. 5.

32. Verify that, if $X = ax^2 + bx + c$,

$$\frac{d}{dx}\left(x^{n-1}\sqrt{X}\right) = \frac{anx^n + b(n - \frac{1}{2})x^{n-1} + c(n - 1)x^{n-2}}{\sqrt{X}},$$

so that the integral of the left member, $x^{n-1}\sqrt{X}$

$$= an\int\frac{x^n}{\sqrt{X}}\,dx + b\left(n - \frac{1}{2}\right)\int\frac{x^{n-1}}{\sqrt{X}}\,dx + c(n - 1)\int\frac{x^{n-2}}{\sqrt{X}}\,dx.$$

Use this to deduce the reduction formula (105) of the text.

33. Verify that, if $X = ax^2 + bx + c$, $S = ar^2 + br + c$, $T = 2ar + b$,

$$\frac{d}{dx}\left[\frac{\sqrt{X}}{(x - r)^m}\right] = \frac{-a(m - 1)}{(x - r)^{m-1}\sqrt{X}} - \frac{(m - \frac{1}{2})T}{(x - r)^m\sqrt{X}} - \frac{mS}{(x - r)^{m+1}\sqrt{X}},$$

so that

$$\frac{\sqrt{X}}{(x - r)^m} = -a(m - 1)\int\frac{dx}{(x - r)^{m-1}\sqrt{X}}$$
$$- \left(m - \frac{1}{2}\right)T\int\frac{dx}{(x - r)^m\sqrt{X}} - mS\int\frac{dx}{(x - r)^{m+1}\sqrt{X}}.$$

Use this, with $S = 0$ and $m = k$, to deduce formula (108) of the text; and, with $S \neq 0$ and $m = k - 1$, to deduce (107) of the text.

34. Show that the integral $\displaystyle\int\frac{dx}{a + b\cos x + c\sin x}$ is equal to

$$\frac{2}{\sqrt{a^2 - b^2 - c^2}}\tan^{-1}\left[\frac{c + (a - b)\tan\frac{x}{2}}{\sqrt{a^2 - b^2 - c^2}}\right],$$ if $a^2 > b^2 + c^2$; and to

$$\frac{1}{\sqrt{b^2 + c^2 - a^2}}\log\left|\frac{\sqrt{b^2 + c^2 - a^2} - c - (a - b)\tan\frac{x}{2}}{\sqrt{b^2 + c^2 - a^2} + c + (a - b)\tan\frac{x}{2}}\right|,$$

if $a^2 < b^2 + c^2$.

35. Show that if $a^2 = b^2 + c^2$ and $a \neq b$, the integral of Prob. 34 is equal to $\displaystyle\frac{-2}{c + (a - b)\tan\frac{x}{2}}$. If $a^2 = b^2 + c^2$ and $a = b$, so that $c = 0$

the integral is $\displaystyle\int\frac{dx}{a + a\cos x} = \frac{1}{a}\tan\frac{x}{2}$.

36. By taking real and imaginary parts of

$$\int e^{(a+bi)x}dx = \frac{e^{(a+bi)x}}{a+bi},$$

deduce the indefinite integrals

$$\int e^{ax} \cos bx \, dx = \frac{e^{ax}(a \cos bx + b \sin bx)}{a^2 + b^2}$$

and

$$\int e^{ax} \sin bx \, dx = \frac{e^{ax}(a \sin bx - b \cos bx)}{a^2 + b^2}.$$

37. By considering the integrand or indefinite integral near $x = 0$, show that $\int_{-1}^{1} (4 + 1/x^2)dx$ diverges. Thus the "area" under the arc $y = 4 + 1/x^2$, between -1 and 1 is infinite. Note that a simple-minded use of the indefinite integral would lead to an incorrect conclusion, since $4x - \dfrac{1}{x} \Big|_{-1}^{1} = 6$.

38. The double integral $\int_R \rho(r,\theta)r \, dr \, d\theta$ represents the mass of a plate if $\rho(r,\theta)$ is the density, or mass per unit area, in terms of polar coordinates. Find the mass of a plate in the form of a triangle with vertices at $(r,\theta) = (0,0)$, $(1,0)$, and $(\sqrt{2}, \pi/4)$ if its density is $\rho = 12r^2$.

39. Check Prob. 38 by using Cartesian coordinates. The mass is now $\int_R \rho(x,y)dx \, dy$, the density $\rho = 12(x^2 + y^2)$, and the vertices $(x,y) = (0,0)$, $(1,0)$, and $(1,1)$.

40. Let M_x and M_y denote the moments of a plate about the x and y axes. Then $M_x = \int_R y\rho \, dx \, dy$ and $M_y = \int_R x\rho \, dx \, dy$. Find these for the plate of Prob. 39. Hence find its center of gravity $(\bar{x},\bar{y})$ from $\bar{x} = M_y/M$ and $\bar{y} = M_x/M$.

41. The moments M_x and M_y of Prob. 40, in terms of polar coordinates, are $M_x = \int_R \rho r^2 \sin \theta \, dr \, d\theta$, $M_y = \int_R \rho r^2 \cos \theta \, dr \, d\theta$. Use these to check the values found in Prob. 40.

42. Let I_x, I_y, and I_0 denote the moments of inertia of a plate about the x, y, and z axes. Then $I_x = \int_R \rho y^2 dx \, dy$, $I_y = \int_R \rho x^2 dx \, dy$, $I_0 = \int_R \rho(x^2 + y^2)dx \, dy = I_x + I_y$. Compute I_x, I_y, and I_0 for the plate of Prob. 39.

43. The moments of inertia of Prob. 42, in terms of polar coordinates, are $I_x = \int_R \rho r^3 \sin^2 \theta \, dr \, d\theta$, $I_y = \int_R \rho r^3 \cos^2 \theta \, dr \, d\theta$, $I_0 = \int_R \rho r^3 dr \, d\theta$. Use these to check the values found in Prob. 42.

44. A plate formed of that quarter of the circle $x^2 + y^2 = 4$ for which $x \geqq 0$ and $y \geqq 0$ has its density $\rho = 1$. Find its center of gravity $(\bar{x}, \bar{y})$. See Probs. 41 and 40.

45. Find the moments of inertia I_x, I_y, I_0 for the plate of Prob. 44. See Prob. 43.

46. The total water pressure on a gate, filling the region R of a vertical xy plane, is $P = \displaystyle\int_R wy\, dx\, dy$. The x axis is in the water level, the y axis is downward, and $w = 62.5$ lb./ft.[3] Show that $P = wM_x = wM\bar{y}$, where $M\bar{y} = M_x$ has the meaning of Prob. 40 for a plate covering R of density $\rho = 1$. Find the pressure on a vertical circle of radius 2 ft. whose center is 4 ft. below the surface of the water. Strictly speaking, P is the total force on one side of R due to liquid pressure, or force per unit area.

47. Let F_y denote the component parallel to the y axis of the attractive force of a plate on a particle of mass m at the origin. The value of $F_y = m\gamma \displaystyle\int_R \frac{\rho y}{(x^2 + y^2)^{3/2}}\, dx\, dy$. Show that in polar coordinates this is $F_y = m\gamma \displaystyle\int_R \frac{\rho \sin\theta}{r}\, dr\, d\theta$.

48. A plate formed of that half of the circle $x^2 + y^2 = 2ay$ for which $y \geqq a$ has its density $\rho = k$, a constant. Find the attractive force of this plate on a particle of mass m at the origin. See Prob. 47 for F_y and note that $F_x = 0$.

49. Compute the volume of that octant of the sphere of radius a $x^2 + y^2 + z^2 = a^2$ for which $x \geqq 0$, $y \geqq 0$, $z \geqq 0$ by using the triple integral $V = \int dx\, dy\, dz$.

50. Compute the volume of Prob. 49 by using the triple integral $\int r^2 \sin\phi\, d\theta\, d\phi\, dr$. See Sec. 59.

51. Compute the volume of Prob. 49 by using the double integral $V = \int z\, dx\, dy$.

52. Compute the volume of Prob. 49 by using the double integral $V = \int zr\, dr\, d\theta$.

53. Let M_z denote the moment of a solid of density ρ with respect to the xy plane whose equation is $z = 0$. Then $M_z = \int \rho z\, dx\, dy\, dz$. Show that, in the coordinates of Probs. 50 to 52,

$$M_z = \int \rho r^3 \cos\phi \sin\phi\, d\theta\, d\phi\, dr = \int \frac{\rho}{2} z^2 dx\, dy = \int \frac{\rho}{2} z^2 r\, dr\, d\theta.$$

54. A solid of uniform density $\rho = k$ covers that half of the sphere $x^2 + y^2 + z^2 = a^2$ for which $z \geqq 0$. Find M_z from the last expression in Prob. 53. Hence, find its center of gravity $(0,0,\bar{z})$ from $\bar{z} = M_z/M$, where $M = \int \rho\, dV$, or kV, since $\rho = k$.

55. By successive differentiation of $\int_0^\infty e^{-ax}dx = 1/a$ with respect to a, deduce that $\int_0^\infty x^n e^{-ax}dx = n!/a^{n+1}$, for n any positive integer.

56. By successive differentiation of $\int_0^1 x^b dx = 1/(b+1)$ with respect to b, deduce that $\int_0^1 x^b (\log x)^n dx = (-1)^n n!/(b+1)^{n+1}$, for n any positive integer.

57. Check the result of Prob. 56 by applying the substitution $e^{-x} = t$ to the result of Prob. 55 and putting $a = b + 1$.

58. From $\int_0^1 x^u dx = \dfrac{1}{u+1}$, by integration with respect to u, show that $\int_0^1 \dfrac{x^d - x^c}{\log x} dx = \log \dfrac{d+1}{c+1}$, if $d > c > -1$.

59. Check Prob. 58 by applying the substitution $e^{-x} = t$ to the integral of Eq. (207) of the text and putting $a = c + 1$, $b = d + 1$.

60. It follows from Prob. 34 that $\int_0^\pi \dfrac{dx}{a - \cos x} = \dfrac{\pi}{\sqrt{a^2 - 1}}$, if $a > 1$. By differentiating with respect to a, show that the integral $\int_0^\pi \dfrac{dx}{(a - \cos x)^2} = \dfrac{\pi a}{(a^2 - 1)^{3/2}}$, if $a > 1$.

61. Show that $\int_0^\infty \dfrac{dx}{x^2 + a^2} = \dfrac{\pi}{2a}$, if $a > 0$. By differentiation with respect to a, deduce that $\int_0^\infty \dfrac{dx}{(x^2 + a^2)^2} = \dfrac{\pi}{4a^3}$, if $a > 0$.

62. By repeating the procedure of Prob. 61 n times, show also that $\int_0^\infty \dfrac{dx}{(x^2 + a^2)^n} = \dfrac{\pi}{2a^{2n-1}} \dfrac{1 \cdot 3 \cdot 5 \cdots (2n-3)}{2 \cdot 4 \cdot 6 \cdots (2n-2)}$, $a > 0$, n a positive integer.

63. By putting $x = a \tan t$ in the integral of Prob. 62 and suitably changing the notation, show that for n a positive integer, the integral $\int_0^{\pi/2} \cos^{2n} x \, dx = \dfrac{\pi}{2} \dfrac{1 \cdot 3 \cdot 5 \cdots (2n-1)}{2 \cdot 4 \cdot 6 \cdots 2n}$.

64. Show that $\int_0^\infty \dfrac{dx}{(x^2 + a^2)^{3/2}} = \dfrac{1}{a^2}$. By differentiation with respect to a, deduce that $\int_0^\infty \dfrac{dx}{(x^2 + a^2)^{5/2}} = \dfrac{2}{3a^4}$.

65. By repeating the procedure of Prob. 64 n times, show that $\int_0^\infty \dfrac{dx}{(x^2 + a^2)^{n+1/2}} = \dfrac{1}{a^{2n}} \dfrac{2 \cdot 4 \cdot 6 \cdots (2n-2)}{3 \cdot 5 \cdot 7 \cdots (2n-1)}$, n a positive integer.

66. By putting $x = a \tan t$ in the integral of Prob. 65 and suitably changing the notation, show that for n a positive integer, the integral $\int_0^{\pi/2} \cos^{2n+1} x \, dx = \dfrac{2 \cdot 4 \cdot 6 \cdots 2n}{3 \cdot 5 \cdot 7 \cdots (2n+1)}$.

67. By Prob. 1, $\int_0^{\pi/2} \sin^m x \, dx = \int_0^{\pi/2} \cos^m x \, dx$. Show that this leads to the evaluation when m is any positive integer by using Prob. 63 for m even and Prob. 66 for m odd.

68. From $\int_0^\infty \dfrac{dx}{1 + u^2x^2} = \dfrac{\pi}{2u}$, $u > 0$, by integration with respect to u, deduce that $\int_0^\infty \dfrac{\tan^{-1} bx - \tan^{-1} ax}{x} \, dx = \dfrac{\pi}{2} \log \dfrac{b}{a}$, $b > a > 0$.

69. Using Prob. 36, evaluate the two following improper integrals $\int_0^\infty e^{-ax} \cos bx \, dx = \dfrac{a}{a^2 + b^2}$, $\int_0^\infty e^{-ax} \sin bx \, dx = \dfrac{b}{a^2 + b^2}$, $a > 0$.

70. From Prob. 69, by differentiation with respect to a, show that

$$\int_0^\infty xe^{-ax} \cos bx \, dx = \frac{a^2 - b^2}{(a^2 + b^2)^2}, \qquad a > 0, \text{ and}$$

$$\int_0^\infty xe^{-ax} \sin bx \, dx = \frac{2ab}{(a^2 + b^2)^2}, \qquad a > 0.$$

71. Check the results of Prob. 70 by differentiation of the relations of Prob. 69 with respect to b.

72. From Prob. 69, by integrating with respect to a from $a = 0$ to $a = c$, deduce that if $c > 0$ and $b > 0$,

$$\int_0^\infty \frac{(1 - e^{-cx}) \cos bx}{x} \, dx = \frac{1}{2} \log \frac{c^2 + b^2}{b^2}, \text{ and}$$

$$\int_0^\infty \frac{(1 - e^{-cx}) \sin bx}{x} \, dx = \frac{\pi}{2} - \tan^{-1} \frac{b}{c}.$$

73. From Prob. 69, by integrating with respect to b from p to q, show that $\int_0^\infty \dfrac{e^{-ax} (\sin qx - \sin px)}{x} \, dx = \tan^{-1} \dfrac{q}{a} - \tan^{-1} \dfrac{p}{a}$, and also that $\int_0^\infty \dfrac{e^{-ax} (\cos qx - \cos px)}{x} \, dx = \dfrac{1}{2} \log \dfrac{a^2 + p^2}{a^2 + q^2}$. Assume $q > p \geqq 0$.

74. If $a \to 0$, the second equation of Prob. 73 assumes the form $\int_0^\infty \dfrac{\cos qx - \cos px}{x} \, dx = \log \dfrac{p}{q}$. Combine this with the first equation of Prob. 72 written first with $c = r$, $b = p$ and then with $c = s$, $b = q$ to deduce $\int_0^\infty \dfrac{e^{-rx} \cos px - e^{-sx} \cos qx}{x} \, dx = \dfrac{1}{2} \log \dfrac{s^2 + q^2}{r^2 + p^2}$.

75. With $p = 0$, the first equation of Prob. 73 is simplified to $\int_0^\infty \dfrac{e^{-ax} \sin qx}{x} \, dx = \tan^{-1} \dfrac{q}{a}$. By letting $a \to 0$, deduce further that $\int_0^\infty \dfrac{\sin qx}{x} \, dx = \dfrac{\pi}{2}$ if $q > 0$, $= 0$ if $q = 0$, and $= -\dfrac{\pi}{2}$ if $q < 0$.

76. Let $I(q) = \int_0^\infty \frac{\sin qx}{x}\, dx$. Show that the derivative dI/dq cannot be found by using Eq. (44), since $\int_0^\infty \sin qx\, dx$ is divergent and we have possibility 1. But, by using the values found in Prob. 75, show that if $q \neq 0$, $dI/dq = 0$.

77. Show that $\int_0^\infty \frac{\sin ax \cos bx}{x}\, dx = \frac{\pi}{2}$, if $a > |b|$, $\frac{\pi}{4}$ if $a = |b|$, and $= 0$ if $a < |b|$. Hint: Use Prob. 75.

78. Show that $\int_0^\infty \frac{\sin^2 ax}{x^2}\, dx = |a|\frac{\pi}{2}$. Hint: Integrate by parts and use Prob. 75.

79. Using the method or result of Prob. 78, show that the integral $\int_0^\infty \frac{\cos ax - \cos bx}{x^2}\, dx = (|b| - |a|)\frac{\pi}{2}$.

80. Show that $\int_0^\infty \frac{a \sin x - \sin ax}{x^2}\, dx = a \log |a|$. Hint: Integrate by parts and use Prob. 74.

81. Let $N(x)$ be expressible as a sum of terms, each of the form $Ae^{-rx} \sin ax$ or $Be^{-sx} \cos bx$, with $r \geqq 0$ and $s \geqq 0$. Suppose $N(x)$ is such that the integral $\int_0^\infty \frac{N(x)}{x^n}\, dx$ converges for some particular integer n greater than one. Show that this integral may be evaluated by integrating by parts n times and using the results of Probs. 74 and 75. Problems 78 to 80 are illustrations.

82. Let V denote the volume in the first octant ($x \geqq 0$, $y \geqq 0$, $z \geqq 0$) bounded above the surface $z = e^{-x^2-y^2}$. Show that the volume

$$V = \int z\, dx\, dy = \int_0^\infty dx \int_0^\infty e^{-x^2-y^2} dy = \int_0^\infty e^{-x^2} dx \int_0^\infty e^{-y^2} dy$$

$$= \left(\int_0^\infty e^{-x^2} dx\right)^2.$$ And in polar coordinates the value of the volume is

$$V = \int zr\, dr\, d\theta = \int_0^{\pi/2} d\theta \int_0^\infty e^{-r^2} r\, dr = \pi/4.$$ Use these relations to deduce that $\int_0^\infty e^{-x^2} dx = \sqrt{\pi}/2$.

83. Show that $\int_0^1 \frac{dx}{\sqrt{|\log x|}} = \sqrt{\pi}$. Hint: Put $x = e^{-t^2}$ and use Prob. 82.

84. Show that $\int_0^\infty e^{-ax^2} dx = \sqrt{\pi}/(2\sqrt{a})$, $a > 0$. Hint: Substitute $x = t/\sqrt{a}$ and use Prob. 82.

85. By differentiation of the integral of Prob. 84 with respect to a, deduce that $\int_0^\infty x^2 e^{-ax^2} dx = \frac{\sqrt{\pi}}{4a\sqrt{a}}$, $a > 0$.

86. By repeating the procedure of Prob. 85 n times, show that
$$\int_0^\infty x^{2n}e^{-ax^2}dx = \frac{\sqrt{\pi}}{\sqrt{a}}\frac{1\cdot 3\cdot 5\cdots(2n-1)}{2^{n+1}a^n}, \; n \text{ a positive integer.}$$

87. For a Gaussian or normal distribution, the frequency of an error x is $ke^{-h^2x^2}$. This means that the probability of an error x falling between a and b is $\int_a^b ke^{-h^2x^2}dx$. The probability of an error of some size is certainty. This leads to the relation $\int_{-\infty}^\infty ke^{-h^2x^2}dx = 1$. From this relation, Probs. 84 and 2 show that $k = h/\sqrt{\pi}$.

88. With the notation of Prob. 87, the mean square error is defined by $\mu^2 = \int_{-\infty}^\infty x^2ke^{-h^2x^2}dx$, where $k = h/\sqrt{\pi}$. From these relations, Probs. 85 and 2 show that $\mu = 1/(h\sqrt{2})$.

89. The error function of x, erf x, is usually defined by the equation erf $x = \dfrac{2}{\sqrt{\pi}}\int_0^x e^{-t^2}dt$. With the notation of Prob. 87, the probability of an error falling between $-c$ and c is $P_c = \int_{-c}^c \dfrac{h}{\sqrt{\pi}}e^{-h^2x^2}dx$. By putting $hx = t$ and using Prob. 2, show that $P_c = \text{erf } (ch)$. Most mathematical tables include values of the error function, computed from the series found in Prob. 68 of Exercises I (page 42) or for large values from Prob. 90 which follows. The probable error ϵ is defined as the number such that the probability of an error falling between $-\epsilon$ and ϵ is $\dfrac{1}{2}$. Show that $\dfrac{1}{2} = \text{erf } \epsilon h$, so that $\epsilon h = \text{erf}^{-1} 0.5 = 0.4769$, from the tables. Thus $\epsilon = 0.4769/h$.

90. By successive integration by parts, derive the asymptotic series
$$\int_x^\infty e^{-x^2}dx = e^{-x^2}\left(\frac{1}{2x} - \frac{1}{2^2x^3} + \frac{1\cdot 3}{2^3x^5} - \frac{1\cdot 3\cdot 5}{2^4x^7} + \cdots\right).$$
From Probs. 89 and 82 deduce that erf $x = 1 - \dfrac{2}{\sqrt{\pi}}\int_x^\infty e^{-x^2}dx$, so that the asymptotic series of this problem enables us to compute erf x easily when x is large compared with unity.

91. From Prob. 84, by integrating with respect to a from p to q, show that $\int_0^\infty \dfrac{e^{-px^2} - e^{-qx^2}}{x^2}dx = (\sqrt{q} - \sqrt{p})\sqrt{\pi}, \; q > p > 0$.

92. Show that $\int_0^\infty e^{-x^2-(a^2/x^2)}dx = \dfrac{\sqrt{\pi}}{2}e^{-2a}$. HINT: Let the integral be $I(a)$. Find dI/da and from the substitution $x = a/t$ in the resulting integral deduce that $dI/da = -2I$, so that $d(\log I)/da = -2$ and $I = ke^{-2a}$. Finally, evaluate k by putting $a = 0$ and using Prob. 82.

93. Show that $\int_0^\infty e^{-x^2} \cos ax\, dx = \frac{\sqrt{\pi}}{2} e^{-a^2/4}$. HINT: Let the integral be $I(a)$. Find dI/da and by integrating the resulting integral by parts deduce that $dI/da = -\frac{a}{2} I$. Then proceed as in Prob. 92.

94. Show that $\int_0^\infty xe^{-x^2} \sin ax\, dx = a \frac{\sqrt{\pi}}{4} e^{-a^2/4}$. HINT: Use Prob. 93 and differentiate with respect to a.

95. Show that $\int_0^{\pi/2} \log \sin x\, dx = -\frac{\pi}{2} \log 2$. HINT: By Prob. 1,

$$I = \int_0^{\pi/2} \log \sin x\, dx = \int_0^{\pi/2} \log \cos x\, dx.$$ Hence the integral

$$J = \int_0^{\pi/2} \log \sin 2x\, dx = \int_0^{\pi/2} (\log \sin x + \log \cos x + \log 2)dx \text{ or}$$

$= 2I + \frac{\pi}{2} \log 2$. But if we make the subsitution $t = x + \frac{\pi}{2}$, we find that

$$\int_{\pi/2}^\pi \log \sin t\, dt = \int_0^{\pi/2} \log \cos x\, dx = I. \text{ And if we place } x = \frac{t}{2},$$

$$J = \frac{1}{2} \int_0^\pi \log \sin t\, dt = \frac{1}{2} \left(\int_0^{\pi/2} \log \sin t\, dt + \int_{\pi/2}^\pi \log \sin t\, dt \right) \text{ or}$$

$= \frac{1}{2} (2I) = I$. Thus $2I + \frac{\pi}{2} \log 2 = J = I$, and $I = -\frac{\pi}{2} \log 2$.

96. Show that $\int_0^\pi x \log \sin x\, dx = -\frac{\pi^2}{2} \log 2$. HINT: If $x = \pi - t$,

$$K = \int_0^\pi x \log \sin x\, dx = \int_0^\pi (\pi - t) \log \sin t\, dt = 2\pi I - K, \text{ where } I$$

is the integral of Prob. 95, so that $K = 2\pi I - K$ and $K = \pi I$.

97. Show that $\int_0^\pi \log (a + b \cos x)dx = \pi \log \frac{a + \sqrt{a^2 - b^2}}{2}$, $a > |b|$.

HINT: Differentiate with respect to a, use Prob. 34 to obtain the result

$$\int_0^\pi \frac{dx}{a + b \cos x} = \frac{\pi}{\sqrt{a^2 - b^2}},$$ then integrate with respect to a and deter-

mine the constant by subtracting $\int_0^\pi \log a\, dx = \pi \log a$ to deduce that

$$\int_0^\pi \log \left(1 + \frac{b}{a} \cos x \right) dx = \pi \log \left(1 + \sqrt{1 + \frac{b^2}{a^2}} \right) + C, \text{ and letting}$$

$a \to \infty$.

98. Show that $\int_{-\pi/2}^{\pi/2} \log (a + b \sin x)dx = \pi \log \frac{a + \sqrt{a^2 - b^2}}{2}$, if

$a > |b|$. HINT: Use the method of Prob. 97, or else put $x = \frac{\pi}{2} - t$ in the result of that problem.

99. Show that $\int_0^\pi \log (p^2 + q^2 + 2pq \cos x)dx = 2\pi \log |p|$, if $|p| < |q|$, and $2\pi \log |q|$, if $|q| > |p|$.   HINT: Use Prob. 97.

100. The relations of Prob. 99 suggest that if $q = p$, or $q = -p$, the value of the integral is $2\pi \log |p|$.   Check this by showing that

$$\int_0^\pi \log (2p^2 + 2p^2 \cos x)dx = 4 \int_0^{\pi/2} \log (2 |p| \cos t)dt \text{ and}$$

$$\int_0^\pi \log (2p^2 - 2p^2 \cos x)dx = 4 \int_0^{\pi/2} \log (2 |p| \sin t)dt$$

when $x = 2t$, and using Prob. 95.

101. Show that $\int_0^\pi \dfrac{\log (1 + b \cos x)}{\cos x} dx = \pi \sin^{-1} b$, $|b| < 1$.   HINT: Differentiate with respect to b and use Prob. 34.   Then integrate with respect to b and put $b = 0$ to determine the constant.

102. Show that $\int_0^{\pi/2} \log \left(\dfrac{1 + b \sin x}{1 - b \sin x}\right) \dfrac{dx}{\sin x} =$

$\int_{-\pi/2}^{\pi/2} \dfrac{\log (1 + b \sin x)}{\sin x} dx = \pi \sin^{-1} b$, $|b| < 1$.   HINT: Use the method or result of Prob. 101.

By successive integration by parts, derive the following asymptotic series:

103. $\int_x^\infty \sin x^2 dx = \dfrac{\cos x^2}{2x} + \dfrac{\sin x^2}{2^2 x^3} - \dfrac{3 \cos x^2}{2^3 x^5} - \dfrac{3 \cdot 5 \sin x^2}{2^4 x^7} + \cdots$

104. $\int_x^\infty \cos x^2 dx = - \dfrac{\sin x^2}{2x} + \dfrac{\cos x^2}{2^2 x^3} + \dfrac{3 \sin x^2}{2^3 x^5} - \dfrac{3 \cdot 5 \cos x^2}{2^4 x^7} - \cdots$

105. $\int_x^\infty \dfrac{\sin x}{x} dx = \dfrac{\cos x}{x} + \dfrac{\sin x}{x^2} - \dfrac{2! \cos x}{x^3} - \dfrac{3! \sin x}{x^4} + \cdots$

106. $\int_x^\infty \dfrac{\cos x}{x} dx = - \dfrac{\sin x}{x} + \dfrac{\cos x}{x^2} + \dfrac{2! \sin x}{x^3} - \dfrac{3! \cos x}{x^4} - \cdots$

107. Show that $\int_0^{\pi/2} \log \dfrac{\sin x}{x} dx = \dfrac{\pi}{2} (1 - \log \pi)$.   HINT: The integral $= \int_0^{\pi/2} \log \sin x \, dx - \int_0^{\pi/2} \log x \, dx$.   See Prob. 95 for the first integral and Sec. 70 for the second.

Compute an approximate value of each of the following integrals by using Simpson's rule, with $n = 10$.   Compare your results with the numerical values found by the alternative method indicated.

108. $\int_1^2 \dfrac{dx}{x} = \log 2 = 0.69315$, from the indefinite integral.

109. $\int_0^1 \dfrac{dx}{1 + x^2} = \dfrac{\pi}{4} = 0.785398$, from the indefinite integral.

110. $\int_0^1 e^{-x^2}dx = 0.74682$, from Prob. 72 of Exercises I (page 42).

111. $\int_0^1 \sin x^2 dx = 0.3103$, from Prob. 73 of Exercises I (page 42).

112. $\int_0^1 \cosh x^2 dx = 1.1047$, from Prob. 74 of Exercises I (page 42).

113. $\int_0^{0.5} \frac{\sin x}{x} dx = 0.4931$, from Prob. 75 of Exercises I (page 42).

114. $\int_0^{\pi/2} \log \frac{\sin x}{x} dx = -0.22734$, from Prob. 107 above.

115. Let OA and AB be two movable rods, hinged together at A. and let OA rotate about the fixed point O. If S is the area traced out by the rods in moving from a fixed to a variable position, shaded in

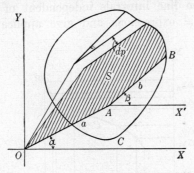

Fig. 79, show that $dS = \frac{1}{2}a^2 d\alpha + \frac{1}{2}b^2 d\beta + b\,dp$. In this expression $\alpha = \angle XOA$, $OA = a$, $\beta = \angle X'AB$, $AB = b$ and the differential dp is measured perpendicular to the instantaneous position of AB. If B describes a closed curve C, not containing O, it follows that

$$\text{Area } C = \int dS = b(p_2 - p_1).$$

This is the theory of the Amsler polar planimeter. The difference $p_2 - p_1$ is proportional to the angle of rotation of a small wheel with sharpened edges having its axle along AB. Hence we need merely read a dial before and after traversing C, form the difference of the readings, and multiply by the proper constant to measure the area enclosed by C.

CHAPTER V

LINE INTEGRALS. COMPLEX VARIABLES

Certain physical quantities are most easily computed by integrals taken along a curved arc, known as *line* or *contour* *integrals*. We define such integrals for a curved path in the plane and describe some of their properties. We show the relation between line integrals independent of the path and exact differential expressions and give applications of these

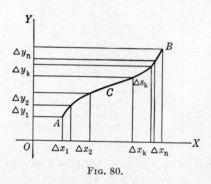

FIG. 80.

ideas in mechanics and thermodynamics. We then consider integrals of complex functions, and the relation between integrals independent of the path, the Cauchy-Riemann equations, and analytic functions of a complex variable. We define residues and illustrate their use by evaluating several real definite integrals. Finally we study the two-dimensional irrotational motion of an incompressible fluid, the relation of such a flow to a pair of conjugate functions, and the transformation of such flows by conformal mapping, in particular by the Schwarz transformation.

80. Line Integrals. Let C be an arc of a smooth curve, with initial point A and terminal point B. And let $h(x,y)$ be a function of two variables x and y, defined and continuous for x,y any point of the arc AB. We divide C into n arcs $\Delta s_1, \Delta s_2, \cdots,$ Δs_n. Each Δs_k has a projection Δx_k on the x axis and a projection

Δy_k on the y axis. Choose x_k, y_k an arbitrary point on the arc Δs_k, and form the sums

$$\sum_{k=1}^{n} h(x_k, y_k)\Delta s_k, \qquad \sum_{k=1}^{n} h(x_k, y_k)\Delta x_k, \qquad \sum_{k=1}^{n} h(x_k, y_k)\Delta y_k. \quad (1)$$

If we let n increase indefinitely and take the Δs_k in such a way that the largest Δs_k approaches zero as n becomes infinite, each of these three sums, like the S_n of Sec. 62 will approach a limit. These limits are called *line integrals*, or *contour integrals*, and are denoted by

$$\int_C h(x,y)ds, \qquad \int_C h(x,y)dx, \qquad \int_C h(x,y)dy, \quad (2)$$

respectively. The shorter form

$$\int_C h\,ds, \qquad \int_C h\,dx, \qquad \int_C h\,dy \quad (3)$$

is often used. The curve C is called the *path* or *contour*.

If the equations of the curve C are given in terms of a parameter t in the form

$$x = f(t), \qquad y = g(t), \quad (4)$$

the integrals (2) may be reduced to ordinary integrals in t by writing in the integrals,

$$h(x,y) = h[f(t),g(t)], \qquad dx = f'(t)dt, \qquad dy = g'(t)dt,$$
$$ds = \sqrt{f'(t)^2 + g'(t)^2}\,dt. \quad (5)$$

If the equation of the path is given in the form $y = G(x)$ or $x = F(y)$, a corresponding reduction may be made. For example, if $y = G(x)$, the second integral is

$$\int_C h(x,y)dx = \int_C h[x,G(x)]dx. \quad (6)$$

Again, if $x = F(y)$, the third integral is

$$\int_C h(x,y)dy = \int_C h[F(y),y]dy. \quad (7)$$

If we take any line integral over C from B to A, the value will be the negative of that over C from A to B. This follows from the fact that the signs of the Δs_k, Δx_k, and Δy_k in the sums (1) will all be reversed.

If a continuous curve C^* is made up of several segments each

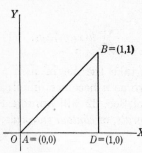

Fig. 81.

of type C, the line integral over C^* is defined to be the sum of those over the separate segments. Thus the line integral over a polygon is the sum of the integrals over its sides. Similarly, if the path of integration is made up of parts having different equations of the form (4), we may compute the line integral by adding up the results for the separate parts.

Line integrals often occur in the form of a sum of integrals of the last two types,

$$\int_C [P(x,y)dx + Q(x,y)dy] \qquad \text{or} \qquad \int_C (P\,dx + Q\,dy). \quad (8)$$

As an illustration of the evaluation, consider the line integral

$$\int (y\,dx - x\,dy) \qquad (9)$$

taken from $A = (0,0)$ to $B = (1,1)$, first along the straight line AB and then along the broken line composed of AD and DB, where $D = (1,0)$. On AB, $y = x$ and

$$y\,dx - x\,dy = x\,dx - x\,dx = 0,$$

so that

$$\int_{AB} (y\,dx - x\,dy) = 0. \qquad (10)$$

On AD, $y = 0$, $dy = 0$, $y\,dx - x\,dy = 0$, but on DB, $x = 1$, $dx = 0$ so that $y\,dx - x\,dy = -dy$. Thus

$$\int_{ADB} (y\,dx - x\,dy) = \int_{DB} (-dy) = -\int_0^1 dy = -1. \qquad (11)$$

This illustrates that when no restrictions are imposed on $P(x,y)$ and $Q(x,y)$ in the integral (8), the value depends on the path, as well as on the end points.

In some cases we use a closed path C, which returns to itself. When we wish to emphasize that the path is closed, we write

$$\oint [P(x,y)dx + Q(x,y)dy] \qquad \text{or} \qquad \oint (P\,dx + Q\,dy). \quad (12)$$

Considerations similar to those of Secs. 71 and 72 apply to line integrals for which the path extends to infinity, or for which the function $h(x,y)$ becomes infinite at one or more points. These improper line integrals converge when they are the limits of certain proper line integrals.

81. Green's Theorem. Let T be a two-dimensional region of the plane, and B_T its complete boundary. At each point of B_T we may draw a vector along the normal pointing into the region, and a vector along the tangent in such a way that the 90° turn which takes the tangent into the inner normal is the same as

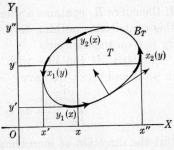

FIG. 82.

that which takes the positive x axis into the positive y axis. This determines the positive direction along the tangent to B_T, and hence the positive direction along B_T itself.

The theorem of Green asserts that, under certain conditions

$$\int_{B_T} (P \, dx + Q \, dy) = \int_T \left(\frac{\partial Q}{\partial x} - \frac{\partial P}{\partial y} \right) dx \, dy. \qquad (13)$$

Thus the theorem enables us to express certain line integrals as double integrals.   The conditions are

1. The functions $P(x,y)$, $Q(x,y)$ as well as their partial derivatives $\partial Q/\partial x$, $\partial P/\partial y$ are continuous functions of the two variables x,y in T and on B_T.

2. The line integral on the left is taken along B_T in the positive direction determined by regarding B_T as bounding T.

Consider first a region T like that in Fig. 82, which is such that every straight line through an interior point and parallel to either axis cuts the boundary in exactly two points.   Then, if the line with coordinate y cuts the boundary in the points $x_1(y)$ and $x_2(y)$, we have

$$\int_{x_1(y)}^{x_2(y)} \frac{\partial Q}{\partial x} \, dx = Q(x_2,y) - Q(x_1,y). \qquad (14)$$

Since the segment x_1,x_2 is inside the area, the direction of increasing y is the positive direction along B_T for the point at x_2 but the direction of increasing y is opposite to the positive direction along B_T for the point at x_1.   Hence, if y' and y'' are the least and greatest values of y on B_T, we shall have

$$\int_{y'}^{y''} Q(x_2,y)dy - \int_{y'}^{y''} Q(x_1,y)dy = \int_{B_T} Q(x,y)dy. \quad (15)$$

If the curve B_T contains a whole segment with $y = y'$ or $y = y''$, this contributes nothing to the line integral on the right, since $dy = 0$ on the segment.

Similarly, if the line with coordinate x cuts the boundary in $y_1(x)$ and $y_2(x)$, we have

$$\int_{y_1(x)}^{y_2(x)} \frac{\partial P}{\partial y} \, dy = P(x,y_2) - P(x,y_1). \quad (16)$$

But the direction of increasing x is the positive direction along B_T for the point at y_1, and the direction of increasing x is opposite to the positive direction along B_T for the point at y_2. Hence we have

$$\int_{x'}^{x''} P(x,y_2)dx - \int_{x'}^{x''} P(x,y_1)dx = - \int_{B_T} P(x,y)dx, \quad (17)$$

where x' and x'' are the least and greatest values of x on B_T.

We may conclude from the last four equations that

$$\int_{B_T} (P \, dx + Q \, dy) = \int_{y'}^{y''} dy \int_{x_1(y)}^{x_2(y)} \frac{\partial Q}{\partial x} \, dx$$
$$- \int_{x'}^{x''} dx \int_{y_1(x)}^{y_2(x)} \frac{\partial P}{\partial y} \, dy. \quad (18)$$

Since each of these repeated integrals is equivalent to a double integral over T, the result (13) follows.

The equation may now be extended to hold for any region T which is the sum of a finite number of pieces of the kind just used, provided that the integral on the right is taken over the total area and the left over the entire boundary, which may consist of one or more closed curves. If any of the curves bounding parts of T have arcs in common, these will be traversed in opposite directions for the two parts. Thus, when we add the equations for the separate parts, these arcs may be neglected, since the integrals for them cancel. Two cases are illustrated in Figs. 83 and 84.

A region such that any two points in it can be joined by a curve lying wholly inside the region is said to be *connected*. A *simply connected* region is one that is deformable into the interior of a circle. In this case all points inside any closed curve in the region belong to the region. If this is not true, there are holes and the connected region is said to be *multiply connected*. The omission of a single point is regarded as a hole. Thus a circle with the center omitted is a multiply connected region.

Our definition of positive direction along a boundary is such that for a simply connected region the positive direction is

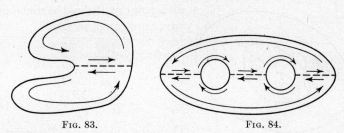

FIG. 83.   FIG. 84.

counterclockwise. The large regions of Figs. 82 and 83, and the parts into which the regions of Figs. 83 and 84 have been divided are examples. For a hole, regarded as part of the boundary of a multiply connected region outside of it, the positive direction is clockwise. This is illustrated in Fig. 84. For all parts of the boundary of any region, the positive direction is regarded as forward by an observer walking along the boundary with the region on his left.

As an example of Green's theorem, let $P(x,y) = -y$ and $Q(x,y) = x$. Then $\partial Q/\partial x = 1$, $\partial P/\partial y = -1$ so that

$$\oint_{B_T} (-y\,dx + x\,dy) = \int_T (1+1)dx\,dy = 2\int_T dx\,dy = 2A_T, \quad (19)$$

where A_T is the area of T. This shows that

$$A_T = \tfrac{1}{2} \int_{B_T} (x\,dy - y\,dx), \qquad (20)$$

a convenient formula for calculating areas when x and y are given in terms of a parameter. Compare Prob. 29 of Exercises I (page 38).

Let us use (20) to check the calculations made in connection with (9), whose integrand is the negative of that in (20). If T is the triangle of Fig. 81, $B_T = ADB + BA = ADB - AB$. Hence from Eqs. (10) and (11),

$$\int_{B_T} (y\,dx - x\,dy) = -1 \quad \text{and} \quad \tfrac{1}{2}\int_{B_T}(x\,dy - y\,dx) = \tfrac{1}{2}.$$

$$(21)$$

This is in agreement with (20), since the area of triangle T is $\frac{1}{2}$.

82. Exact Differential Expressions. Let R be a simply connected region, and let the functions $P(x,y)$, $Q(x,y)$ as well as their partial derivatives $\partial Q/\partial x$, $\partial P/\partial y$ be continuous functions of the two variables x,y in R. Let us further suppose that at each point of R these partial derivatives are equal, so that

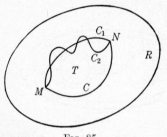

FIG. 85.

$$\frac{\partial Q}{\partial x} = \frac{\partial P}{\partial y}$$

or

$$\frac{\partial Q}{\partial x} - \frac{\partial P}{\partial y} = 0. \qquad (22)$$

Then for any region T consisting entirely of points of R the right member of (13) will be zero. Hence the line integral

$$\int (P\,dx + Q\,dy)$$

will be zero over every closed path in R which is the boundary of a region T.

Let M and N be any two points in R, and consider two arcs C_1 and C which join M to N and together bound a region T in R. Then

$$\int_C (P\,dx + Q\,dy) - \int_{C_1} (P\,dx + Q\,dy) = 0. \qquad (23)$$

For the difference is the integral over a closed curve, proceeding from M to N along C and then from N to M along C_1 reversed. Hence it is zero by Eq. (13). It follows from Eq. (23) that the line integral along C equals the line integral along C_1.

If we consider two paths joining M to N like C_1 and C_2, which intersect in several points and so do not bound a single region T, we may find a third arc C in R which bounds a region T when taken with C_1, and also when taken with C_2. In this case the preceding argument shows that the line integral over C_2 equals that over C, and hence equals that over C_1.

To indicate the situation just described, we say that the differential expression $(P\,dx + Q\,dy)$ is "exact" in R. If x_0,y_0

is a fixed point in R, and x,y a variable point in R, we may write

$$\int_{x_0,y_0}^{x,y} (P\,dx + Q\,dy) = G(x,y). \tag{24}$$

The integral is calculated along any path lying in R.   This determines $G(x,y)$ as a single valued function of x and y, since the foregoing discussion shows that the value of the integral is the same for any two paths in R.

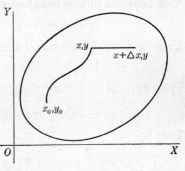

Fig. 86.

In particular, let us take x,y and $x + \Delta x,\ y$ in R and calculate the values of $G(x,y)$ and $G(x + \Delta x,y)$ using two paths that differ only by a straight-line segment parallel to the x axis.   Then we have

$$G(x + \Delta x,y) - G(x,y) = \int_{x,y}^{x+\Delta x,y} (P\,dx + Q\,dy) = \int_{x,y}^{x+\Delta x,y} P\,dx, \tag{25}$$

since $dy = 0$ along the straight segment.   The last form is an ordinary integral in x, as y is constant.   On dividing both sides by Δx and reasoning as we did in Sec. 64, we may deduce that

$$\frac{\partial G}{\partial x} = P(x,y). \tag{26}$$

In the same way we may prove that

$$\frac{\partial G}{\partial y} = Q(x,y). \tag{27}$$

It follows from the last two equations that

$$dG = \frac{\partial G}{\partial x}\,dx + \frac{\partial G}{\partial y}\,dy = P\,dx + Q\,dy. \tag{28}$$

Thus when $(P\,dx + Q\,dy)$ is an exact differential expression in the sense of this section, it is also the total differential, as defined in Sec. 21, of the function $G(x,y)$ given by (24).   Taking a different point x_0,y_0 would merely change this function by a constant, equal to the integral from the new point to x_0,y_0.

Suppose next that by any process we have found a function $F(x,y)$ which has $(P\,dx + Q\,dy)$ as its total differential. Then

$$dF = P\,dx + Q\,dy \qquad \text{and} \qquad \frac{\partial F}{\partial x} = P, \qquad \frac{\partial F}{\partial y} = Q. \quad (29)$$

A comparison of this equation and Eq. (28) shows that

$$dF = dG \qquad \text{or} \qquad d(F - G) = 0. \quad (30)$$

Since its total differential is zero, $(F - G)$ is constant and

$$F - G = k, \qquad \text{or} \qquad F(x,y) = G(x,y) + k. \quad (31)$$

From Eq. (24) it follows that $G(x_0,y_0) = 0$, and hence

$$G(x,y) = G(x,y) - G(x_0,y_0) = F(x,y) - F(x_0,y_0). \quad (32)$$

That is,

$$\int_{x_0,y_0}^{x,y} (P\,dx + Q\,dy) = F(x,y) \Big|_{x_0,y_0}^{x,y} = F(x,y) - F(x_0,y_0). \quad (33)$$

This expresses the line integral of the exact integrand in terms of any indefinite integral $F(x,y)$ that satisfies (29).

To show how such indefinite integrals may be found by ordinary integration, let us consider the particular example,

$$P\,dx + Q\,dy = (3x^2 + 2xy^3)dx + (3x^2y^2 + 2y)dy. \quad (34)$$

The condition for exactness [Eq. (22)] is satisfied, since

$$\frac{\partial P}{\partial y} = 6xy^2 \qquad \text{and} \qquad \frac{\partial Q}{\partial x} = 6xy^2. \quad (35)$$

The condition

$$\frac{\partial F}{\partial x} = 3x^2 + 2xy^3 \text{ gives } F = x^3 + x^2y^3 + f(y) \quad (36)$$

by integrating with respect to x, keeping y constant. The constant of integration is written $f(y)$, since it may depend on y which was kept constant during the integration. The condition

$$\partial F/\partial y = 3x^2y^2 + 2y \text{ combined with } \partial F/\partial y = 3x^2y^2 + f'(y), \quad (37)$$

obtained from (36), leads to

$$f'(y) = 2y \qquad \text{and} \qquad f(y) = y^2 + k. \quad (38)$$

Hence the indefinite integral of (34) is

$$F = x^3 + x^2y^3 + y^2 + k.$$

The success of this procedure is contingent on the disappearance of x at the stage corresponding to (38). But x will disappear at this stage whenever the original expression is exact.

We note that any differential expression $(P\,dx + Q\,dy)$ obtained by taking the total differential of a function $F(x,y)$ is exact. For if

$$P\,dx + Q\,dy = dF = \frac{\partial F}{\partial x}\,dx + \frac{\partial F}{\partial y}\,dy,$$

$$P = \frac{\partial F}{\partial x} \quad \text{and} \quad Q = \frac{\partial F}{\partial y}, \tag{39}$$

so that by Sec. 23

$$\frac{\partial Q}{\partial x} = \frac{\partial^2 F}{\partial x\,\partial y} = \frac{\partial^2 F}{\partial y\,\partial x} = \frac{\partial P}{\partial y} \quad \text{and} \quad \frac{\partial Q}{\partial x} - \frac{\partial P}{\partial y} = 0. \tag{40}$$

The discussion of this section shows that the existence of continuous partial derivatives $\partial Q/\partial x$ and $\partial P/\partial y$, satisfying the condition

$$\frac{\partial Q}{\partial x} = \frac{\partial P}{\partial y}, \tag{41}$$

is both necessary and sufficient for the existence of a function $F(x,y)$ which has $(P\,dx + Q\,dy)$ as its total differential.

When the condition holds, we call $(P\,dx + Q\,dy)$ an *exact* differential expression. The integral in Eq. (24) is independent of the path, provided that the path lies inside a simply connected region in which the condition for exactness holds.

83. Work. If X and Y are constant and the force vector

$$\mathbf{F} = X\mathbf{i} + Y\mathbf{j} \tag{42}$$

acts on a particle during a vector displacement

$$d\mathbf{s} = dx\,\mathbf{i} + dy\,\mathbf{j}, \quad \text{with } |d\mathbf{s}| = ds, \tag{43}$$

the work done is

$$ds\,\text{Proj}_{ds}\,\mathbf{F} = d\mathbf{s}\cdot\mathbf{F} = X\,dx + Y\,dy, \tag{44}$$

by Eqs. (40) and (52) of Sec. 45.

Now suppose that X and Y are variable so that

$$\mathbf{F}(x,y) = X(x,y)\mathbf{i} + Y(x,y)\mathbf{j}, \tag{45}$$

and we wish to consider the work W_c done on a particle during its motion along a curved arc C. The relation (44) suggests that

$$W_c = \int_C [X(x,y)dx + Y(x,y)dy] = \int_C (X\,dx + Y\,dy). \tag{46}$$

This is the definition of the work done by the variable force field $F(x,y)$ of (45) on a particle moving along a curved path.

The force field is *conservative* if the work depends only on the end points of C and otherwise is independent of the path. Thus for a conservative field the expression $(X\,dx + Y\,dy)$ is exact, and there is a function $W(x,y)$ having this expression as its total differential. The function $W(x,y)$ is called the *force potential*, while $U(x,y) = -W(x,y)$ is the *potential energy*. Thus for a conservative field we have

$$\frac{\partial X}{\partial y} = \frac{\partial Y}{\partial x} \quad \text{and} \quad X\,dx + Y\,dy = dW = -dU. \quad (47)$$

And the relations

$$X = \frac{\partial W}{\partial x} = -\frac{\partial U}{\partial x}, \quad Y = \frac{\partial W}{\partial y} = -\frac{\partial U}{\partial y} \quad (48)$$

express the force components in terms of the potentials.

84. Thermodynamics. The distinction between exact and inexact differential expressions is of importance in thermodynamics. Consider as a system a fixed mass of homogeneous fluid. Its thermodynamical state is characterized by three quantities: pressure p, volume v, and absolute temperature T. Any two of these determine the third, since there is a relationship

$$T = f(p,v) \quad (49)$$

which for the case of an ideal gas enclosed in a container takes the form

$$T = \left(\frac{T_0}{p_0 v_0}\right) pv. \quad (50)$$

If we think of p and v as determining the state of the gas, a change of state will be represented by a curve C in the pv plane or pv diagram. During this change of state, the amount of heat lost or absorbed will be given by an integral of the form

$$Q_C = \int_C [P(p,v)dp + V(p,v)dv]. \quad (51)$$

Here, in general, $\partial P/\partial v \neq \partial V/\partial p$, so that the integrand is not an exact differential expression. Hence Q_C depends on the path and is not a function of p and v. However, the notation dQ is used as an abbreviation for the integrand,

$$dQ = P(p,v)dp + V(p,v)dv. \quad (52)$$

The work done during the change of state is

$$W_C = \int_C p\, dv. \tag{53}$$

This also depends on the path and is not a function of p and v. But the notation

$$dW = p\, dv$$

is used.

With the abbreviated notation, the first law of thermodynamics asserts that the difference of the two inexact differential expressions $dQ - dW$ is an exact differential expression. We call the function that has this as its total differential the *internal energy* of the system and denote it by E. Thus

$$dE = \frac{\partial E}{\partial p} dp + \frac{\partial E}{\partial v} dv = dQ - dW$$
$$= P(p,v)dp + [V(p,v) - p]dv, \tag{54}$$

and there is a function $E(p,v)$ such that

$$\frac{\partial E}{\partial p} = P(p,v) \qquad \text{and} \qquad \frac{\partial E}{\partial v} = V(p,v) - p. \tag{55}$$

It is a consequence of the second law of thermodynamics that dQ/T is an exact differential expression. We call the function that has this as its total differential the *entropy* of the system and denote it by S. Thus

$$dS = \frac{\partial S}{\partial p} dp + \frac{\partial S}{\partial v} dv = \frac{dQ}{T}$$
$$= \frac{P(p,v)}{T} dp + \frac{Q(p,v)}{T} dv, \tag{56}$$

and there is a function $S(p,v)$ such that

$$\frac{\partial S}{\partial p} = \frac{P(p,v)}{T} \qquad \text{and} \qquad \frac{\partial S}{\partial v} = \frac{Q(p,v)}{T}. \tag{57}$$

85. Analytic Functions of a Complex Variable. Let $z = x + iy$ be a complex variable, and R any region of the xy plane or z plane. And suppose that, for all values of z in R, $w = f(z)$ is an analytic function of z as defined in Sec. 11. We denote the real part of w by u, and the imaginary part by v, so that

$$w = u + iv. \tag{58}$$

The values of x and y determine $z = x + iy$, and hence $w = f(z)$. Thus u and v are each functions of x and y, so that

$$f(x + iy) = u(x,y) + iv(x,y). \tag{59}$$

two functions $u(x,y)$ and $v(x,y)$ obtained in this way are called *conjugate functions*.

We stated in Sec. 11 that, under these conditions, $f(z)$ possesses derivatives of all orders for all z in R. It is a consequence of this fact that the conjugate functions $u(x,y)$ and $v(x,y)$, regarded as functions of two real variables, each possess partial derivatives of all orders for x,y in R. And as was indicated in Sec. 12, $f(z)$ has a Taylor's expansion in powers of $(z - z_0)$ about any point z_0 inside R. This expansion will converge if z lies inside some circle in R with center at z_0. It follows from this fact that $u(x,y)$ and $v(x,y)$ may each be expanded in a Taylor's series in two variables of the type discussed in Sec. 31 in powers of $(x - x_0)$ and $(y - y_0)$. These series will surely converge if x,y lies inside some circle in R with center at x_0,y_0.

For example, let $w = e^z$ which is analytic for all finite values of z. Then by Eq. (26) of Sec. 3,

$$e^z = e^x \cos y + ie^x \sin y \tag{60}$$

so that

$$u(x,y) = e^x \cos y, \qquad v(x,y) = e^x \sin y. \tag{61}$$

The Taylor's series about any point, *e.g.*, the origin, will converge for all values of x and y. These series may be obtained as real and imaginary parts of

$$c^z = 1 + (x + iy) + \frac{(x + iy)^2}{2!} + \frac{(x + iy)^3}{3!} + \cdots, \tag{62}$$

or more simply by multiplying the series for e^x by that for $\cos y$, and then by that for $\sin y$.

86. Cauchy-Riemann Differential Equations. We wish now to derive a pair of equations satisfied by $u(x,y)$ and $v(x,y)$ which follow from the analytic character of $f(z)$. To say that $f(z)$ is analytic means that there is a derivative

$$f'(z) = \frac{dw}{dz} = \lim_{\Delta z \to 0} \frac{\Delta w}{\Delta z}, \tag{63}$$

where the limit on the right is the same for all methods of approach of Δz to zero.   We find from $w = u + iv$ that

$$\Delta w = \Delta u + i\,\Delta v, \qquad \text{and} \qquad \frac{\Delta w}{\Delta z} = \frac{\Delta u}{\Delta z} + i\,\frac{\Delta v}{\Delta z}. \qquad (64)$$

In particular, if we put $\Delta y = 0$, $\Delta z = \Delta x$ and

$$f'(z) = \lim_{\Delta x \to 0}\left(\frac{\Delta u}{\Delta x} + i\,\frac{\Delta v}{\Delta x}\right) = \frac{\partial u}{\partial x} + i\,\frac{\partial v}{\partial x}. \qquad (65)$$

On the other hand, if we put $\Delta x = 0$, $\Delta z = i\,\Delta y$ and

$$f'(z) = \lim_{\Delta y \to 0}\left(\frac{1}{i}\,\frac{\Delta u}{\Delta y} + \frac{\Delta v}{\Delta y}\right) = -i\,\frac{\partial u}{\partial y} + \frac{\partial v}{\partial y}. \qquad (66)$$

If these two values are equal, we must have

$$\frac{\partial u}{\partial x} = \frac{\partial v}{\partial y} \qquad \text{and} \qquad \frac{\partial v}{\partial x} = -\,\frac{\partial u}{\partial y}. \qquad (67)$$

These are known as the *Cauchy-Riemann differential equations* and are the relations that we sought to prove.

Functions (61) satisfy these equations, since they make

$$\frac{\partial u}{\partial x} = e^x \cos y, \; \frac{\partial u}{\partial y} = -e^x \sin y, \; \frac{\partial v}{\partial x} = e^x \sin y, \; \frac{\partial v}{\partial y} = e^x \cos y.$$

We omit the proof of the fact that, conversely, if the partial derivatives of $u(x,y)$ and $v(x,y)$ are continuous and satisfy Eqs. (67) in R, the function $u + iv$ is an analytic function of $z = x + iy$ in R.   Thus u and v are conjugate functions.

We may consider the function $w = f(z)$ as effecting a mapping, or transformation of the points of the z plane on or into the points of the w plane.   Let z_0 be mapped on w_0, and write the derivative $f'(z_0)$, assumed $\neq 0$, in polar form,

$$f'(z_0) = ae^{iA}. \qquad (68)$$

Then for z near z_0, $\Delta z = z - z_0$ will be small and by (63)

$$\Delta w = f'(z_0)\Delta z \quad \text{or} \quad ae^{iA}\Delta z \text{ approximately.} \qquad (69)$$

By Sec. 6, this means that each element Δz is (approximately) turned through an angle A and has its length multiplied by a. Thus a small figure near z_0, like the triangle of Fig. 87, will go into a nearly similar figure, like the curvilinear triangle of Fig. 88. And the angle between two curves at z_0 will be the same as the angle between the image curves at w_0. This similarity and preservation of angles at a point are described by the word *conformal*. Hence we may say that the mapping or transformation induced by the function $w = f(z)$ is conformal at any point where $f(z)$ is analytic and $f'(z) \neq 0$. This is in agreement with Probs. 116 to 124, in particular 122, of Exercises III (page 140) where Eqs. (67), with the partial derivatives not all zero, was found as a condition for a conformal map.

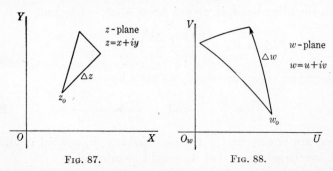

Fig. 87.   Fig. 88.

In the z plane the curves $u(x,y) = u_0$, $v(x,y) = v_0$ cut at right angles at z_0. For their image curves in the w plane are the lines through w_0 parallel to the axes, $u = u_0$, $v = v_0$.

87. Laplace's Equation. It follows from the Cauchy-Riemann equations (67) and Sec. 23, that

$$\frac{\partial^2 u}{\partial x^2} = \frac{\partial^2 v}{\partial x \, \partial y} = \frac{\partial^2 v}{\partial y \, \partial x} = -\frac{\partial^2 u}{\partial y^2}. \tag{70}$$

Consequently,

$$\frac{\partial^2 u}{\partial x^2} + \frac{\partial^2 u}{\partial y^2} = 0. \tag{71}$$

This equation is known as *Laplace's equation* in two dimensions. It may be shown that any function $u(x,y)$ that satisfies Laplace's equation at all points of a region R necessarily has continuous partial derivatives of all orders at any interior point of R.

Any function $u(x,y)$ that satisfies Laplace's equation at all points of a simply connected region R may be obtained as the real part of a function $f(z) = u + iv$, analytic in R. We may find v from

$$v = \int_{x_0,y_0}^{x,y} \left(-\frac{\partial u}{\partial y} \, dx + \frac{\partial u}{\partial x} \, dy \right). \tag{72}$$

This function is single-valued in R, since the condition for exactness of the integrand of (72) reduces to Laplace's equation (71).   And for an exact integrand, Eq. (72) implies

$$\frac{\partial v}{\partial x} = -\frac{\partial u}{\partial y} \quad \text{and} \quad \frac{\partial v}{\partial y} = \frac{\partial u}{\partial x}, \tag{73}$$

which are the Cauchy-Riemann equations (67), so that $u + iv$ is an analytic function.

A similar argument shows that v satisfies Laplace's equation

$$\frac{\partial^2 v}{\partial x^2} + \frac{\partial^2 v}{\partial y^2} = 0, \tag{74}$$

and that, if $v(x,y)$ satisfies this equation in a simply connected region R, the function $u + iv$ is analytic in R if

$$u = \int_{x_0,y_0}^{x,y} \left(\frac{\partial v}{\partial y} dx - \frac{\partial v}{\partial x} dy \right). \tag{75}$$

For example, the function $x^2 - y^2$ is a solution of Laplace's equation.   If we take this as u, we find from Eq. (72) that

$$v = \int_{0,0}^{x,y} (2y\, dx + 2x\, dy) = 2xy. \tag{76}$$

Thus $x^2 - y^2$ is the real part of

$$x^2 - y^2 + 2xyi = (x + iy)^2 = z^2. \tag{77}$$

If we take $x^2 - y^2$ as v, and use Eq. (75), we find

$$u = \int_{0,0}^{x,y} (-2y\, dx - 2x\, dy) = -2xy.$$

Thus $x^2 - y^2$ is the imaginary part of

$$-2xy + i(x^2 - y^2) = i(x + iy)^2 = iz^2. \tag{78}$$

88. Integrals of Complex Functions. The integral of the complex function $f(z)$ along a path C is defined as the line integral along C of the integrand

$$f(z)dz = (u + iv)(dx + i\, dy) = (u\, dx - v\, dy) + i(v\, dx + u\, dy). \tag{79}$$

That is

$$\int_C f(z)dz = \int_C (u\, dx - v\, dy) + i \int_C (v\, dx + u\, dy). \tag{80}$$

Each of the integrals on the right is a real line integral, similar to (8) of Sec. 80, and could be evaluated by the method given in that section.

Our definition implies a relation analogous to Eq. (11) of Sec. 61, namely,

$$\int_C f(z)dz = \lim_{n \to \infty} \sum_{k=1}^{n} f(z_k)\Delta z_k, \qquad \text{if } \lim_{n \to \infty} d_n = 0. \tag{81}$$

Here d_n is the largest value of $|\Delta z_k|$ for any n. And for each n we form subdivisions and take intermediate points on C as in Sec. 80, and put $z_k = x_k + iy_k$, $\Delta z_k = \Delta x_k + i\,\Delta y_k$.

Again, analogous to Eq. (53) of Sec. 66, we have the rule of substitution

$$\int_C f(z)dz = \int_{C_Z} f[g(Z)]g'(Z)dZ, \tag{82}$$

if $g(Z)$ is analytic and $g'(Z) \neq 0$ on C_Z, and the points of C_Z are mapped on the points of C by $z = g(Z)$.

From Sec. 6, for any two complex numbers A and B,

$$|AB| = |A| \cdot |B| \qquad \text{and} \qquad |A + B| \leqq |A| + |B|. \tag{83}$$

Hence, if $|f(z)| \leqq M$,

$$\left| \sum_{k=1}^{n} f(z_k)\Delta z_k \right| \leqq \sum_{k=1}^{n} |f(z_k)||\Delta z_k| \leqq M \sum_{k=1}^{n} |\Delta z_k|. \tag{84}$$

But

$$|dz|^2 = |dx + i\,dy|^2 = dx^2 + dy^2 = ds^2, \tag{85}$$

so that relation (84) leads to the relation

$$\left| \int_C f(z)dz \right| \leqq M \int_C |dz| \text{ or } M \int_C ds = ML, \tag{86}$$

where L is the length of the path C.

Similarly if $|f(z)| \leqq |g(z)|$ on C,

$$\left| \int_C f(z)dz \right| \leqq \int_C |f(z)|ds \leqq \int_C |g(z)|ds. \tag{87}$$

This may be applied to improper integrals as the basis of a comparison test similar to that of Sec. 72, since we may deduce the convergence of the complex integral in the left member of (87) from the convergence of the real integral on the right.

89. Integrals of Analytic Functions. Let B_T be the complete boundary of a region T, as in Sec. 81. And suppose further that

$u + iv = f(z)$ is an analytic function of z for all z in T and on B_T. Then we may use B_T as the path C in Eq. (80) and transform the right member by Green's theorem (13).   The result is

$$\int_{B_T} (u\,dx - v\,dy) + i \int_{B_T} (v\,dx + u\,dy)$$

$$= \int_T \left(-\frac{\partial v}{\partial x} - \frac{\partial u}{\partial y} \right) dx\,dy + i \int_T \left(\frac{\partial u}{\partial x} - \frac{\partial v}{\partial y} \right) dx\,dy. \quad (88)$$

Since $f(z)$ is analytic in T, Eqs. (67) hold and the integrands on the right are zero.   Hence the left member is zero and, by (80),

$$\int_{B_T} f(z)dz = 0. \quad (89)$$

That is, the integral of $f(z)$ is zero over every closed path B_T such that $f(z)$ is analytic at all points on the path B_T and in the region T which has B_T as its complete boundary. This result is known as *Cauchy's integral theorem.*

As in Sec. 82, it follows that the value of the integral between two fixed points of a simply connected region R is independent of the path of integration, restricted to lie in R. Otherwise expressed, the value of the integral of $f(z)$ from z_0 to z is the same for any two paths that may be deformed into one another, crossing over only points at which $f(z)$ is analytic.

In a simply connected region R in which $f(z)$ is analytic, we may write

$$\int_{z_0}^{z} f(z)dz = F(z). \quad (90)$$

By reasoning like that of Sec. 64, we could deduce from this that

$$\frac{dF}{dz} = F'(z) = f(z). \quad (91)$$

Thus $F(z)$ is an indefinite integral of $f(z)$. And, since it has a derivative in R, it is analytic in R.

It follows directly from Eq. (90) that

$$\int_{z_1}^{z_2} f(z)dz = F(z) \Big|_{z_1}^{z_2} = F(z_2) - F(z_1). \quad (92)$$

An argument like that of Sec. 61 shows that any other indefinite integral of $f(z)$ can differ from $F(z)$ only by a constant, so that it may be used in place of $f(z)$ in Eq. (92).

The fact that the indefinite integral of an analytic function is analytic and may be used to calculate the definite integral as in (92) has already been illustrated for the special case of power series in Sec. 11.

Suppose that $f(x)$ is an elementary function for which an indefinite integral $F(x)$ can be found in integral tables or by the methods of Chap. IV. Then the results or methods may be used to find $F(z)$, an indefinite integral of $f(z)$. The function so found will be elementary and so be analytic except for certain singular points. These will necessarily be located at the singularities of $f(z)$. In such a case the integral of $f(z)$ between z_1 and z_2 for any path not containing a singular point of $f(z)$ may be computed from Eq. (92).

For example, on any path joining z_1 and z_2,

$$\int_{z_1}^{z_2} e^z dz = e^z \Big|_{z_1}^{z_2} \quad \text{and} \quad \int_{z_1}^{z_2} e^{kz} dz = \frac{e^{kz}}{k} \Big|_{z_1}^{z_2}. \tag{93}$$

The second integral, with $k = a + bi$ and z_1, z_2, and the path on the real axis, has been used in Probs. 3, 4 of Exercises I (page 37).

Similarly, for any path joining z_1 and z_2,

$$\int_{z_1}^{z_2} z^n dz = \frac{z^{n+1}}{n+1} \Big|_{z_1}^{z_2}, \qquad n \text{ a positive integer.} \tag{94}$$

The integrands in Eqs. (93) and (94) have no finite singular points. Hence the indefinite integrals are single-valued. In such cases the integral around any closed path, for which $z_2 = z_1$, is zero. This is in accord with Cauchy's integral theorem.

When the integrand $f(z)$ has finite singular points, the indefinite integral $F(z)$ may be multiple-valued, and in using Eq. (92) we must be careful to use that value of $F(z_2)$ which arises from $F(z_1)$ by continuous variation along the path of integration. For example, on any path joining z_1 and z_2 that does not pass through the origin,

$$\int_{z_1}^{z_2} \frac{dz}{z} = \log z \Big|_{z_1}^{z_2} = (\log r + i\theta) \Big|_{r_1,\theta_1}^{r_2,\theta_2} \tag{95}$$

by Eqs. (62) and (56) of Sec. 5. Here $r = |z|$ is single-valued, but the value of θ_2 must be derived from θ_1 by continuous variation along the path. In particular, consider a closed path that winds once about O in the counterclockwise direction. We call such a path a *positive circuit* about O and denote it by C_0. Then on C_0, θ will increase by 2π, and we shall have

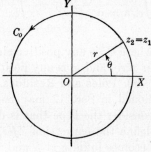

$$\int_{C_0} \frac{dz}{z} = 2\pi i. \qquad (96)$$

In indefinite integration formulas involving logarithms, it is customary to insert absolute value signs to avoid logarithms of negative numbers, when all the variables are real. These absolute value signs must be

FIG. 89.

omitted to obtain analytic integrals, valid in the complex plane. Thus

$$\int \frac{dx}{x} = \log |x|, \quad x \text{ real}, \quad \text{but} \quad \int \frac{dz}{z} = \log z, \quad z \text{ complex}. \qquad (97)$$

As a second example of a multiple-valued indefinite integral, we note that on any path not passing through the origin,

$$\int_{z_1}^{z_2} z^a dz = \frac{z^{a+1}}{a+1} \Big|_{z_1}^{z_2} = \frac{r^{a+1} e^{i(a+1)\theta}}{a+1} \Big|_{r_1, \theta_1}^{r_2, \theta_2}, \quad a \neq -1, \qquad (98)$$

by Sec. 7. In this case, for C_0 a positive circuit about O, since $e^{2\pi i} = 1$, $e^{2\pi(a+1)i} = e^{2\pi a i}$ and

$$\int_{C_0} z^a dz = \frac{(z_1{}^a)z_1}{a+1} (e^{2\pi a i} - 1), \quad a \neq -1. \qquad (99)$$

This is different from zero unless a is a positive or negative integer. Here the integrand z^a is itself multiple-valued, and the value of $z_1{}^a$ to be used is the value of the integrand selected at z_1, where we start the circuit.

The substitution $z - \alpha = Z$ takes C_α, any positive circuit about α in the z plane into C_0, a positive circuit about O in the Z plane. And it makes $dz = dZ$, so that

$$\int_{C_\alpha} (z - \alpha)^a dz = \int_{C_0} Z^a dZ, \qquad (100)$$

by the rule of substitution (82). Hence we may deduce from Eqs. (96) and (99) that

$$\int_{C_\alpha} \frac{dz}{z - \alpha} = 2\pi i, \qquad \int_{C_\alpha} (z - \alpha)^n dz = 0, \qquad \int_{C_\alpha} \frac{dz}{(z - \alpha)^m} = 0,$$
$$(101)$$

where C_α is any positive circuit about α, n is any positive integer or zero, and m is any positive integer greater than one.

90. Poles and Residues. The singularities of functions mentioned in Sec. 12 may be of various types. We wish here to consider the type that is due to a vanishing denominator. We define the expression "$f(z)$ has a pole at α" to mean that $f(z)$ becomes infinite at α and, in some circle with α as a center, the function $f(z)$ is single-valued and analytic except at α. It may be proved that, under these conditions, there is some positive integer m such that $|f(z)|$ behaves like $|z - \alpha|^{-m}$ at α, and the function

$$g(z) = (z - \alpha)^m f(z) \tag{102}$$

is analytic at α with $g(\alpha) \neq 0$. The number m, known as the *order* of the pole, may be determined practically as the smallest integer m for which $(z - \alpha)^m f(z)$ remains finite as $z \to \alpha$.

By Sec. 11, we may expand $g(z)$ in a Taylor's series

$$g(z) = A_0 + A_1(z - \alpha) + \cdots + A_m(z - \alpha)^m$$
$$+ A_{m+1}(z - \alpha)^{m+1} + \cdots, \tag{103}$$

where, as we note for future reference,

$$A_{m-1} = \frac{g^{(m-1)}(\alpha)}{(m - 1)!}, \qquad g^{(m-1)}(z) = \frac{d^{m-1}g}{dz^{m-1}}. \tag{104}$$

It follows from this and Eq. (102) that

$$f(z) = \frac{A_0}{(z - \alpha)^m} + \cdots + \frac{A_{m-1}}{z - \alpha} + A_m + A_{m+1}(z - \alpha) + \cdots.$$
$$(105)$$

Now consider the integral of $f(z)$ along C_α, a positive circuit about α. If the circuit is sufficiently small, it will be inside the circle of convergence of the series (103) and hence of the series made up of the terms with positive powers in (105). Thus we may integrate the series termwise. But, by Eq. (101), the integral of every term is zero except the term containing $1/(z - \alpha)$, whose integral is $2\pi i$. Consequently, we have

$$\int_{C\alpha} f(z)dz = A_{m-1} \int_{C\alpha} \frac{dz}{z - \alpha} = 2\pi i A_{m-1}. \qquad (106)$$

The coefficient of $1/(z - \alpha)$ in the expansion (105), which is the only coefficient needed to calculate the value of the integral of $f(z)$ along C_α, is called the *residue* of the pole.

For a pole of the first order, or simple pole, the residue is given by

$$R(\alpha) = A_0 = g(\alpha) = \lim_{z \to \alpha} (z - \alpha)f(z). \qquad (107)$$

If $f(z)$ is written in the form $P(z)/D(z)$, with $P(\alpha)$ finite, this limit may be evaluated by l'Hospital's rule, as in Eq. (56) of Sec. 67. The result is

$$R(\alpha) = \frac{P(\alpha)}{D'(\alpha)} \qquad \text{for } f(z) = \frac{P(z)}{D(z)} \text{ with } P(\alpha) \text{ finite.} \quad (108)$$

Whenever $f(\alpha) = \infty$ and the right member of Eq. (107) or the first equation in (108) is finite, there is a pole of the first order at α and the finite value is its residue.

For a pole of higher order than the first, we may compute the residue from Eq. (104), which shows that

$$R(\alpha) = \frac{g^{(m-1)}(\alpha)}{(m - 1)!} \qquad \text{if } g(z) = (z - \alpha)^m f(z), \qquad (109)$$

and $f(z)$ has a pole of the mth order at α.

Let B_T be the complete boundary of a region T, as in Sec. 81. We wish to calculate the integral of $f(z)$ along B_T in the positive direction, where $f(z)$ is analytic at all points of T and B_T except a certain number of points α_1, α_2, $\cdots$, α_n in T at which it has poles. Let the residue of $f(z)$ at any one of these points, α_k, be $R(\alpha_k)$. By Eq. (106) the integral of $f(z)$ along C_k, any sufficiently small circuit about α_k is given by

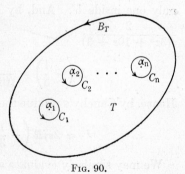

Fig. 90.

$$\int_{C_k} f(z)dz = 2\pi i R(\alpha_k). \qquad (110)$$

But the path of integration B_T may be deformed into the circuits $C_1, C_2, \cdots, C_n$, crossing only points at which $f(z)$ is analytic. Hence

$$\int_{B_r} f(z)dz = \sum_{k=1}^{n} \int_{C_k} f(z)dz = 2\pi i \sum_{k=1}^{n} R(\alpha_k), \qquad (111)$$

by Cauchy's integral theorem and Eq. (110).

Thus the integral of $f(z)$ around the complete boundary of a region in which $f(z)$ is analytic except for poles is equal to $2\pi i$ times the sum of the residues of $f(z)$ at the poles. This is *Cauchy's residue theorem.*

91. Evaluation of Definite Integrals. Many real definite integrals can be evaluated by means of complete integrals around suitable closed contours. We illustrate the procedure by a few typical examples.

EXAMPLE 1. $I_1 = \displaystyle\int_0^{2\pi} \frac{dt}{5 + 3 \cos t}.$ (112)

Let us make the substitution $it = \log z$. Then by Secs. 2 and 5, z traverses the unit circle U when t moves through real values from 0 to 2π, and

$$dt = \frac{dz}{iz}, \qquad e^{it} = z, \qquad \cos t = \frac{z^2 + 1}{2z}, \qquad \sin t = \frac{z^2 - 1}{2iz}. \quad (113)$$

Thus in terms of z,

$$I_1 = \frac{2}{i} \int_U \frac{dz}{3z^2 + 10z + 3}. \qquad (114)$$

The denominator has roots at -3 and $-\tfrac{1}{3}$. The second is the only one inside U. And, by Eq. (108), the residue at $-\tfrac{1}{3}$ of $\dfrac{2}{i(3z^2 + 10z + 3)}$ is

$$R\left(-\frac{1}{3}\right) = \frac{2}{i(6z + 10)}\bigg|_{-\frac{1}{3}} = \frac{1}{4i}. \qquad (115)$$

Hence, by Cauchy's residue theorem [Eq. (111)], the value of I_1 is

$$I_1 = 2\pi i R\left(-\frac{1}{3}\right) = 2\pi i \left(\frac{1}{4i}\right) = \frac{\pi}{2}. \qquad (116)$$

We may similarly evaluate any integral of the type

$$\int_a^{a+2\pi} f(\cos t, \sin t)dt$$

where $f(x,y)$ is a rational function and $f(\cos t,\ \sin t)$ is finite for all real t. For the substitution (113) will reduce the integral to $\int_U Q(z)dz$, where $Q(z)$ is a rational function of z with no poles on U.

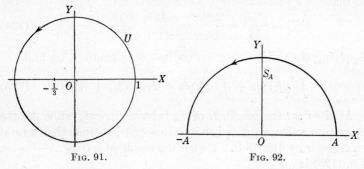

FIG. 91.   FIG. 92.

If the integrand is an *even* function of t, by Probs. 2 and 8 of Exercises IV (page 186) we shall have

$$\int_0^\pi f\, dt = \tfrac{1}{2}\int_{-\pi}^\pi f\, dt = \tfrac{1}{2}\int_0^{2\pi} f\, dt. \qquad (117)$$

Thus we may deduce from Example 1 that

$$\int_0^\pi \frac{dt}{5 + 3\cos t} = \frac{1}{2}I_1 = \frac{\pi}{4}. \qquad (118)$$

EXAMPLE 2. $I_2 = \displaystyle\int_{-\infty}^\infty \frac{x^4 dx}{(x^2 + 1)^2(x^2 + 4)}. \qquad (119)$

We consider I_2 as the limit, when $A \to \infty$, of

$$\int_{-A}^A f(z)dz \qquad \text{where } f(z) = \frac{z^4}{(z^2 + 1)^2(z^2 + 4)}. \qquad (120)$$

and the integral is taken along the real axis. We close the contour with S_A, a semicircle of radius A drawn in the upper half of the z plane from A to $-A$.

For large A, the poles of $f(z)$ inside the semicircle are at i and $2i$. At $2i$, we use Eq. (108) with

$$P(z) = \frac{z^4}{(z^2 + 1)^2}, \qquad D(z) = z^2 + 4, \qquad D'(z) = 2z \qquad (121)$$

so that

$$R(2i) = \frac{P(2i)}{D'(2i)} = \frac{4}{9i}. \qquad (122)$$

At i, which is a pole of order 2, we must use Eq. (109) with

$$g(z) = (z - i)^2 \frac{z^4}{(z^2 + 1)^2(z^2 + 4)} = \frac{z^4}{(z + i)^2(z^2 + 4)}. \quad (123)$$

so that

$$R(i) = \frac{g'(i)}{1!} = \frac{2z^3(iz^2 + 4z + 8i)}{(z + i)^3(z^2 + 4)^2}\bigg|_i = -\frac{11}{36i}. \quad (124)$$

Applying the residue theorem to the closed contour, we find

$$\int_{-A}^{A} f(z)dz + \int_{S_A} f(z)dz = 2\pi i[R(2i) + R(i)]. \quad (125)$$

As $A \to \infty$, the length L of S_A behaves like A, while M, the maximum value of $|f(z)|$ behaves like $1/A^2$, so that the integral on $S_A \to 0$ by Eq. (86). Hence the result of letting $A \to \infty$ in Eq. (125) is

$$I_2 = 2\pi i[R(2i) + R(i)] = 2\pi i\left(\frac{4}{9i} - \frac{11}{36i}\right) = \frac{5\pi}{18}. \quad (126)$$

The reasoning used for I_2 applies to any integral of the type $\int_{-\infty}^{\infty} Q(x)dx$, provided that $Q(x)$ is a rational function whose denominator is of degree at least *two* higher than the numerator and has no real roots. If the roots of the denominator in the upper half of the z plane are $\alpha_1, \alpha_2, \cdots, \alpha_p$, the conclusion is that

$$\int_{-\infty}^{\infty} Q(x)dx = 2\pi i[R(\alpha_1) + R(\alpha_2) + \cdots + R(\alpha_p)], \quad (127)$$

which is a formula for evaluating integrals of the type described.

If the integrand is an *even* function of x, we may find $\int_{0}^{\infty} Q(x)dx$ as $\frac{1}{2}\int_{-\infty}^{\infty} Q(x)dx$. Thus from Example 2,

$$\int_{0}^{\infty} \frac{x^4 dx}{(x^2 + 1)^2(x^2 + 4)} = \frac{1}{2} I_2 = \frac{5\pi}{36}. \quad (128)$$

EXAMPLE 3. $\quad I_3 = \int_{0}^{\infty} \frac{\cos 2x}{x^2 + 9} dx. \quad (129)$

This may be deduced from the real part of the complex integral

$$I_c = \int_{-\infty}^{\infty} \frac{e^{2ix}dx}{x^2 + 9}, \quad \text{since } \mathbf{R}I_c = \int_{-\infty}^{\infty} \frac{\cos 2x}{x^2 + 9} dx = 2I_3. \quad (130)$$

We now treat I_c as we did I_2 in Example 2. We consider I_c as the limit, when $A \to \infty$, of

$$\int_{-A}^{A} f(z)\,az, \qquad \text{where } f(z) = \frac{e^{2iz}}{z^2 + 9} \tag{131}$$

and the integral is taken along the real axis. We close the contour by the semicircle S_A of Fig. 92.

For large A, the function $f(z)$ has one pole inside the semicircle, at $z = 3i$. And by Eq. (108) its residue at this pole is

$$R(3i) = \frac{e^{2iz}}{2z}\bigg|_{3i} = \frac{e^{-6}}{6i}. \tag{132}$$

If we apply the residue theorem to the closed contour, we find

$$\int_{-A}^{A} f(z)dz + \int_{S_A} f(z)dz = 2\pi i R(3i). \tag{133}$$

If $z = x + iy$,

$$e^{2iz} = e^{-2y+2xi} = e^{-2y}(\cos 2x + i \sin 2x) \qquad \text{and} \qquad |e^{2iz}| = e^{-2y}. \tag{134}$$

Since this is at most unity on S_A, the maximum value of $|f(z)|$ again behaves like $1/A^2$ as $A \to \infty$, and the integral on $S_A \to 0$. Hence the result of letting $A \to \infty$ in Eq. (133) is

$$I_c = 2\pi i R(3i) = 2\pi i \frac{e^{-6}}{6i} = \frac{\pi}{3} e^{-6}. \tag{135}$$

And, from Eq. (130),

$$I_3 = \frac{1}{2} \mathbf{R} I_c = \frac{\pi}{6} e^{-6}. \tag{136}$$

Equation (134) shows that $|e^{2iz}|$ is small for y large and positive, but large for y large and negative. Also $|e^{-2iz}|$ is large for y large and positive, but small for y large and negative. Hence $|\cos 2z|$ is large for y large with either sign. This explains why we could not use the original integrand.

Equating imaginary parts of Eq. (135) leads to

$$\int_{-\infty}^{\infty} \frac{\sin 2x}{x^2 + 9} \, dx = \mathbf{I} I_c = 0. \tag{137}$$

This also follows from Prob. 5 of Exercises IV (page 186).

By more refined reasoning than that used above, it may be shown that the integral on S_A approaches zero as $A \to \infty$ if $f(z)$

has the form $e^{imz}Q(z)$, $m > 0$, and the maximum value of $|Q(z)|$ behaves like $1/A$. This enables us to evaluate any integral of the type $\int_{-\infty}^{\infty} e^{imx}Q(x)dx$, provided that $Q(x)$ is a rational function whose denominator is of degree at least *one* higher than the numerator and has no real roots. If the roots of the denominator in the upper half of the z plane are $\alpha_1, \alpha_2, \cdots, \alpha_p$,

$$\int_{-\infty}^{\infty} e^{imx}Q(x)dx = 2\pi i[R(\alpha_1) + R(\alpha_2) + \cdots + R(\alpha_p)]. \quad (138)$$

Here $m > 0$, and the residues are those of $f(z) = e^{imz}Q(z)$.

If the coefficients of $Q(x)$ are *real*, the real and imaginary parts of the left member of (138) are

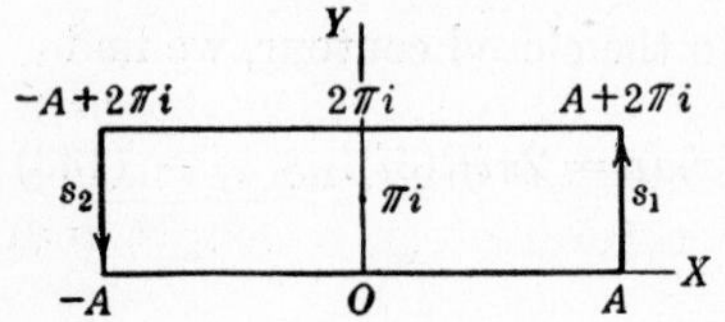

Fig. 93.

$$\int_{-\infty}^{\infty} \cos mx \, Q(x)dx$$

and

$$\int_{-\infty}^{\infty} \sin mx \, Q(x)dx. \quad (139)$$

Hence these integrals may be found by equating the real and imaginary parts of Eq. (138).

If one of the integrands in (139) is *even*, the corresponding integral from 0 to ∞ may be found as one-half that from $-\infty$ to ∞.

EXAMPLE 4. $I_4 = \int_{-\infty}^{\infty} \dfrac{e^{px}}{1 + e^x} dx, \qquad 0 < p < 1. \quad (140)$

As before, we consider this as the limit when $A \to \infty$ of

$$\int_{-A}^{A} f(z)dz, \qquad \text{where } f(z) = \frac{e^{pz}}{1 + e^z}, \quad (141)$$

and the integral is taken along the real axis. But here we take the closed contour as the rectangle of Fig. 93 whose sides are parts of the lines $y = 0$, $y = 2\pi$, $x = A$, and $x = -A$.

The poles of $f(z)$ are found from

$$1 + e^z = 0, \qquad z = \log(-1) = \pi i \pm 2k\pi i. \quad (142)$$

Thus there is one pole inside the contour, at $z = \pi i$. And, by Eq. (108), the residue of $f(z)$ at this pole is

$$R(\pi i) = \frac{e^{pz}}{e^z}\bigg|_{\pi i} = -e^{p\pi i}. \quad (143)$$

If we apply the residue theorem to the closed contour, we find

$$\int_{-A}^{A} f(z)dz + \int_{s_1} f(z)dz + \int_{A+2\pi i}^{-A+2\pi i} f(z)dz + \int_{s_2} f(z)dz = 2\pi i R(\pi i),$$

(144)

in which s_1 denotes the side from A to $A + 2\pi i$ and s_2 the side from $-A + 2\pi i$ to $-A$.

If $z = x + iy$,

$$e^{pz} = e^{px+pyi} = e^{px}(\cos py + i \sin py) \qquad \text{and} \qquad |e^{pz}| = e^{px}.$$

(145)

Similarly $|e^z| = e^x$. It follows that as $A \to \infty$, M, the maximum value of $|f(z)|$, behaves like $e^{-(1-p)A}$ on s_1 and like e^{-pA} on s_2. Since the restriction on p, $0 < p < 1$, makes each of these functions approach zero, and the length L of s_1 and s_2 remains constant, it follows from Eq. (86) that the integrals along s_1 and s_2 each approach zero as $A \to \infty$.

Since $e^{2\pi i} = 1$, we have

$$f(Z + 2\pi i) = \frac{e^{p(Z+2\pi i)}}{1 + e^{Z+2\pi i}} = \frac{e^{2p\pi i}e^{pZ}}{1 + e^{Z}} = e^{2p\pi i}f(Z). \qquad (146)$$

Consequently the substitution $z = Z + 2\pi i$ makes

$$\int_{A+2\pi i}^{-A+2\pi i} f(z)dz = \int_{A}^{-A} f(Z + 2\pi i)dZ = -e^{2p\pi i} \int_{-A}^{A} f(Z)dZ.$$

(147)

Hence the third integral in (144) differs from the first by a simple constant factor only. This explains why we chose the line $y = 2\pi i$ as part of the contour.

Now let $A \to \infty$ in Eq. (144), taking account of Eq. (147). The result is

$$I_4 - e^{2p\pi i}I_4 = 2\pi i R(\pi i) = -2\pi i e^{p\pi i}. \qquad (148)$$

We may solve this for I_4 to obtain

$$I_4 = \frac{-2\pi i e^{p\pi i}}{1 - e^{2p\pi i}} = \pi \left(\frac{2i}{e^{p\pi i} - e^{-p\pi i}} \right) = \frac{\pi}{\sin p\pi}. \qquad (149)$$

This result may be used to show that

$$\int_{0}^{\infty} \frac{x^{p-1}}{1 + x} \, dx = \frac{\pi}{\sin p\pi}, \qquad 0 < p < 1. \qquad (150)$$

For the substitution $x = e^t$ makes

$$\int_0^\infty \frac{x^{p-1}}{1+x}\, dx = \int_{-\infty}^\infty \frac{e^{pt}}{1+e^t}\, dt = I_4 = \frac{\pi}{\sin p\pi}. \quad (151)$$

92. Indented Contours. Let us consider an example.

EXAMPLE 5. $\quad I_5 = \int_{-\infty}^\infty \frac{\sin x}{x}\, dx = 2 \int_0^\infty \frac{\sin x}{x}\, dx. \quad (152)$

This would be of type (139), if it were not for the fact that the denominator has a real root, zero, which causes the function

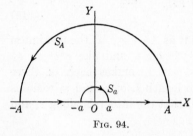

FIG. 94.

$$f(z) = \frac{e^{iz}}{z} \quad (153)$$

to have a pole at the origin. To avoid this pole, we modify the contour used in Example 3 by drawing a small semicircle S_a of radius a about the origin. This gives the closed contour of Fig. 94. Since there are no poles inside this contour, we have

$$\int_a^A f(z)dz + \int_{S_A} f(z)dz + \int_{-A}^{-a} f(z)dz + \int_{S_a} f(z)dz = 0, \quad (154)$$

where S_a is traversed in the clockwise direction.

If we put $z = -Z$ in the third integral of (154), we find

$$\int_{-A}^{-a} \frac{e^{iz}}{z}\, dz = \int_A^a \frac{e^{-iZ}}{Z}\, dZ = -\int_a^A \frac{e^{-iZ}}{Z}\, dZ. \quad (155)$$

Consequently the sum of the first and third integrals is

$$\int_a^A f(z)dz + \int_{-A}^{-a} f(z)dz = \int_a^A \frac{e^{iz}-e^{-iz}}{z}\, dz = 2i \int_a^A \frac{\sin z}{z}\, dz. \quad (156)$$

The limit of this, as $A \to \infty$ and $a \to 0$ is iI_5. The integral along S_A approaches zero when $A \to \infty$, since the integrand has the form $e^{imz}Q(z)$ with $m > 0$, and maximum $|Q(z)|$ behaving like $1/A$.

Along S_a, $z \to 0$ and $e^{iz} \to 1$ when $a \to 0$. It follows from this that when $a \to 0$, the limit of the integral of $f(z)$ along S_a is the same as the limit of

$$\int_{S_a} \frac{dz}{z} = \int_{-a}^a \frac{dz}{z} = \log z \Big|_{-a}^a = (\log r + i\theta)\Big|_{a,\pi}^{a,0} = -i\pi. \quad (157)$$

Now let $A \to \infty$ and $a \to 0$ in Eq. (154), taking account of Eqs. (156) and (157). The result is

$$iI_5 - i\pi = 0, \qquad \text{so that } I_5 = \pi. \qquad (158)$$

When a contour includes part of a small circle with center α, inserted to avoid a singularity of the integrand $f(z)$ at α, the contour is said to be *indented* at α. For example, the contour of Fig. 94 is the contour of Fig. 92 indented at O.

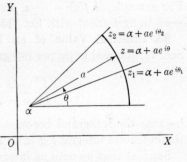

Let each indented arc S_a be that part of the circle of radius a about α between two straight lines through α. Then, if $f(z)$ has a simple pole at α, the limit of the integral of $f(z)$ along S_a when $a \to 0$ may be found as follows.

Fig. 95.

Let θ denote the angle from the positive x axis to the radius from α to z, any point on the arc S_a. Then on S_a,

$$z - \alpha = ae^{i\theta} \qquad \text{and} \qquad \log(z - \alpha) = \log a + i\theta.$$

And, if the end points of S_a are z_1 and z_2, with angles θ_1 and θ_2,

$$\int_{S_a} \frac{dz}{z - \alpha} = \log(z - \alpha) \Big|_{z_1}^{z_2} = (\log a + i\theta) \Big|_{\theta_1}^{\theta_2} = i(\theta_2 - \theta_1). \quad (159)$$

For a simple pole, $m = 1$ in Eq. (105) and we may write

$$f(z) = \frac{R(\alpha)}{z - \alpha} + \phi(z), \qquad (160)$$

where $R(\alpha)$ is the residue of $f(z)$ at α, and $\phi(z)$ is analytic at α. Along S_a, $z \to \alpha$ when $a \to 0$. Hence M, the maximum value of $|\phi(z)|$ on S_a, approaches $|\phi(\alpha)|$. But L, the length of S_a, approaches zero. Hence by Eq. (86) the integral of $\phi(z)$ along S_a approaches zero when $a \to 0$. Consequently,

$$\lim_{a \to 0} \int_{S_a} f(z) dz = \lim_{a \to 0} \int_{S_a} \frac{R(\alpha) dz}{z - \alpha} = R(\alpha) i(\theta_2 - \theta_1), \quad (161)$$

by Eq. (159).

If S_a is C_α, a complete counterclockwise circuit about α, $\theta_2 - \theta_1 = 2\pi$, and the factor $2\pi i$ is in accord with the residue theorem. If S_a is a semicircle traversed clockwise, $\theta_2 - \theta_1 = -\pi$, and

$$\lim_{a \to 0} \int_{S_a} f(z) dz = -\pi i R(\alpha). \tag{162}$$

For example, if $f(z) = e^{iz}/z$, $R(0) = 1$ and the right member is $-\pi i$, in agreement with Eq. (157).

93. Principal Value of an Integral. By the definition of Sec. 71, the real improper integral

$$\int_0^6 \frac{dx}{x - 2} \text{ diverges}, \tag{163}$$

because the integrand becomes infinite at $x = 2$, and as $x \to 2$ the indefinite integral $\log |x - 2| \to -\infty$.

Suppose that we omit an interval with center at the singularity, in this case from $2 - a$ to $2 + a$, and then let $a \to 0$. For any small a greater than zero we find

$$\int_0^{a-2} \frac{dx}{x - 2} = \log |x - 2| \Big|_0^{a-2} = \log a - \log 2, \tag{164}$$

and

$$\int_{2+a}^6 \frac{dx}{x - a} = \log |x - 2| \Big|_{2+a}^6 = \log 4 - \log a. \tag{165}$$

Thus the sum is $\log 2$, which approaches the limit $\log 2$ when $a \to 0$. The number obtained by this process is known as the *principal value* of the integral and is indicated by **P**, so that

$$\mathbf{P} \int_0^6 \frac{dx}{x - 2} = \lim_{a \to 0} \left[\int_0^{2-a} \frac{dx}{x - 2} + \int_{2+a}^6 \frac{dx}{x - 2} \right] = \log 2. \tag{166}$$

The term *Cauchy principal value* is sometimes used, and the symbol **P** is often omitted in technical literature.

To show how contour integration may be used to find a principal value, we discuss a case.

EXAMPLE 6. $I_6 = \mathbf{P} \int_{-\infty}^{\infty} \frac{e^{px}}{1 - e^x} dx, \qquad 0 < p < 1. \tag{167}$

This is the limit, for $A \to \infty$ and $a \to 0$ of

$$\int_{-A}^{-a} f(z)dz + \int_{a}^{A} f(z)dz, \qquad \text{where } f(z) = \frac{e^{pz}}{1 - e^z}. \quad (168)$$

The poles of $f(z)$ are found from

$$1 - e^z = 0, \qquad z = \log(1) = 0 \pm 2k\pi i.$$

The pole at zero makes the integral divergent and necessitates the use of a principal value. Since the poles at O and $2\pi i$ are on the boundary of the contour used in Example 4, we shall indent the contour of Fig. 93 at these points to obtain the modified contour of Fig. 96. Since there are no poles inside the indented contour, we find

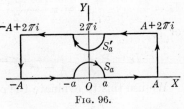

Fig. 96.

$$\int_{-A}^{-a} f(z)dz + \int_{S_a} f(z)dz + \int_{a}^{A} f(z)dz + \int_{s_2} f(z)dz + \int_{A+2\pi i}^{a+2\pi i} f(z)dz$$
$$+ \int_{S_{a'}} f(z)dz + \int_{-a+2\pi i}^{-A+2\pi i} f(z)dz + \int_{s_1} f(z)dz = 0. \quad (169)$$

The reasoning used in Example 4 shows that when $A \to \infty$ the integrals along s_1 and s_2 each approach zero. And, using the substitution $z = Z + 2\pi i$ as we did to deduce (147), we find that here

$$\int_{A+2\pi i}^{a+2\pi i} f(z)dz + \int_{-a+2\pi i}^{-A+2\pi i} f(z)dz$$
$$= -e^{2p\pi i} \left[\int_{-A}^{-a} f(z)dz + \int_{a}^{A} f(z)dz \right]. \quad (170)$$

By Eq. (108) the residues of $f(z)$ at the simple poles O and $2\pi i$ are

$$R(0) = \frac{e^{pz}}{-e^z}\bigg|_0 = -1 \quad \text{and} \quad R(2\pi i) = \frac{e^{pz}}{-e^z}\bigg|_{2\pi i} = -e^{2p\pi i}.$$
$$(171)$$

Since S_a and $S_{a'}$ are each semicircles traversed clockwise, Eq. (162) applies and

$$\lim_{a \to 0} \int_{S_a} f(z)dz = -\pi i R(0) = \pi i, \qquad (172)$$

$$\lim_{a \to 0} \int_{S_{a'}} f(z)dz = -\pi i R(2\pi i) = \pi i e^{2p\pi i}. \qquad (173)$$

Now let $A \to \infty$ and $a \to 0$ in Eq. (169), combining the first and third integrals to give the limit I_6 and using Eq. (170) to transform the sum of the fifth and seventh integrals. The result is

$$I_6 + \pi i - e^{2p\pi i} I_6 + \pi i e^{2p\pi i} = 0. \tag{174}$$

We may solve this for I_6 to obtain

$$I_6 = \frac{\pi i (e^{2p\pi i} + 1)}{e^{2p\pi i} - 1} = \pi \frac{e^{p\pi i} + e^{-p\pi i}}{2} \frac{2i}{e^{p\pi i} - e^{-p\pi i}} = \pi \frac{\cos p\pi}{\sin p\pi} \tag{175}$$

or

$$I_6 = \mathbf{P} \int_{-\infty}^{\infty} \frac{e^{px}}{1 - e^x} \, dx = \pi \cot p\pi, \qquad 0 < p < 1. \tag{176}$$

We use this to evaluate the *convergent* improper integral

$$\int_{-\infty}^{\infty} \frac{e^{px} - e^{qx}}{1 - e^x} \, dx = \pi(\cot p\pi - \cot q\pi). \tag{177}$$

94. Two-dimensional Flow. We wish to study the steady two-dimensional motion of an incompressible fluid in a plane. We consider a simply connected region R, in which there are no sources or sinks. Let the velocity of the particle at the point x,y be the vector

$$\mathbf{q}(x,y) = q_1(x,y)\mathbf{i} + q_2(x,y)\mathbf{j}. \tag{178}$$

A curve such as BB', tangent at each of its points to the vector $\mathbf{q}(x,y)$ for that point is called a *streamline*. Now draw two curves from $A = (a,b)$, a fixed point to $B = (x,y)$, any point in R. Since the fluid is incompressible, the amount of fluid crossing each of these curves C and C^*, in the clockwise sense about A, will be the same. Let us calculate it for C. Since the vector

$$d\mathbf{s} = dx\,\mathbf{i} + dy\,\mathbf{j} \tag{179}$$

is tangent to C, the vector

$$\mathbf{n} = dy\,\mathbf{i} - dx\,\mathbf{j} \tag{180}$$

will be normal to C. And it is of length ds. Hence the flow in unit time across an element of C will be

$$ds\,\text{Proj}_\mathbf{n}\,\mathbf{q} = \mathbf{n} \cdot \mathbf{q} = q_1 dy - q_2 dx. \tag{181}$$

Thus the flow across AB will be

$$S(x,y) = \int_{a,b}^{x,y} (-q_2 dx + q_1 dy). \tag{182}$$

We write the limits only, instead of indicating the path, since the value does not depend on the path. Regarded as a function of x,y this flow in unit time is called the *stream function*. Furthermore, since no fluid crosses the curve BB', the stream function will be the same at B and B'. And the streamlines will be those curves for which the stream function is constant.

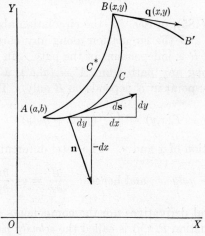

Fig. 97.

Since the integral in Eq. (182) is independent of the path, it follows from the condition (41) that

$$\frac{\partial q_1}{\partial x} = \frac{\partial(-q_2)}{\partial y} \qquad \text{or} \qquad \frac{\partial q_1}{\partial x} + \frac{\partial q_2}{\partial y} = 0. \qquad (183)$$

This is known as the *equation of continuity*.

For the steady streaming of a fluid, the *circulation* along a curve is defined as the integral of the tangential velocity component times ds, or

$$ds \operatorname{Proj}_{ds} \mathbf{q} = ds \cdot \mathbf{q} = q_1 dx + q_2 dy. \qquad (184)$$

The circulation K about any closed curve B_T bounding a region T is

$$K = \int_{B_T} (q_1 dx + q_2 dy) = \int_T \left(\frac{\partial q_2}{\partial x} - \frac{\partial q_1}{\partial y}\right) dx\, dy, \qquad (185)$$

by Green's theorem (13). The quantity

$$\omega = \frac{1}{2}\left(\frac{\partial q_2}{\partial x} - \frac{\partial q_1}{\partial y}\right) \qquad (186)$$

is called the *rotation*, since $\omega(x,y)$ is the angular velocity of an element of the fluid at x,y. If $\omega = 0$ for all points of the region considered, the motion is said to be *irrotational*.

We now assume that our motion is irrotational, so that

$$\frac{\partial q_2}{\partial x} = \frac{\partial q_1}{\partial y}. \tag{187}$$

Then by Eq. (185), or Sec. 82, the circulation about any closed curve is zero, and the circulation along any curve joining two fixed points in R is independent of the path. In particular, the circulation along any path from $A' = (a',b')$, a fixed point to $B = (x,y)$, any point in R depends on B only. Thus

$$P(x,y) = \int_{a',b'}^{x,y} (q_1 dx + q_2 dy) \tag{188}$$

defines a function of x and y. The total differential of $P(x,y)$ is

$$dP = q_1 dx + q_2 dy \qquad \text{and hence} \qquad \frac{\partial P}{\partial x} = q_1, \frac{\partial P}{\partial y} = q_2. \tag{189}$$

Since its partial derivatives are the components of the velocity vector, the function $P(x,y)$ is called the *velocity potential*.

By Eq. (182) the total differential of $S(x,y)$ is

$$dS = -q_2 dx + q_1 dy \qquad \text{and hence} \qquad \frac{\partial S}{\partial x} = -q_2, \frac{\partial S}{\partial y} = q_1. \tag{190}$$

A comparison of this equation with (189) shows that

$$\frac{\partial P}{\partial x} = \frac{\partial S}{\partial y} \qquad \text{and} \qquad \frac{\partial S}{\partial x} = -\frac{\partial P}{\partial y}. \tag{191}$$

These have the same form as the Cauchy-Riemann equations (67). It follows that the function $F(z)$ obtained by setting

$$F(z) = P(x,y) + iS(x,y) \tag{192}$$

is an analytic function of $z = x + iy$ in R. Thus the velocity potential and stream function are a pair of conjugate functions, with all the properties discussed in Secs. 85–87. In particular, they each satisfy Laplace's equation.

Any given analytic function $F(z)$ determines a possible plane irrotational motion of an incompressible fluid, whose velocity potential and stream function are given by Eq. (192).

We note that, from Eq. (65)

$$\frac{dF}{dz} = F'(z) = \frac{\partial P}{\partial x} + i\frac{\partial S}{\partial x} = q_1 - iq_2. \tag{193}$$

Hence the velocity vector corresponds to the complex number

$$q_1 + iq_2 = \overline{F'(z)}, \qquad \text{conjugate to } F'(z). \tag{194}$$

This fact may be used to find the velocity components if $F(z)$ is given. For example, the function

$$F(z) = c \log z, \qquad c \text{ a real constant}, \tag{195}$$

is analytic in any simply connected region R not including the origin. Here

$$F'(z) = \frac{c}{z}, \qquad \text{so that } q_1 + iq_2 = \overline{F'(z)} = \frac{c}{\bar{z}}. \tag{196}$$

Let us set

$$z = re^{i\theta}, \ \bar{z} = re^{-i\theta}, \qquad \text{and} \qquad \frac{c}{\bar{z}} = \frac{c}{re^{-i\theta}} = \frac{c}{r}e^{i\theta}. \tag{197}$$

This shows that the velocity is along the radius vector and that its magnitude is inversely proportional to r.

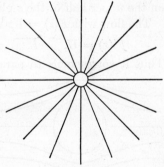

FIG. 98.

We may consider such velocities in the multiply connected region consisting of the plane with the origin removed. Then the flow corresponds to a source at the origin of strength $2\pi c$, since fluid crosses any circle about the origin at a rate

$$2\pi r\left(\frac{c}{r}\right) = 2\pi c.$$

If we wished to have the functions $P(x,y)$ and $S(x,y)$ as obtained from (192) exactly those of Eqs. (188) and (182) with $A = (a,b)$ and $A' = (a',b')$ both at z_0, we would have to use $c \log z - c \log z_0$ in place of $F(z)$. However, additive constants in any of the functions $P(x,y)$, $S(x,y)$, and $F(z)$ are usually unimportant, since the chief significance of these functions is the relation of their derivatives to the velocity.

To show how one flow may be mapped into another by a
suitable conformal transformation, or analytic function, let us
consider the relation

$$z = \frac{1}{2}\left(w + \frac{1}{w}\right) \qquad (198)$$

as a mapping of part of the w plane on the upper half of the
z plane.   The function takes the part of the u axis with $|u| > 1$

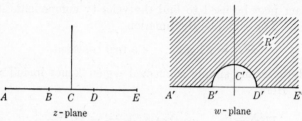

z-plane w-plane

Fig. 99.

into the part of the x axis with $|x| > 1$.   And the unit semicircle
$B'C'D'$ in the w plane goes into the segment of the x axis BCD
(Fig. 99), since

$$w = e^{i\theta} \text{ makes } z = \tfrac{1}{2}(e^{i\theta} + e^{-i\theta}) = \cos\theta. \qquad (199)$$

In fact, R', the part of the w plane above $A'B'C'D'E'$ is mapped
on the upper half of the z plane.

The flow with $F(z) = Uz$ with U real has

$$F'(z) = U, \qquad \overline{F'(z)} = U, \qquad q_1 = U, \qquad q_2 = 0. \qquad (200)$$

Thus it corresponds to parallel streaming, or streaming in the

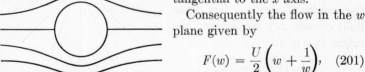

upper half z plane with velocity
tangential to the x axis.

Consequently the flow in the w
plane given by

$$F(w) = \frac{U}{2}\left(w + \frac{1}{w}\right), \qquad (201)$$

Fig. 100.   will correspond to streaming in the
region R' with the velocity tangential to the boundary
$A'B'C'D'E'$, or streaming past a circular barrier.   The streamlines shown in Fig. 100 are obtained from

$$S(u,v) = \frac{U}{2}\left(v - \frac{v}{u^2 + v^2}\right) = k, \qquad (202)$$

They are the images of $y = k/U$ under the transformation.

A method of finding the proper transformation for simple polygonal barriers is given in Sec. 95.

In discussing flow we have used the terminology of hydro-dynamics for the sake of concreteness. However, much of the discussion applies to the flow of electricity and heat. More-

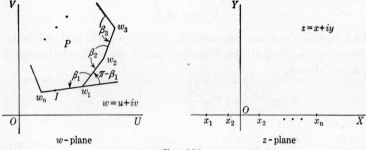

w-plane

z-plane

FIG. 101.

over, the conformal transformation of conjugate functions often simplifies the solution of Laplace's equation in two dimensions for given boundary conditions. And that solution may represent velocity potential, electrostatic potential, magnetic potential, gravitational potential, or steady-state temperature.

95. The Schwarz Transformation. There is a general expression, due to Schwarz, for a function $w(z)$ which will map the

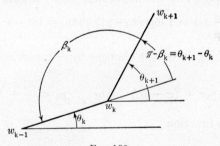

FIG. 102.

upper half of the z plane, where $z = x + iy$, on the interior of a given polygon P in the w plane, where $w = u + iv$. Call the vertices of the polygon in the w plane $w_1, w_2, \cdots, w_n$. And let their images on the real axis of the z plane be $x_1, x_2, \cdots, x_n$. The subscripts are chosen in such a way that $x_1 < x_2 < \cdots < x_n$. Then the vertices $w_1, w_2, \cdots, w_n$ will necessarily follow around P in the positive direction, and there will be a point I on the side $w_n w_1$ which is the image of infinity in the z plane. Denote the interior angle of the polygon at w_k by β_k. Then the exterior angle at w_k will be $\pi - \beta_k$.

For any complex number, the polar angle θ is the imaginary part of the logarithm, since $z = re^{i\theta}$ implies $\log z = \log r + i\theta$ or

$$\mathbf{I} \log z = \theta.$$

As x passes along any segment $x_{k-1} x_k$, $\Delta z = \Delta x$ is real, while Δw along $w_{k-1} w_k$ makes the constant angle θ_k with the positive u axis. Hence

$$\mathbf{I} \log \frac{\Delta w}{\Delta z} = \mathbf{I} \log \frac{dw}{dz} = \theta_k \text{ along } w_{k-1} w_k. \tag{203}$$

Similarly

$$\mathbf{I} \log \frac{dw}{dz} = \theta_{k+1} \text{ along } w_k w_{k+1}. \tag{204}$$

Thus when z passes along the x axis through x_k,

$$\mathbf{I} \log \frac{dw}{dz} \text{ changes by } (\theta_{k+1} - \theta_k) = (\pi - \beta_k) \text{ at } x_k. \tag{205}$$

Let us seek a function that behaves in this way. Now $x - x_k$ is negative before x reaches x_k, and positive after x_k. Since it rotates through $-\pi$ in the upper half plane, it follows that

$$\mathbf{I} \log (z - x_k) = \mathbf{I} \log (x - x_k) \text{ changes by } -\pi \text{ at } x_k. \tag{206}$$

And

$$\mathbf{I} \log (z - x_k)^{p_k} \text{ changes by } -p_k \pi \text{ at } x_k. \tag{207}$$

If we set

$$-p_k \pi = (\pi - \beta_k) \qquad \text{or} \qquad p_k = \frac{\beta_k}{\pi} - 1, \tag{208}$$

we obtain the function

$$(z - x_k)^{p_k}, \qquad p_k = \frac{\beta_k}{\pi} - 1. \tag{209}$$

This suggests that dw/dz has the form

$$\frac{dw}{dz} = G(z - x_1)^{p_1}(z - x_2)^{p_2} \cdots (z - x_n)^{p_n}, \tag{210}$$

so that

$$w = G \int (z - x_1)^{p_1}(z - x_2)^{p_2} \cdots (z - x_n)^{p_n} dz + A. \tag{211}$$

Here G and A are complex constants, and

$$p_k = \frac{\beta_k}{\pi} - 1. \tag{212}$$

In fact, for any value of the constants involved, the function $w(z)$ obtained from (211) will map the x axis in the z plane on some polygon P^* in the w plane. And at w_k, the image of x_k, the interior angle of the polygon will be β_k, related to the p_k by (212). For the angle made by Δw with the positive u axis will be constant along the image of each segment $x_{k-1}x_k$ and will increase by $\pi - \beta_k$ at each vertex w_k.

The constant of integration A determines the position of P^* with respect to the origin, so that changing A displaces P^* parallel to itself.

The constant $G = ge^{i\gamma}$ determines the size and orientation of P^*. To change the size by a given constant scale factor, we multiply g by this factor. To rotate the polygon through a constant angle about the origin, we add this constant to γ.

The constants x_k determine the ratios of the sides of P^*. If any three of the x_k are chosen at random, the remaining $n - 3$ may be so determined that P^* has the shape of any polygon with interior angles β_k. This is related to the fact that the shape of a polygon of n sides with given angles depends on $n - 3$ parameters.

The foregoing discussion makes plausible the following properties of the Schwarz transformation [Eq. (211)], which we state without proof.

I. With any three of the x_k chosen arbitrarily, the remaining constants G, A, and the x_k in (211) may be so determined that the function $w(z)$ maps the x axis on the boundary of the polygon P, each traversed in the positive sense.

II. This function $w(z)$ will then map the points of the upper half z plane on the points of the interior of the polygon P in the w plane in a one-to-one manner.

The form of dw/dz shows that all its singularities are on the real axis and that it is never zero in the upper half z plane. Hence the function $w(z)$ is analytic, and the mapping is conformal at all points of the upper half z plane. Moreover, the inverse function $z = z(w)$ obtained by solving $w = w(z)$ is analytic at all points inside the polygon P in the w plane.

The transformation may be applied in some cases where the polygon P does not have all its vertices located in the finite part of the plane, as will be seen from our examples.

EXAMPLE 1. Let the polygon P be the opening between two straight lines, making an angle β. Here there is just one finite vertex, so that we may take $x_1 = 0$, and

$$p_1 = p = \frac{\beta}{\pi} - 1. \tag{213}$$

Thus

$$\frac{dw}{dz} = Gz^p, \qquad w = \frac{G}{p+1} z^{p+1} + A. \tag{214}$$

We take $A = 0$, which makes $w(0) = 0$, and hence $w_1 = 0$. And we set the coefficient $G/(p+1) = c$ and take c real. This makes the positive u axis the image of the positive x axis. This leads us to the transformation

$$w = cz^m, \qquad m = p + 1 = \frac{\beta}{\pi}. \tag{215}$$

Since the lines $y = $ constant in Fig. 103 are the streamlines for parallel flow in the upper half z plane past the x axis, their

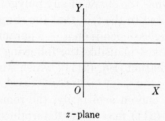
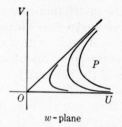

z-plane w-plane

FIG. 103.

images under the transformation (215) will be the streamlines for flow around two straight barriers meeting at an angle β. For a particular m and any convenient choice of the scale factor c, the image of $y = y_0$ may be obtained from

$$w = c(x + iy_0)^m. \tag{216}$$

A series of values of x, inserted in (216), will yield a series of values of $w = u + iv$ and hence of points u,v on the image curve.

Some of these curves are shown in the figures. For flow inside a 45° opening, $\beta = \pi/4$ and $m = \frac{1}{4}$ (Fig. 103). For flow inside

a square corner, $\beta = \pi/2$ and $m = \frac{1}{2}$ (Fig. 104). For flow outside a square corner, $\beta = 3\pi/2$ and $m = \frac{3}{2}$ (Fig. 105). For
flow around the two sides of a single barrier, $\beta = 2\pi$ and $m = 2$
(Fig. 106).

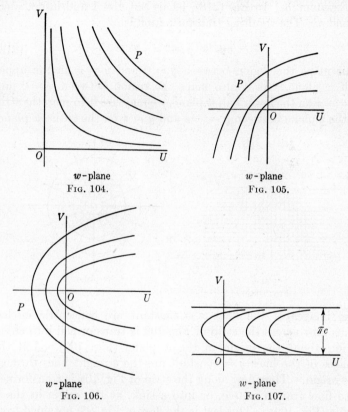

w - plane
FIG. 104.

w - plane
FIG. 105.

w - plane
FIG. 106.

w - plane
FIG. 107.

EXAMPLE 2.   Let us consider the limiting case of the polygon
of Example 1 obtained by letting $\beta \to 0$, while w_1 moves to
infinity.   When $\beta \to 0$ in (213), $p \to -1$ and

$$\frac{dw}{dz} = Gz^{-1}, \qquad w = G \log z + A. \qquad (217)$$

With $A = 0$ and $G = c$, a real constant, this becomes

$$w = c \log z. \qquad (218)$$

This maps the space between the lines $v = 0$ and $v = \pi c$ in the

w plane on the upper half z lane.   The images of the curves
y = constant, the streamlines of a flow along one plate and back
along a parallel plate are shown in Fig. 107.   Here c depends on
the distance between the parallel barriers.

EXAMPLE 3.   In Eq. (218), let us put $c = 1$ and interchange
w and z.   The resulting transformation is

$$z = \log w \qquad \text{or} \qquad w = e^z. \tag{219}$$

This maps the region between $y = 0$ and $y = \pi$ on the upper
half w plane.   As it also maps the region between $y = 0$ and
$y = -\pi$ on the lower half w plane, we may use it to map the strip
of the z plane between $y = -\pi$ and $y = \pi$ on the entire w plane.

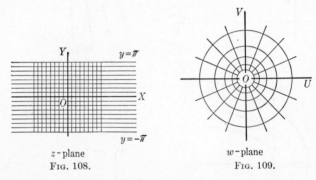

z-plane
FIG. 108.

w-plane
FIG. 109.

The images of the lines x = constant are concentric circles.
Thus flow across the strip of Fig. 108 is transformed into circulation about the origin in the w plane (Fig. 109).   And the
images of the lines y = constant are the straight lines through
the origin.   Thus flow along the strip of Fig. 108 is transformed
into flow from a source, or into a sink, at the origin in the w
plane (Fig. 109).   This last is the flow of Fig. 98, obtained from
Eq. (195).

EXAMPLE 4.   Let the polygon P be bounded by three straight
lines with two square corners (Fig. 110).   Then

$$\beta_1 = \beta_2 = \frac{\pi}{2}, \qquad \text{so that } p_1 = p_2 = -\frac{1}{2}. \tag{220}$$

Hence, if we take $x_1 = -1$ and $x_2 = 1$, we shall have

$$\frac{dw}{dz} = G(z + 1)^{-\frac{1}{2}}(z - 1)^{-\frac{1}{2}} = \frac{G}{i\sqrt{1 - z^2}}. \tag{221}$$

and

$$w = \frac{G}{i} \sin^{-1} z + A, \quad \text{or} \quad w = c \sin^{-1} z, \quad (222)$$

if we put $A = 0$ and $G/i = c$, a real constant. This maps the segment of the u axis between $-c\pi/2$ and $c\pi/2$ on the segment of the x axis between -1 and 1. Thus the semiinfinite rectangle of Fig. 110 is related to the axes as shown. The curves sketched are streamlines for flow along the sides of the rectangle, the images of the lines $y = $ constant in the z plane (Fig. 111).

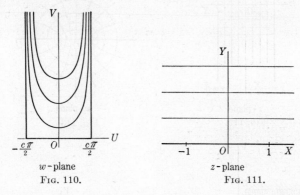

w-plane
Fig. 110.

z-plane
Fig. 111.

EXAMPLE 5. In Eq. (222) let us put $c = 1$ and interchange w and z. The resulting transformation is

$$z = \sin^{-1} w \quad \text{or} \quad w = \sin z. \quad (223)$$

This maps the region with $-\pi/2 \leqq x \leqq \pi/2$, $y \geqq 0$ in the z plane on the upper half w plane. As it also maps the region with $-\pi/2 \leqq x \leqq \pi/2$, $y \leqq 0$ on the lower half w plane, we may use it to map the infinite strip $-\pi/2 \leqq x \leqq \pi/2$ on the entire w plane. The images of the lines $y = $ constant are confocal ellipses with foci at $w = -1$ and $w = 1$. They are the streamlines for flow about a barrier in the w plane (Fig. 113) along the part of the u axis between -1 and 1. The images of the lines x constant are confocal hyperbolas with foci at $w = -1$ and $w = 1$. They are the streamlines for flow around two barriers along the u axis, separated by a slot from -1 to 1 through which the flow takes place.

EXAMPLE 6. Let us start with the strip of Example 2 (Fig. 107), which had one angle zero at infinity. And consider the strip formed from it by folding back the right half of the upper edge about any point of this edge, along itself to give an angle 2π.   Thus

$$\beta_1 = 2\pi, \qquad \beta_2 = 0, \qquad \text{so that } p_1 = 1, p_2 = -1. \quad (224)$$

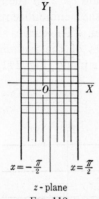

z - plane
FIG. 112.

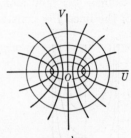

w - plane
FIG. 113.

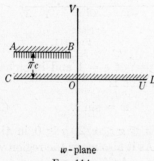

w - plane
FIG. 114.

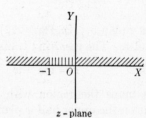

z - plane
FIG. 115.

And, if we take $x_1 = -1$ and $x_2 = 0$, we shall have

$$\frac{dw}{dz} = G(z+1)z^{-1} = G\left(1 + \frac{1}{z}\right), \qquad w = G(z + \log z) + A. \quad (225)$$

With $A = 0$ and $G = c$, a real constant, this becomes

$$w = c(z + \log z). \tag{226}$$

The image of $x_1 = -1$ is $w_1 = c(-1 + \pi i)$, point B in Fig. 114. And the segments AB (upper side), BA (lower side), CD in the w plane (Fig. 114) are mapped on the segments $x < -1$, $-1 < x < 0$, $x > 0$ of the x axis in the z plane (Fig. 115).

EXAMPLE 7.   Let us combine the transformation of Example 3 with that of Example 6.   With Z in place of w, Eq. (219) is

$$z = \log Z \quad \text{or} \quad Z = e^z. \tag{227}$$

And with Z in place of z, Eq. (226) is

$$w = c(Z + \log Z). \tag{228}$$

The result of eliminating Z from these equations is

$$w = c(e^z + z). \tag{229}$$

The lines $y = $ constant in the upper half z plane are mapped by (227) into the lines radiating out from a source at the origin in the upper half Z plane.   Then by (228) these lines are mapped into the streamlines for flow from a source at infinity in the channel between AB and CD, flowing through the channel and fanning out into the upper half plane. The transformation (229), like those of Examples 3 and 5, may be extended symmetrically into the lower half plane.   Thus the images of the lines $y = $ constant in the z plane by the transformation (229), shown in Fig. 116, give the streamlines for flow out of a channel.

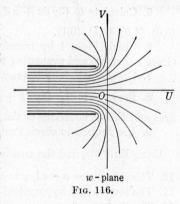

w - plane

FIG. 116.

This transformation is also used in connection with the electrostatic field near the edge of a parallel plate condenser.

96. References.   For further details on the applications of line integrals and complex variables, the student may consult *The Elements of Aerofoil and Airscrew Theory* by H. Glauert, *Complex Variable and Operational Calculus with Technical Applications* by N. W. Mclachlan, *Conjugate Functions for Engineers* by M. Walker, and *Theory of Functions as Applied to Engineering Problems* by Rothe, Ollendorf, and Pohlhausen.

Justification of the calculations on residues used here will be found in the author's *Treatise on Advanced Calculus*, Chap. XIII.   A comprehensive text on complex variables which includes the Schwarz transformation is the *Vorlesungen über allgemeine Funktionentheorie und elliptische Funktionen* by R. Courant and A. Hurwitz.

EXERCISES V

1. Calculate $\int_{0,0}^{2,4} (2y^2dx - 3xy\ dy)$ over the path C_1 along $y = 2x$ and also over C_2 along $y^2 = 8x$.

2. Calculate $\int_{0,0}^{3,1} (2xy\ dx + 3x^2dy)$ over the path C_1 along $x^2 = 9y$ and also over C_2 along $x = 3y$.

3. Calculate $\oint (4y\ dx + 2x\ dy)$ around the circle $x = \cos\ t$, $y = \sin t$.

4. Calculate $\oint (2y\ dx - 5x\ dy)$ around the ellipse $x = 4\cos t$, $y = 2\sin t$.

5. Calculate $\oint (3y\ dx + x\ dy)$ around the square with vertices at $(0,0)$, $(1,0)$, $(1,1)$, $(0,1)$.

6. Check Prob. 1 by transforming the integral over $C_1 - C_2$ by Green's theorem and evaluating the double integral.

7. Check Prob. 2 by the method of Prob. 6.

8. Prove that $\int_{B_T} (ay\ dx + bx\ dy) = (b - a)A_T$, where A_T is the area and B_T the boundary of the region T.

9. Use Prob. 8 to check Probs. 3, 4, and 5.

Using Eq. (20), find the area bounded by

10. The ellipse $x = a\cos t$, $y = b\sin t$.

11. The four-cusped hypocycloid $x = a\cos^3 t$, $y = a\sin^3 t$.

12. The lines $y = 0$, $x = -a$, and the involute, $0 < t < \pi$,

$$x = a(\cos t + t\sin t), \qquad y = a(\sin t - t\cos t).$$

13. The epicycloid of $(n - 1)$ cusps, $0 < t < 2\pi$,

$$x = a(n\cos t - \cos nt), \qquad y = a(n\sin t - \sin nt).$$

14. The hypocycloid of $(n + 1)$ cusps, $0 < t < 2\pi$,

$$x = a(n\cos t + \cos nt), \qquad y = a(n\sin t - \sin nt).$$

15. The loop of the strophoid, $-\pi/4 < t < \pi/4$,

$$x = a\cos 2t, \qquad y = a\tan t\cos 2t.$$

For each of the following exact differential expressions, find an indefinite integral $F(x,y)$ whose total differential dF equals the given expression:

16. $(x^3 + 12x^2y)dx + (2y + 4x^3)dy$.

17. $(x^2 + y^2)^2(x\,dx + y\,dy)$.

18. $(e^x + e^y)dx + (1 + x)e^y dy$.

19. $(x + \cos y)dx + (y - x \sin y)dy$.

20. $\dfrac{y\,dx - x\,dy}{x^2 + 4y^2}$, $(x,y) \neq (0,0)$.

21. $\dfrac{-y\,dx + x\,dy}{4x^2 - y^2}$, $4x^2 \neq y^2$.

22. $ax^m y^n[(m + 1)y\,dx + (n + 1)x]dy$, $m > 0$, $n > 0$.

23. If the potential energy is $U(x,y) = k(x^2 + y^2)^{-\frac{1}{2}}$, show that the force is an attraction toward the origin inversely proportional to the square of the distance.

24. With the notation of Prob. 62 of Exercises III (page 137), let $d\mathbf{s} = \mathbf{i}_1 dr + \mathbf{j}_1 r\,d\theta$. Hence if the force is $\mathbf{F} = F_r \mathbf{i}_1 + F_\theta \mathbf{j}_1$, the element of work is $dW = F_r dr + rF_\theta d\theta$. Deduce from this that if there is a potential energy function $U(r,\theta)$ such that $dU = -dW$, then as a consequence $F_r = -\dfrac{\partial U}{\partial r}$ and $F_\theta = -\dfrac{1}{r}\dfrac{\partial U}{\partial \theta}$.

25. Check Prob. 23 by using Prob. 24 with $U = k/r$.

26. For an ideal gas, Eq. (50) holds and $pv = RT$, R constant. Assume that $dQ = c\,dT + p\,dv$, c constant. This means that for $dT = 0$, $dQ = p\,dv$. And for $dv = 0$, $dQ/dT = c$, the specific heat at constant volume. Derive the equation $dQ = (c + R)dT - v\,dp$, and use it to show that the specific heat at constant pressure C is constant and equal to $c + R$.

27. From $pv = RT$, $dQ = c\,dT + p\,dv$, and $c + R = C$, Prob. 26, deduce that $dS = \dfrac{dQ}{T} = c\dfrac{dp}{p} + C\dfrac{dv}{v}$. Hence show that the change in entropy along any path from p_0, v_0 to p, v is

$$S(p,v) - S(p_0,v_0) = c \log p + C \log v - c \log p_0 - C \log v_0.$$

28. An adiabatic curve in the pv diagram is one on which $dQ = 0$. Hence $dS = 0$, and the entropy is constant. Show that for the system of Probs. 26 and 27 the adiabatic through p_0, v_0 is $pv^k = p_0 v_0^k$, where $k = C/c = 1 + R/c$. In air $k = 1.4$ and the adiabatic is $pv^{1.4} = p_0 v_0^{1.4}$.

For each given $f(z)$ find the conjugate functions $u(x,y)$ and $v(x,y)$ such that $f(x + iy) = u + iv$. Also verify directly that Eqs. (67), (71), and (74) hold.

29. $(2 + 3i)z$.   **30.** $3z^2$.   **31.** e^{3z}.   **32.** iz^3.

33. $\sin 2z$.   **34.** $\cos z$.   **35.** $\sinh z$.   **36.** $\cosh 3z$.

Verify that the given function satisfies Laplace's equation, and find $f(z)$ such that $f(z) = u + iv$ is analytic if

37. $u = x + 2y$.   **38.** $u = 6xy$.   **39.** $u = e^x \sin y$.

40. $v = \cos x \sinh y$.   **41.** $v = 6x^2 y - 2y^3$.   **42.** $v = e^y \cos x$.

43. Let $w = f(z)$ be analytic. Write $z = re^{i\theta}$ in $w = u + iv$ so that $f(re^{i\theta}) = u(r,\theta) + iv(r,\theta)$. Show that when θ is constant $dz = e^{i\theta}dr$ and $\dfrac{dw}{dz} = e^{-i\theta}\left(\dfrac{\partial u}{\partial r} + i\dfrac{\partial v}{\partial r}\right)$. And that when r is constant the relations are $dz = ire^{i\theta}d\theta$ and $\dfrac{dw}{dz} = e^{-i\theta}\left(-\dfrac{i}{r}\dfrac{\partial u}{\partial \theta} + \dfrac{1}{r}\dfrac{\partial v}{\partial \theta}\right)$.

44. Use Prob. 43 to derive the polar form of the Cauchy-Riemann equations $\dfrac{\partial u}{\partial r} = \dfrac{1}{r}\dfrac{\partial v}{\partial \theta}$ and $\dfrac{\partial v}{\partial r} = -\dfrac{1}{r}\dfrac{\partial u}{\partial \theta}$.

45. Check Prob. 44 by finding the condition for exactness of the real and imaginary parts of $\dfrac{f(z)}{z}\,dz = (u + iv)\left(\dfrac{dr}{r} + i\,d\theta\right)$.

46. By eliminating v from the equations of Prob. 44 show that $r\dfrac{\partial}{\partial r}\left(r\dfrac{\partial u}{\partial r}\right) + \dfrac{\partial^2 u}{\partial \theta^2} = 0$. This is the polar form of Laplace's equation. Also show that $r\dfrac{\partial}{\partial r}\left(r\dfrac{\partial v}{\partial r}\right) + \dfrac{\partial^2 v}{\partial \theta^2} = 0$.

For each given $f(z)$ find the conjugate functions $u(r,\theta)$ and $v(r,\theta)$ such that $f(re^{i\theta}) = u + iv$. Also verify directly that the equations of Probs. 44 and 46 hold.

47. $\log z$.   **48.** $4i \log z$.   **49.** $3iz^2$.   **50.** $2z^3$.
51. $1/z$.   **52.** $z^{1/2}$.   **53.** $5e^{2iz}$.   **54.** ae^{iAz^p}, a, A, p, real.

Find the value, over any path joining the given end points, of each of the following integrals:

55. $\displaystyle\int_0^i (4z^3 + 4z)dz.$ **56.** $\displaystyle\int_2^{2+i} (z - 2)^2 dz.$ **57.** $\displaystyle\int_{\pi i}^{2\pi i} e^z dz.$

Calculate each of the following integrals over the path C_1, the upper half of the circle $x^2 + y^2 = 25$. Also over C_2, the lower half of the same circle.

58. $\displaystyle\int_{-5}^{5} \dfrac{2z + 3}{z^2}\,dz.$ **59.** $\displaystyle\int_{-5}^{5} \dfrac{2\,dz}{z^2 - 1}.$ **60.** $\displaystyle\int_{-5}^{5} \dfrac{dz}{z - 1}.$

61. Check the last three problems by using the residue theorem to evaluate each integral over $C_2 - C_1$.

62. Show that, over any path not passing through the origin, $\displaystyle\int_{-1}^{1}\left(4 + \dfrac{1}{z^2}\right)dz = 6$. Compare Prob. 37 of Exercises IV (page 189).

63. Prove Cauchy's *integral formula*, $f(z) = \dfrac{1}{2\pi i}\displaystyle\int_{C_z} \dfrac{f(t)dt}{t - z}$, where C_z denotes a positive circuit about z, and C_z is inside some region in which $f(z)$ is analytic. HINT: Replace t, z, C_z by z, α, C_α and apply the residue theorem to the integral.

64. With the notation of Prob. 63, prove that the nth derivative of $f(z)$, $f^{(n)}(z) = \dfrac{n!}{2\pi i} \displaystyle\int_{C_z} \dfrac{f(t)dt}{(t-z)^{n+1}}$. See the hint to Prob. 63 and compute the residue by Eq. (109).

65. Let $f(z)$ be analytic inside T and on B_T. Assume that $f(z) \neq 0$ on B_T, and let N denote the number of roots of $f(z) = 0$, or zeros of $f(z)$, inside T, where a zero of order m is counted m times. Show that $N = \dfrac{1}{2\pi i} \displaystyle\int_{B_T} \dfrac{f'(z)}{f(z)}\, dz$. HINT: If $f(z)$ has an m-fold zero at the point α,

$$f(z) = (z - \alpha)^m g(z), \qquad g(\alpha) \neq 0. \quad \text{Hence } \frac{f'(z)}{f(z)} = \frac{m}{z - \alpha} + \frac{g'(z)}{g(z)}. \quad \text{Now}$$

apply the residue theorem to this function, using a circuit C in which $g(z) \neq 0$.

66. Let $f(z)$ be analytic inside T and on B_T. Assume that $f(z) \neq 0$ on B_T and that $f(z) = 0$ has only one simple root α inside T. Show that $\alpha = \dfrac{1}{2\pi i} \displaystyle\int_{B_T} \dfrac{z f'(z)}{f(z)}\, dz$. HINT: The integrand has a simple pole at α, with $R(\alpha) = \alpha$.

Using complex integration as in Sec. 91, verify that

67. $\displaystyle\int_0^\pi \frac{dx}{5 - 4\cos x} = \frac{\pi}{3}.$ **68.** $\displaystyle\int_0^\pi \frac{dx}{(5 - 4\cos x)^2} = \frac{5\pi}{27}.$

69. $\displaystyle\int_0^\pi \frac{dx}{a + b\cos x} = \frac{\pi}{\sqrt{a^2 - b^2}}, \qquad a >]b|.$

70. $\displaystyle\int_0^{\pi/2} \sin^4 x\, dx = \frac{1}{4}\int_0^{2\pi} \sin^4 x\, dx = \frac{3\pi}{16}.$

71. $\displaystyle\int_0^{\pi/2} \cos^{2n} x\, dx = \frac{\pi}{2}\frac{1 \cdot 3 \cdot 5 \cdots (2n-1)}{2 \cdot 4 \cdot 6 \cdots 2n}, \qquad n$ a positive integer.

72. $\displaystyle\int_0^\infty \frac{dx}{(x^2 + a^2)(x^2 + b^2)} = \frac{\pi}{2ab(a+b)}, \qquad a > 0, b > 0.$

73. $\displaystyle\int_0^\infty \frac{dx}{x^4 + 1} = \frac{\pi}{2\sqrt{2}}.$ **74.** $\displaystyle\int_0^\infty \frac{x^2\, dx}{x^6 + 1} = \frac{\pi}{6}.$

75. $\displaystyle\int_0^\infty \frac{dx}{x^4 - 6x^2 + 25} = \frac{\pi}{20}.$ HINT: $x^4 - 6x^2 + 25$
$$= (x^2 + 5)^2 - (4x)^2.$$

76. $\displaystyle\int_0^\infty \frac{\cos mx}{a^2 + x^2}\, dx = \frac{\pi e^{-am}}{2a}, \qquad a > 0, m > 0.$

77. $\displaystyle\int_0^\infty \frac{x \sin mx}{a^2 + x^2}\, dx = \frac{\pi e^{-am}}{2}, \qquad a > 0, m > 0.$

78. $\displaystyle\int_0^\infty \frac{\cos mx}{4 + x^4}\, dx = \frac{\pi}{8} e^{-m}(\cos m + \sin m), \qquad m > 0.$

79. From Prob. 69, by differentiation with respect to a, deduce that
$$\int_0^\pi \frac{dx}{(a + b \cos x)^2} = \frac{\pi a}{(a^2 - b^2)^{3/2}}, \qquad a > |b|. \quad \text{Use this to check Prob. 68.}$$

80. Using complex integration as in Sec. 92, show that
$$\int_0^\infty \frac{\sin mx}{x(a^2 + x^2)} \, dx = \frac{\pi}{2a^2} (1 - e^{-am}), \qquad a > 0, \, m > 0.$$

81. Check Probs. 76 and 77 by differentiating the result of Prob. 80 twice with respect to m.

82. From Prob. 80, by differentiation with respect to a, deduce that
$$\int_0^\infty \frac{\sin mx}{x(a^2 + x^2)^2} \, dx = \frac{\pi}{2a^4} \left(1 - \frac{2 + am}{2} e^{-am} \right), \qquad a > 0, \, m > 0.$$

83. Show that the integral $\displaystyle\int_0^\infty \frac{x^m dx}{x^n + 1} = \frac{\pi}{n \sin \left(\dfrac{m + 1}{n} \pi \right)}$, if $0 < m + 1 < n$. HINT: Make the substitution $x^n = t$ and use Eq. (150).

84. Use Prob. 83 to check Probs. 73 and 74.

85. Show that $\displaystyle\int_{-\infty}^\infty \frac{e^{2ax}}{\cosh \pi x} \, dx = \sec a, \qquad -\frac{\pi}{2} < a < \frac{\pi}{2}.$ HINT: Make the substitution $2\pi x = t$ and use Eq. (151).

86. Given $\displaystyle\int_0^\infty e^{-x^2} dx = \frac{\sqrt{\pi}}{2}$, derived in Prob. 82 of Exercises IV (page 193), show that $\displaystyle\int_0^\infty e^{-x^2} \cos 2bx \, dx = \frac{\sqrt{\pi}}{2} e^{-b^2}$. HINT: Integrate e^{-z^2} around a rectangle bounded by $y = 0$, $y = b$, $x = -A$, $x = A$.

87. Using the integral given in Prob. 86, deduce that
$$\int_0^\infty \cos x^2 dx = \int_0^\infty \sin x^2 dx = \frac{\sqrt{2\pi}}{4}.$$
HINT: Integrate e^{-z^2} around the sector of the circle of radius A bounded by the lines $y = 0$ and $y = x$, together with a circular arc S_A. As $A \to \infty$, the integral on $S_A \to 0$. On $y = 0$, the integral approaches $\displaystyle\int_0^\infty e^{-x^2} dx = \frac{\sqrt{\pi}}{2}$. And on $y = x$, if we put $z = \dfrac{1 + i}{\sqrt{2}} t$, the integral approaches
$$\int_0^\infty e^{-z^2} dz = \int_0^\infty (\cos t^2 - i \sin t^2) \frac{1 + i}{\sqrt{2}} \, dt.$$

88. If a two-dimensional flow has $\mathbf{q} = -ay\mathbf{i} + ax\mathbf{j}$, show that the rotation defined in Eq. (186) is constant, $\omega = a$. By Sec. 52, the fluid is moving like a rigid plane rotating about the z axis with angular velocity a, since $a\mathbf{k} \times (x\mathbf{i} + y\mathbf{j}) = -ay\mathbf{i} + ax\mathbf{j}$.

89. For a steady plane flow with no external forces,
$$\frac{\partial q_1}{\partial x} q_1 + \frac{\partial q_1}{\partial y} q_2 = -\frac{1}{\rho} \frac{\partial p}{\partial x} \quad \text{and} \quad \frac{\partial q_2}{\partial x} q_1 + \frac{\partial q_2}{\partial y} q_2 = -\frac{1}{\rho} \frac{\partial p}{\partial y}. \quad \text{Here } p(x,y)$$

is the pressure in pounds per square foot and $\rho = D/g$ is the constant density in slugs per cubic foot. Assume that the motion is irrotational so that by Eq. (187) $\partial q_2/\partial x = \partial q_1/\partial y$. Deduce from these equations that $dp = -\rho(q_1 dq_1 + q_2 dq_2)$ and hence that $p = -\dfrac{\rho}{2}(q_1{}^2 + q_2{}^2) + c$.

90. If the motion of Prob. 89 is related to $F(z)$ by equation (192), show that the pressure $p = -\dfrac{\rho}{2}|F'(z)|^2 + c$.

91. Show that $S(x,y) = x^2 + 2xy - y^2 - x - y$ determines an irrotational motion, and find $P(x,y)$ and $F(z) = P + iS$. At what point is the fluid at rest?

92. Find the pressure difference between $(0,0)$ and $(5,10)$ for the motion of Prob. 91, if the conditions of Probs. 89 and 90 hold and (a) the fluid is water with $\rho = 1.93$ slugs/ft.³, (b) the fluid is air with $\rho = 0.00238$ slug/ft.³

Using Eq. (194) and Prob. 90, find the velocity components q_1, q_2 and the pressure p for the fluid motion determined by each of the following functions $F(z)$:

93. z.   **94.** z^2.   **95.** e^z.   **96.** $-\cos z$.   **97.** $\sinh z$.

98. As in Prob. 24 write $d\mathbf{s} = \mathbf{i}_1 dr + \mathbf{j}_1 r\, d\theta$. And let the velocity $\mathbf{q} = q_r \mathbf{i}_1 + q_\theta \mathbf{j}_1$. And if K is the circulation of Eq. (185), show that
$$K = \int_{B_r} (q_r dr + r q_\theta d\theta) = \int_T \left(q_\theta + r\frac{\partial q_\theta}{\partial r} - \frac{\partial q_r}{\partial \theta} \right) dr\, d\theta.$$ Also that $K = \displaystyle\int_T 2\omega r\, dr\, d\theta$. Deduce that $\omega = \dfrac{1}{2}\left(\dfrac{q_\theta}{r} + \dfrac{\partial q_\theta}{\partial r} - \dfrac{1}{r}\dfrac{\partial q_r}{\partial \theta} \right)$. For irrotational motion, $\omega = 0$, and there is a velocity potential $P(r,\theta)$ such that $dP = q_r dr + r q_\theta d\theta$, and hence $q_r = \dfrac{\partial P}{\partial r}$, $q_\theta = \dfrac{1}{r}\dfrac{\partial P}{\partial \theta}$.

99. With the notation of Prob. 98, $\mathbf{n}$ of Eq. (180) is $\mathbf{i}_1 r\, d\theta - \mathbf{j}_1 dr$. Show that the stream function $S(r,\theta)$ is the integral of $-q_\theta dr + r q_r d\theta$, and hence $q_\theta = -\dfrac{\partial S}{\partial r}$, $q_r = \dfrac{1}{r}\dfrac{\partial S}{\partial \theta}$.

100. Show that the functions P and S of Probs. 98 and 99 satisfy the equations $\dfrac{\partial P}{\partial r} = \dfrac{1}{r}\dfrac{\partial S}{\partial \theta}$ and $\dfrac{\partial S}{\partial r} = -\dfrac{1}{r}\dfrac{\partial P}{\partial \theta}$. These have the same form as those derived in Prob. 44.

101. Using Probs. 43, 99, and 100 show that the polar components of the velocity may be obtained from $F(z) = F(re^{i\theta}) = P(r,\theta) + iS(r,\theta)$ by means of the relation $e^{i\theta}F'(z) = q_r - iq_\theta$.

Using Probs. 101 and 90, find the velocity components q_r, q_θ and the pressure p in terms of r and θ for the fluid motion determined by each of the following functions $F(z)$:

102. $\log z$.   **103.** z^4.   **104.** $1/z$.   **105.** $z^{2/3}$.   **106.** z^m, m real.

107. If $F(z) = \log\ (z - \alpha_1)^{k_1} \cdots (z - \alpha_n)^{k_n}$ show that the flow with $P + iS = F(z)$ has a "source" with strength $2\pi k_p$ at $z = \alpha_p$. If the sum of the k's is not zero, we must think of an additional "source" at infinity of strength $-2\pi(k_1 + k_2 + \cdots + k_n)$. A "source" of negative strength is a sink.

108. Plot by points the streamline $S = 1$ if $F(z) = \log\ (z^2 - 1)$.

109. Show that if $F(z) = \log \dfrac{z - 1}{z + 1}$, the streamlines $S = $ constant, as well as the equipotentials $P = $ constant are "circles," including straight lines as degenerate cases.

110. If $F(z) = -ic \log z$, show that the streamlines are circles about O, and that the circulation around C_O, any positive circuit about O, is $2\pi c$.

111. Show that $F(z) = b(z + a^2/z)$, for $|z| > a$, corresponds to streaming past a barrier in the form of a circle of radius a. The velocity at infinity is b, since for z large, $F(z)$ is nearly bz.

112. Probs. 110 and 111 show that $F(z) = -ic \log z + b(z + a^2/z)$ corresponds to streaming past a circle of radius a, combined with circulation $2\pi c$ around the circle. Plot the streamline $S = 1$ if $a = b = c = 1$.

113. Plot, by points, the curve in the w plane which is the image of the circle $(x - 0.2)^2 + (y - 0.3)^2 = 1.53$ under the transformation $w = z + 1/z$. HINT: For any point on the circle, measure r, calculate $1/r$, and plot $1/z$ with polar coordinates $1/r$, θ. Then add to z by the graphical construction of Sec. 6.

The curve is an example of the Joukowski airfoil. It is possible to find the streamlines for flow past it by first finding them for the circle as in Prob. 112 and then mapping them on the w plane by $w = z + 1/z$.

114. Plot the streamlines of liquid flow from a channel obtained as the images of $y = 0$, $\pi/4$, $\pi/2$ under $w = e^z + z$.

115. Plot the lines of force of a parallel-plate condenser, obtained as the images of $x = 0$, $\frac{1}{2}$, 1 under $w = e^z + z$.

116. Show that the elliptic integral $w = \displaystyle\int_0^z \dfrac{dz}{\sqrt{(1 - z^2)(1 - k^2z^2)}}$, $k < 1$, maps the upper half z plane on a rectangle in the w plane. The points $x_1 = -1/k$, $x_2 = -1$, $x_3 = 1$, $x_4 = 1/k$ go into the vertices $w_1 = -K + iK'$, $w_2 = -K$, $w_3 = K$, $w_4 = K + iK'$, where

$$K = \int_0^1 \frac{dx}{\sqrt{(1 - x^2)(1 - k^2x^2)}} \qquad \text{and} \qquad K' = \int_1^{1/k} \frac{dx}{\sqrt{(x^2 - 1)(1 - k^2x^2)}}.$$

117. Let t be any real or complex number not equal to 0 or $\pm k\pi$, one of the poles of $\cot z$. For any integer n such that $n\pi > |t|$, let S_n be the square whose sides are $x = \pm(n + \frac{1}{2})\pi$, $y = \pm(n + \frac{1}{2})\pi$. Show that

$$\int_{S_n} \left(\cot z - \frac{1}{z}\right)\left(\frac{1}{z - t} - \frac{1}{z}\right) dz = 2\pi i \left(\cot t - \sum_{k=1}^{n} \frac{2t}{t^2 - n^2\pi^2}\right).$$

As $n \to \infty$, the integral on $S_n \to 0$. Assuming this, deduce that

$$\cot t - \frac{1}{t} = \sum_{k=1}^{\infty} \frac{2t}{t^2 - n^2\pi^2}.$$

118. By integrating the result of Prob. 117 from 0 to z, show that

$\log\left(\frac{\sin z}{z}\right) = \sum_{n=1}^{\infty} \log\left(1 - \frac{z^2}{n^2\pi^2}\right)$, and hence

$\sin z = z\left[1 - \left(\frac{z}{\pi}\right)^2\right]\left[1 - \left(\frac{z}{2\pi}\right)^2\right]\left[1 - \left(\frac{z}{3\pi}\right)^2\right]\left[1 - \left(\frac{z}{4\pi}\right)^2\right] \cdots .$

CHAPTER VI

THE GAMMA FUNCTION
AND RELATED DEFINITE INTEGRALS

The Gamma function, a generalization of the factorial function, is defined by an integral between fixed limits which contains the independent variable as a parameter. In this chapter we discuss the Gamma function and certain integrals expressible in terms of it.

97. The Gamma Function. The integral

$$\int_0^\infty x^{p-1}e^{-x}dx \tag{1}$$

is improper because of the infinite limit and, if $p < 1$, because of the discontinuity for $x = 0$. However the tests of Sec. 72 show that the integral converges whenever $p > 0$. For positive values it defines the Gamma function of p, $\Gamma(p)$. Thus

$$\Gamma(p) = \int_0^\infty x^{p-1}e^{-x}dx, \qquad p > 0. \tag{2}$$

If we integrate by parts, we find that

$$\int_0^\infty x^p e^{-x}dx = -x^p e^{-x}\Big|_0^\infty + p\int_0^\infty x^{p-1}e^{-x}dx$$
$$= p\int_0^\infty x^{p-1}e^{-x}dx, \tag{3}$$

since the integrated part is zero at the upper limit by Eq. (224) of Sec. 17, and at the lower limit because $x^p = 0$. By the definition [Eq. (2)], Eq. (3) may be rewritten as

$$\Gamma(p + 1) = p\Gamma(p). \tag{4}$$

If we replace p by $p - 1$, this becomes

$$\Gamma(p) = (p - 1)\Gamma(p - 1). \tag{5}$$

For $p = 1$, we have

$$\Gamma(1) = \int_0^\infty e^{-x}dx = -e^{-x}\Big|_0^\infty = 1. \tag{6}$$

It follows by Eq. (5) that

$$\Gamma(2) = 1\Gamma(1) = 1; \qquad \Gamma(3) = 2\Gamma(2) = 2 \cdot 1;$$
$$\Gamma(4) = 3\Gamma(3) = 3 \cdot 2 \cdot 1. \quad (7)$$

Continuing in this way, we find that for any positive integer n,

$$\Gamma(n) = (n-1)(n-2) \cdots 3 \cdot 2 \cdot 1 = (n-1)! \qquad (8)$$

and

$$\Gamma(n+1) = n(n-1) \cdots 3 \cdot 2 \cdot 1 = n! \qquad (9)$$

where $n!$, read "factorial n," is the product of the integers from 1 up to n. This shows that the function $\Gamma(p+1)$ is a generalization of $p!$, originally defined for integral values only. And many expressions involving factorials of positive integers may be extended to other values by defining

$$p! = \Gamma(p+1) \qquad (10)$$

when p is not a positive integer. The usual definition of 0! as 1 is a special case, since it makes $0! = \Gamma(1)$.

Suppose that the values of $\Gamma(p)$ are known for all values of p in some unit interval, e.g., $1 \leqq p \leqq 2$. Then by using Eq. (5) we may find the value of $\Gamma(p)$ for any p in the next unit interval, $2 < p \leqq 3$, since this makes $1 < p - 1 \leqq 2$. Similarly, we may from these find the value of $\Gamma(p)$ for any p in the interval $3 < p \leqq 4$, and so on for all values of $p > 1$.

Or we may, by repeated use of Eq. (5), deduce that

$$\Gamma(p) = (p-1)(p-2) \cdots (p-n)\Gamma(p-n) \qquad (11)$$

for any positive integer n less than p. Then for any $p > 2$, $p - n$ will lie in the interval $1 \leqq p - n \leqq 2$ if n is the integer between $p - 2$ and $p - 1$.

The solved form of Eq. (4),

$$\Gamma(p) = \frac{\Gamma(p+1)}{p}, \qquad (12)$$

may be used to find the value of $\Gamma(p)$ if $0 < p < 1$.

We use Eq. (4), or its equivalent (12), to define the Gamma function for negative values of the argument. Thus we may regard Eq. (12) as giving the value of $\Gamma(p)$ for $-1 < p < 0$, in terms of $\Gamma(p+1)$ with $0 < p + 1 < 1$. The values for $-2 < p < -1$ are then determined from those for

$$-1 < p + 1 < 0,$$

and so on.

Or we may by repeated use of (12) deduce that

$$\Gamma(p) = \frac{\Gamma(p + n)}{p(p + 1) \cdots (p + n - 1)} \tag{13}$$

for any positive integer n. Then for any $p < 0$ and not a negative integer, $p + n$ will lie in the interval $1 < p + n < 2$ if n is the integer between $-p + 1$ and $-p + 2$. Equation (13) shows that $\Gamma(p)$ becomes infinite as p approaches zero, or any negative integer.

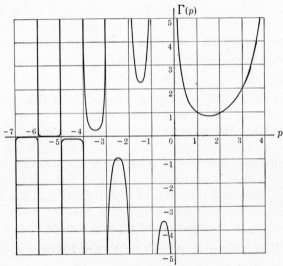

Graph of the Gamma function.
FIG. 117.

We illustrate the remarks just made by computing the values of $\Gamma(3.2)$ and $\Gamma(-1.2)$ from a table of values of $\log_{10} \Gamma(p)$ for $1 < p < 2$, as given in Peirce's *Tables*. We have

$$\Gamma(3.2) = (2.2)(1.2)\Gamma(1.2), \qquad \log_{10} \Gamma(1.2) = \bar{1}.9629$$
$$\log_{10} \Gamma(3.2) = 0.3424 + 0.0792 + \bar{1}.9629 = 0.3845$$
$$\Gamma(3.2) = 2.424. \tag{14}$$

$$\Gamma(-1.2) = \frac{\Gamma(1.8)}{(-1.2)(-0.2)(0.8)}, \qquad \log_{10} \Gamma(1.8) = \bar{1}.9691$$
$$\log_{10} \Gamma(-1.2) = \bar{1}.9691 - (0.0792 + \bar{1}.3010 + \bar{1}.9031) = 0.6858$$
$$\Gamma(-1.2) = 4.851. \tag{15}$$

By computing a sufficient number of values in this way we may construct the graph, as shown in Fig. 117.

98. The Beta Function.   The integral

$$\int_0^1 x^{p-1}(1-x)^{q-1}dx \tag{16}$$

is improper because of the discontinuity at $x = 0$ if $p < 1$, and because of the discontinuity at 1 if $q < 1$.   However, the tests of Sec. 72 show that the integral is convergent if $p > 0$ and $q > 0$.   For positive values it defines the Beta function of p and q, $B(p,q)$.   Thus

$$B(p,q) = \int_0^1 x^{p-1}(1-x)^{q-1}dx, \qquad p > 0, \qquad q > 0. \tag{17}$$

We may express the Beta function in terms of Gamma functions by the following device.   Put $x = y^2$, $dx = 2y\, dy$ in Eq. (2) to obtain

$$\Gamma(p) = \int_0^\infty x^{p-1}e^{-x}dx = 2\int_0^\infty y^{2p-1}e^{-y^2}dy. \tag{18}$$

From this, on replacing p by q and y by x, we find

$$\Gamma(q) = 2\int_0^\infty x^{2q-1}e^{-x^2}dx. \tag{19}$$

It follows that

$$\Gamma(q)\Gamma(p) = 4\int_0^\infty x^{2q-1}e^{-x^2}dx \int_0^\infty y^{2p-1}e^{-y^2}dy. \tag{20}$$

We may regard the repeated integral on the right as a double integral over the first quadrant.   To change to polar coordinates, we replace $dx\, dy$ by $r\, dr\, d\theta$ and obtain

$$\Gamma(q)\Gamma(p) = 4\int_0^{\pi/2} d\theta \int_0^\infty (r\cos\theta)^{2q-1}(r\sin\theta)^{2p-1}e^{-r^2}r\, dr$$
$$= \left[2\int_0^\infty r^{2(p+q)-1}e^{-r^2}dr\right]\left[2\int_0^{\pi/2}\cos^{2q-1}\theta\,\sin^{2p-1}\theta\,d\theta\right]. \tag{21}$$

With $p + q$ in place of q, and r in place of x, (19) becomes

$$\Gamma(p+q) = 2\int_0^\infty r^{2(p+q)-1}e^{-r^2}dr. \tag{22}$$

And the result of substituting

$$x = \sin^2\theta, \qquad 1 - x = \cos^2\theta, \qquad dx = 2\cos\theta\sin\theta\,d\theta \tag{23}$$

in Eq. (17) is

$$B(p,q) = \int_0^1 x^{p-1}(1-x)^{q-1}dx = 2\int_0^{\pi/2}\cos^{2q-1}\theta\,\sin^{2p-1}\theta\,d\theta. \tag{24}$$

A comparison of Eqs. (21), (22), and (24) shows that

$$\Gamma(q)\Gamma(p) = \Gamma(p+q)B(p,q) \text{ and hence } B(p,q) = \frac{\Gamma(p)\Gamma(q)}{\Gamma(p+q)}. \quad (25)$$

This enables us to reduce the evaluation of the Beta function to the calculation of Gamma functions. The symmetrical form shows that $B(p,q) = B(q,p)$.

If we put $p = q = \frac{1}{2}$ in Eq. (25) and then use Eqs. (6) and (24), we find

$$\Gamma(\tfrac{1}{2})\Gamma(\tfrac{1}{2}) = \Gamma(1)B(\tfrac{1}{2},\tfrac{1}{2}) = 2\int_0^{\pi/2} d\theta = \pi. \quad (26)$$

Hence

$$[\Gamma(\tfrac{1}{2})]^2 = \pi \quad \text{and} \quad \Gamma(\tfrac{1}{2}) = \sqrt{\pi}. \quad (27)$$

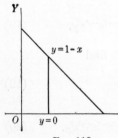

FIG. 118.

The value of the Gamma function for any p that is half an odd integer may be deduced from this by using Eq. (11) when $p = n + \frac{1}{2}$ and Eq. (13) when $p = -n + \frac{1}{2}$.

99. Dirichlet's Multiple Integrals. Consider the double integral of $x^p y^q$ over the triangle defined by

$$x \geqq 0, \qquad y \geqq 0, \qquad x + y \leqq 1. \quad (28)$$

The integral equals

$$\int_0^1 dx \int_0^{1-x} x^p y^q dy = \frac{1}{Q+1}\int_0^1 x^P(1-x)^{Q+1}dx$$

$$= \frac{1}{Q+1} B(p+1, Q+2) \quad (29)$$

by Eq. (17) with $P+1$ in place of p and $Q+2$ in place of q. By Eq. (25) the right member is

$$\frac{1}{Q+1}\frac{\Gamma(P+1)\Gamma(Q+2)}{\Gamma(P+Q+3)} \quad \text{or} \quad \frac{\Gamma(P+1)\Gamma(Q+1)}{\Gamma(P+Q+3)} \quad (30)$$

by (4) with p replaced by $Q+1$. Hence,

$$\int_0^1 dx \int_0^{1-x} x^p y^q dy = \frac{\Gamma(P+1)\Gamma(Q+1)}{\Gamma(P+Q+3)},$$

$$P > -1, Q > -1. \quad (31)$$

The double integral of $x^P y^Q$ over the area defined by

$$x \geqq 0, \qquad y \geqq 0, \qquad \left(\frac{x}{a}\right)^A + \left(\frac{y}{b}\right)^B \leqq 1 \tag{32}$$

may be deduced from (31) by a suitable change of variables. For if

$$u = \left(\frac{x}{a}\right)^A, v = \left(\frac{y}{b}\right)^B; \qquad x = au^{1/A}, y = bv^{1/B}, \tag{33}$$

and

$$\int_0^a dx \int_0^{b[1-(x/a)^A]^{1/B}} x^P y^Q dy$$

$$= \frac{a^{P+1}b^{Q+1}}{AB} \int_0^1 du \int_0^{1-v} u^{\frac{P+1}{A}-1} v^{\frac{Q+1}{B}-1} dv$$

$$= \frac{a^{P+1}b^{Q+1}}{AB} \frac{\Gamma\left(\frac{P+1}{A}\right)\Gamma\left(\frac{Q+1}{B}\right)}{\Gamma\left(\frac{P+1}{A} + \frac{Q+1}{B} + 1\right)}$$

$$P > -1, Q > -1, \tag{34}$$

by Eq. (31).

Similar results hold for integrals of this type in more than two variables. Thus

$$\int_0^1 dx \int_0^{1-x} dy \int_0^{1-x-y} x^P y^Q z^R dz$$

$$= \int_0^1 dx \int_0^{1-x} x^P y^Q \frac{(1-x-y)^{R+1}}{R+1} dy. \tag{35}$$

But, if $y = (1-x)u$,

$$\int_0^{1-x} y^Q (1-x-y)^{R+1} dy = (1-x)^{Q+R+2} \int_0^1 u^Q (1-u)^{R+1} du. \tag{36}$$

Since the integral in u is $B(Q+1, R+2)$, the triple integral in (35) is

$$\frac{B(Q+1, R+2)}{R+1} \int_0^1 x^P (1-x)^{Q+R+2} dx$$

$$= \frac{B(Q+1, R+2)B(P+1, Q+R+3)}{R+1}. \tag{37}$$

By Eqs. (25) and (4) this is

$$\frac{\Gamma(Q + 1)\Gamma(R + 2)\Gamma(P + 1)\Gamma(Q + R + 3)}{(R + 1)\Gamma(Q + R + 3)\Gamma(P + Q + R + 4)}$$
$$= \frac{\Gamma(P + 1)\Gamma(Q + 1)\Gamma(R + 1)}{(P + Q + R + 4)}. \quad (38)$$

And, by a change of variable, we find that the integral of $x^P y^Q z^R$ taken over the volume for which

$$x \geqq 0, \qquad y \geqq 0, \qquad z \geqq 0, \qquad \left(\frac{x}{a}\right)^A + \left(\frac{y}{b}\right)^B + \left(\frac{z}{c}\right)^C \leqq 1 \quad (39)$$

is equal to

$$\frac{a^{P+1}b^{Q+1}c^{R+1}}{ABC} \frac{\Gamma\left(\frac{P + 1}{A}\right) \Gamma\left(\frac{Q + 1}{B}\right) \Gamma\left(\frac{R + 1}{C}\right)}{\Gamma\left(\frac{P + 1}{A} + \frac{Q + 1}{B} + \frac{R + 1}{C} + 1\right)}. \quad (40)$$

Equations (34) and (40) enable us to find the mass, center of gravity, and moments of inertia of uniform plates bounded by the coordinate axes and curves of the form

$$\left(\frac{x}{a}\right)^A + \left(\frac{y}{b}\right)^B = 1, \quad (41)$$

or of uniform solids bounded by the coordinate planes and surfaces of the form

$$\left(\frac{x}{a}\right)^A + \left(\frac{y}{b}\right)^B + \left(\frac{z}{c}\right)^C = 1. \quad (42)$$

As an illustration, consider the first octant of the sphere

$$x^2 + y^2 + z^2 = a^2. \quad (43)$$

When $b = c = a$, $A = B = C = 2$, and $P = Q = R = 0$, the expression (40) is

$$\frac{a^3}{8} \frac{[\Gamma(\frac{1}{2})]^3}{\Gamma(\frac{5}{2})} = \frac{a^3}{8} \frac{[\Gamma(\frac{1}{2})]^3}{\frac{3}{2} \cdot \frac{1}{2}\Gamma(\frac{1}{2})} = \frac{\pi a^3}{6}. \quad (44)$$

This is the volume of one octant of the sphere (43). When $b = c = a$, $A = B = C = 2$, $Q = R = 0$, but $P = 1$, the expression (40) is

$$\frac{a^4}{8} \frac{\Gamma(1)[\Gamma(\frac{1}{2})]^2}{\Gamma(3)} = \frac{a^4}{8} \frac{[\Gamma(\frac{1}{2})]^2}{2!} = \frac{\pi a^4}{16}. \quad (45)$$

Divided by the value found in (44), this gives $\frac{3}{8}a$, the distance from one plane face to the center of gravity of the octant. When $b = c = a$, $A = B = C = 2$, $Q = R = 0$, but $P = 2$, the expression (40) is

$$\frac{a^5}{8} \frac{\Gamma(\frac{3}{2})[\Gamma(\frac{1}{2})]^2}{\Gamma(\frac{7}{2})} = \frac{a^5}{8} \frac{[\Gamma(\frac{1}{2})]^2 \Gamma(\frac{3}{2})}{\frac{5}{2} \cdot \frac{3}{2}\Gamma(\frac{3}{2})} = \frac{\pi a^5}{30}. \tag{46}$$

By symmetry, twice this will give the inertial integral of $(x^2 + y^2)$. Doubling and dividing by the value found in (44) gives $\frac{2}{5}a^2$. And the moment of inertia of the octant about the z axis is $\frac{2}{5}Ma^2$.

100. Alternative Forms. If we put $x = -q \log y$, $q > 0$, in the defining equation for $\Gamma(p)$, (2), we obtain

$$\Gamma(p) = \int_0^\infty x^{p-1}e^{-x}dx = -q^p \int_1^0 y^{q-1}(-\log y)^{p-1}dy \tag{47}$$

or

$$\Gamma(p) = q^p \int_0^1 y^{q-1}\left(\log \frac{1}{y}\right)^{p-1} dy. \tag{48}$$

The special case with $q = 1$, $\int_0^1 \left(\log \frac{1}{y}\right)^{p-1} dy$ is sometimes taken as the integral defining the Gamma function, $\Gamma(p)$.

If we start with the integral, it is more natural to change the notation and write

$$\int_0^1 x^a \left(\log \frac{1}{x}\right)^b dx = \frac{\Gamma(b + 1)}{(a + 1)^{b+1}}, \qquad a > -1, b > -1. \tag{49}$$

The integral of a power of x times the exponential of a power of x from 0 to ∞ is reducible to a Gamma function. Thus with $bx^c = y$,

$$\int_0^\infty x^a e^{-bx^c}dx = \frac{1}{cb^{\frac{a+1}{c}}} \int_0^\infty e^{-y}y^{\frac{a+1}{c}-1}dy = \frac{\Gamma\left(\dfrac{a+1}{c}\right)}{cb^{\frac{a+1}{c}}},$$

$$a > -1, b > 0, c > 0. \tag{50}$$

As examples with $b = h^2$ and $c = 2$ we have

$$\int_0^\infty e^{-h^2x^2}dx = \frac{\Gamma(\frac{1}{2})}{2h} = \frac{\sqrt{\pi}}{2h}. \tag{51}$$

$$\int_0^\infty xe^{-h^2x^2}dx = \frac{\Gamma(1)}{2h^2} = \frac{1}{2h^2}. \tag{52}$$

$$\int_0^\infty x^2e^{-h^2x^2}dx = \frac{\Gamma(\frac{3}{2})}{2h^3} = \frac{\frac{1}{2}\Gamma(\frac{1}{2})}{2h^3} = \frac{\sqrt{\pi}}{4h^3}. \tag{53}$$

These integrals occur in the theory of errors with normal probability distribution. Compare Probs. 87 to 89 of Exercises IV (page 194).

Equations (17) and (25) show that

$$\int_0^1 x^{p-1}(1-x)^{q-1}dx = \mathrm{B}(p,q) = \frac{\Gamma(p)\Gamma(q)}{\Gamma(p+q)}. \tag{54}$$

The integral of any product of two first-degree factors, each of which vanishes at one of the limits, is reducible to Beta functions. Thus with $x - a = (b-a)y$,

$$\int_a^b (x-a)^P(b-x)^Q dx = (b-a)^{P+Q+1}\mathrm{B}(P+1,\,Q+1)$$
$$= (b-a)^{P+Q+1}\frac{\Gamma(P+1)\Gamma(Q+1)}{\Gamma(P+Q+2)},$$
$$b > a, P > -1, Q > -1. \tag{55}$$

And the substitution $x^c = y$ will reduce the integrals

$$\int_a^b (x^c - a^c)^P(b^c - x^c)^Q x^{c-1}dx \quad \text{and} \quad \int_0^b x^R(b^c - x^c)^Q dx \tag{56}$$

to the type evaluated in Eq. (55).

The Beta function may be converted to an integral from 0 to ∞ by making the change of variable

$$x = \frac{y}{1+y}, \qquad 1 - x = \frac{1}{1+y}, \qquad dx = \frac{dy}{(1+y)^2} \tag{57}$$

in

$$\mathrm{B}(p,q) = \int_0^1 x^{p-1}(1-x)^{q-1}dx = \int_0^\infty \frac{y^{p-1}}{(1+y)^{p+q}}\,dy. \tag{58}$$

And the substitution $bx^c = ay$ makes

$$\int_0^\infty \frac{x^P dx}{(a+bx^c)^Q} = \frac{a^{\frac{P+1}{c}-Q}}{cb^{\frac{P+1}{c}}}\int_0^\infty \frac{y^{\frac{P+1}{c}-1}}{(1+y)^Q}\,dy$$
$$= \frac{a^{\frac{P+1}{c}-Q}}{cb^{\frac{P+1}{c}}}\,\mathrm{B}\left(\frac{P+1}{c},\,Q-\frac{P+1}{c}\right), \tag{59}$$

by Eq. (58).

If we put $q = 1 - p$ in Eq. (58), we find

$$\int_0^\infty \frac{y^{p-1}}{1+y}\,dy = \mathrm{B}(p,1-p) = \frac{\Gamma(p)\Gamma(1-p)}{\Gamma(1)}$$
$$= \Gamma(p)\Gamma(1-p). \tag{60}$$

But the particular integral on the left was evaluated in Eq. (150) of Sec. 91. Using the value there given, we find

$$\Gamma(p)\Gamma(1 - p) = \frac{\pi}{\sin p\pi}. \tag{61}$$

The argument just given assumes that $0 < p < 1$. But, if we replace p by $p + 1$ in the left member, we find from Eqs. (4) and (12)

$$\Gamma(p + 1)\Gamma(-p) = p\Gamma(p)\frac{\Gamma(-p + 1)}{-p} = -\Gamma(p)\Gamma(1 - p). \tag{62}$$

Thus the sign is reversed. And with $p + 1$ in place of p the left member also reverses its sign, since $\sin (p + 1)\pi = -\sin p\pi$. This shows that, since Eq. (61) holds for $0 < p < 1$, it holds for $1 < p < 2$, and then for $2 < p < 3$, and so on. And similarly we may replace p by $p - 1$ and show that the equation holds for $-1 < p < 0$, $-2 < p < -1$, and so on. Thus Eq. (61) holds for all real nonintegral values of p.

101. Trigonometric Integrals. An expression for the Beta function in terms of trigonometric functions is given in (24):

$$B(p,q) = 2 \int_0^{\pi/2} \cos^{2q-1} \theta \sin^{2p-1} \theta \, d\theta. \tag{63}$$

If we start with the integral and change the notation, we find

$$\int_0^{\pi/2} \cos^Q \theta \sin^P \theta \, d\theta = \frac{1}{2} B\left(\frac{P + 1}{2}, \frac{Q + 1}{2}\right),$$
$$P > -1, Q > -1. \tag{64}$$

For $P = 0$ or $Q = 0$ this becomes Wallis's integral,

$$W_P = \int_0^{\pi/2} \cos^P \theta \, d\theta = \int_0^{\pi/2} \sin^P \theta \, d\theta$$

$$= \frac{1}{2} B\left(\frac{1}{2}, \frac{P + 1}{2}\right) = \frac{\sqrt{\pi} \, \Gamma\left(\dfrac{P + 1}{2}\right)}{2\Gamma\left(\dfrac{P}{2} + 1\right)}. \tag{65}$$

For a positive integer n, $\Gamma(n) = (n - 1)!$ and

$$\Gamma\left(n + \frac{1}{2}\right) = \left(n - \frac{1}{2}\right)\left(n - \frac{3}{2}\right) \cdots \frac{1}{2} \Gamma\left(\frac{1}{2}\right)$$

$$= \frac{(2n - 1)(2n - 3) \cdots 3 \cdot 1 \sqrt{\pi}}{2^n}. \tag{66}$$

It follows that when $P = 2m + 1$, an odd positive integer, in (65)

$$W_{2m+1} = \frac{2^m m!}{(2m + 1)(2m - 1) \cdots 3 \cdot 1}$$

$$= \frac{2 \cdot 4 \cdots (2m - 2)(2m)}{3 \cdot 5 \cdots (2m - 1)(2m + 1)}. \quad (67)$$

And when $P = 2m$, an even positive integer, in Eq. (65)

$$W_{2m} = \frac{(2m - 1)(2m - 3) \cdots 3 \cdot 1}{2^{m+1} m!} \pi$$

$$= \frac{\pi}{2} \frac{1 \cdot 3 \cdots (2m - 3)(2m - 1)}{2 \cdot 4 \cdots (2m - 2)(2m)}. \quad (68)$$

The expressions (67) and (68) for the value of either integral of Eq. (65) when P is a positive integer are collectively known as *Wallis's formula.* They may be used to deduce Wallis's infinite product for π. We first note that W_P decreases when P is increased by unity, since this multiplies the positive integrand by $\cos \theta$, and $0 < \cos \theta < 1$ for $0 < \theta < \pi/2$. It follows that

$$W_{2m} > W_{2m+1} > W_{2m+2} \text{ and hence } \frac{\pi}{2} > \frac{\pi}{2} \frac{W_{2m+1}}{W_{2m}} > \frac{\pi}{2} \frac{W_{2m+2}}{W_{2m}}. \quad (69)$$

From (68), as written and with $m + 1$ in place of m, we find

$$\frac{W_{2m+2}}{W_{2m}} = \frac{2m + 1}{2m + 2} \to 1 \text{ when } m \to \infty, \quad \text{and}$$

$$\lim_{m \to \infty} \frac{\pi}{2} \frac{W_{2m+2}}{W_{2m}} = \frac{\pi}{2}. \quad (70)$$

And from Eqs. (67) and (68) we find

$$\frac{\pi}{2} \frac{W_{2m+1}}{W_{2m}}$$

$$= \frac{2 \cdot 2 \cdot 4 \cdot 4 \cdots (2m - 2)(2m - 2)(2m)(2m)}{1 \cdot 3 \cdot 3 \cdot 5 \cdots (2m - 3)(2m - 1)(2m - 1)(2m + 1)}. \quad (71)$$

This approaches $\pi/2$ when $m \to \infty$, since the relation (69) shows that it is less than $\pi/2$ and greater than a number that approaches $\pi/2$ by Eq. (70). Consequently,

$$\frac{\pi}{2} = \frac{2}{1} \cdot \frac{2}{3} \cdot \frac{4}{3} \cdot \frac{4}{5} \cdot \frac{6}{5} \cdot \frac{6}{7} \cdots = \lim_{m \to \infty} \frac{2^{4m}(m!)^4}{[(2m)!]^2(2m + 1)}, \quad (72)$$

since the expression (71) may be written

$$\left[\frac{2\cdot 4 \cdots (2m)}{1\cdot 3 \cdots (2m-1)}\right]^2 \frac{1}{2m+1} \left[\frac{2\cdot 4 \cdots (2m)}{2\cdot 4 \cdots (2m)}\right]^2$$

$$= \frac{[2^m 1\cdot 2\cdot 3 \cdots m]^4}{[1\cdot 2\cdot 3 \cdots (2m)]^2 (2m+1)}. \quad (73)$$

102. Stirling's Formula for Factorial *n*. If n is a positive integer, $n! = 1\cdot 2\cdot 3 \cdots n$ and

$$\log (n!) = \log 1 + \log 2 + \log 3 + \cdots + \log n. \quad (74)$$

For n large this sum will be of the order of magnitude of

$$\int_1^n \log x \, dx = (x \log x - x) \Big|_1^n = n \log n - n + 1. \quad (75)$$

If we neglect the 1, we have $n^n e^{-n}$ as a rough estimate of the size of $n!$. A better estimate is $n^{n+\frac{1}{2}}e^{-n}$. To show this, we consider the logarithm of the ratio

$$h(m) = \log \frac{m!}{m^{m+\frac{1}{2}}e^{-m}} = \log (m!) + m - \left(m + \frac{1}{2}\right)\log m. \quad (76)$$

From this

$$h(m) - h(m-1) = \log m + 1 - \left(m + \frac{1}{2}\right)\log m$$

$$+ \left(m - \frac{1}{2}\right)\log (m-1)$$

$$= 1 + \left(m - \frac{1}{2}\right)\log \frac{m-1}{m}. \quad (77)$$

When $m \geqq 2$, $1/m < 1$, and by Eq. (126) of Sec. 11,

$$\log \frac{m-1}{m} = \log \left(1 - \frac{1}{m}\right)$$

$$= -\frac{1}{m} - \frac{1}{2m^2} - \frac{1}{3m^3} - \frac{1}{4m^4} - \cdots. \quad (78)$$

Consequently

$$\left(m - \frac{1}{2}\right)\log \frac{m-1}{m} = -1 - \frac{1}{12m^2} - \frac{1}{12m^3} - \frac{3}{40m^4} - \cdots. \quad (79)$$

It follows from this and Eq. (77) that

$$h(m) - h(m-1) = -\frac{1}{12m^2} - R_m, \quad (80)$$

where for $m \geqq 2$,

$$0 < R_m < \frac{1}{12m^2} \qquad \text{so that} \quad \sum_{m=2}^{n} R_m < \sum_{m=2}^{n} \frac{1}{12m^2}. \qquad (81)$$

Let us next observe that

$$h(n) - h(2) = h(3) - h(2) + h(4) - h(3) + \cdots + h(n) \\ - h(n-1)$$

$$= \sum_{m=2}^{n} [h(m) - h(m-1)]$$

$$= - \sum_{m=2}^{n} \frac{1}{12m^2} - \sum_{m=2}^{n} R_m, \qquad (82)$$

by Eq. (80). For n large

$$\int_n^\infty \frac{1}{12x^2} \, dx = - \frac{1}{12x} \Big|_n^\infty = \frac{1}{12n} \qquad \text{and} \qquad \sum_{n=2}^{\infty} \frac{1}{12m^2} \qquad (83)$$

have the same order of magnitude. Hence for $n \to \infty$ the first sum on the right of (82) converges. And the convergence of the second sum for $n \to \infty$ then follows from the relation (81). Thus we may write

$$\lim_{n \to \infty} h(n) = h(2) - \sum_{m=2}^{\infty} \frac{1}{12m^2} - \sum_{m=2}^{\infty} R_m = \log K, \qquad (84)$$

where K is the constant whose logarithm is defined by this equation.

It follows from Eqs. (76) and (84) that

$$\lim_{n \to \infty} \frac{n!}{n^{n+\frac{1}{2}} e^{-n}} = K, \qquad \text{or} \qquad \lim_{n \to \infty} \frac{n!}{K n^{n+\frac{1}{2}} e^{-n}} = 1. \qquad (85)$$

This confirms our statement that for large n, $n^{n+\frac{1}{2}} e^{-n}$ gives a good estimate of the size of $n!$.

To find the value of K, we use the relation

$$\pi = \lim_{m \to \infty} \frac{2^{4m}(m!)^4}{[(2m)!]^2 m} \qquad (86)$$

which follows from Eq. (72) since $2m/(2m+1) \to 1$ as $m \to \infty$. By the second equation in (85), with $n = m$ and with $n = 2m$, the limit in (86) is the same as the limit of

$$\frac{2^{4m}K^4m^{4m+2}e^{-4m}}{K^2(2m)^{4m+1}e^{-4m}m} = \frac{K^2}{2}, \quad \text{so that } \frac{K^2}{2} = \pi \text{ and } K = \sqrt{2\pi}. \quad (87)$$

The relation obtained by inserting this in Eq. (85),

$$\lim_{n \to \infty} \frac{n!}{\sqrt{2\pi}\ n^{n+\frac{1}{2}}e^{-n}} = 1, \quad (88)$$

is known as *Stirling's formula* for $n!$. It shows that in evaluating the limits, as $n \to \infty$ of expressions containing $n!$ as a factor, we may replace $n!$ by the denominator. This procedure has many applications in the theory of probability.

103. Computation of $\Gamma(x)$ by Stirling's Formula. The denominator of expression (88) has a steadily increasing graph for $n > 2$. And the function $\Gamma(x + 1)$ has a smooth graph, interpolating between the values $\Gamma(n + 1) = n!$ for $x = n$, a positive integer. Hence, we should expect

$$\lim_{x \to \infty} \frac{\Gamma(x + 1)}{\sqrt{2\pi}\ x^{x+\frac{1}{2}}e^{-x}} = \lim_{x \to \infty} \frac{\Gamma(x)}{\sqrt{2\pi}\ x^{x-\frac{1}{2}}e^{-x}} = 1 \quad (89)$$

to hold when x is not restricted to integral values, since for $x = n$ it reduces to Eq. (88).

Equation (89) is a special consequence of the expansion

$$\log \Gamma(x) = \log\left(\sqrt{2\pi}\ x^{x-\frac{1}{2}}e^{-x}\right)$$
$$+ \frac{1}{12x} - \frac{1}{360x^3} + \frac{1}{1260x^5} - \cdots. \quad (90)$$

This has the property that for any positive x each partial sum of terms on the right approximates the left member with an error numerically less than the last term retained. We shall not prove this, merely noting that the term $1/(12x)$ is not unrelated to the $1/(12n)$ in Eq. (83). Regarded as an infinite series, the right member of (90) diverges for all values of x, so that it is an asymptotic expansion as defined in Sec. 76.

For practical computation, we rewrite Eq. (90) in the form

$$\log_{10} \Gamma(x) = 0.39909 + \left(x - \frac{1}{2}\right)\log_{10} x$$
$$- 0.434294\left(x - \frac{1}{12x} + \frac{1}{360x^3} - \cdots\right). \quad (91)$$

For a four-place result we may stop with the term in $1/x^3$ if x exceeds 2, and with the term in $1/x$ if x exceeds 4.

As an example, let $x = 3.2$. Then

$$\log_{10} \Gamma(3.2) = 0.39909 + (2.7)(0.50515)$$
$$- 0.434294 \left(3.2 - \frac{1}{12(3.2)} + \frac{1}{360(3.2)^3} \right)$$
$$= 0.39909 + 1.36390 - 1.38974 + 0.01131 - 0.00004$$
$$= 0.38452. \tag{92}$$

This is in agreement with the value found in Eq. (14).

For negative x, we may not use (91) directly but may use it to compute $\Gamma(1 - x)$, since if $x < 0$, $1 - x > 1$. And then, by Eq. (61),

$$\Gamma(x) = \frac{\pi}{\sin \pi x} \frac{1}{\Gamma(1 - x)}. \tag{93}$$

With $-x$ in place of x, this procedure leads to the equation

$$\log_{10} \Gamma(-x) = 0.09806 - \log_{10} \sin (-180x)^\circ$$
$$- \left(x + \frac{1}{2} \right) \log_{10} (x + 1)$$
$$+ 0.434294 \left[x + 1 - \frac{1}{12(x + 1)} + \frac{1}{360(x + 1)^3} - \cdots \right]. \tag{94}$$

Here $x > 0$, and $\Gamma(-x)$ has the same algebraic sign as

$$\sin (-180x)^\circ.$$

For numerically large arguments the use of Eq. (91) or (94) is less tedious and more accurate than the reduction to tabular values by the method of Sec. 97.

104. References. Short tables of the Gamma function or its logarithm will be found in most mathematical handbooks. An introduction to the theory of the Gamma function is given in Chap. XVI of the author's *Treatise on Advanced Calculus*.

Comprehensive tables, a survey of the theory, and a bibliography will all be found in Vol. I of *Tables of Higher Mathematical Functions*, by H. T. Davis.

EXERCISES VI

Use tables to evaluate

1. $\int_0^\infty x^{4/5} e^{-x} dx.$ **2.** $\int_0^\infty x^{5/4} e^{-x} dx.$ **3.** $\int_0^\infty x^{3/8} e^{-x} dx.$

4. $\Gamma(3.8)$.   **5.** $\Gamma(-2.4)$.   **6.** $\displaystyle\int_0^1 x^{-1/5}(1-x)^{-2/5}dx$

7. Show that $\displaystyle\frac{d\Gamma(p)}{dp} = \int_0^\infty x^{p-1}e^{-x} \log x \, dx$.

8. Show that $\displaystyle\frac{d^n\Gamma(p)}{dp^n} = \int_0^\infty x^{p-1}e^{-x} (\log x)^n dx$.

For $a > -1$, $b > 0$, and n a positive integer show that

9. $\displaystyle\int_0^\infty x^a e^{-bx}dx = \frac{\Gamma(a+1)}{b^{a+1}}$.   **10.** $\displaystyle\int_0^\infty x^n e^{-bx}dx = \frac{n!}{b^{n+1}}$.

11. $\displaystyle\int_0^\infty x^a b^{-x}dx \frac{\Gamma(a+1)}{(\log b)^{a+1}}$.   **12.** $\displaystyle\int_0^\infty x^n b^{-x}dx = \frac{n!}{(\log b)^{n+1}}$.

Use Eq. (34) to find the area in the first quadrant bounded by the axes and each of the following curves:

13. $x^{1/2} + y^{1/2} = a^{1/2}$.   **14.** $x^{2/3} + y^{2/3} = a^{2/3}$.   **15.** $\left(\dfrac{x}{a}\right)^2 + \left(\dfrac{y}{b}\right)^2 = 1$.

16. Find the center of gravity of the area of Prob. 13.

17. For the area of Prob. 14, find the moment of inertia about OX.

18. If the area of Prob. 15 is revolved about OY, find the volume generated.

19. A plate covering the area of Prob. 13 has its density $\rho = 2x^4$. Find the mass of the plate.

20. A plate covering the area of Prob. 14 has its density $\rho = x^2 + y^2$. Find the center of gravity of the plate.

21. For the solid of Prob. 18, find the moment of inertia about its axis OY.

Use Eq. (40) to find the volume in the first octant bounded by the coordinate planes and each of the following surfaces:

22. $x^{1/2} + y^{1/2} + z^{1/2} = a^{1/2}$.   **23.** $x^{2/3} + y^{2/3} + z^{2/3} = a^{2/3}$.

24. $\left(\dfrac{x}{a}\right)^2 + \left(\dfrac{y}{b}\right)^2 + \left(\dfrac{z}{c}\right)^2 = 1$.   **25.** $x^2 + y^4 + z^6 = 1$.

26. Find the center of gravity of the volume of Prob. 22.

27. For the volume of Prob. 23, find the moment of inertia about OZ.

28. A solid filling the volume of Prob. 22 has its density $\rho = x^3$. Find the mass of the solid.

Evaluate each of the following integrals:

29. $\displaystyle\int_0^1 x^2 \left(\log \frac{1}{x}\right)^3 dx$.   **30.** $\displaystyle\int_0^1 \sqrt[5]{\log x} \, dx$.   **31.** $\displaystyle\int_0^\infty e^{-x^3}dx$.

32. $\displaystyle\int_0^\infty x^4 e^{-x^3}dx$.   **33.** $\displaystyle\int_0^2 x^2(2-x)^{13}dx$.

34. $\int_1^3 (x-1)^{-\frac14}(3-x)^{-\frac34}dx.$ **35.** $\int_2^4 (x-2)^{-\frac16}(4-x)^{-\frac56}dx.$

36. $\int_0^1 \dfrac{dx}{\sqrt{1-x^3}}.$ **37.** $\int_0^1 \dfrac{dx}{\sqrt{1-x^4}}.$ **38.** $\int_0^1 \dfrac{x^2dx}{\sqrt{1-x^4}}.$

39. $\int_0^\infty \dfrac{dx}{1+x^4}.$ **40.** $\int_0^\infty \dfrac{x\,dx}{1+x^6}.$ **41.** $\int_0^\infty \dfrac{x\,dx}{1+x^3}.$

42. $\int_0^{\pi/2} \sin^{\frac53} x \cos^{\frac43} x\,dx.$ **43.** $\int_0^{\pi/2} \sqrt{\dfrac{\sin^5 x}{\cos x}}\,dx.$

44. For $0 < p < 1$, show that the value of the definite integral

$$\int_0^{\pi/2} \tan^p x\,dx = \int_0^{\pi/2} \cot^p x\,dx = \frac12 B\left(\frac{1+p}{2}, \frac{1-p}{2}\right) = \frac{\pi}{2\cos\dfrac{p\pi}{2}}.$$

Use Prob. 44 to evaluate

45. $\int_0^{\pi/2} \tan^{\frac25} x\,dx.$ **46.** $\int_0^{\pi/2} \cot^{\frac23} x\,dx.$ **47.** $\int_0^{\pi/2} \sqrt{\tan x}\,dx.$

For $a > -1, b > 0, c > -1$, and n a positive integer show that

48. $\int_0^1 x^a(1-x^b)^c dx = \dfrac{1}{b} B\left(\dfrac{a+1}{b}, c+1\right) = \dfrac{1}{b}\dfrac{\Gamma\left(\dfrac{a+1}{b}\right)\Gamma(c+1)}{\Gamma\left(\dfrac{a+1}{b}+c+1\right)}$

49. $\int_0^1 x^{bn-1}(1-x^b)^c dx = \dfrac{(n-1)!}{b(c+1)(c+2)\cdots(c+n)}.$

50. $\int_0^1 x^{bn-bc-1}(1-x^b)^c dx = \dfrac{\pi c(1-c)(2-c)\cdots(n-1-c)}{bn!\sin c\pi}$, if c is

not zero or an integer. When c is an integer m,

$$\int_0^1 x^{bn-bm-1}(1-x^b)^m dx = \frac{m!(n-m-1)!}{bn!}.$$

51. $\int_0^1 \dfrac{dx}{\sqrt{1-x^b}} = \dfrac{\sqrt{\pi}\,\Gamma\left(\dfrac{1}{b}\right)}{b\Gamma\left(\dfrac{1}{b}+\dfrac12\right)}, \int_0^1 \dfrac{dx}{\sqrt{1-x^{1/n}}} = \dfrac{2\cdot4\cdots(2n)}{1\cdot3\cdots(2n-1)}.$

52. Show that for $a > -1, b > 0, bc > a+1$, the definite integral

$$\int_0^\infty \frac{x^a dx}{(1+x^b)^c} = \frac{1}{b} B\left(\frac{a+1}{b}, c-\frac{a+1}{b}\right) = \frac{\Gamma\left(\dfrac{a+1}{b}\right)\Gamma\left(c-\dfrac{a+1}{b}\right)}{b\Gamma(c)}.$$

53. From Prob. 52 and Eq. (61) deduce that

$$\int_0^\infty \frac{x^a dx}{1+x^b} = \frac{\pi}{b\sin\left(\dfrac{a+1}{b}\pi\right)}, \qquad 0 < a+1 < b.$$

54. Use Prob. 52 to show that $\int_0^\infty \frac{dx}{(x^2+1)^c} = \frac{\sqrt{\pi}\,\Gamma(c-\frac{1}{2})}{2\Gamma(c)}$,

$c > \frac{1}{2}$. Check Probs. 62 and 65 of Exercises IV (page 191) by putting $c = n$, and $c = n + \frac{1}{2}$.

55. A particle starts from rest at $x = a$ and moves along the x axis toward O under the law of force $F = -k/x$. The energy equation is $\frac{m}{2}\left(\frac{dx}{dt}\right)^2 + k \log x = k \log a$. Derive the equation

$$t = -\sqrt{\frac{m}{2k}}\int_a^x \left(\log\frac{a}{x}\right)^{-\frac{1}{2}} dx = a\sqrt{\frac{m}{2k}}\int_{x/a}^1 \left(\log\frac{1}{u}\right)^{-\frac{1}{2}} du \text{ and show}$$

that the time required to reach O is $a\sqrt{m\pi/2k}$.

56. A particle starts from rest at $x = a$ and moves along the x axis toward O under the law of force $F = -k/x^{p+1}$, $p > 0$. The energy equation is $\frac{m}{2}\left(\frac{dx}{dt}\right)^2 - \frac{k}{px^p} = -\frac{k}{pa^p}$. Derive the equation of motion

$$t = -\sqrt{\frac{mp}{2k}}\int_a^x (x^{-p}-a^{-p})^{-\frac{1}{2}}dx = a^{p/2+1}\sqrt{\frac{mp}{2k}}\int_{x/a}^1 \frac{u^{p/2}du}{\sqrt{1-u^p}} \text{ and show}$$

that the time required to reach 0 is $a^{p/2+1}\sqrt{\frac{m\pi}{2kp}}\dfrac{\Gamma\left(\frac{1}{p}+\frac{1}{2}\right)}{\Gamma\left(\frac{1}{p}+1\right)}$.

57. The energy equation for a pendulum making $180°$ swings is $\frac{ml^2}{2}\left(\frac{d\theta}{dt}\right)^2 - mg\cos\theta = 0$. If $t = 0$ when $\theta = \pi/2$, derive the equation

$$t = -\sqrt{\frac{l}{2g}}\int_{\pi/2}^\theta \cos^{-\frac{1}{2}}\theta\, d\theta,$$ and show that the period of vibration is $P = 7.416\sqrt{l/g}$.

58. Show that the total length of the lemniscate $r^2 = a^2\cos 2\theta$ is $$4a\int_0^{\pi/4}\cos^{-\frac{1}{2}}2\theta\, d\theta = 2a\int_0^{\pi/2}\cos^{-\frac{1}{2}}u\, du = 5.244a.$$

59. Show that the area of the oval $y^2 = \dfrac{1-x^2}{1+x^2}$ in terms of $t = \sin^{-1} x^2$ is $$4\int_0^1 y\, dx = 2\int_0^{\pi/2}(\sin^{-\frac{1}{2}}t - \sin^{\frac{1}{2}}t)dt = 2.848.$$

For the loop of $r = \sin^p\theta\cos^q\theta$, $p > 0$, $q > 0$, $0 < \theta < \dfrac{\pi}{2}$, show that

60. The area A is $\dfrac{1}{2}\displaystyle\int_0^{\pi/2} r^2 d\theta = \dfrac{1}{4}B(p+\frac{1}{2}, q+\frac{1}{2})$.

61. The moment $A\bar{x}$ is $\dfrac{1}{3}\displaystyle\int_0^{\pi/2} r^3\cos\theta\, d\theta = \dfrac{1}{6}B\left(\dfrac{3p+1}{2}, \dfrac{3q}{2}+1\right)$.

62. The moment $A\bar{y}$ is $\dfrac{1}{3}\displaystyle\int_0^{\pi/2} r^3\sin\theta\, d\theta = \dfrac{1}{6}B\left(\dfrac{3p}{2}+1, \dfrac{3q+1}{2}\right)$.

63. The polar moment of inertia I_0 is expressed by the definite integral

$$\tfrac{1}{4} \int_0^{\pi/2} r^4 d\theta = \tfrac{1}{8} B(2p + \tfrac{1}{2}, 2q + \tfrac{1}{2}).$$

For the loop of $r^4 = \sin^3 \theta \cos \theta, 0 < \theta < \pi/2$,

64. Find the area by Prob. 60.

65. Find the center of gravity, $\bar{x}, \bar{y}$ by Probs. 61, 62, and 64.

66. Find the polar moment of inertia by Prob. 63.

67. Using Prob. 9 and Eq. (58), evaluate each side of the equation

$$\int_0^\infty x^{p+q-1} e^{-x} dx \int_0^\infty y^{p-1} e^{-xy} dy = \int_0^\infty y^{p-1} dy \int_0^\infty x^{p+q-1} e^{-(1+y)x} dx,$$

thus giving a new demonstration of Eq. (25).

68. For $b > 0$ and $0 < p < 1$, simplify each member of the equation

$$\int_0^\infty \cos bx \, dx \int_0^\infty y^{p-1} e^{-xy} dy = \int_0^\infty y^{p-1} dy \int_0^\infty \cos bx e^{-xy} dx, \quad \text{and so}$$

prove that $\displaystyle \int_0^\infty \frac{\cos bx}{x^p} \, dx = \frac{b^{p-1}\pi}{\Gamma(p) 2 \cos \dfrac{p\pi}{2}} = b^{p-1} \Gamma(1 - p) \sin \frac{p\pi}{2}.$

HINT: Use Prob. 69 of Exercises IV (page 192), Probs. 53 and 9 above, and for the final step Eq. (61).

69. By the method of Prob. 61, show that for $b > 0, 0 < p < 1$,

$$\int_0^\infty \frac{\sin bx}{x^p} \, dx = \frac{b^{p-1}\pi}{\Gamma(p) 2 \sin \dfrac{p\pi}{2}} = b^{p-1} \Gamma(1 - p) \cos \frac{p\pi}{2}.$$

70. By putting $u = x^k$ and using Probs. 68 and 69, demonstrate that

$$\int_0^\infty \cos (bx^k) dx = \frac{\Gamma(1/k)}{kb^{1/k}} \cos \frac{\pi}{2k}, \int_0^\infty \sin (bx^k) dx = \frac{\Gamma(1/k)}{kb^{1/k}} \sin \frac{\pi}{2k},$$

$b > 0, k > 1$.

71. From Probs. 68, 69, and 70 deduce that

$$\int_0^\infty \frac{\cos x}{\sqrt{x}} \, dx = \int_0^\infty \frac{\sin x}{\sqrt{x}} \, dx = \frac{\sqrt{2\pi}}{2},$$

$$\int_0^\infty \cos x^2 dx = \int_0^\infty \sin x^2 dx = \frac{\sqrt{2\pi}}{4}.$$

72. Using Eq. (58), show that

$$\int_0^1 \frac{x^{p-1} + x^{q-1}}{(1 + x)^{p+q}} \, dx = B(p,q).$$

HINT: $\displaystyle \int_0^1 \frac{x^{q-1} dx}{(1 + x)^{p+q}} = \int_1^\infty \frac{u^{p-1} du}{(1 + u)^{p+q}}, \quad$ if $x = \dfrac{1}{u}$.

73. Show that $B(p,p) = 2^{1-2p} B(p, \tfrac{1}{2})$. HINT: Let $P = 2p - 1$. Then if $t = 2x$,

$$2 \int_0^{\pi/2} \sin^P x \cos^P x \, dx = 2^{-P} \int_0^{\pi} \sin^P t \, dt = 2^{-P} \left(2 \int_0^{\pi/2} \sin^P t \, dt \right).$$

74. From Prob. 73 deduce that $\sqrt{\pi} \, \Gamma(2p) = 2^{2p-1} \Gamma(p) \Gamma(p + \frac{1}{2})$.

75. The numerical values of the Riemann Zeta-function $\zeta(p)$ have been tabulated, where $\zeta(p) = \frac{1}{1^p} + \frac{1}{2^p} + \frac{1}{3^p} + \cdots$, $\quad p > 1$. Let $s_p = \frac{1}{1^p} + \frac{1}{3^p} + \frac{1}{5^p} + \cdots$ and $t_p = \frac{1}{1^p} - \frac{1}{2^p} + \frac{1}{3^p} - \cdots$. Show that $s_p = (1 - 2^{-p})\zeta(p)$ and $t_p = 2s_p - \zeta(p) = (1 - 2^{-p+1})\zeta(p)$. HINT: $\zeta(p) = s_p(1 + 2^{-p} + 2^{-2p} + 2^{-3p} + \cdots)$.

76. It follows from Prob. 117 of Exercises V (page 250) that we may write $1 - t \cot t = \sum_{n=1}^{\infty} \frac{2t^2}{n^2\pi^2} \left(1 - \frac{t^2}{n^2\pi^2} \right)^{-1}$. This becomes the series $\frac{t^2}{3} + \frac{t^4}{45} + \cdots = \frac{2t^2}{\pi^2} \sum_{n=1}^{\infty} \frac{1}{n^2} + \frac{2t^4}{\pi^4} \sum_{n=1}^{\infty} \frac{1}{n^4} + \cdots$ if both sides are expanded in powers of t by the methods of Sec. 13. Using Prob. 75, deduce that $\zeta(2) = \pi^2/6$, $s_2 = \pi^2/8$, $t_2 = \pi^2/12$, while $\zeta(4) = \pi^4/90$, $s_4 = \pi^4/96$, $t_4 = 7\pi^4/720$.

77. Using $\frac{1}{1 - x} = 1 + x^{-1} + x^{-2} + \cdots$ and Prob. 75, show that

$$\int_0^1 \frac{(-\log x)^p}{1 - x} \, dx = \Gamma(p + 1)\zeta(p + 1), \quad p > 0.$$

78. Using $\frac{1}{1 + x} = 1 - x^{-1} + x^{-2} - \cdots$ and Prob. 75, show that

$$\int_0^1 \frac{(-\log x)^p}{1 + x} \, dx = \Gamma(p + 1)t_{p+1} = (1 - 2^{-p})\Gamma(p + 1)\zeta(p + 1), \text{ if}$$

$p > 0$.

79. Integrate by parts and use Probs. 77 and 76 to demonstrate that

$$\int_0^1 \log (1 - x) \frac{dx}{x} = \int_0^1 \frac{\log x}{1 - x} \, dx = -\frac{\pi^2}{6}.$$

80. Integrate by parts and use Probs. 78 and 76 to demonstrate that

$$\int_0^1 \log (1 + x) \frac{dx}{x} = \int_0^1 \frac{-\log x}{1 + x} \, dx = \frac{\pi^2}{12}.$$

81. The radiation density ψ, according to Planck's law, is given by

$$\psi = \frac{8\pi h}{c^3} \int_0^{\infty} \frac{\nu^3 d\nu}{e^{h\nu/KT} - 1}.$$ Show that this may be evaluated as

$$\psi = \frac{8\pi h}{c^3} \left(\frac{KT}{h} \right)^4 \int_0^1 \frac{(-\log x)^3}{1 - x} \, dx = \frac{8\pi^5 K^4 T^4}{15c^3 h^3}.$$ HINT: Use a new variable $h\nu = -KT \log x$ and use Probs. 77 and 76.

82. Use Eq. (90) to show that the error made by replacing $n!$ by Stirling's approximation $\sqrt{2\pi} \, n^{n+\frac{1}{2}} e^{-n}$ is less than 0.1 per cent if n exceeds 100, less than 1 per cent if n exceeds 10, and less than 10 per cent if n exceeds 1. Note that $n! = n\Gamma(n)$.

83. The number of possible arrangements of an ordinary deck of cards is 52!. Show that this is about 8.07×10^{67}.

84. Calculate $\Gamma(11) = 10!$ by Eq. (90) and compare with the exact value 3,628,800.

85. Use Eq. (94) to compute $\Gamma(-1.2)$ and so check the value found from the tables in Eq. (15).

CHAPTER VII

ELLIPTIC INTEGRALS

The integral that expresses the length of arc of an ellipse cannot be evaluated by elementary methods. It is one of a large class of nonelementary integrals, called *elliptic integrals*. In this chapter we shall show how certain problems that lead to elliptic integrals may be solved by using tables of two special functions, $F(k,\phi)$ and $E(k,\phi)$.

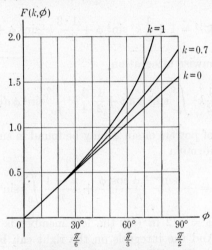

The elliptic integral of the first kind.
Fig. 119.

105. The Function $F(k,\phi)$. The equation

$$F(k,\phi) = \int_0^\phi \frac{d\phi}{\sqrt{1 - k^2 \sin^2 \phi}}, \qquad 0 \leq k \leq 1 \qquad (1)$$

defines Legendre's normal form of the elliptic integral of the first kind $F(k,\phi)$ as a function of the *amplitude* ϕ and of the *modulus* k. For $k = 0$ or 1, we have

$$F(0,\phi) = \phi \qquad \text{and} \qquad F(1,\phi) = \log (\tan \phi + \sec \phi). \qquad (2)$$

For other values of k, the graph of $F(k,\phi)$ as a function of ϕ for fixed k lies between these two, as indicated in Fig. 119.

The integral in (1) is called *complete* if $\phi = \pi/2$. The complete integral of the first kind $F(k, \pi/2)$ is usually denoted by $K(k)$, or by K when the modulus k is indicated by the context. Thus

$$K = K(k) = F\left(k, \frac{\pi}{2}\right) = \int_0^{\pi/2} \frac{d\phi}{\sqrt{1 - k^2 \sin^2 \phi}}, \quad 0 \leqq k \leqq 1. \quad (3)$$

When k is not 0 or 1, the integral in (1) is nonelementary. That is, it cannot be expressed in terms of a finite combination of elementary functions. However, its value can be found from an infinite series. For, by the binomial theorem, Eq. (127) of Sec. 11,

$$(1 - k^2 \sin^2 \phi)^{-\frac{1}{2}} = 1 + \frac{1}{2} k^2 \sin^2 \phi + \frac{1 \cdot 3}{2 \cdot 4} k^4 \sin^4 \phi + \cdots. \quad (4)$$

Hence, by termwise integration,

$$F(k,\phi) = \phi + \frac{1}{2} k^2 \int_0^\phi \sin^2 \phi \, d\phi + \frac{1 \cdot 3}{2 \cdot 4} k^4 \int_0^\phi \sin^4 \phi \, d\phi + \cdots. \quad (5)$$

The integrals of powers of $\sin \phi$ may be found in succession from the recursion formula

$$\int_0^\phi \sin^n \phi \, d\phi = -\frac{\sin^{n-1} \phi \cos \phi}{n} + \frac{n-1}{n} \int_0^\phi \sin^{n-2} \phi \, d\phi. \quad (6)$$

If we put $\phi = \pi/2$ in (5), the left member is the complete integral K. And the integrals on the right can be found from Wallis's formula [Eq. (68) of Sec. 101]. In this way we find

$$K = \frac{\pi}{2}\left[1 + \left(\frac{1}{2}\right)^2 k^2 + \left(\frac{1 \cdot 3}{2 \cdot 4}\right)^2 k^4 + \left(\frac{1 \cdot 3 \cdot 5}{2 \cdot 4 \cdot 6}\right)^2 k^6 + \cdots\right]. \quad (7)$$

The integrand of (1) is an even function of ϕ. Hence

$$F(k, -\phi) = -F(k,\phi) \quad (8)$$

by Prob. 2 of Exercises IV (page 186).

And the integrand of (1) is a periodic function having the period π. Hence by Prob. 8 of Exercises IV (page 186),

$$F(k, n\pi + \phi) = nF(k,\pi) + F(k,\phi), \quad n \text{ any integer.} \quad (9)$$

In particular, if $n = 1$ and $\phi = -\pi/2$,

$$F\left(k, \frac{\pi}{2}\right) = F(k,\pi) + F\left(k, -\frac{\pi}{2}\right) \quad \text{or} \quad K = F(k,\pi) - K. \quad (10)$$

Consequently,

$$F(k,\pi) = 2K \quad \text{and} \quad F(k,n\pi + \phi) = 2nK + F(k,\phi). \quad (11)$$

Equations (8) and (11) enable us to determine $F(k,\phi)$ for any amplitude ϕ from values of $F(k,\phi)$ tabulated for the range $0 \leqq \phi \leqq \pi/2$. If $-\pi/2 \leqq \phi < 0$, we use Eq. (8). Any amplitude greater than $\pi/2$ or less than $-\pi/2$ may be written in the form $n\pi + \phi$, with n a positive or negative integer and

$$-\pi/2 \leqq \phi \leqq \pi/2.$$

Hence, if $|\phi| > \pi/2$, we use Eq. (11).

Instead of k, most tables use the parameter α defined by

$$\sin \alpha = k, \quad 0 < \alpha < 90°. \quad (12)$$

As an example, let us find $F(0.41, 0.3584)$. Here $\sin \alpha = 0.41$ and $\phi = 0.3584$ radian. Consequently $\alpha = 24.20°$ and

$$\phi = 20.54°.$$

USING PEIRCE'S TABLES				USING JAHNKE-EMDE'S TABLES			
α φ	15°	24.20°	30°	α φ	20°	24.20°	25°
20°	0.3495	(0.3503)	0.3508	20°	0.3499	(0.3502)	0.3503
20.54°		[0.3598]		20.54°		[0.3595]	
25°	0.4372	(0.4387)	0.4397	21°	0.3671	(0.3674)	0.3675

The corner values are the nearest ones found in the tables. The values in parentheses are found by these by interpolating on α, and finally the values in square brackets are found by interpolating on ϕ. Thus from Peirce's tables we find the three-place value 0.360 and from Jahnke-Emde's tables the four-place value 0.3595.

To find $F(0.41, 3.5)$, where $\phi = 3.5 > \pi/2$, we observe that

$$3.5 - 3.1416 = 0.3584, \quad \text{so that } 3.5 = \pi + 0.3584. \quad (13)$$

Hence, by Eq. (11),

$$F(0.41, 3.5) = 2K(0.41) + F(0.41, 0.3584)$$
$$= 2(1.6439) + 0.3595 = 3.6473. \quad (14)$$

The value of $K(0.41)$, for $\alpha = 24.20°$, is found by interpolating between the values $K = 1.6426$ for $\alpha = 24°$ and $K = 1.6490$ for $\alpha = 25°$, found in either of the tables mentioned.

For small values of k, a direct computation of the series (7) is sometimes preferable to the use of the tables.

We note that, when the lower limit is not zero,

$$\int_{\phi_1}^{\phi_2} \frac{d\phi}{\sqrt{1 - k^2 \sin^2 \phi}} = F(k,\phi_2) - F(k,\phi_1) = F(k,\phi) \Big|_{\phi_1}^{\phi_2}. \quad (15)$$

106. The Pendulum Problem.

In many physical and geometrical problems we encounter an integral of the type

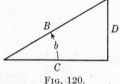

FIG. 120.

$$I_1 = \int_{u_1}^{u_2} \frac{du}{\sqrt{A + C \cos u + D \sin u}}. \quad (16)$$

The procedure for reducing such an integral to an expression whose value can be found from tables of $F(k,\phi)$ is as follows. We first find B,b the polar coordinates of the point C,D from

$$B = \sqrt{C^2 + D^2}, \qquad b = \tan^{-1} \frac{D}{C}, \quad (17)$$

choosing B positive and b in such a quadrant that

$$C = B \cos b, \qquad D = B \sin b. \quad (18)$$

This makes

$$C \cos u + D \sin u = B \cos b \cos u + B \sin b \sin u$$
$$= B \cos (u - b). \quad (19)$$

Now change I_1 by the substitution

$$u - b = 2v, \qquad \text{so that } \cos (u - b) = 1 - 2 \sin^2 v. \quad (20)$$

Then

$$I_1 = \int_{v_1}^{v_2} \frac{2dv}{\sqrt{A + B - 2B \sin^2 v}}$$

$$= \frac{2}{\sqrt{A + B}} \int_{v_1}^{v_2} \frac{dv}{\sqrt{1 - \dfrac{2B}{A + B} \sin^2 v}}. \quad (21)$$

Since $B > 0$ and for real values the radicand must be positive, $A + B > 0$. We must now distinguish two cases, according as $A \geqq B$ or $A < B$.

Case I. $A \geqq B$.   We put

$$c^2 = \frac{A + B}{2B}, \qquad \text{where } c^2 \geqq 1 \text{ since } A + B \geqq 2B. \quad (22)$$

Then from Eq. (15) and the second form in (21),

$$I_1 = \int_{u_1}^{u_2} \frac{du}{\sqrt{A + B \cos (u - b)}}$$
$$= \frac{2}{\sqrt{A + B}} \left[F\left(\frac{1}{c}, v_2\right) - F\left(\frac{1}{c}, v_1\right) \right], \qquad \text{if } A \geqq B, \quad (23)$$

where

$$\frac{1}{c} = \sqrt{\frac{2B}{A + B}} \leqq 1 \qquad \text{and} \qquad v_2 = \frac{u_2 - b}{2}, v_1 = \frac{u_1 - b}{2}. \quad (24)$$

Case II. $A < B$.   We again put

$$c^2 = \frac{A + B}{2B}, \qquad \text{where now } c^2 < 1 \text{ since } A + B < 2B. \quad (25)$$

We make the further change of variable

$$\sqrt{2B} \sin v = \sqrt{A + B} \sin w,$$
$$\sqrt{2B} \cos v \, dv = \sqrt{A + B} \cos w \, dw. \quad (26)$$

The radical in the second integral of (21) becomes $\cos w$, so that

$$I_1 = \int \frac{2 \, dv}{\sqrt{A + B} \cos w}$$
$$= \int \frac{2 \, dw}{\sqrt{2B} \cos v} = \int \frac{2 \, dw}{\sqrt{2B - (A + B) \sin^2 w}}. \quad (27)$$

Hence

$$I_1 = \frac{2}{\sqrt{2B}} \int_{w_1}^{w_2} \frac{dw}{\sqrt{1 - \dfrac{A + B}{2B} \sin^2 w}}$$
$$= \frac{2}{\sqrt{2B}} [F(c, w_2) - F(c, w_1)] \quad (28)$$

by Eq. (15). That is,

$$I_1 = \int_{u_1}^{u_2} \frac{du}{\sqrt{A + B \cos (u - b)}}$$
$$= \frac{2}{\sqrt{2B}} [F(c, w_2) - F(c, w_1)] \qquad \text{if } A < B, \quad (29)$$

where

$$c = \sqrt{\frac{A + B}{2B}} < 1 \qquad \text{and} \qquad \sin w_2 = \frac{1}{c} \sin \frac{u_2 - b}{2},$$

$$\sin w_1 = \frac{1}{c} \sin \frac{u_1 - b}{2}. \quad (30)$$

As an application of these reductions, we consider the motion

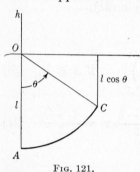

FIG. 121.

of a simple pendulum of mass m slugs and length l feet. The position is determined by θ, the angular displacement from the position of stable equilibrium. If we take O, the pivot, as the level of zero potential energy, the height above this is

$$h = -l \cos \theta,$$

and the potential energy is

$$U = wh = -mgl \cos \theta. \quad (31)$$

Since the moment of inertia about O is ml^2, the kinetic energy is

$$T = \frac{1}{2} ml^2 \left(\frac{d\theta}{dt}\right)^2. \quad (32)$$

The total energy $T + U$ is constant. Hence the equation of motion is

$$\frac{1}{2} ml^2 \left(\frac{d\theta}{dt}\right)^2 - mgl \cos \theta = \frac{1}{2} ml^2 \omega_0^2 - mgl, \quad (33)$$

where ω_0 is the value of $d\theta/dt$ at $\theta = 0$.

This may be written

$$\left(\frac{d\theta}{dt}\right)^2 = \omega_0^2 - \frac{2g}{l} + \frac{2g}{l} \cos \theta = A + B \cos \theta, \quad (34)$$

with A and B abbreviations for the coefficients, defined by

$$A = \omega_0^2 - \frac{2g}{l} \qquad \text{and} \qquad B = \frac{2g}{l}. \quad (35)$$

It follows from this that with the proper sign for the radical,

$$\frac{d\theta}{dt} = \sqrt{A + B \cos \theta} \qquad \text{and} \qquad dt = \frac{d\theta}{\sqrt{A + B \cos \theta}}. \quad (36)$$

If we take $t = 0$ when $\theta = 0$, this leads to

$$t = \int_0^\theta \frac{d\theta}{\sqrt{A + B \cos \theta}}, \tag{37}$$

which is an integral of the type in Eq. (16). There are three types of motion according as $A > B$, $A < B$, or $A = B$.

Type I. *Complete Revolutions.* Suppose that $A > B$. Then we may apply Eq. (23) to the integral (37) to obtain

$$t = \frac{2}{\sqrt{A + B}} F\left(\sqrt{\frac{2B}{A + B}}, \frac{\theta}{2}\right) = \frac{2}{\omega_0} F\left(\frac{2}{\omega_0}\sqrt{\frac{g}{l}}, \frac{\theta}{2}\right). \tag{38}$$

This applies for all values of, t since the condition $A > B$ implies that the radical in (37) is never zero and hence preserves its sign. The pendulum rotates around the circle in one direction with periodically varying speed. And the period of the motion P, or time for one complete revolution, is

$$P = \frac{2}{\omega_0} F\left(\frac{2}{\omega_0}\sqrt{\frac{g}{l}}, \pi\right) = \frac{4}{\omega_0} K\left(\frac{2}{\omega_0}\sqrt{\frac{g}{l}}\right) \tag{39}$$

by Eq. (11).

From Eq. (35), the condition $A > B$ is equivalent to

$$\omega_0{}^2 > \frac{4g}{l} \quad \text{or} \quad T_0 = \frac{1}{2} ml^2\omega_0{}^2 > mg(2l). \tag{40}$$

Thus the motion is of Type I if $\omega_0 > 2\sqrt{g/l}$, that is, if T_0 the initial kinetic energy is larger than $mg(2l)$, the work necessary to raise the bob from the bottom to the top of the circle.

Type II. *Vibratory Motion.* Suppose that $A < B$. Then we may apply Eq. (29) to the integral (37) to obtain

$$t = \sqrt{\frac{l}{g}} F\left(\frac{\omega_0}{2}\sqrt{\frac{l}{g}}, \phi\right) \quad \text{where } \sin \phi = \frac{2}{\omega_0}\sqrt{\frac{g}{l}} \sin \frac{\theta}{2}. \tag{41}$$

The parameter α of this elliptic integral is defined by

$$\sin \alpha = \frac{\omega_0}{2}\sqrt{\frac{l}{g}}, \quad 0 < \alpha < 90°. \tag{42}$$

Thus

$$\sin \frac{\theta}{2} = \sin \alpha \sin \phi, \quad \text{and} \quad A + B \cos \theta = \frac{4g}{l} \sin^2 \alpha \cos^2 \phi. \tag{43}$$

Initially the radical in (37) is positive if θ is increasing when $t = 0$. As θ increases from 0 to 2α, ϕ increases from 0 to $\pi/2$, by the first equation in (43). And hence, by the second equation in (43) the radicand $A + B \cos \theta$ decreases from $A + B$ to 0. Since the radical would become imaginary if θ increased further, at this time the sign before the radical must be reversed. Hence, if we let ϕ increase steadily through $\pi/2$, we may replace the radical in (37) with its proper sign by

$$2 \sqrt{\frac{g}{l}} \sin \alpha \cos \phi, \tag{44}$$

both before and after $\pi/2$. A similar situation holds when θ decreases to -2α and ϕ increases to $3\pi/2$. Consequently, Eqs. (41) will apply for all positive values of t and ϕ if we take θ such that

$$\sin \frac{\theta}{2} = \sin \alpha \sin \phi \qquad \text{and} \qquad -2\alpha \leqq \theta \leqq 2\alpha. \tag{45}$$

The pendulum oscillates between the positions $\theta = 2\alpha$ and $\theta = -2\alpha$. The period of the motion, or time for one complete swing and return, is

$$P = \sqrt{\frac{l}{g}} \, F(\sin \alpha, \, 2\pi) = 4 \sqrt{\frac{l}{g}} \, K(\sin \alpha) = 4 \sqrt{\frac{l}{g}} \, K\left(\frac{\omega_0}{2} \sqrt{\frac{l}{g}}\right). \tag{46}$$

When $A < B$ we must reverse the inequality signs in (40). Hence the motion is of Type II if $\omega_0 < 2 \sqrt{g/l}$, that is, if T_0, the initial kinetic energy, is less than the work necessary to raise the bob from the bottom to the top of the circle.

Type III. *Asymptotic Approach to a* 180° *Deflection.* If $A = B$, Eq. (38) becomes

$$t = \frac{2}{\omega_0} F\left(l, \frac{\theta}{2}\right) = \frac{2}{\omega_0} \log\left(\tan \frac{\theta}{2} + \sec \frac{\theta}{2}\right), \tag{47}$$

by Eq. (2). In this case, the radicand approaches zero as $\theta \to \pi$. But when $\theta = \pi$, $t = \infty$. Thus the pendulum approaches a 180° deflection but does not reach it in finite time.

When $A = B$ we must replace the inequality signs in (40) by equality signs. Hence the motion is of Type III if $\omega_0 = 2 \sqrt{g/l}$, that is, if T_0, the initial kinetic energy, is just equal to the work necessary to raise the bob from the bottom to the top of the circle.

107. The Function $E(k,\phi)$.   The equation

$$E(k,\phi) = \int_0^\phi \sqrt{1 - k^2 \sin^2 \phi} \, d\phi, \qquad 0 \leqq k \leqq 1 \qquad (48)$$

defines the Legendre's normal form of the elliptic integral of the second kind $E(k,\phi)$, as a function of the *amplitude* ϕ and of the *modulus* k.   For $k = 0$ or 1 we have

$$E(0,\phi) = \phi \qquad \text{and} \qquad E(1,\phi) = \sin \phi. \qquad (49)$$

For other values of k, the graph of $E(k,\phi)$ as a function of ϕ for fixed k lies between these two, as indicated in Fig. 122.

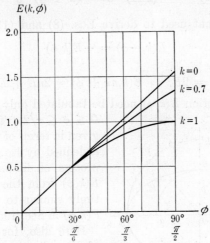

The elliptic integral of the second kind.
Fig. 122.

The integral in (48) is called *complete* if $\phi = \pi/2$.   The complete integral of the second kind $E(k,\pi/2)$ is usually denoted by $E(k)$ or by E when the modulus is indicated by the context. Thus

$$E = E(k) = E\left(k, \frac{\pi}{2}\right) = \int_0^{\pi/2} \sqrt{1 - k^2 \sin^2 \phi} \, d\phi,$$
$$0 \leqq k \leqq 1. \quad (50)$$

When k is not 0 or 1, the integral in (48) is nonelementary. But its value can be found from an infinite series.   For, by the binomial theorem, Eq. (127) of Sec. 11,

$$(1 - k^2 \sin^2 \phi)^{1/2} = 1 - \frac{1}{2} k^2 \sin^2 \phi - \frac{1 \cdot 1}{2 \cdot 4} k^4 \sin^4 \phi - \cdots. \quad (51)$$

Hence, by termwise integration,

$$E(k,\phi) = \phi - \frac{1}{2}\,k^2 \int_0^\phi \sin^2 \phi\, d\phi - \frac{1\cdot 1}{2\cdot 4}\,k^4 \int_0^\phi \sin^4 \phi\, d\phi - \cdots.$$
$$(52)$$

The integrals may be found from Eq. (6).

If we put $\phi = \pi/2$ in (52), the left member is the complete integral E. And the integrals on the right can be found from Wallis's formula [Eq. (68) of Sec. 101]. In this way we find

$$E = \frac{\pi}{2}\left[1 - \left(\frac{1}{2}\right)^2 k^2 - \left(\frac{1\cdot 3}{2\cdot 4}\right)^2 \frac{k^4}{3} - \left(\frac{1\cdot 3\cdot 5}{2\cdot 4\cdot 6}\right)^2 \frac{k^6}{5} - \cdots \right]. \quad (53)$$

The argument used to derive Eqs. (8) and (11) shows that

$$E(k,-\phi) = -E(k,\phi) \quad (54)$$

and that

$$E(k,\pi) = 2E, \qquad E(k,n\pi + \phi) = 2nE + E(k,\phi). \quad (55)$$

Thus the function $E(k,\phi)$ need be tabulated only for the range $0 \leqq \phi \leqq \pi/2$. The tables are given in terms of the parameter α defined by Eq. (12), and the process of finding a value of $E(k,\phi)$ from the tables is entirely similar to that used for $F(k,\phi)$ in Sec. 105.

Here also, for small values of k, a direct computation of the series (53) is sometimes preferable to the use of the tables.

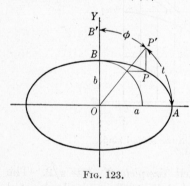

Fig. 123.

When the lower limit of our integral is not zero,

$$\int_{\phi_1}^{\phi_2} \sqrt{1 - k^2 \sin^2 \phi}\, d\phi = E(k,\phi_2) - E(k,\phi_1) = E(k,\phi)\,\Big|_{\phi_1}^{\phi_2}. \quad (56)$$

As an application of this equation, let us determine the following:

The Length of an Arc of an Ellipse. Take the parametric equations for the ellipse as

$$x = a\cos t, \qquad y = b\sin t, \qquad \text{with } a > b. \quad (57)$$

Then

$$ds^2 = dx^2 + dy^2 = (a^2 \sin^2 t + b^2 \cos^2 t)dt, \quad (58)$$

so that the arc AP is

$$s = \int_0^t \sqrt{a^2 \sin^2 t + b^2 \cos^2 t} \, dt. \tag{59}$$

We note that

$$a^2 \sin^2 t + b^2 \cos^2 t = a^2 - (a^2 - b^2) \cos^2 t$$
$$= a^2(1 - e^2 \cos^2 t) \tag{60}$$

where e is the eccentricity of the ellipse,

$$e = \frac{c}{a} = \frac{\sqrt{a^2 - b^2}}{a} < 1. \tag{61}$$

To replace $\cos t$ by $\sin \phi$, we use the substitution

$$t = \frac{\pi}{2} - \phi, \qquad \text{which makes } \cos t = \sin \phi \text{ and } dt = -d\phi. \tag{62}$$

It follows from Eqs. (59), (60), and (62) that

$$s = a \int_\phi^{\pi/2} \sqrt{1 - e^2 \sin^2 \phi} \, d\phi = a[E(e) - E(e,\phi)]. \tag{63}$$

It follows that, if AB is a quadrant of the ellipse,

$$\text{Arc } AB = aE(e) \qquad \text{and} \qquad \text{arc } PB = aE(e,\phi). \tag{64}$$

Let $AP'B'$ be a 90° circular arc and PP' be parallel to OB. Then angle $P'OB' = \phi$. This leads to a geometric representation of any value of $E(k,\phi)$ by an arc PB on an ellipse with $a = 1$ and $c = e = k$.

108. A Trigonometric Integral. The integral

$$I_2 = \int_{u_1}^{u_2} \sqrt{A + C \cos u + D \sin u} \, du \tag{65}$$

can always be expressed in terms of the two functions $E(k,\phi)$ and $F(k,\phi)$. The procedure for reducing I_2 is somewhat similar to that for I_1 described in Sec. 106. We first use the transformation (19) and substitution (20), $u - b = 2v$, to obtain

$$I_2 = \int_{u_1}^{u_2} \sqrt{A + B \cos (u - b)} \, du$$
$$= 2 \int_{v_1}^{v_2} \sqrt{A + B - 2B \sin^2 v} \, dv. \tag{66}$$

We next distinguish two cases according as $A \geqq B$ or $A < B$.

Case I. $A \geqq B$. As in (22), we put

$$c^2 = \frac{A + B}{2B}, \qquad \text{where } c^2 \geqq 1 \text{ since } A + B \geqq 2B. \tag{67}$$

Then from Eqs. (66) and (56),

$$I_2 = \int_{u_1}^{u_2} \sqrt{A + B \cos (u - b)} \, du$$
$$= 2 \sqrt{A + B} \left[E\left(\frac{1}{c}, v_2\right) - E\left(\frac{1}{c}, v_1\right) \right], \quad \text{if } A \geqq B, \quad (68)$$

where

$$\frac{1}{c} = \sqrt{\frac{2B}{A + B}} \leqq 1 \quad \text{and} \quad v_2 = \frac{u_2 - b}{2}, \quad v_1 = \frac{u_1 - b}{2}. \quad (69)$$

Case II. $A < B$.   As in (25) we put

$$c^2 = \frac{A + B}{2B}, \quad \text{where } c^2 < 1 \text{ since } A + B < 2B. \quad (70)$$

And we make the further change of variable (26)

$$\sqrt{2B} \sin v = \sqrt{A + B} \sin w,$$
$$\sqrt{2B} \cos v \, dv = \sqrt{A + B} \cos w \, dw. \quad (71)$$

The radical of Eq. (66) becomes $\sqrt{A + B} \cos w$, so that

$$I_2 = 2 \sqrt{A + B} \int \cos w \, dv = \int \frac{2(A + B) \cos^2 w \, dw}{\sqrt{2B} \cos v}$$
$$= \int \frac{2(A + B) \cos^2 w \, dw}{\sqrt{2B - (A + B) \sin^2 w}}. \quad (72)$$

We next combine the last integral with the identity

$$2(A + B) \cos^2 w = 2(A - B) + 2[2B - (A + B) \sin^2 w] \quad (73)$$

to deduce that

$$I_2 = \frac{2(A - B)}{\sqrt{2B}} \int_{w_1}^{w_2} \frac{dw}{\sqrt{1 - c^2 \sin^2 w}}$$
$$+ 2 \sqrt{2B} \int_{w_1}^{w_2} \sqrt{1 - c^2 \sin^2 w} \, dw. \quad (74)$$

Then from Eqs. (15) and (56),

$$I_2 = \int_{u_1}^{u_2} \sqrt{A + B \cos (u - b)} \, du$$
$$= \left[\frac{2(A - B)}{\sqrt{2B}} F(c, w) + 2 \sqrt{2B} \, E(c, w) \right]_{w_1}^{w_2}, \quad \text{if } A < B, \quad (75)$$

where

$$c = \sqrt{\frac{A + B}{2B}} < 1 \qquad \text{and} \qquad \sin w_2 = \frac{1}{c} \sin \frac{u_2 - b}{2},$$

$$\sin w_1 = \frac{1}{c} \sin \frac{u_1 - b}{2}. \quad (76)$$

109. The General Elliptic Integral. Let $R(u,v)$ denote any rational function of the two variables with real coefficients and

$$X = ax^4 + bx^3 + cx^2 + dx + e \qquad (77)$$

be a real polynomial. Consider the integral

$$R(x,\sqrt{X})dx. \qquad (78)$$

If $a = b = 0$, the polynomial X is of the first or second degree. And if $X = 0$ has two equal roots, we may write

$$\sqrt{X} = \sqrt{(x - r)^2(px^2 + qx + r)}$$
$$= (x - r) \sqrt{px^2 + qx + r}. \quad (79)$$

In both cases the integral (78) reduces to the type shown in Sec. 68 to be expressible in terms of elementary functions. We exclude these degenerate cases and assume that X is a polynomial of the third or fourth degree with all its roots distinct.

Then the integral (78) is called an *elliptic integral* and in general is nonelementary. However, any such integral can always be expressed in terms of integrals which are elementary, together with three new types of integrals, namely,

$$\int_0^x \frac{dx}{\sqrt{(1 - x^2)(1 - k^2x^2)}}, \qquad \int_0^x \sqrt{\frac{1 - k^2x^2}{1 - x^2}}\, dx,$$

and $\qquad\qquad\qquad\qquad\qquad\qquad\qquad\qquad\qquad\qquad\qquad (80)$

$$\int_0^x \frac{dx}{(1 + nx^2)\sqrt{(1 - x^2)(1 - k^2x^2)}} \qquad \text{where } 0 < k < 1,$$
$$-1 \leqq x \leqq 1.$$

Here, as the inequalities indicate, k and x are real. But n may be any complex number. The three integrals (80) are Jacobi's normal forms for elliptic integrals of the first, second, and third kinds, respectively. They may be transformed into Legendre's normal forms by the substitution $x = \sin \phi$, which makes

$$\int_0^x \frac{dx}{\sqrt{(1 - x^2)(1 - k^2 x^2)}} = \int_0^\phi \frac{d\phi}{\sqrt{1 - k^2 \sin^2 \phi}} = F(k,\phi), \quad (81)$$

$$\int_0^x \sqrt{\frac{1 - k^2 x^2}{1 - x^2}}\, dx = \int_0^\phi \sqrt{1 - k^2 \sin^2 \phi}\, d\phi = E(k,\phi), \quad (82)$$

$$\int_0^x \frac{dx}{(1 + nx^2)\, \sqrt{(1 - x^2)(1 - k^2 x^2)}}$$
$$= \int_0^\phi \frac{d\phi}{(1 + n \sin^2 \phi)\, \sqrt{1 - k^2 \sin^2 \phi}} = \pi(n,k,\phi). \quad (83)$$

The functions $F(k,\phi)$ and $E(k,\phi)$ have been discussed in Secs. 105 and 107. It is theoretically possible by using $F(k,\phi)$ and elementary functions to express $A\pi(n,k,\phi) + \bar{A}\pi(\bar{n},k,\phi)$, where $A, \bar{A}$ and $n, \bar{n}$ are any two pairs of conjugate complex numbers, in terms of two functions $\pi(m_1,k,\phi)$ and $\pi(m_2,k,\phi)$ with m_1 and m_2 real; and similarly to express $\pi(n,k,\phi)$ with $n > 1$ or $n < 1$ in terms of $\pi(m,k,\phi)$ with $-1 \leqq m \leqq 1$. But even with this restriction, there are still three parameters, and tabulation is not practicable. It is also possible to express the complete function $\pi\left(n,k,\dfrac{\pi}{2}\right)$, $-1 \leqq n \leqq 1$, in terms of elementary functions and the functions $F(k,\phi)$ and $E(k,\phi)$.

Sections 110 and 111 are devoted to two classes of elliptic integrals that may be expressed in terms of $F(k,\phi)$ and $E(k,\phi)$ and hence practically evaluated. For most other elliptic integrals, the reduction would lead to integrals of the third kind. And if numerical values are required, one must resort to a direct use of Simpson's rule or to a series expansion.

110. Integrals of the First Kind. The integral of $dx/\sqrt{X}$ is always reducible to a constant times the integral of (15). The evaluation is easily effected if there is at hand a substitution which makes

$$\frac{dx}{\sqrt{X}} = C \frac{d\phi}{\sqrt{1 - k^2 \sin^2 \phi}}, \quad \text{and hence} \int_{x_1}^{x_2} \frac{dx}{\sqrt{X}}$$
$$= C[F(k,\phi_2) - F(k,\phi_1)]. \quad (84)$$

We give such a substitution for each of six possible cases. This enables us to compute ϕ_2 from x_2 and ϕ_1 from x_1. We also give the formulas for computing the constant C and the modulus k. The constants a,b, etc., are all real.

Case I. $X = \pm(x - a)(x - b)(x - c)(x - d)$.

The substitution

$$\sin^2 \phi = \frac{(b - d)(x - c)}{(b - c)(x - d)}, \qquad 0 < \phi < \frac{\pi}{2}, \qquad (85)$$

will make Eq. (84) hold with

$$C^2 = \frac{4}{(a - c)(b - d)} \qquad \text{and} \qquad k^2 = \frac{(b - c)(a - d)}{(a - c)(b - d)}. \quad (86)$$

The modulus k is positive, and the sign of C is determined by the following table:

Upper sign: $d < c < x < b < a$, or $x < b < a < d < c$,
$$C > 0; \quad (87)$$
$$a < b < x < c < d, \text{ or } c < d < a < b < x,$$
$$C < 0. \quad (88)$$
Lower sign: $c < x < b < a < d, C > 0; d < a < b < x < c,$
$$C < 0. \quad (89)$$

For x in any interval of integration which makes $\sqrt{X}$ real, it is always possible so to letter the four roots that one of these relations is satisfied.   This will ensure that the given expression for C^2 is positive and that the expressions for $\sin^2 \phi$ and k^2 will each be between 0 and 1.

Case II. $X = \pm (x - a)(x - b)[(x - c)^2 + d^2]$.

The substitution

$$\tan^2 \frac{\phi}{2} = \pm \frac{N}{M} \frac{x - a}{x - b}, \qquad 0 < \phi < \pi, \qquad (90)$$

where M and N are the positive square roots of

$$M^2 = (c - a)^2 + d^2, \qquad N^2 = (c - b)^2 + d^2, \qquad (91)$$

will make Eq. (84) hold with

$$C^2 = \frac{1}{MN} \qquad \text{and} \qquad k^2 = \frac{(M \pm N)^2 - (a - b)^2}{\pm 4MN}. \quad (92)$$

The modulus k is positive, and the constant C is positive if

Upper sign: $x < b < a$,   or $b < a < x$.   (93)
Lower sign: $a < x < b$.   (94)

For x in any interval of integration that makes $\sqrt{X}$ real, it is always possible so to letter the two real roots that one of

these relations is satisfied. This will ensure that the given
expression for $\tan^2 \phi/2$ is positive, and that the expression for
k^2 will be between 0 and 1.

Case III. $X = [(x - a)^2 + b^2][(x - c)^2 + d^2], \qquad a \neq c.$

Let p and q be the roots, necessarily real, of the quadratic
equation

$$(a - c)p^2 + (c^2 + d^2 - a^2 - b^2)p + (ca^2 + cb^2 - ac^2 - ad^2) = 0. \quad (95)$$

Calculate

$$M = [(q - a)^2 + b^2][(p - c)^2 + d^2] \qquad \text{and}$$
$$N = [(p - a)^2 + b^2][(q - c)^2 + d^2]. \quad (96)$$

The notation may be so chosen that $p > q$ and that $M \geqq N$,
since an interchange of a,b with c,d will not affect p and q but
will interchange M and N.   Then the substitution

$$\tan \phi = \sqrt{\frac{(q - a)^2 + b^2}{(p - a)^2 + b^2}} \frac{x - q}{p - x}, \qquad -\frac{\pi}{4} < \phi < \frac{3\pi}{4}, \quad (97)$$

will make Eq. (84) hold with

$$C = \frac{p - q}{\sqrt{M}} \qquad \text{and} \qquad k = \sqrt{1 - \frac{N}{M}}, \quad (98)$$

where the indicated square roots in Eqs. (97) and (98) are all
to be taken as positive.

Case IV. $X = [(x - a)^2 + b^2][(x - a)^2 + c^2], \qquad 0 < b < c.$

The substitution

$$\tan \phi = \frac{x - a}{b}, \qquad -\frac{\pi}{2} < \phi < \frac{\pi}{2}, \quad (99)$$

will make Eq. (84) hold with

$$C = \frac{1}{c} \qquad \text{and} \qquad k = \sqrt{1 - \frac{b^2}{c^2}}. \quad (100)$$

Case V. $X = \pm (x - a)(x - b)(x - c).$

The substitution

$$\sin^2 \phi = \frac{x - c}{b - c}, \qquad 0 < \phi < \frac{\pi}{2}, \quad (101)$$

will make Eq. (84) hold with

$$C^2 = \frac{\pm 4}{a - c} \quad \text{and} \quad k^2 = \frac{b - c}{a - c}, \tag{102}$$

if the sign of C is determined from the table:

Upper sign: $c < x < b < a,$ $C > 0.$ (103)
Lower sign: $a < b < x < c,$ $C < 0.$ (104)

And the substitution

$$\sin^2 \phi = \frac{b - c}{x - c}, \quad 0 < \phi < \frac{\pi}{2}, \tag{105}$$

will make Eq. (84) hold with

$$C^2 = \frac{\pm 4}{b - c} \quad \text{and} \quad k^2 = \frac{a - c}{b - c}, \tag{106}$$

if the sign of C is determined from the table:

Upper sign: $c < a < b < x,$ $C > 0.$ (107)
Lower sign: $x < b < a < c,$ $C < 0.$ (108)

For x is any interval of integration which makes $\sqrt{X}$ real, it is always possible so to letter the three roots that one of the relations (103), (104) or (107), (108) is satisfied.

Case VI. $X = \pm (x - a)[(x - b)^2 + c^2]$.

Let M be the positive square root of

$$M^2 = (b - a)^2 + c^2. \tag{109}$$

Then for the upper sign $x > a$, and the substitution

$$\tan^2 \frac{\phi}{2} = \frac{x - a}{M}, \quad 0 < \phi < \pi, \tag{110}$$

makes Eq. (84) hold with C and k the positive square roots of

$$C^2 = \frac{1}{M} \quad \text{and} \quad k^2 = \frac{M + b - a}{2M}. \tag{111}$$

For the lower sign $x < a$, and the substitution

$$\tan^2 \frac{\phi}{2} = \frac{a - x}{M}, \quad 0 < \phi < \pi, \tag{112}$$

makes Eq. (84) hold with C negative and k positive where

$$C^2 = \frac{1}{M} \quad \text{and} \quad k^2 = \frac{M + a - b}{2M}. \tag{113}$$

111. Integrals of the First and Second Kinds. One of the intermediate steps in the reduction of an elliptic integral (78) is a substitution that transforms the radicand to the product of two real factors without odd powers of x,

$$X = (Ax^2 + B)(A'x^2 + B') = ax^4 + bx^2 + c. \tag{114}$$

This substitution will, in general, introduce denominators outside the radical that eventually lead to integrals of the third kind. In fact, if the original radicand X is an unrestricted third- or fourth-degree polynomial, we can be sure of avoiding this difficulty only if the integral has the form $dx/\sqrt{X}$ discussed in Sec. 110.

However, if X has the partly reduced form (114), the integral

$$\frac{x^n}{\sqrt{X}} \, dx, \qquad n \text{ any positive or negative integer,} \tag{115}$$

is always reducible to integrals that are either elementary or expressible in terms of $F(k,\phi)$ and $E(k,\phi)$. If n is odd,

$$n = 2m + 1,$$

the integral (115) is elementary, since the substitution $x^2 = t$ makes

$$\int \frac{x^{2m+1}}{\sqrt{X}} \, dx = \int \frac{t^m dt}{2\sqrt{at^2 + bt + c}}, \tag{116}$$

which is an integral of the type treated in Sec. 68. Hence we need consider only integrals (115) with exponent n even.

We start with the relation

$$\frac{d}{dx}\left(x^n \sqrt{X}\right) = \frac{a(n + 2)x^{n+3} + b(n + 1)x^{n+1} + cnx^{n-1}}{\sqrt{X}}. \tag{117}$$

If we put $n = 2m - 3$ we may deduce that

$$\int \frac{x^{2m}}{\sqrt{X}} \, dx = \frac{x^{2m-3}\sqrt{X}}{a(2m - 1)} - \frac{2b(m - 1)}{a(2m - 1)} \int \frac{x^{2m-2}}{\sqrt{X}} \, dx$$
$$- \frac{c(2m - 3)}{a(2m - 1)} \int \frac{x^{2m-4}}{\sqrt{X}} \, dx. \tag{118}$$

This enables us to reduce any integral (115) with positive exponent to two others with smaller exponents if $m > 1$. Again, we may put $n = -2m + 1$ in (117) and deduce that

$$\int \frac{x^{-2m}}{\sqrt{X}}\, dx = -\frac{x^{-2m+1}\sqrt{X}}{c(2m-1)} - \frac{2b(m-1)}{c(2m-1)} \int \frac{x^{-2(m-1)}}{\sqrt{X}}\, dx$$
$$-\frac{a(2m-3)}{c(2m-1)} \int \frac{x^{-2(m-2)}}{\sqrt{X}}\, dx. \quad (119)$$

This enables us to reduce any integral (115) with negative exponent to two others with algebraically greater exponents. Thus, by successive use of the two formulas, any single integral, or linear combination of integrals, of the type of (115) may be expressed in terms of the two integrals

$$\frac{dx}{\sqrt{X}} \quad \text{and} \quad \frac{x^2 dx}{\sqrt{X}}. \quad (120)$$

The first of these is of the type evaluated in Sec. 110. The second may be transformed as follows. Choose the signs of A, B, A', B' in such a way that the two factors of X in (114) are both positive for x in the interval of integration. We shall require two substitutions.

Substitution I. The substitution $z^2 = Ax^2 + B$ makes

$$\int \frac{x^2 dx}{\sqrt{X}} = \frac{-B}{|A|} \int \frac{dz}{\sqrt{Z}} + \frac{1}{|A|} \int \frac{z^2 dz}{\sqrt{Z}}, \quad (121)$$

where, written with positive factors,

$$Z = (z^2 - B)(A'z^2 + AB' - A'B), \quad \text{if } A > 0, \quad (122)$$

and

$$Z = (-z^2 + B)(-A'z^2 - AB' + A'B), \quad \text{if } A < 0. \quad (123)$$

The first integral on the right in (121) is reducible by the method of Sec. 110, and the second integral is of the same type as our original integral, but with new radicand given by (122) or (123).

Substitution II. The substitution $z = -1/x$ makes

$$\int \frac{x^2 dx}{\sqrt{X}} = \int \frac{z^{-2} dz}{\sqrt{Z}} = -\frac{\sqrt{Z}}{AA'z} + \frac{BB'}{AA'} \int \frac{z^2 dz}{\sqrt{Z}}, \quad (124)$$

by Eq. (119) with $m = 1$, where

$$Z = (Bz^2 + A)(B'z^2 + A'). \quad (125)$$

Thus Substitutions I and II enable us to express the second integral (120) in terms of a new integral of the same type with new radicand given by Eq. (122), (123), or (125). After each substitution we may replace z by x and redefine the letters so that the radicand is again $(Ax^2 + B)(A'x^2 + B')$.

If B and B' are both negative, Substitution II will make the new B and B' both positive.

If B and B' are of opposite sign, choose the notation so that B is negative and B' positive. Then Substitution I will make the new B and B' both positive.

This reduces all cases to that in which B and B' are both positive. And in that case we may take the factor $\sqrt{BB'}$ outside the radical, and with revised notation write

$$X = (1 + Ax^2)(1 + A'x^2). \tag{126}$$

If A and A' are of opposite sign, choose the notation so that A is negative and A' positive. Apply Substitution I. Then from (123) with $B = B' = 1$, the new radicand will be

$$Z = (1 - z^2)(A' - A - A'z^2)$$
$$= (A' - A)(1 - z^2)\left(1 - \frac{A'}{A' - A} z^2\right). \tag{127}$$

If A and A' are both positive, choose the notation so that $A' > A$. Then Substitution I [Eq. (122)], followed by Substitution II, will make the new radicand

$$Z = (1 - z^2)[A' + (A - A')z^2] = A'(1 - z^2)\left(1 - \frac{A' - A}{A'} z^2\right). \tag{128}$$

This reduces all cases to that in which A and A' are negative. And in that case we may write the radicand (126) in the form

$$X = (1 - a^2x^2)(1 - b^2x^2), \qquad \text{with } a > b > 0. \tag{129}$$

Our integral is now reduced to normal form by the substitution

$$\sin \phi = ax, \qquad -\frac{\pi}{2} < \phi < \frac{\pi}{2}, \tag{130}$$

which makes

$$\int \frac{x^2 dx}{\sqrt{(1 - a^2x^2)(1 - b^2x^2)}} = \frac{1}{ab^2} \int \frac{k^2 \sin^2 \phi \, d\phi}{\sqrt{1 - k^2 \sin^2 \phi}}, \tag{131}$$
$$\text{where } k = \frac{b}{a},$$

or

$$= \frac{1}{ab^2} \int \frac{d\phi}{\sqrt{1 - k^2 \sin^2 \phi}} - \frac{1}{ab^2} \int \sqrt{1 - k^2 \sin^2 \phi}\, d\phi. \quad (132)$$

And these two integrals may be found in terms of $F(k,\phi)$ and $E(k,\phi)$ by means of Eqs. (15) and (56).

112. Jacobi's Elliptic Functions. For fixed modulus k and $x = \sin \phi$, the equation

$$u = F(k,\phi) = \int_0^\phi \frac{d\phi}{\sqrt{1 - k^2 \sin^2 \phi}} = \int_0^x \frac{dx}{\sqrt{(1 - x^2)(1 - k^2 x^2)}} \quad (133)$$

defines u as a function of ϕ or of x. It also defines ϕ as a function of u, $\phi = \text{am } u$ (read *amplitude* of u). The sine amplitude of u, cosine amplitude of u, and delta amplitude of u are then defined by the equations,

$$\text{sn } u = \sin (\text{am } u) = \sin \phi = x, \quad (134)$$
$$\text{cn } u = \cos (\text{am } u) = \cos \phi = \sqrt{1 - x^2}, \quad (135)$$
$$\text{dn } u = \Delta(\text{am } u) = \Delta\phi = \sqrt{1 - k^2 \sin^2 \phi} = \sqrt{1 - k^2 x^2}. \quad (136)$$

When u is real, all these functions are real and we use the positive square root in Eq. (136). In particular, if $u = 0$, $\phi = 0$ and

$$\text{sn } 0 = 0, \qquad \text{cn } 0 = 1, \qquad \text{dn } 0 = 1. \quad (137)$$

The function sn u is odd, while cn u and dn u are even. That is

$$\text{sn } (-u) = - \text{sn } u, \qquad \text{cn } (-u) = \text{cn } u \qquad \text{dn } (-u) = \text{dn } u. \quad (138)$$

We shall omit the deduction of the addition theorems for these functions, which are as follows (see Prob. 87 of Exercises VII):

$$\text{sn } (u \pm v) = \frac{\text{sn } u \text{ cn } v \text{ dn } v \pm \text{cn } u \sin v \text{ dn } u}{1 - k^2 \text{ sn}^2 u \text{ sn}^2 v}, \quad (139)$$

$$\text{cn } (u \pm v) = \frac{\text{cn } u \text{ cn } v \mp \text{sn } u \text{ sn } v \text{ dn } u \text{ dn } v}{1 - k^2 \text{ sn}^2 u \text{ sn}^2 v}, \quad (140)$$

$$\text{dn } (u \pm v) = \frac{\text{dn } u \text{ dn } v \mp k^2 \text{ sn } u \text{ sn } v \text{ cn } u \text{ cn } v}{1 - k^2 \text{ sn}^2 u \text{ sn}^2 v}. \quad (141)$$

When $u = K = F(k,\pi/2)$, $\phi = \pi/2$ so that

$$\text{sn } K = 1, \qquad \text{cn } K = 0, \qquad \text{dn } K = \sqrt{1 - k^2} = k'. \quad (142)$$

This positive root k' is called the *complementary modulus.*

And by Prob. 90, when $u = K + iK'$, where $K' = F(k',\pi/2)$, sn $u = x = 1/k$ so that

$$\text{sn } (K + iK') = \frac{1}{k}, \qquad \text{cn } (K + iK') = -\frac{ik'}{k},$$
$$\text{dn } (K + iK') = 0. \quad (143)$$

From these values and the addition theorems, it follows that each of the functions sn u, cn u, dn u admits the real period $4K$ and the imaginary period $4iK'$. The smaller periods $2iK'$ for sn u and $2K$ for dn u, as well as the alternative period $2K + 2iK'$ for cn u may be used.

All three of the normal integrals of Sec. 109 may be expressed in terms of sn u and simple integrals involving sn u. Thus

$$F(k,\sin^{-1} x) = \int_0^x \frac{dx}{\sqrt{(1 - x^2)(1 - k^2x^2)}} = u = \text{sn}^{-1} x \text{ or sn}^{-1} (x,k)$$
$$(144)$$

if we wish to indicate the parameter.

If $\phi = \text{am } u$, we find from Eqs. (133) and (136) that

$$\frac{du}{d\phi} = \frac{1}{\Delta\phi} = \frac{1}{\text{dn } u} \quad \text{and} \quad \text{dn}^2 u = 1 - k^2 \text{ sn}^2 u. \quad (145)$$

Hence

$$E(k,\phi) = \int_0^\phi \Delta\phi \, d\phi = \int_0^u \text{dn}^2 u \, du = u - k^2 \int_0^u \text{sn}^2 u \, du. \quad (146)$$

And when $x = \sin \phi = \text{sn } u$, from this and Eq. (82),

$$E(k,\sin^{-1} x) = \int_0^x \frac{\sqrt{1 - k^2x^2}}{\sqrt{1 - x^2}} \, dx = \text{sn}^{-1} x - k^2 \int_0^{\text{sn}^{-1} x} \text{sn}^2 u \, du. \quad (147)$$

Similarly, from Eq. (83),

$$\pi(n,k,\phi) = \pi(n,k,\sin^{-1} x) = \int_0^x \frac{dx}{(1 + nx^2) \sqrt{(1 - x^2)(1 - k^2x^2)}}$$
$$= \int_0^{\text{sn}^{-1} x} \frac{du}{(1 + n \text{ sn}^2 u)}. \quad (148)$$

113. References. Tables of the complete integrals K and E as functions of α are included in many mathematical handbooks. Those in H. B. Dwight's *Mathematical Tables* list K and E as functions of the argument k^2, which is usually the known parameter. The brief table of the incomplete integrals $F(k,\phi)$ and $E(k,\phi)$ given in B. O. Peirce's *Short Table of Integrals* and the fuller one in Jahnke-Emde's *Tables of Functions* have been mentioned in Sec. 105.

A proof of the possibility of expressing any elliptic integral in terms of the three normal forms will be found in Chap. VI of the author's *Treatise on Advanced Calculus*. For a comprehensive treatment of the theory of elliptic integrals and functions, the reader may consult A. Enneper's *Elliptische Funktionen*.

EXERCISES VII

Use tables to evaluate

1. $K(0.23)$.   **2.** $F(0.23, 0.96)$.   **3.** $F(0.23, 1.85)$.

4. $\int_0^{\pi/4} \dfrac{d\phi}{\sqrt{1 - 0.36 \sin^2 \phi}}$.   **5.** $\int_0^{\pi/2} \dfrac{d\phi}{\sqrt{1 - 0.83 \sin^2 \phi}}$.

6. $\int_{-\pi}^{2\pi} \dfrac{d\phi}{\sqrt{1 - 0.54 \sin^2 \phi}}$.   **7.** $\int_{\pi/18}^{\pi/9} \dfrac{d\phi}{\sqrt{1 - 0.25 \sin^2 \phi}}$.

By means of the series (7), compute the value of the elliptic integral

8. $K(0.1)$.   **9.** $K(0.08)$.   **10.** $K(0.2)$.

11. From Eqs. (5), (6), and (7), deduce that
$$F(k,\phi) = \frac{2}{\pi} K\phi - \sin 2\phi \frac{k^2}{4} \left(\frac{1}{2} + \frac{3}{4} C_2 \frac{k^2}{4} + \frac{3 \cdot 5}{4 \cdot 6} C_4 \frac{k^4}{6} \right.$$
$$\left. + \frac{3 \cdot 5 \cdot 7}{4 \cdot 6 \cdot 8} C_6 \frac{k^6}{8} + \cdots \right), \text{ where}$$
$$C_2 = \sin^2 \phi + \frac{3}{2}, \qquad C_4 = \sin^4 \phi + \frac{5}{4} \sin^2 \phi + \frac{5 \cdot 3}{4 \cdot 2},$$
$$C_6 = \sin^6 \phi + \frac{7}{6} \sin^4 \phi + \frac{7 \cdot 5}{6 \cdot 4} \sin^2 \phi + \frac{7 \cdot 5 \cdot 3}{6 \cdot 4 \cdot 2}, \text{ etc.}$$

12. Using Probs. 11 and 8, compute the value of the elliptic integral
$$\int_0^{\pi/4} \frac{d\phi}{\sqrt{1 - 0.01 \sin^2 \phi}} = F\left(0.1, \frac{\pi}{4}\right).$$

Use Eqs. (23) and (29) and the tables to evaluate

13. $\int_0^{\pi/9} \dfrac{du}{\sqrt{3 + \cos u}}$.   **14.** $\int_0^{\pi/9} \dfrac{du}{\sqrt{3 - \cos u}}$.   **15.** $\int_0^{\pi/2} \dfrac{du}{\sqrt{7 - \sin u}}$.

16. $\int_0^{\pi/3} \dfrac{du}{\sqrt{\cos u}}$.   **17.** $\int_0^{\pi/3} \dfrac{du}{\sqrt{\sin u}}$.

18. $\int_0^{\pi/2} \dfrac{du}{\sqrt{\cos u}} = \int_0^{\pi/2} \dfrac{du}{\sqrt{\sin u}}$.

19. Let $P = (r, \theta)$ be a point on the lemniscate $r^2 = a^2 \cos 2\theta$ with $0 < \theta \leq \pi/4$ and let A be the vertex $(a, 0)$. Show that the length of the arc AP is equal to any one of the following expressions:

$$\int_0^\theta \frac{a\, d\theta}{\sqrt{\cos 2\theta}} = \int_0^{2\theta} \frac{a\, du}{2\sqrt{\cos u}} = \frac{a}{\sqrt{2}} F\left[\frac{1}{\sqrt{2}}, \sin^{-1}(\sqrt{2} \sin \theta)\right].$$

20. Evaluate the arc AP in Prob. 19 if $\theta = \pi/6$; also if $\theta = \pi/4$, when AP is a quadrant. Use this to check Prob. 58 of Exercises VI (page 269).

21. Let O be the pivot and C the center of gravity of a compound pendulum. Then $T = \frac{1}{2} I (d\theta/dt)^2$, $U = -mgr \cos \theta$ where I is the moment of inertia about O, m is the mass, and $r = OC$. Show that the discussion of Sec. 106 applies if we replace l by I/mr in Eq. (34) and all later relations.

22. Use Eq. (46) to find the period of a simple pendulum making 180° swings, and so check Prob. 57 of Exercises VI (page 269).

23. For the pendulum of Prob. 22, find the time required for θ to increase from 0° to 30°, from 30° to 60°, and from 60° to 90°.

24. If β is the maximum angular deflection of a vibrating pendulum, show that the period $P = 2\pi \sqrt{\frac{l}{g}} \left(1 + \frac{1}{4} \sin^2 \frac{\beta}{2} + \frac{9}{64} \sin^4 \frac{\beta}{2} + \cdots\right)$

or $2\pi \sqrt{\frac{l}{g}} \left(1 + \frac{1}{16} \beta^2 + \frac{11}{3072} \beta^4 + \cdots\right)$ if β is small.

25. Check Prob. 22, within 2 per cent, by using three terms of the first series of Prob. 24.

26. If the maximum velocity of a pendulum making complete revolutions is one-half the minimum velocity, find the period.

27. Show that the elliptic integral involving trigonometric functions

$$\int \frac{dv}{\sqrt{P + Q \sin^2 v + R \cos^2 v + S \cos v \sin v}}$$ takes the form of I_1 given in Eq. (16) if $u = 2v$.

Use Prob. 27 to evaluate

28. $\int_0^{\pi/2} \dfrac{dv}{\sqrt{1 + 3 \sin^2 v}}.$

29. $\int_0^{\pi/2} \dfrac{dv}{\sqrt{1 + 3 \cos^2 v}}.$

30. $\int_0^{\pi/3} \dfrac{dv}{\sqrt{3 - 4 \sin^2 v}}.$

31. $\int_{\pi/6}^{\pi/2} \dfrac{dv}{\sqrt{3 - 4 \cos^2 v}}.$

32. $\int_0^{\pi/6} \dfrac{dv}{\sqrt{1 - 4 \sin^2 v}}.$

33. $\int_{\pi/3}^{\pi/2} \dfrac{dv}{\sqrt{1 - 4 \cos^2 v}}.$

Use tables to evaluate

34. $E(0.70).$ **35.** $E(0.70, 1).$ **36.** $E(0.70, 2).$

37. $\int_0^{\pi/5} \sqrt{1 - 0.36 \sin^2 \phi}\, d\phi.$ **38.** $\int_0^{\pi/2} \sqrt{1 - 0.72 \sin^2 \phi}\, d\phi.$

39. $\int_{-2\pi}^{\pi} \sqrt{1 - 0.41 \sin^2 \phi} \, d\phi.$ **40.** $\int_{\pi/10}^{\pi/5} \sqrt{1 - 0.25 \sin^2 \phi} \, d\phi.$

By means of the series (53) compute the value of

41. $E(0.1).$ **42.** $E(0.06).$ **43.** $E(0.2).$

44. From Eqs. (52), (6), and (53), deduce that the elliptic integral
$$E(k,\phi) = \frac{2}{\pi} E\phi + \sin 2\phi \frac{k^2}{4} \left(\frac{1}{2} + \frac{1}{4} C_2 \frac{k^2}{4} + \frac{1 \cdot 3}{4 \cdot 6} C_4 \frac{k^4}{6} \right.$$
$$\left. + \frac{1 \cdot 3 \cdot 5}{4 \cdot 6 \cdot 8} C_6 \frac{k^6}{8} + \cdots \right), \text{ where the } C_n \text{ are given in Prob. 11.}$$

45. Using Probs. 44 and 41, compute the value of the integral
$\int_0^{\pi/4} \sqrt{1 - 0.01 \sin^2 \phi} \, d\phi = E(0.1, \pi/4).$

Find the entire length of the ellipse

46. $8x^2 + 9y^2 = 72.$ **47.** $x^2 + 4y^2 = 4.$ **48.** $x^2 + 2y^2 = 16.$

On the ellipse of Prob. 48, find

49. The length of the minor arc joining $(2, \sqrt{6})$ and $(2\sqrt{2}, 2).$
50. The point that bisects the arc of the first quadrant.
51. The end of a unit arc measured from $(0, 2\sqrt{2})$ to the right.

52. Show that the total length of an ellipse is equal to the expression
$2\pi a(1 - \tfrac{1}{4}e^2 - \tfrac{3}{64}e^4 - \tfrac{5}{256}e^6 - \tfrac{175}{16384}e^8 - \cdots).$
53. Check Prob. 46 by using the series of Prob. 52.
54. Show that the length of one arch of $y = a \sin x$ may be expressed
in the form $2\sqrt{a^2 + 1} \, E \left(\dfrac{a}{\sqrt{a^2 + 1}} \right).$
55. Use Prob. 54 to find the length of one arch of $y = \sin x.$

Given the right circular cylinder $C: r = a \sin \theta$ and the sphere
$S: r^2 = z^2 + b^2$, with $b \geqq a$, show that

56. The area on the cylinder C inside the sphere S is $4abE(a/b).$
57. The area on S inside C is $2b^2[\pi - 2E(a/b)].$

58. Compute the areas of Probs. 56 and 57 when $a = 1, b = 2.$

Use Eqs. (68) and (75) and the tables to evaluate

59. $\int_0^{\pi/2} \sqrt{\cos u} \, du.$ **60.** $\int_0^{\pi/2} \sqrt{\sin u} \, du.$
61. $\int_0^{\pi/3} \sqrt{3 + \cos u} \, du.$

62. Express $\int \dfrac{P' + Q' \sin^2 v + R' \cos^2 v}{\sqrt{P + Q \sin^2 v + R \cos^2 v}}\, dv$ in terms of the integrals

reduced in Secs. 106 and 108 by putting $u = 2v$ and using the identity

$$\dfrac{A' + B' \cos u}{\sqrt{A + B \cos u}} = \dfrac{B'}{B} \sqrt{A + B \cos u} + \dfrac{A'B - AB'}{B}\dfrac{1}{\sqrt{A + B \cos u}}.$$

Use the appropriate reduction of Sec. 110 to evaluate

63. $\displaystyle\int_2^3 \dfrac{dx}{\sqrt{(x-1)(x-2)(x-3)(x-4)}}.$ **64.** $\displaystyle\int_0^1 \dfrac{dx}{\sqrt{1-x^4}}.$

65. $\displaystyle\int_0^\infty \dfrac{dx}{\sqrt{x^4 + 6x^2 + 8}}.$ **66.** $\displaystyle\int_1^2 \dfrac{dx}{\sqrt{(x-1)(x-2)(x-3)}}.$

67. $\displaystyle\int_0^1 \dfrac{dx}{\sqrt{(1-x)(4-x^2)}}.$ **68.** $\displaystyle\int_0^1 \dfrac{dx}{\sqrt{1-x^3}}.$

69. Check Prob. 63 by putting $2x = \sin \phi + 5$.

70. From Case I of Sec. 110 with $d,c,b,a = -1/m, -1, 1, 1/m;\ m < 1$:

$$2K(m) = \int_{-1}^1 \dfrac{dx}{\sqrt{(1-x^2)(1-m^2x^2)}} = \dfrac{2}{1+m} K\left(\dfrac{2\sqrt{m}}{1+m}\right).$$ Now put

$k = \dfrac{2\sqrt{m}}{1+m}$ and deduce that $K(k) = (1+m)K(m)$, where $m = \dfrac{1-k'}{1+k'}$,

$k' = \sqrt{1-k^2}$. This is one case of Landen's transformation. Since $m < k$, the series (7) for $K(m)$ converges faster than that for $K(k)$.

Use the substitutions of Sec. 111 to evaluate

71. $\displaystyle\int_0^1 \dfrac{x^2\,dx}{\sqrt{1-x^4}}.$ **72.** $\displaystyle\int_0^1 \dfrac{x^2\,dx}{\sqrt{x^4 + 6x^2 + 8}}.$

73. The area of the oval $y^2 = \dfrac{1-x^2}{1+x^2}$ is $A = 4\displaystyle\int_0^1 \dfrac{(1-x^2)\,dx}{\sqrt{(1-x^2)(1+x^2)}}.$

Section 111 suggests $z^2 = 1 - x^2$ and $\sin \phi = z$, or $x = \cos \phi$. Use

this to show that $A = 4\sqrt{2}\left[K\left(\dfrac{1}{\sqrt{2}}\right) - E\left(\dfrac{1}{\sqrt{2}}\right)\right] = 2.848$, check-

ing Prob. 59 of Exercises VI (page 269).

74. Verify that

$$(1 - k^2)\int_0^\phi \dfrac{\sec^2 \phi}{\Delta\phi}\, d\phi = \int_0^\phi \sec^2 \phi\, \Delta\phi\, d\phi - k^2 F(k,\phi)$$ and also that

$\displaystyle\int_0^\phi \sec^2 \phi\, \Delta\phi\, d\phi = \tan \phi\, \Delta\phi + F(k,\phi) - E(k,\phi)$, if as usual we write

$\Delta\phi = \sqrt{1 - k^2 \sin^2 \phi}$.

75. Let $A = (a,0)$ be the vertex and $P = (x,y)$ be a point with posi-

tive coordinates on the hyperbola $\dfrac{x^2}{a^2} - \dfrac{y^2}{b^2} = 1$. Put $\tan \phi = \dfrac{cy}{b^2}$, where

$c = \sqrt{a^2 + b^2}$, and show that the length of arc AP is equivalent to

$\dfrac{b^2}{c} F\left(\dfrac{a}{c}, \phi\right) - cE\left(\dfrac{a}{c}, \phi\right) + \tan\phi\,\sqrt{c^2 - a^2}\,\sin^2\phi.$ HINT: Use Prob. 74.

76. Use Prob. 75 to find the length of the arc joining (4,0) and $(\frac{4}{3}\sqrt{13}, 2)$ on the hyperbola $9x^2 - 16y^2 = 144$.

77. Show that the volume cut out of the cylinder $x^2 + z^2 = a^2$ by the cylinder $x^2 + y^2 = b^2$, $b \leqq a$, is

$V = \dfrac{8a}{3}\left[(a^2 + b^2)E\left(\dfrac{b}{a}\right) - (a^2 - b^2)F\left(\dfrac{b}{a}\right) \right].$ HINT: If $x = \cos\phi$, and

$k = \dfrac{b}{a}$; $V = 8ab^2 \displaystyle\int_0^{\pi/2} \cos^2\phi\,\Delta\phi\,d\phi$. Now use the following identity

$3\cos^2\phi\,\Delta\phi = \dfrac{d}{d\phi}(\sin\phi\cos\phi\,\Delta\phi) + (k^{-2} + 1)\Delta\phi - (k^{-2} - 1)\dfrac{1}{\Delta\phi}.$

78. Compute the volume of Prob. 77 if $a = 3$ and $b = 2$.

Let an electric current I flow around a circular loop C of radius a. The magnetic field intensity H at O, any point in the plane of C and at distance b from its center, may be found as follows. If O is the origin and the center of C has polar coordinates $(b,0)$, the equation of C is $r^2 - 2br\cos\theta + b^2 = a^2$, and the expression for the field intensity is

$H = \displaystyle\int \dfrac{I\sin(r,ds)}{r^2}\,ds = I\int\int\dfrac{d\theta}{r}$, taken over C. Show that

79. For O inside C, $b < a$; $\dfrac{1}{r} = \dfrac{\sqrt{a^2 - b^2\sin^2\theta} - b\cos\theta}{a^2 - b^2}$ and hence

$H = I\displaystyle\int_0^{2\pi} \dfrac{d\theta}{r} = \dfrac{4Ia}{a^2 - b^2} K\left(\dfrac{b}{a}\right).$

80. For O outside C, $b > a$; if $\theta < \alpha$, where $\sin\alpha = a/b$ there are two values of r on C. If these are r_1 and $r_2 > r_1$; $d\theta_2 = -d\theta_1$, while now

$\dfrac{1}{r_1} - \dfrac{1}{r_2} = \dfrac{2\sqrt{a^2 - b^2\sin^2\theta}}{b^2 - a^2}.$ Hence the expression for the intensity is

$H = 2I\displaystyle\int_0^\alpha \left(\dfrac{d\theta_1}{r_1} + \dfrac{d\theta_2}{r_2}\right) = \dfrac{4I}{b^2 - a^2}\int_0^\alpha \sqrt{a^2 - b^2\sin^2\theta}\,d\theta.$ And hence

$H = 4I\left[\dfrac{bE(a/b)}{b^2 - a^2} - \dfrac{1}{b}K\left(\dfrac{a}{b}\right)\right].$

81. If a spring, originally straight and along the x axis, is bowed up by a compressive force F acting on its ends, the equation $\dfrac{EI}{\rho} = -Fy$ holds. Put $EI = Fc^2$, $p = \dfrac{dy}{dx}$ so that $\dfrac{1}{\rho} = \dfrac{p\,dp/dy}{(1 + p^2)^{3/2}}$. Let $x = 0$, $y = b$ when $p = 0$ and $x = \pm a$ when $y = 0$. Then it follows that $y\,dy = -c^2 p\,dp(1 + p^2)^{-3/2}$, $y^2 - b^2 = 2c^2[(1 + p^2)^{-1/2} - 1]$. And with $y = b\cos\phi$, $k = \dfrac{b}{2c}$, deduce that the following relations are all valid. $(1 + p^2)^{-1/2} = 1 - 2k^2\sin^2\phi = 2(\Delta\phi)^2 - 1$, and hence for $0 < x \leqq a$,

$-\dfrac{1}{p} = \dfrac{2(\Delta\phi)^2 - 1}{2k \sin\phi\,\Delta\phi}.$ But $-\dfrac{1}{p} = -\dfrac{dx}{dy} = \dfrac{dx}{b \sin\phi\,d\phi}$, so that we have

$dx = 2c\,\Delta\phi\,d\phi - \dfrac{c\,d\phi}{\Delta\phi}$ and $x = c[2E(k,\phi) - F(k,\phi)]$. Also with s

measured from $(0,b)$, $\dfrac{ds}{dy} = -\dfrac{(1 + p^2)^{1/2}}{p}$, so that $ds = \dfrac{c\,d\phi}{\Delta\phi}$ and hence

$s = cF(k,\phi)$. For the whole spring from $-a$ to a, the length becomes $L = 2cK(k)$, the span $2a = 2c[2E(k) - K(k)]$, and the maximum deflection $b = 2ck$.

82. Suppose the spring of Prob. 81 is of steel for which $E = 3 \times 10^7$ lb./in.^{2} has uncompressed length $L = 10$ in. and is $\frac{1}{2}$ in. wide and $\frac{1}{64}$ in. thick, so that $I = 1/(3 \times 2^{21})$ in.^{4} Find the maximum deflection and span if the thrust F is 1 lb.

83. When gravity is neglected compared with the centrifugal force and tension T, the equation for the curve of a skipping rope reduces to $\dfrac{d}{ds}\left(Tg\dfrac{dy}{dx}\right) = -m\omega^2 y$. Put $m\omega^2 c^2 = Tg$ and $p = dy/dx$. Let $x = 0,2a$ when $y = 0$ and $x = a$, $y = b$ when $p = 0$. Then it follows that $c^2 p\,dp(1 + p^2)^{-1/2} = -y\,dy$, $2c^2[(1 + p^2)^{1/2} - 1] = b^2 - y^2$. And with $y = b \sin\phi$, $k^2 = \dfrac{b^2}{4c^2 + b^2}$, deduce that $(1 + p^2)^{1/2} = \dfrac{b^2}{2c^2 k^2}(\Delta\phi)^2 - 1$,

and for $0 \leqq x < a$, $\dfrac{1}{p} = \dfrac{2kc^2}{b^2 \cos\phi\,\Delta\phi}$. But $\dfrac{1}{p} = \dfrac{dx}{dy} = \dfrac{dx}{b \cos\phi\,d\phi}$, so

that $dx = \dfrac{2kc^2\,d\phi}{b\,\Delta\phi}$ and $x = \dfrac{2kc^2}{b}F(k,\phi)$. Also $\dfrac{ds}{dx} = (1 + p^2)^{1/2}$, so that $ds = \left(\dfrac{b}{k}\Delta\phi - \dfrac{2kc^2}{b\,\Delta\phi}\right)d\phi$ and $s = \dfrac{b}{k}E(k,\phi) - \dfrac{2kc^2}{b}F(k,\phi)$.

84. In Fig. 124, $B'AB$ is the arc of a circle of radius l on which the bob of a simple pendulum is vibrating. BCB' and UWU' are horizontal lines cutting the vertical diameter AD in C and W. The small circle has diameter AC and cuts UU' in VV'. Angle $AOB = 2\alpha$, angle $AOU = \theta$, and the time t is given by Eq. (41). Show that $AW = 2l \sin^2\dfrac{\theta}{2}$, $AC = 2\,l\sin^2\alpha$, so that $AV = \sqrt{AW \cdot AC} = 2l \sin\dfrac{\theta}{2}\sin\alpha = AC \sin\phi$. Deduce that angle $ACV = \phi$, and if $u = \sqrt{g/l}\,t$, the functions of Sec. 112 are sn $u = WV/CV$, cn $u = CW/CV$, dn $u = DW/DU$, since $\mathrm{dn}^2 u = 1 - \sin^2\alpha \sin^2\phi = \cos^2\dfrac{\theta}{2}$.

85. Use Case V of Sec. 110 to show that, if $e_3 < e_2 < e_1 < p$, then

$$u = \int_p^\infty \dfrac{dx}{\sqrt{4(x - e_1)(x - e_2)(x - e_3)}}$$

$$= \dfrac{1}{\sqrt{e_1 - e_3}}\,F\left(\sqrt{\dfrac{e_2 - e_3}{e_1 - e_3}},\ \sin^{-1}\sqrt{\dfrac{e_1 - e_3}{p - e_3}}\right).$$

Deduce that $p(u) = e_3 + \dfrac{e_1 - e_3}{\text{sn}^2 (\sqrt{e_1 - e_3}\, u)}$, where $k = \sqrt{\dfrac{e_2 - e_3}{e_1 - e_3}}$ is the modulus of the sine amplitude. When $e_1 + e_2 + e_3 = 0$, the function $p(u)$ is the Weierstrass $\wp$ function.

86. From Eqs. (134) to (136) and (145), $\dfrac{d\phi}{du} = \text{dn}\,u$, deduce that

$$\frac{d(\text{sn}\,u)}{du} = \text{cn}\,u\,\text{dn}\,u, \quad \frac{d(\text{cn}\,u)}{du} = -\text{sn}\,u\,\text{dn}\,u, \quad \frac{d(\text{dn}\,u)}{du} = -k^2\,\text{sn}\,u\,\text{cn}\,u.$$

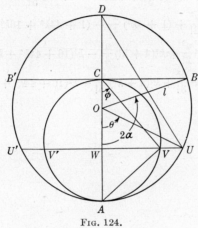

FIG. 124.

87. If $u + v = c$, $\dfrac{dv}{du} = -1$. Let $\text{sn}\,u = s$, $\text{sn}\,v = S$, and use primes for u differentiation. From Prob. 86, we have $s'^2 = (1 - s^2)(1 - k^2 s^2)$, $s'' = 2k^2 s^3 - (1 + k^2)s$, and similarly $S'^2 = (1 - S^2)(1 - k^2 S^2)$ $S'' = 2k^2 S^3 - (1 + k^2)S$, so that $s''S - S''s = 2k^2 sS(s^2 - S^2)$ and $s'^2 S^2 - S'^2 s^2 = (1 - k^2 s^2 S^2)(S^2 - s^2)$. Hence derive the relation $\dfrac{s''S - S''s}{s'S - S's} = -\dfrac{2k^2 sS(s'S + S's)}{1 - k^2 s^2 S^2}$, and from this by integration deduce $\log (s'S - S's) = \log (1 - k^2 s^2 S^2) + C$. This may be rewritten as $\dfrac{\text{cn}\,u\,\text{dn}\,u\,\text{sn}\,v + \text{cn}\,v\,\text{dn}\,v\,\text{sn}\,u}{1 - k^2\,\text{sn}^2 u\,\text{sn}^2 v} = e^C$. When $v = 0$, $u = c$, and so $e^C = \text{sn}\,c$ or $\text{sn}\,(u + v)$. This verifies the first addition theorem, Eq. (139).

88. Show that when $k = 0$, $u = \phi$, $\text{sn}\,u = \sin u$, $\text{cn}\,u = \cos u$, $\text{dn}\,u = 1$, and Eqs. (139) and (140) become familiar trigonometric formulas.

89. Show that when $k = 1$, $u = \text{gd}^{-1}\,\phi$, where $\phi = \text{gd}\,u$ is the function of Probs. 31 and 32 of Exercises I (page 39) and also show that $\text{sn}\,u = \tanh u$, $\text{cn}\,u = \text{sech}\,u$, $\text{dn}\,u = \text{sech}\,u$. Also verify that Eqs. (139) and (140) become consequences of formulas given in Sec. 4.

90. In Eq. (133), u becomes complex if $x > 1$. Show that when $x = 1/k$, $u = K + iK'$, where we may evaluate $K = F(k, \pi/2)$ and $K' = F(\sqrt{1 - k^2}, \pi/2)$. HINT: See Prob. 116 of Exercises V (page 250) and put $1 - k^2x^2 = (1 - k^2) \sin^2 \phi$ in the integral for K'.

Use Prob. 86 to check the first two terms of each of the following series. They all converge if $|u| < K'$, defined in Prob. 90.

91. $\operatorname{sn} u = u - (1 + k^2) \dfrac{u^3}{3!} + (1 + 14k^2 + k^4) \dfrac{u^5}{5!} - \cdots$.

92. $\operatorname{cn} u = 1 - \dfrac{u^2}{2!} + (1 + 4k^2) \dfrac{u^4}{4!} - (1 + 44k^2 + 16k^4) \dfrac{u^6}{6!} + \cdots$.

93. $\operatorname{dn} u = 1 - k^2\dfrac{u^2}{2!} + k^2(4 + k^2) \dfrac{u^4}{4!} - k^2(16 + 44k^2 + k^4) \dfrac{u^6}{6!} + \cdots$.

94. $\operatorname{am} u = u - k^2 \dfrac{u^3}{3!} + k^2(4 + k^2) \dfrac{u^5}{5!} - k^2(16 + 44k^2 + k^4) \dfrac{u^7}{7!} + \cdots$.

CHAPTER VIII

VECTOR ANALYSIS

The algebra and ordinary differentiation of vectors were introduced in Chap. III as an aid to the study of curves and surfaces in space. Most of this chapter deals with the symbolic vector del, which is a vector partial differential operator, and three expressions involving del known as the *gradient, divergence,* and *curl.* These expressions simplify the discussion of certain useful relations between volume integrals, surface integrals, and line integrals in space. We show how results formulated in terms of del may be expressed in any system of orthogonal curvilinear coordinates. Symbolic vectors occur frequently in mathematical physics. We illustrate this by deriving the condition for a force field to be conservative, the Fourier equation of heat flow, Euler's hydrodynamic equations, and Poisson's equation for electrical or gravitational potential.

114. Vector Algebra. We begin with a summary of those properties of vectors or directed magnitudes which were developed in Chap. III. Vectors may be represented in terms of their components along the axes, as

$$\mathbf{a} = a_x\mathbf{i} + a_y\mathbf{j} + a_z\mathbf{k}, \qquad \mathbf{b} = b_x\mathbf{i} + b_y\mathbf{j} + b_z\mathbf{k}, \text{ etc.} \qquad (1)$$

The operations of addition, subtraction, multiplication by a scalar, and differentiation with respect to a scalar parameter can all be carried out by performing these operations on the components of the vectors involved. The length of the vector a is

$$a = |\mathbf{a}| = \sqrt{a_x{}^2 + a_y{}^2 + a_z{}^2}. \qquad (2)$$

The scalar product or dot product of Sec. 45, $\mathbf{a} \cdot \mathbf{b}$, is

$$\mathbf{a} \cdot \mathbf{b} = a_xb_x + a_yb_y + a_zb_z. \qquad (3)$$

The scalar product is commutative, $\mathbf{a} \cdot \mathbf{b} = \mathbf{b} \cdot \mathbf{a}$, and

$$\mathbf{a} \cdot \mathbf{b} = a \operatorname{Proj_a} \mathbf{b} = ab \cos \theta. \qquad (4)$$

303

The vector product or cross product of Sec. 51, $\mathbf{a} \times \mathbf{b}$, is

$$\mathbf{a} \times \mathbf{b} = \begin{vmatrix} \mathbf{i} & \mathbf{j} & \mathbf{k} \\ a_x & a_y & a_z \\ b_x & b_y & b_z \end{vmatrix} = \begin{vmatrix} a_y & a_z \\ b_y & b_z \end{vmatrix} \mathbf{i} + \begin{vmatrix} a_z & a_x \\ b_z & b_x \end{vmatrix} \mathbf{j} + \begin{vmatrix} a_x & a_y \\ b_x & b_y \end{vmatrix} \mathbf{k}. \quad (5)$$

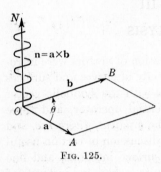

Fig. 125.

The expanded form is

$$\mathbf{a} \times \mathbf{b} = (a_y b_z - a_z b_y)\mathbf{i} +$$
$$(a_z b_x - a_x b_z)\mathbf{j} + (a_x b_y - a_y b_x)\mathbf{k}. \quad (6)$$

The vector product is *not* commutative, but

$$\mathbf{a} \times \mathbf{b} = -\mathbf{b} \times \mathbf{a}, \qquad \text{while}$$
$$|\mathbf{a} \times \mathbf{b}| = |\mathbf{b} \times \mathbf{a}| = ab \sin \theta. \quad (7)$$

The triple scalar product of Sec. 53 is

$$\mathbf{a} \cdot (\mathbf{b} \times \mathbf{c}) = (\mathbf{a} \times \mathbf{b}) \cdot \mathbf{c} = \begin{vmatrix} a_x & a_y & a_z \\ b_x & b_y & b_z \\ c_x & c_y & c_z \end{vmatrix}. \quad (8)$$

115. The Symbolic Vector Del. The equation

$$\nabla = \frac{\partial}{\partial x}\mathbf{i} + \frac{\partial}{\partial y}\mathbf{j} + \frac{\partial}{\partial z}\mathbf{k} \quad (9)$$

defines the symbolic vector, or vector differential operator ∇, read *del*. To interpret ∇ in combination with a scalar point function $f(x,y,z)$, we treat $\partial/\partial x$, $\partial/\partial y$, $\partial/\partial z$ as if they were numerical components, and in the final form replace the product of $\partial/\partial x$ times f by $\partial f/\partial x$, that of $\partial/\partial y$ times f by $\partial f/\partial y$, and that of $\partial/\partial z$ times f by $\partial f/\partial z$. Thus the *gradient* of f, ∇f, is

$$\nabla f = \frac{\partial}{\partial x}f\mathbf{i} + \frac{\partial}{\partial y}f\mathbf{j} + \frac{\partial}{\partial z}f\mathbf{k} = \frac{\partial f}{\partial x}\mathbf{i} + \frac{\partial f}{\partial y}\mathbf{j} + \frac{\partial f}{\partial z}\mathbf{k}. \quad (10)$$

Similarly for a combination with a vector point function

$$\mathbf{Q}(x,y,z) = Q_x(x,y,z)\mathbf{i} + Q_y(x,y,z)\mathbf{j} + Q_z(x,y,z)\mathbf{k} \quad (11)$$

we replace products such as $\partial/\partial x$ times Q_x by $\partial Q_x/\partial x$. Thus the *divergence* of $\mathbf{Q}$, $\nabla \cdot \mathbf{Q}$, is by Eq. (3)

$$\nabla \cdot \mathbf{Q} = \frac{\partial}{\partial x}Q_x + \frac{\partial}{\partial y}Q_y + \frac{\partial}{\partial z}Q_z = \frac{\partial Q_x}{\partial x} + \frac{\partial Q_y}{\partial y} + \frac{\partial Q_z}{\partial z}. \quad (12)$$

And from Eq. (5) the *curl* of **Q**, $\nabla \times \mathbf{Q}$, is

$$\nabla \times \mathbf{Q} = \begin{vmatrix} \mathbf{i} & \mathbf{j} & \mathbf{k} \\ \dfrac{\partial}{\partial x} & \dfrac{\partial}{\partial y} & \dfrac{\partial}{\partial z} \\ Q_x & Q_y & Q_z \end{vmatrix} = \left(\frac{\partial Q_z}{\partial y} - \frac{\partial Q_y}{\partial z} \right) \mathbf{i} + \left(\frac{\partial Q_x}{\partial z} - \frac{\partial Q_z}{\partial x} \right) \mathbf{j}$$

$$+ \left(\frac{\partial Q_y}{\partial x} - \frac{\partial Q_x}{\partial y} \right) \mathbf{k}. \quad (13)$$

The notation

$$\operatorname{grad} f = \nabla f, \qquad \operatorname{div} \mathbf{Q} = \nabla \cdot \mathbf{Q}, \qquad \operatorname{curl} \mathbf{Q} = \nabla \times \mathbf{Q} \quad (14)$$

is often used. The reason for the terms gradient, divergence, and curl will be explained in Secs. 116, 117, and 128. The physical interpretations there given show that the expressions (10), (12), and (13) have a significance independent of the choice of coordinate axes. This is not at once obvious, since del was defined in terms of **i**,**j**,**k** and x,y,z for a particular choice of axes. And we cannot geometrically interpret del or the scalar and vector products involving del by the methods used for ordinary vectors. Actually, under a rotation of the coordinate axes, the formulas of transformation for the component differential operators of ∇ are identical with those for the components of an ordinary vector. Any scalar or vector expression that has a geometric meaning when applied to ordinary vectors must lead to an expression with a meaning independent of the axes when one or more of the vectors is replaced by ∇. Consequently all simple expressions of this type are likely to be useful in mathematical physics. For example,

$$\nabla \cdot \nabla f = \frac{\partial^2 f}{\partial x^2} + \frac{\partial^2 f}{\partial y^2} + \frac{\partial^2 f}{\partial z^2} \quad (15)$$

is the Laplacian operator. We usually write ∇^2 for $\nabla \cdot \nabla$.

Many of the rules of differentiation apply to ∇. In particular the product rule suggests that

$$\nabla(fg) = (\nabla f)g + f(\nabla g), \quad \nabla \cdot (f\mathbf{Q}) = (\nabla f) \cdot \mathbf{Q} + f \nabla \cdot \mathbf{Q}, \quad (16)$$
$$\nabla \times (f\mathbf{Q}) = (\nabla f) \times \mathbf{Q} + f \nabla \times \mathbf{Q},$$
$$\nabla \cdot (\mathbf{P} \times \mathbf{Q}) = \mathbf{Q} \cdot (\nabla \times \mathbf{P}) - \mathbf{P} \cdot (\nabla \times \mathbf{Q}). \quad (17)$$

If the vector **Q** is a gradient, $\mathbf{Q} = \nabla f$,

$$\mathbf{Q} \cdot (\nabla Q_x) = \mathbf{Q} \cdot \left(\nabla \frac{\partial f}{\partial x} \right) = \mathbf{Q} \cdot \frac{\partial(\nabla f)}{\partial x} = \mathbf{Q} \cdot \frac{\partial \mathbf{Q}}{\partial x} = \frac{1}{2} \frac{\partial}{\partial x} (\mathbf{Q} \cdot \mathbf{Q}). \quad (18)$$

On replacing $\mathbf{Q}$ by ∇f in Eq. (13) we find

$$\nabla \times \nabla f = 0. \tag{19}$$

From this and the second equation in (17) we may deduce that

$$\nabla \cdot (\nabla f \times \nabla g) = \nabla g \cdot (\nabla \times \nabla f) - \nabla f \cdot (\nabla \times \nabla g) = 0. \tag{20}$$

116. The Gradient. Let $U(x,y,z)$ be any scalar point function, for example, a potential function. Then we may pass an equipotential surface,

$$U(x,y,z) = c \tag{21}$$

through any given point $P = (x,y,z)$. By Sec. 49, the vector

$$\nabla U = \frac{\partial U}{\partial x} \mathbf{i} + \frac{\partial U}{\partial y} \mathbf{j} + \frac{\partial U}{\partial z} \mathbf{k} \tag{22}$$

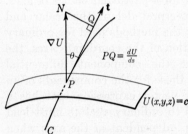

is normal to the surface (21) at P. Thus the gradient of the potential function at any point is normal to the equipotential surface through the point.

Let C be a space curve passing through P, and s the arc length measured along C. Then on the curve x,y,z are functions of s, and hence U is a function of s. We call dU/ds the *directional derivative* of U

Fig. 126.

along C. From Eq. (25) of Sec. 21

$$\frac{dU}{ds} = \frac{\partial U}{\partial x} \frac{dx}{ds} + \frac{\partial U}{\partial y} \frac{dy}{ds} + \frac{\partial U}{\partial z} \frac{dz}{ds}. \tag{23}$$

But $\mathbf{t}$, the unit vector tangent to the curve C at the point P, is

$$\mathbf{t} = \frac{dx}{ds} \mathbf{i} + \frac{dy}{ds} \mathbf{j} + \frac{dz}{ds} \mathbf{k} \tag{24}$$

by Eqs. (172) to (174) of Sec. 54. It follows that

$$\frac{dU}{ds} = (\nabla U) \cdot \mathbf{t} = \mathbf{t} \cdot (\nabla U). \tag{25}$$

Let θ be the angle between the gradient and the vector $\mathbf{t}$. Put

$$|\mathrm{grad}\ U| = |\nabla U| = \sqrt{\left(\frac{\partial U}{\partial x}\right)^2 + \left(\frac{\partial U}{\partial y}\right)^2 + \left(\frac{\partial U}{\partial z}\right)^2}. \tag{26}$$

Since **t** is of length one, we find from Eq. (4),

$$\frac{dU}{ds} = |\text{grad } U| \cos \theta = \text{Proj}_t (\nabla U). \qquad (27)$$

This shows that dU/ds depends only on the direction of the tangent to C at P and is equal to the projection of the gradient on this tangent. We call dU/ds the *derivative* of U in the direction of **t**. It is a maximum when $\cos \theta = 1$, and $\theta = 0$. That

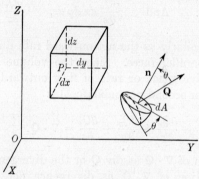

Fig. 127.

is, the gradient ∇U extends in the direction in which the derivative of U is a maximum, and its magnitude $|\text{grad } U|$ of (26) is equal to that maximum derivative.

117. The Divergence. For the flow of a liquid in a three-dimensional region, let

$$\mathbf{Q} = Q_x\mathbf{i} + Q_y\mathbf{j} + Q_z\mathbf{k} \qquad (28)$$

be a vector equal to D times the velocity vector, where D is the variable density in pounds per cubic foot. Thus $|\mathbf{Q}|$ is the quantity of flow, per unit time, through unit area normal to the direction of flow. Consider any element of area dA ft.² Let **n** be the unit vector normal to dA drawn toward the side called *positive*. And let θ be the angle between **n** and **Q**. Then the projection of dA normal to the flow is $dA \cos \theta$, and the rate of flow through dA toward the positive side is

$$|\mathbf{Q}| \, dA \cos \theta = \mathbf{Q} \cdot \mathbf{n} \, dA. \qquad (29)$$

Let us apply this result to the faces of the parallelepiped, or box of Fig. 127, with one vertex at $P(x,y,z)$ and with sides of length dx, dy, dz parallel to the axes. Then the rate of flow into the left-hand face is

$$\mathbf{Q} \cdot \mathbf{j} \, dx \, dz = Q_y \, dx \, dz, \qquad \text{while} \left(Q_y + \frac{\partial Q_y}{\partial y} \, dy \right) dx \, dz \quad (30)$$

is the rate of flow out of the right-hand face. The net outward rate of flow due to these two faces is

$$\frac{\partial Q_y}{\partial y} \, dy \, dx \, dz. \qquad \text{And} \qquad \frac{\partial Q_x}{\partial x} \, dx \, dy \, dz, \qquad \frac{\partial Q_z}{\partial z} \, dz \, dx \, dy \quad (31)$$

are obtained similarly as the net outward rate due to the other two pairs of parallel faces. Since the volume of the box is $dx \, dy \, dz$, the divergence or rate of flow outward per unit volume (pounds per second per cubic foot) is

$$\frac{\partial Q_x}{\partial x} + \frac{\partial Q_y}{\partial y} + \frac{\partial Q_z}{\partial z} = \nabla \cdot \mathbf{Q}. \quad (32)$$

The designation of $\nabla \cdot \mathbf{Q}$ as div $\mathbf{Q}$ or the divergence anticipated this interpretation of $\nabla \cdot \mathbf{Q}$ as divergence per unit time per unit volume.

118. The Divergence Theorem. Let $\mathbf{Q}(x,y,z)$ be a vector point function and R a region of space throughout which $\mathbf{Q}$ is

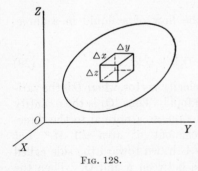

FIG. 128.

regular, that is, without singularities. Then in R we may associate $\mathbf{Q}$ with the ideal flow of a compressible fluid in the manner described in Sec. 117.

Let S consist of one or more closed surfaces that collectively bound a volume V in R. If we subdivide R into small boxes by a series of planes parallel to the axes, V will be subdivided into boxes and parts of boxes. For each small box wholly in V, the outward flow per unit time will be

$$\nabla \cdot \mathbf{Q} \, \Delta x \, \Delta y \, \Delta z = \nabla \cdot \mathbf{Q} \, \Delta V \quad (33)$$

to within infinitesimals of higher order, by Eq. (32). As in Sec. 74, neglecting the parts of boxes near S or replacing them by whole boxes will not affect the limit of the sum, which will be

$$\int_V \nabla \cdot \mathbf{Q} \, dV. \tag{34}$$

The flow out from any face of an interior box will be into the face of an adjacent box. Consequently the integral (34) will represent the total net rate of flow from V out through S.

The rate of flow out through an element dS of S is

$$\mathbf{Q} \cdot \mathbf{n} \, dS, \tag{35}$$

by Eq. (29), where

$$\mathbf{n} = \cos \alpha \, \mathbf{i} + \cos \beta \, \mathbf{j} + \cos \gamma \, \mathbf{k} \tag{36}$$

is the *outward* drawn unit vector normal to dS. Hence the total net rate of flow out through S is

$$\int_S \mathbf{Q} \cdot \mathbf{n} \, dS. \tag{37}$$

By equating this to the expression found in (34), we find

$$\int_V \nabla \cdot \mathbf{Q} \, dV = \int_S \mathbf{Q} \cdot \mathbf{n} \, dS. \tag{38}$$

This is the *divergence theorem*. From Eqs. (28), (32), and (36) we may derive the expanded form for Cartesian coordinates

$$\int_V \left(\frac{\partial Q_x}{\partial x} + \frac{\partial Q_y}{\partial y} + \frac{\partial Q_z}{\partial z} \right) dx \, dy \, dz$$
$$= \int_S (Q_x \cos \alpha + Q_y \cos \beta + Q_z \cos \gamma) dS. \tag{39}$$

Let us use parameters u and v on S, so chosen that the vector $\mathbf{A}$ of Eq. (278) in Sec. 56 has the direction of the outward drawn normal. Then from Secs. 56, 57, and 58

$$\cos \alpha \, dS = \frac{\partial(y,z)}{\partial(u,v)} \, du \, dv = \pm dy \, dz. \tag{40}$$

And the right member of Eq. (39) may be written

$$\int \left[\frac{\partial(y,z)}{\partial(u,v)} Q_x + \frac{\partial(z,x)}{\partial(u,v)} Q_y + \frac{\partial(x,y)}{\partial(u,v)} Q_z \right] du \, dv$$
$$= \int_S (\pm Q_x dy \, dz \pm Q_y dz \, dx \pm Q_z dx \, dy). \tag{41}$$

The last form follows from Sec. 58. The signs in (40) and (41) are determinate at each point as those of the Jacobians in Eq. (41), or those of the cosines in Eq. (36). With each term we may associate the coordinate axis of the variable whose dif-

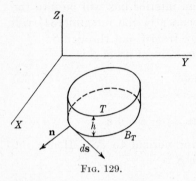

ferential is omitted. Then the sign is plus if the projection of the outer normal to S on this axis is positive and minus if this projection is negative.

119. Green's Theorem for a Plane Region. Let T be a simple region in the xy plane. Define the positive direction on its boundary B_T, as in Sec. 81. Erect a right cylinder C of height h on T as a lower base.

Fig. 129.

Then we may apply the divergence theorem to the cylinder C, using the vector point function

$$\mathbf{Q} = Q(x,y)\mathbf{i} - P(x,y)\mathbf{j}, \qquad \text{so that } Q_x = Q,$$
$$Q_y = -P, \ Q_z = 0. \quad (42)$$

On the top and bottom of the cylinder, $\mathbf{Q} \cdot \mathbf{n} = 0$. And on the lateral surface

$$\mathbf{n} = \left(\frac{dx}{ds}\mathbf{i} + \frac{dy}{ds}\mathbf{j}\right) \times \mathbf{k} = \mathbf{i}\frac{dy}{ds} - \mathbf{j}\frac{dx}{ds}, \qquad dS = h\,ds. \quad (43)$$

Since no quantity depends on z, we may take $dV = h\,dx\,dy$ and Eq. (38) becomes

$$\int_T \left(\frac{\partial Q}{\partial x} - \frac{\partial P}{\partial y}\right) h\,dx\,dy = \int_{B_T} \left(Q\frac{dy}{ds} + P\frac{dx}{ds}\right) h\,ds. \quad (44)$$

It follows that

$$\int_{B_T} (P\,dx + Q\,dy) = \int_T \left(\frac{\partial Q}{\partial x} - \frac{\partial P}{\partial y}\right) dx\,dy, \qquad (45)$$

which is Green's theorem as stated in Sec. 81.

We shall next obtain a vector form in which the coordinates do not appear explicitly. Let $\mathbf{Q}$ be any vector point function [Eq. (11)] and put

$$P(x,y) = Q_x(x,y,0), \qquad Q(x,y) = Q_y(x,y,0). \quad (46)$$

At all points of T, $z = 0$, so that by Eq. (13)

$$\mathbf{k} \cdot (\nabla \times \mathbf{Q}) = \left(\frac{\partial Q_y}{\partial x} - \frac{\partial Q_x}{\partial y}\right)\bigg|_{z=0} = \left(\frac{\partial Q}{\partial x} - \frac{\partial P}{\partial y}\right). \quad (47)$$

Let dT be the element of area of T, and $\mathbf{n}_T$ the unit vector normal to T. Then $dT = dx\,dy$ and $\mathbf{n}_T = \mathbf{k}$, so that the right member of Eq. (45) is

$$\int_T \left(\frac{\partial Q}{\partial x} - \frac{\partial P}{\partial y}\right) dx\,dy = \int_T \mathbf{n}_T \cdot (\nabla \times \mathbf{Q})dT. \quad (48)$$

Again, if $d\mathbf{s}$ is the vector of length ds along the tangent to B_T, $d\mathbf{s} = dx\,\mathbf{i} + dy\,\mathbf{j}$ and

$$\mathbf{Q} \cdot d\mathbf{s} = Q_x dx + Q_y dy = P\,dx + Q\,dy \quad (49)$$

on B_T, since $z = 0$ there. Hence the left member of Eq. (45) is

$$\int_{B_T} (P\,dx + Q\,dy) = \int_{B_T} \mathbf{Q} \cdot d\mathbf{s}. \quad (50)$$

Equations (48) and (50) lead to the alternative form of (45),

$$\int_{B_T} \mathbf{Q} \cdot d\mathbf{s} = \int_T \mathbf{n}_T \cdot (\nabla \times \mathbf{Q})dT. \quad (51)$$

Here all the terms have a meaning independent of the choice of axes. With that meaning the equation holds for a region T in any plane.

120. Stokes's Theorem. Let S be a portion of a surface in space bounded by a simple closed curve B_S. The positive direction on B_S is that regarded as forward by an observer on the positive side of the surface walking along the boundary with the region on his left. It is

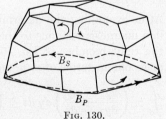

Fig. 130.

possible to approximate the curved surface S by a polyhedral cap P each of whose faces T is in a plane tangent to S at an interior point. Let d_m be the largest dimension of any polygonal face. Then if d_m is small enough, the skew polygon B_P which bounds the cap will approximate B_S, the bounding curve of S.

With Q any vector point function, we may apply Eq. (51) to each plane face T. The sum over all the faces of the cap is

$$\sum \int_{B_T} \mathbf{Q} \cdot d\mathbf{s} = \sum \int_T \mathbf{n}_T \cdot (\nabla \times \mathbf{Q})dT. \quad (52)$$

Each inner edge of the cap is traversed twice in opposite directions.   Consequently the sum on the left reduces to the integral
over the skew polygon B_P which bounds the cap. The line
integral over a skew polygon or space curve is defined by a
procedure analogous to that used for the plane case in Sec. 80.
And we may consider the sum on the right as a surface integral
over the cap.   Hence

$$\int_{B_P} \mathbf{Q} \cdot d\mathbf{s} = \int_P \mathbf{n}_T \cdot (\nabla \times \mathbf{Q}) dS. \tag{53}$$

Applied to a sequence of approximating polyhedral caps with
$d_m \to 0$, this leads to the limiting relation

$$\int_{B_S} \mathbf{Q} \cdot d\mathbf{s} = \int_S \mathbf{n} \cdot (\nabla \times \mathbf{Q}) dS, \tag{54}$$

where $\mathbf{n}$ is the unit vector normal to S drawn toward the positive
side. This is *Stokes's theorem*. Let the components of the
positive normal $\mathbf{n}$ be given by Eqs. (36) and (40).   Then from
Eq. (13) we may derive a Cartesian form of Stokes's theorem:

$$\int_{B_S} (Q_x dx + Q_y dy + Q_z dz) = \int_S \begin{vmatrix} \cos \alpha & \cos \beta & \cos \gamma \\ \dfrac{\partial}{\partial x} & \dfrac{\partial}{\partial y} & \dfrac{\partial}{\partial z} \\ Q_x & Q_y & Q_z \end{vmatrix} dS. \tag{55}$$

After expanding the determinant, we may use the relation (40)
in a manner analogous to that used to derive Eq. (41), to express
the right member of Eq. (55) as a double integral in u and v,
or as one in terms of x, y, and z.   The latter is

$$\int_S \pm \left(\frac{\partial Q_z}{\partial y} - \frac{\partial Q_y}{\partial z} \right) dy \, dz \pm \left(\frac{\partial Q_x}{\partial z} - \frac{\partial Q_z}{\partial x} \right) dz \, dx$$
$$\pm \left(\frac{\partial Q_y}{\partial x} - \frac{\partial Q_x}{\partial y} \right) dx \, dy, \tag{56}$$

where at each point the signs may be determined by the method
given for determining the signs in Eq. (41).

121. Exact Differential Expressions.   Consider the differential
expression

$$P(x,y,z)dx + Q(x,y,z)dy + R(x,y,z)dz \tag{57}$$

for x, y, z in T, some three-dimensional region of simple type.
If the first partial derivatives of P,Q,R with respect to x,y,z are

continuous and satisfy the conditions

$$\frac{\partial R}{\partial y} - \frac{\partial Q}{\partial z} = 0, \qquad \frac{\partial P}{\partial z} - \frac{\partial R}{\partial x} = 0, \qquad \frac{\partial Q}{\partial x} - \frac{\partial P}{\partial y} = 0 \quad (58)$$

throughout T, the differential expression (57) is said to be *exact*. If we introduce the vector

$$\mathbf{F} = P\mathbf{i} + Q\mathbf{j} + R\mathbf{k}, \tag{59}$$

the condition for exactness (58) may be written

$$\nabla \times \mathbf{F} = 0 \qquad \text{or} \qquad \text{curl } \mathbf{F} = 0. \tag{60}$$

Let B_s be any closed path bounding a portion of a surface S in the region T. Then by Eq. (59) and Stokes's theorem (54)

$$\int_{B_s} (P\,dx + Q\,dy + R\,dz) = \int_{B_s} \mathbf{F} \cdot d\mathbf{s} = \int_S \mathbf{n} \cdot (\nabla \times \mathbf{F})dS. \tag{61}$$

The last integral is zero by Eq. (60). Hence the first integral is zero over any closed curve of simple type. By an argument like that of Sec. 82, we may deduce from this that

$$f = \int_M^N (P\,dx + Q\,dy + R\,dz), \tag{62}$$

taken over any path joining M to N lying in the region T, is independent of the path. And we may then take $M = (x_0, y_0, z_0)$, $N = (x, y, z)$ and so obtain a function $f(x, y, z)$ such that

$$\frac{\partial f}{\partial x} = P, \qquad \frac{\partial f}{\partial y} = Q, \qquad \frac{\partial f}{\partial z} = R, \qquad \text{or} \qquad \nabla f = \mathbf{F}. \tag{63}$$

The total differential of f will equal the original expression,

$$df = P\,dx + Q\,dy + R\,dz. \tag{64}$$

Conversely, let us start with a function $f(x, y, z)$ and define P, Q, R by Eq. (64). Then

$$\nabla f = \mathbf{F} \qquad \text{and} \qquad \nabla \times \mathbf{F} = \nabla \times \nabla f = 0, \tag{65}$$

by Eq. (19). Hence the total differential df is exact.

We may find f when the exact expression is given by a method like that used for the two variable cases. Consider the expression

$$(yz + 3x^2)dx + (xz + 3y^2)dy + (xy + 3z^2)dz. \tag{66}$$

The condition for exactness (58) is satisfied. Since $\frac{\partial f}{\partial x}$ should equal $yz + 3x^2$,

$$f = xyz + x^3 + g(y,z) \tag{67}$$

by x integration with y and z kept constant. Then

$$\frac{\partial f}{\partial y} = xz + \frac{\partial g}{\partial y} \text{ should equal } xz + 3y^2, \quad \text{so that } \frac{\partial g}{\partial y} = 3y^2. \tag{68}$$

With z kept constant, y integration gives

$$g = y^3 + h(z) \quad \text{and} \quad f = xyz + x^3 + y^3 + h(z). \tag{69}$$

Finally,

$$\frac{\partial f}{\partial z} = xy + \frac{dh}{dz} \text{ should equal } xy + 3z^2, \quad \text{so that } \frac{dh}{dz} = 3z^2. \tag{70}$$

Integrating this gives

$$h = z^3 + c, \quad \text{so that } f = xyz + x^3 + y^3 + z^3 + c. \tag{71}$$

The vector formulation of the principal result of this section is as follows. A necessary and sufficient condition for the continuously differentiable vector $\mathbf{F}$ to be the gradient of a function f, $\mathbf{F} = \nabla f$, is that the curl of $\mathbf{F}$ vanish identically, $\nabla \times \mathbf{F} = 0$.

122. Conservative Force Fields. The discussion of force fields in three dimensions is analogous to that of force fields in the plane given in Sec. 83. Let the variable force vector be

$$\mathbf{F}(x,y,z) = X(x,y,z)\mathbf{i} + Y(x,y,z)\mathbf{j} + Z(x,y,z)\mathbf{k}. \tag{72}$$

Then the work done by the force on a particle moving along any path C, in general a space curve, is

$$W_C = \int_C (X\,dx + Y\,dy + Z\,dz) = \int_C \mathbf{F} \cdot d\mathbf{s}. \tag{73}$$

The force field is *conservative* if the work depends only on the end points of C; otherwise it is independent of the path. In this case the expression $(X\,dx + Y\,dy + Z\,dz)$ is exact, and there is a function $W(x,y,z)$ having this expression as its total differential. The function $W(x,y,z)$ is called the *force potential*, while $U = -W$ is the *potential energy*. Consequently, we have

$$X\,dx + Y\,dy + Z\,dz = dW = -dU \tag{74}$$

In vector form, the condition for a conservative field is

$$\nabla \times \mathbf{F} = 0. \quad \text{And} \quad \mathbf{F} = \nabla W = -\nabla U \tag{75}$$

expresses the force vector in terms of the potentials.

123. Curvilinear Coordinates. Certain problems are simplified by introducing curvilinear coordinates. The systems of most frequent occurrence are *orthogonal* systems, for which the vectors $\mathbf{U},\mathbf{V},\mathbf{W}$, of Sec. 59, tangent to the coordinate curves, are mutually perpendicular, so that

$$\mathbf{U} \cdot \mathbf{V} = 0, \qquad \mathbf{V} \cdot \mathbf{W} = 0, \qquad \mathbf{W} \cdot \mathbf{U} = 0. \tag{76}$$

Here, with subscripts denoting partial derivatives,

$$\mathbf{U} = x_u\mathbf{i} + y_u\mathbf{j} + z_u\mathbf{k}, \qquad \mathbf{V} = x_v\mathbf{i} + y_v\mathbf{j} + z_v\mathbf{k},$$
$$\mathbf{W} = x_w\mathbf{i} + y_w\mathbf{j} + z_w\mathbf{k}. \tag{77}$$

Let h_1, h_2, h_3 be the lengths of $\mathbf{U}$, $\mathbf{V}$, $\mathbf{W}$. Then

$$h_1{}^2 = \mathbf{U} \cdot \mathbf{U}, \qquad h_2{}^2 = \mathbf{V} \cdot \mathbf{V}, \qquad h_3{}^2 = \mathbf{W} \cdot \mathbf{W}. \tag{78}$$

Let us square both sides of each of the equations

$$dx = x_u du + x_v dv + x_w dw, \qquad dy = y_u du + y_v dv + y_w dw,$$
$$dz = z_u du + z_v dv + z_w dw, \tag{79}$$

and add the results. Using Eqs. (76) to (78), we find

$$ds^2 = h_1{}^2 du^2 + h_2{}^2 dv^2 + h_3{}^2 dw^2. \tag{80}$$

Since $h_1 h_2 h_3$ is the volume of the rectangular parallelepiped on $\mathbf{U},\mathbf{V},\mathbf{W}$, by Sec. 53

$$\mathbf{U} \cdot (\mathbf{V} \times \mathbf{W}) = h_1 h_2 h_3. \tag{81}$$

Hence by Sec. 59 volume integrals are transformed by

$$dx\,dy\,dz = h_1 h_2 h_3 du\,dv\,dw. \tag{82}$$

The unit vectors $\mathbf{i},\mathbf{j},\mathbf{k}$ are in the direction of increasing x,y,z. Corresponding to them, at each point we introduce three unit vectors $\mathbf{i}_1,\mathbf{i}_2,\mathbf{i}_3$ along $\mathbf{U},\mathbf{V},\mathbf{W}$. Thus

$$\mathbf{U} = h_1\mathbf{i}_1, \qquad \mathbf{V} = h_2\mathbf{i}_2, \qquad \mathbf{W} = h_3\mathbf{i}_3. \tag{83}$$

Then any vector point function $\mathbf{Q}$ can be represented in terms of these unit vectors

$$\mathbf{Q} = Q_1\mathbf{i}_1 + Q_2\mathbf{i}_2 + Q_3\mathbf{i}_3. \tag{84}$$

By calculating the dot products, and recalling that $\mathbf{i}_1,\mathbf{i}_2,\mathbf{i}_3$ have unit length and are mutually perpendicular, we find that

$$\mathbf{Q} \cdot \mathbf{i}_1 = Q_1, \qquad \mathbf{Q} \cdot \mathbf{i}_2 = Q_2, \qquad \mathbf{Q} \cdot \mathbf{i}_3 = Q_3. \tag{85}$$

These relations may be used to obtain the components of $\mathbf{Q}$.

As an illustration of these ideas, consider the spherical coordinates r,ϕ,θ of Sec. 59. The vector

$$\mathbf{r} = x\mathbf{i} + y\mathbf{j} + z\mathbf{k} = r\mathbf{i}_1 \tag{86}$$

and

$$d\mathbf{s} = dx\,\mathbf{i} + dy\,\mathbf{j} + dz\,\mathbf{k} = dr\,\mathbf{i}_1 + r\,d\phi\,\mathbf{i}_2 + r\,\sin\,\phi\,d\theta\,\mathbf{i}_3. \tag{87}$$

Consequently,

$$h_1 = 1, \qquad h_2 = r, \qquad h_3 = r\,\sin\,\phi \tag{88}$$

and

$$ds^2 = dr^2 + r^2\,d\phi^2 + r^2\,\sin^2\,\phi\,d\theta^2. \tag{89}$$

Also volume integrals are transformed by

$$dx\,dy\,dz = r^2\,\sin\,\phi\,dr\,d\phi\,d\theta. \tag{90}$$

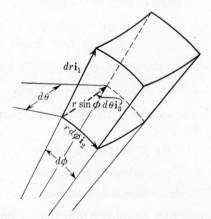

Fig. 131.

124. Del and Curvilinear Coordinates. We shall next obtain the expanded form of the fundamental combinations involving del for a system of orthogonal curvilinear coordinates; that is, in terms of the unit vectors $\mathbf{i}_1,\mathbf{i}_2,\mathbf{i}_3$ and partial derivatives with respect to u,v,w. The gradient of u, ∇u, has the direction normal to the surface $u = $ constant; that is, the direction of $\mathbf{U}$ or $\mathbf{i}_1$. And the magnitude of ∇u is the derivative of u in this direction. But from Eq. (80), when v and w are held fast,

$$\frac{ds}{du} = h_1, \qquad \text{so that } \frac{du}{ds} = \frac{1}{h_1}. \tag{91}$$

Consequently

$$\nabla u = \frac{\mathbf{i}_1}{h_1}. \qquad \text{And similarly} \qquad \nabla v = \frac{\mathbf{i}_2}{h_2}, \qquad \nabla w = \frac{\mathbf{i}_3}{h_3}. \quad (92)$$

It follows from the definition of ∇ and Eq. (26) of Sec. 21 that if $f(u,v,w)$ is any scalar point function,

$$\nabla f = \frac{\partial f}{\partial u} \nabla u + \frac{\partial f}{\partial v} \nabla v + \frac{\partial f}{\partial w} \nabla w. \quad (93)$$

From this and Eq. (92) we may deduce that the gradient

$$\nabla f = \frac{1}{h_1} \frac{\partial f}{\partial u} \mathbf{i}_1 + \frac{1}{h_2} \frac{\partial f}{\partial v} \mathbf{i}_2 + \frac{1}{h_3} \frac{\partial f}{\partial w} \mathbf{i}_3. \quad (94)$$

As a preliminary to finding the expression for $\nabla \cdot \mathbf{Q}$ we note that one consequence of Eq. (94) is

$$(\nabla f) \cdot \mathbf{i}_1 = \frac{1}{h_1} \frac{\partial f}{\partial u}. \quad (95)$$

And from Eq. (92)

$$\nabla v \times \nabla w = \left(\frac{\mathbf{i}_2}{h_2}\right) \times \left(\frac{\mathbf{i}_3}{h_3}\right) = \frac{\mathbf{i}_1}{h_2 h_3}. \quad (96)$$

Since $\mathbf{i}_1$ varies from point to point, $\nabla \cdot \mathbf{i}_1 \neq 0$ in general. But

$$\nabla \cdot \left(\frac{\mathbf{i}_1}{h_2 h_3}\right) = \nabla \cdot (\nabla v \times \nabla w) = 0 \quad (97)$$

by Eq. (20). This leads us to write the first term of (84) as

$$Q_1 \mathbf{i}_1 = (h_2 h_3 Q_1) \left(\frac{\mathbf{i}_1}{h_2 h_3}\right). \quad (98)$$

Then by the second equation in (16)

$$\nabla \cdot (Q_1 \mathbf{i}_1) = \nabla(h_2 h_3 Q_1) \cdot \left(\frac{\mathbf{i}_1}{h_2 h_3}\right) + h_2 h_3 Q_1 \nabla \cdot \left(\frac{\mathbf{i}_1}{h_2 h_3}\right). \quad (99)$$

The last term is zero by Eq. (97). Hence

$$\nabla \cdot (Q_1 \mathbf{i}_1) = \frac{\nabla(h_2 h_3 Q_1) \cdot \mathbf{i}_1}{h_2 h_3} = \frac{1}{h_1 h_2 h_3} \frac{\partial}{\partial u} (h_2 h_3 Q_1), \quad (100)$$

by Eq. (95) with $h_2 h_3 Q_1$ in place of f. On treating the other two terms of Eq. (84) similarly, we find that the divergence

$$\nabla \cdot \mathbf{Q} = \frac{1}{h_1 h_2 h_3} \left[\frac{\partial}{\partial u} (h_2 h_3 Q_1) + \frac{\partial}{\partial v} (h_3 h_1 Q_2) + \frac{\partial}{\partial w} (h_1 h_2 Q_3) \right]. \quad (101)$$

To expand $\nabla \times \mathbf{Q}$, we observe that from Eq. (94)

$$\nabla f \times \mathbf{i}_1 = -\frac{1}{h_2} \frac{\partial f}{\partial v} \mathbf{i}_3 + \frac{1}{h_3} \frac{\partial f}{\partial w} \mathbf{i}_2. \quad (102)$$

And from Eqs. (92) and (19),

$$\nabla \times \left(\frac{\mathbf{i}_1}{h_1} \right) = \nabla \times (\nabla u) = 0. \quad (103)$$

This leads us to write the first term of (84) as

$$Q_1 \mathbf{i}_1 = (h_1 Q_1) \left(\frac{\mathbf{i}_1}{h_1} \right).$$

Then by the first equation in (17)

$$\nabla \times (Q_1 \mathbf{i}_1) = \nabla(h_1 Q_1) \times \left(\frac{\mathbf{i}_1}{h_1} \right) + h_1 Q_1 \nabla \times \left(\frac{\mathbf{i}_1}{h_1} \right). \quad (104)$$

The last term is zero by Eq. (103). Hence

$$\nabla \times (Q_1 \mathbf{i}_1) = \frac{\nabla(h_1 Q_1) \times \mathbf{i}_1}{h_1} = -\frac{1}{h_1 h_2} \frac{\partial(h_1 Q_1)}{\partial v} \mathbf{i}_3$$
$$+ \frac{1}{h_3 h_1} \frac{\partial(h_1 Q_1)}{\partial w} \mathbf{i}_2 \quad (105)$$

by Eq. (102) with $h_1 Q_1$ in place of f. On treating the other two terms of Eq. (84) similarly, we find that the curl of $\mathbf{Q}$

$$\nabla \times \mathbf{Q} = \frac{1}{h_1 h_2 h_3} \begin{vmatrix} h_1 \mathbf{i}_1 & h_2 \mathbf{i}_2 & h_3 \mathbf{i}_3 \\ \dfrac{\partial}{\partial u} & \dfrac{\partial}{\partial v} & \dfrac{\partial}{\partial w} \\ h_1 Q_1 & h_2 Q_2 & h_3 Q_3 \end{vmatrix} = \frac{\mathbf{i}_1}{h_2 h_3} \left[\frac{\partial(h_3 Q_3)}{\partial v} - \frac{\partial(h_2 Q_2)}{\partial w} \right]$$
$$+ \frac{\mathbf{i}_2}{h_3 h_1} \left[\frac{\partial(h_1 Q_1)}{\partial w} - \frac{\partial(h_3 Q_3)}{\partial u} \right] + \frac{\mathbf{i}_3}{h_1 h_2} \left[\frac{\partial(h_2 Q_2)}{\partial u} - \frac{\partial(h_1 Q_1)}{\partial v} \right]. \quad (106)$$

The Laplacian operator of Eq. (15) may be expanded by combining Eqs. (101) and (94). The result is

$$\nabla^2 f = \nabla \cdot \nabla f$$
$$= \frac{1}{h_1 h_2 h_3} \left[\frac{\partial}{\partial u} \left(\frac{h_2 h_3}{h_1} \frac{\partial f}{\partial u} \right) + \frac{\partial}{\partial v} \left(\frac{h_3 h_1}{h_2} \frac{\partial f}{\partial v} \right) + \frac{\partial}{\partial w} \left(\frac{h_1 h_2}{h_3} \frac{\partial f}{\partial w} \right) \right]. \quad (107)$$

Once we know the element of arc (80), or the values of h_1, h_2, h_3 for any orthogonal system of curvilinear coordinates, all the expressions of this section may be found explicitly. For example, in spherical coordinates Eq. (88) holds and

$$u = r, \qquad v = \phi, \qquad w = \theta, \qquad h_1 = 1, \qquad h_2 = r,$$
$$h_3 = r \sin \phi.$$

With these values the expression for the gradient (94) becomes

$$\nabla f = \frac{\partial f}{\partial r} \mathbf{i}_1 + \frac{1}{r} \frac{\partial f}{\partial \phi} \mathbf{i}_2 + \frac{1}{r \sin \phi} \frac{\partial f}{\partial \theta} \mathbf{i}_3. \tag{108}$$

The expansion of the divergence (101) reduces to

$$\nabla \cdot \mathbf{Q} = \frac{1}{r^2} \frac{\partial}{\partial r} (r^2 Q_1) + \frac{1}{r \sin \phi} \frac{\partial}{\partial \phi} (\sin \phi \, Q_2) + \frac{1}{r \sin \phi} \frac{\partial Q_3}{\partial \theta}. \tag{109}$$

And either from these or Eq. (107) the Laplacian is found to be

$$\nabla^2 f = \nabla \cdot \nabla f = \frac{1}{r^2} \frac{\partial}{\partial r} \left(r^2 \frac{\partial f}{\partial r} \right) + \frac{1}{r^2 \sin \phi} \frac{\partial}{\partial \phi} \left(\sin \phi \, \frac{\partial f}{\partial \phi} \right)$$
$$+ \frac{1}{r^2 \sin^2 \phi} \frac{\partial^2 f}{\partial \theta^2} \tag{110}$$

125. Gauss's Theorem. Let S consist of one or more closed surfaces that collectively bound a volume V. For each point x, y, z of S we define r and $\mathbf{i}_1$ by Eq. (86) and denote the outward drawn unit normal by $\mathbf{n}$. Then Gauss's theorem asserts that

$$\int_S \frac{\mathbf{i}_1 \cdot \mathbf{n}}{r^2} \, dS = \begin{cases} 0, & \text{if } O \text{ is outside of } V, \\ 4\pi, & \text{if } O \text{ is inside of } V. \end{cases} \tag{111}$$

Suppose that O is *outside* of V. Then $\mathbf{i}_1/r^2$ is regular in V, and from the divergence theorem (38)

$$\int_V \nabla \cdot \left(\frac{\mathbf{i}_1}{r^2} \right) dV = \int_S \left(\frac{\mathbf{i}_1}{r^2} \right) \cdot \mathbf{n} \, dS. \tag{112}$$

But from Eq. (109)

$$\nabla \cdot \left(\frac{\mathbf{i}_1}{r^2} \right) = \frac{1}{r^2} \frac{\partial}{\partial r} \left(r^2 \frac{1}{r^2} \right) = 0. \tag{113}$$

And in Eq. (112) the left member is zero. Hence the right member is zero. This proves the first case of Gauss's theorem (111).

If V includes O, which is a singularity of $\mathbf{i}_1/r^2$, the divergence theorem is not applicable to V. To circumvent this difficulty, we draw a small sphere s about O, so small that it lies in V. Denote by V' the volume V with the small sphere s removed. The boundary of V' is S together with s, and the outer normal at s, regarded as part of the boundary of V' is $-\mathbf{n}$, where $\mathbf{n}$ is the outer normal of the small sphere. Write

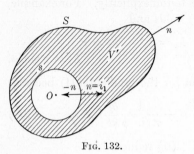

Fig. 132.

$$\int_S \frac{\mathbf{i}_1 \cdot \mathbf{n}}{r^2} dS = \left[\int_S \frac{\mathbf{i}_1 \cdot \mathbf{n}}{r^2} dS + \int_s \frac{\mathbf{i}_1 \cdot (-\mathbf{n})}{r^2} dS \right] + \int_s \frac{\mathbf{i}_1 \cdot \mathbf{n}}{r^2} dS. \quad (114)$$

The bracket equals zero, since we may apply the case of (111) already proved to V', which does not include O. And if the radius of s is a, on s we have

$$\mathbf{n} = \mathbf{i}_1, \qquad r = a, \qquad \text{so that} \int_s \frac{\mathbf{i}_1 \cdot \mathbf{n}}{r^2} dS = \frac{1}{a^2}(4\pi a^2) = 4\pi. \quad (115)$$

This shows that the left member of Eq. (114) equals 4π, and the second case of Gauss's theorem (111) is proved.

126. Poisson's Equation. Let the potential energy $U = e_1 e/r$. Then by Eqs. (75) and (109) the force vector $\mathbf{F}$ is

$$\mathbf{F} = -\nabla U = -\nabla\left(\frac{e_1 e}{r}\right) = -\frac{\partial}{\partial r}\left(\frac{e_1 e}{r}\right)\mathbf{i}_1 = \frac{e_1 e}{r^2}\mathbf{i}_1. \quad (116)$$

Let O be the origin of spherical coordinates, and P the point with spherical coordinates r, ϕ, θ. Then

$$\overline{OP} = r\mathbf{i}_1, \quad (117)$$

and the vector $\mathbf{F}$ at P is the force exerted by an electric charge e at O on a charge e_1 at P. The force on a unit charge at P is $\mathbf{E}$, the electric intensity vector. And the scalar point function Φ, such that $\mathbf{E} = -\nabla\Phi$ is the electric potential. Hence for the single charge e at O,

$$\Phi = \frac{e}{r}, \qquad E = -\nabla\Phi = \frac{e}{r^2}\mathbf{i}_1. \quad (118)$$

All the equations of this section hold for an x,y,z system such that $O = (x_0,y_0,z_0)$ and $P = (x,y,z)$ if we define r and $\mathbf{i}_1$ by

$$r = \sqrt{(x - x_0)^2 + (y - y_0)^2 + (z - z_0)^2} \qquad (119)$$

and

$$r\mathbf{i}_1 = \overline{OP} = (x - x_0)\mathbf{i} + (y - y_0)\mathbf{j} + (z - z_0)\mathbf{k}. \qquad (120)$$

This suggests the correct expression for the potential due to a continuous charge distribution with density of charge $\rho(x_0,y_0,z_0)$ at (x_0,y_0,z_0). If V_0 is the whole of space or a volume including all the charges,

$$\Phi = \int_{V_0} \frac{\rho(x_0,y_0,z_0)}{r} \, dV_0, \qquad \text{where } dV_0 = dx_0 dy_0 dz_0. \quad (121)$$

And, with del acting on the x,y,z without subscripts in r,

$$\mathbf{E} = -\nabla\Phi = \int_{V_0} \frac{\rho(x_0,y_0,z_0)}{r^2} \mathbf{i}_1 dV_0. \qquad (122)$$

Now let S be any closed surface bounding a volume V. By Gauss's theorem (111), with r and $\mathbf{i}_1$ defined by Eqs. (119), (120),

$$\int_S \frac{\mathbf{i}_1 \cdot \mathbf{n}}{r^2} \, dS = \begin{cases} 0, \text{ if } (x_0,y_0,z_0) \text{ is outside of } V, \\ 4\pi, \text{ if } (x_0,y_0,z_0) \text{ is inside of } V. \end{cases} \quad (123)$$

From this and Eq. (122) it follows that

$$\int_S \mathbf{E} \cdot \mathbf{n} \, dS = \int_S dS \int_{V_0} \rho(x_0,y_0,z_0) \cdot \frac{\mathbf{i}_1 \cdot \mathbf{n}}{r^2} \, dV_0$$

$$= 4\pi \int_V \rho(x_0,y_0,z_0) dV_0. \quad (124)$$

With the variables of integration x_0,y_0,z_0 replaced by x,y,z,

$$\int_S \mathbf{E} \cdot \mathbf{n} \, dS = 4\pi \int_V \rho(x,y,z) dV. \qquad (125)$$

But from the divergence theorem (38)

$$\int_S \mathbf{E} \cdot \mathbf{n} \, dS = \int_V \nabla \cdot \mathbf{E} \, dV = - \int_V \nabla \cdot \nabla\Phi \, dV, \quad (126)$$

since $\mathbf{E} = -\nabla\Phi$. A comparison of the last two equations shows that

$$4\pi \int_V \rho(x,y,z) dV = - \int_V \nabla \cdot \nabla\Phi \, dV, \qquad \text{or}$$

$$\int_V [\nabla \cdot \nabla\Phi + 4\pi\rho(x,y,z)] dV = 0. \quad (127)$$

Since this holds for any volume V, the integrand must vanish. Thus

$$\nabla \cdot \nabla\Phi + 4\pi\rho(x,y,z) = 0 \qquad \text{or} \qquad \nabla \cdot \nabla\Phi = -4\pi\rho(x,y,z). \quad (128)$$

This is Poisson's equation. The expanded Cartesian form is

$$\frac{\partial^2\Phi}{\partial x^2} + \frac{\partial^2\Phi}{\partial y^2} + \frac{\partial^2\Phi}{\partial z^2} = -4\pi\rho(x,y,z). \quad (129)$$

It may be expanded for any system of orthogonal coordinates by using Eq. (107). In a region free of charges, $\rho = 0$ and Poisson's equation reduces to Laplace's equation.

We have interpreted Φ as the electric potential due to charges of density ρ. An analogous discussion may be carried out for the magnetic potential due to poles, the gravitational potential due to matter, the steady temperature distribution due to continuously distributed sources of heat, or the velocity potential of an incompressible fluid due to continuously distributed sources or sinks.

127. Heat Flow. In any portion of space where heat is flowing the temperature U is a scalar function of x,y,z and t, the time. Consider any closed surface S bounding a volume V. Then the rate at which heat *escapes* from V through an element dS is $-K\,dU/dn\,dS$, where $\mathbf{n}$ is the *outward* drawn unit vector normal to dS. The constant K is the thermal conductivity in calories per centimeter per second per degree centigrade. And the minus sign is due to the fact that heat flows from a higher to a lower temperature. By Eq. (25) and the divergence theorem (38),

$$\int_S \frac{dU}{dn}\,dS = \int_S (\nabla U) \cdot \mathbf{n}\,dS = \int_V \nabla \cdot \nabla U\,dV. \quad (130)$$

Hence the rate in calories per second at which heat flows *into* the volume V through S is

$$\int_S K\,\frac{dU}{dn}\,dS = \int_V K\,\nabla \cdot \nabla U\,dV. \quad (131)$$

If c cal./gm. °C. is the specific heat and D gm./cm.³ is the density, the rate at which heat is absorbed by an element dV due to the changing temperature is $cD\,\partial U/\partial t\,dV$. And the number of calories per second absorbed by V is

$$\int_V cD \frac{\partial U}{\partial t}\, dV \tag{132}$$

if we assume that there are no sources or sinks of heat in the region under consideration. In that event the heat absorbed by V will equal that which enters through S, and we may equate the expressions (131) and (132). Hence

$$\int_S K \nabla \cdot \nabla U\, dV = \int_V cD \frac{\partial U}{\partial t}\, dV, \qquad \text{or}$$

$$\int_V \left(K \nabla \cdot \nabla U - cD \frac{\partial U}{\partial t} \right) dV = 0. \tag{133}$$

Since this holds for any volume V, the integrand must vanish. Thus

$$K \nabla \cdot \nabla U - cD \frac{\partial U}{\partial t} = 0, \qquad \text{or} \qquad \frac{\partial U}{\partial t} = \frac{K}{cD} \nabla \cdot \nabla U \tag{134}$$

is the equation governing heat flow. If $\alpha^2 = K/cD$, the equation is

$$\frac{\partial U}{\partial t} = \alpha^2 \left[\frac{\partial^2 U}{\partial x^2} + \frac{\partial^2 U}{\partial y^2} + \frac{\partial^2 U}{\partial z^2} \right] \tag{135}$$

in Cartesian coordinates. It may be written for any system of orthogonal coordinates by using Eq. (107).

A similar equation holds for diffusion, whether of a solid through a solution, a liquid through a porous material, or one fluid through another. In fact, if U is the concentration of the diffused substance, and α^2 is the diffusivity, Eq. (135) is the equation governing diffusion phenomena.

128. Fluid Flow. We wish to study the motion of a perfect fluid in space. It is customary to denote the components of $\mathbf{q}$, the velocity vector, by u, v, w (in feet per second), so that

$$\mathbf{q}(x,y,z,t) = u(x,y,z,t)\mathbf{i} + v(x,y,z,t)\mathbf{j} + w(x,y,z,t)\mathbf{k}. \tag{136}$$

Consider any closed surface S bounding a volume V. Let $p(x,y,z,t)$ lb./ft.^{2} be the pressure, which is the same in all directions. Then the *inward* force on any element dS is $-p\mathbf{n}\, dS$, where $\mathbf{n}$ is the *outward* drawn unit vector normal to dS. And the resultant force on S is

$$- \int_S p\mathbf{n} \, dS \quad \text{or} \quad - \int_V \nabla p \, dV, \quad (137)$$

as we see by applying the divergence theorem (38) to each component. For example,

$$\int_S p n_x dS = \int_S (p\mathbf{i}) \cdot \mathbf{n} \, dS = \int_V \nabla \cdot (p\mathbf{i}) dV = \int_V \frac{\partial p}{\partial x} \, dV. \quad (138)$$

Let $\rho(x,y,z,t) = D/g$ (in slugs per cubic foot) be the density at any point of the fluid. Then the mass times acceleration vector for an element dV is $\rho \, dV \, d\mathbf{q}/dt$. And if

$$\mathbf{F} = X\mathbf{i} + Y\mathbf{j} + Z\mathbf{k}$$

(pounds per slug) is the body force per unit mass, the body force on an element dV is $\mathbf{F}\rho \, dV$. For example, $\mathbf{F} = -g\mathbf{k}$ if the z axis is vertically upward and gravity acts as the body force. Equating the resultant mass times acceleration of V to the body force on V plus the resultant force due to pressure on S found in (137) gives

$$\int_V \rho \frac{d\mathbf{q}}{dt} \, dV = \int_V \mathbf{F}\rho \, dV - \int_V \nabla p \, dV. \quad (139)$$

Since this holds for an arbitrary volume V, a similar relation must hold for the integrands and

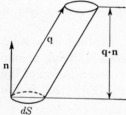

FIG. 133.

$$\rho \frac{d\mathbf{q}}{dt} = \mathbf{F}\rho - \nabla p$$

or

$$\frac{d\mathbf{q}}{dt} = \mathbf{F} - \frac{1}{\rho} \nabla p. \quad (140)$$

This is the vector equation of motion. Another relation may be derived by considering the amount of fluid in V. The rate at which fluid escapes from V through an element dS is $\rho \mathbf{q} \cdot \mathbf{n} \, dS$. Hence the rate (slugs per second) of decrease of mass of V is

$$\int_S (\rho\mathbf{q}) \cdot \mathbf{n} \, dS = \int_V \nabla \cdot (\rho\mathbf{q}) dV \quad (141)$$

by the divergence theorem (38). But the rate of decrease of

mass of an element dV is $-\partial\rho/\partial t \, dV$. The integral of this over V equals the rate of decrease found in (141), so that

$$- \int_V \frac{\partial\rho}{\partial t} \, dV = \int_V \nabla \cdot (\rho\mathbf{q}) dV. \qquad (142)$$

Since this holds for an arbitrary volume V, it follows that

$$- \frac{\partial\rho}{\partial t} = \nabla \cdot (\rho\mathbf{q}), \qquad \text{or} \qquad \nabla \cdot (\rho\mathbf{q}) + \frac{\partial\rho}{\partial t} = 0. \qquad (143)$$

This is known as the *equation of continuity*.

If we kept t fixed in Eq. (136), the motion of a particle would have components

$$\frac{dx}{dt} = u, \qquad \frac{dy}{dt} = v, \qquad \frac{dz}{dt} = w. \qquad (144)$$

The acceleration $d\mathbf{q}/dt$ is due to a space change of this kind, combined with the influence of t in Eq. (136). Thus

$$\frac{d\mathbf{q}}{dt} = \frac{\partial\mathbf{q}}{\partial x}\frac{dx}{dt} + \frac{\partial\mathbf{q}}{\partial y}\frac{dy}{dt} + \frac{\partial\mathbf{q}}{\partial z}\frac{dz}{dt} + \frac{\partial\mathbf{q}}{\partial t} = u\frac{\partial\mathbf{q}}{\partial x} + v\frac{\partial\mathbf{q}}{\partial y} + w\frac{\partial\mathbf{q}}{\partial z} + \frac{\partial\mathbf{q}}{\partial t}. \qquad (145)$$

And on a component of $\mathbf{q}$ or on any scalar, the differential operator

$$\frac{d}{dt} = u\frac{\partial}{\partial x} + v\frac{\partial}{\partial y} + w\frac{\partial}{\partial z} + \frac{\partial}{\partial t} = \mathbf{q} \cdot \nabla + \frac{\partial}{\partial t}. \qquad (146)$$

As a consequence of this and the second equation in (16),

$$\nabla \cdot (\rho\mathbf{q}) + \frac{\partial\rho}{\partial t} = (\nabla\rho) \cdot \mathbf{q} + \rho \nabla \cdot \mathbf{q} + \frac{\partial\rho}{\partial t}$$

$$= \rho \nabla \cdot \mathbf{q} + \left(\mathbf{q} \cdot \nabla + \frac{\partial}{\partial t}\right)\rho = \rho \nabla \cdot \mathbf{q} + \frac{d\rho}{dt}. \qquad (147)$$

Hence the equation of continuity (143) may be written

$$\rho \nabla \cdot \mathbf{q} + \frac{d\rho}{dt} = 0, \qquad \text{or} \qquad \nabla \cdot \mathbf{q} = -\frac{1}{\rho}\frac{d\rho}{dt}. \qquad (148)$$

We may write Eqs. (140) and (148) as follows:

$$u\frac{\partial u}{\partial x} + v\frac{\partial u}{\partial y} + w\frac{\partial u}{\partial z} + \frac{\partial u}{\partial t} = X - \frac{1}{\rho}\frac{\partial p}{\partial x}, \qquad (149)$$

$$u\frac{\partial v}{\partial x} + v\frac{\partial v}{\partial y} + w\frac{\partial v}{\partial z} + \frac{\partial v}{\partial t} = Y - \frac{1}{\rho}\frac{\partial p}{\partial y}, \qquad (150)$$

$$u \frac{\partial w}{\partial x} + v \frac{\partial w}{\partial y} + w \frac{\partial w}{\partial z} + \frac{\partial w}{\partial t} = Z - \frac{1}{\rho} \frac{\partial p}{\partial z}, \qquad (151)$$

$$\frac{\partial u}{\partial x} + \frac{\partial v}{\partial y} + \frac{\partial w}{\partial z} = - \frac{1}{\rho} \left(u \frac{\partial \rho}{\partial x} + v \frac{\partial \rho}{\partial y} + w \frac{\partial \rho}{\partial z} + \frac{\partial \rho}{\partial t} \right). \quad (152)$$

The relation between ρ and p, such as $\rho = kp$ for a perfect gas at constant temperature, or $\rho =$ constant for a liquid, enables us to eliminate ρ. We then have a system of four equations in the four quantities u, v, w, p.

The circulation about any curve is the integral of the tangential component of the velocity times ds, or

$$\mathbf{q} \cdot d\mathbf{s} = u \, dx + v \, dy + w \, dz. \qquad (153)$$

The circulation K about any simple closed curve B_s bounding S, a portion of a surface, is

$$K = \int_{B_s} \mathbf{q} \cdot d\mathbf{s} = \int_S \mathbf{n} \cdot (\nabla \times \mathbf{q}) dS \qquad (154)$$

by Stokes's theorem (54). The vector $\frac{1}{2}(\nabla \times \mathbf{q})$ is called the *rotation* of the fluid, since it represents the instantaneous angular velocity of an element of the fluid. This is responsible for the designation of $\nabla \times \mathbf{q}$ as curl $\mathbf{q}$. The motion is said to be *irrotational* if curl $\mathbf{q}$, and hence the rotation, is zero at all points of the region considered.

Let us assume that the motion is irrotational. Then by Eq. (154) the circulation along any curve from a fixed point (x_0, y_0, z_0) to a variable point (x, y, z) depends only on the end points, and so determines a function $\phi(x, y, z)$. By Sec. 121

$$d\phi = u \, dx + v \, dy + w \, dz, \qquad \frac{\partial \phi}{\partial x} = u, \qquad \frac{\partial \phi}{\partial y} = v,$$

$$\frac{\partial \phi}{\partial z} = w, \qquad \text{and} \qquad \mathbf{q} = \nabla \phi. \quad (155)$$

Since the velocity $\mathbf{q}$ may be obtained from ϕ by this equation, the function ϕ is called the *velocity potential*.

If we make the additional assumption that the body forces are conservative [Eq. (75)], $\mathbf{F} = -\nabla U$ holds. We may then integrate the equations of motion in the following manner. Since $\mathbf{q} = \nabla \phi$, we may use Eq. (18). And the left member of Eq. (149) is

$$\mathbf{q} \cdot \nabla u + \frac{\partial u}{\partial t} = \frac{1}{2} \frac{\partial}{\partial x} (\mathbf{q} \cdot \mathbf{q}) + \frac{\partial}{\partial t} \left(\frac{\partial \phi}{\partial x} \right) = \frac{\partial}{\partial x} \left(\frac{q^2}{2} + \frac{\partial \phi}{\partial t} \right). \quad (156)$$

Since there is a relation $\rho = \rho(p)$, we may define $P(p)$ by

$$P(p) = \int_{p_0}^{p} \frac{dp}{\rho(p)}. \qquad \text{Then} \qquad \frac{\partial P}{\partial x} = \frac{1}{\rho} \frac{\partial p}{\partial x}. \qquad (157)$$

And $\mathbf{F} = -\nabla U$ implies that $X = -\partial U/\partial x$. Consequently the right member of Eq. (149) is

$$X - \frac{1}{\rho} \frac{\partial p}{\partial x} = -\frac{\partial U}{\partial x} - \frac{\partial P}{\partial x}. \qquad (158)$$

It follows from this and Eq. (156) that Eq. (149) is equivalent to

$$\frac{\partial}{\partial x}\left(\frac{q^2}{2} + \frac{\partial \phi}{\partial t} + U + P\right) = 0. \qquad (159)$$

We may treat Eqs. (150) and (151) similarly. Hence the expression in parentheses has all its space derivatives zero, and so can depend only on the time. That is,

$$\frac{q^2}{2} + \frac{\partial \phi}{\partial t} + U + P = \frac{1}{2}(u^2 + v^2 + w^2) + \frac{\partial \phi}{\partial t} + U + \int_{p_0}^{p} \frac{dp}{\rho}$$
$$= f(t). \quad (160)$$

When there are no body forces $U = 0$. And if the motion is steady p, u,v,w and hence ϕ will be independent of the time. Under these further restrictions, Eq. (160) reduces to

$$\frac{q^2}{2} + P = \frac{1}{2}(u^2 + v^2 + w^2) + \int_{p_0}^{p} \frac{dp}{\rho} = c, \qquad (161)$$

which is Bernoulli's equation.

For an incompressible fluid, e.g., a liquid, the density ρ is constant. And the equation of continuity (148) or (152) becomes

$$\nabla \cdot \mathbf{q} = 0 \qquad \text{or} \qquad \frac{\partial u}{\partial x} + \frac{\partial v}{\partial y} + \frac{\partial w}{\partial z} = 0. \qquad (162)$$

For the irrotational motion of an incompressible fluid, it follows from Eqs. (155) and (162) that

$$\nabla \cdot \nabla \phi = 0 \qquad \text{or} \qquad \nabla^2 \phi = \frac{\partial^2 \phi}{\partial x^2} + \frac{\partial^2 \phi}{\partial y^2} + \frac{\partial^2 \phi}{\partial z^2} = 0, \quad (163)$$

so that the velocity potential satisfies Laplace's equation.

For steady, irrotational motion of an incompressible fluid under no body forces, Bernoulli's equation (161) reduces to

$$\frac{q^2}{2} + \frac{p}{\rho} = c \qquad \text{or} \qquad \frac{1}{2}(u^2 + v^2 + w^2) + \frac{p}{\rho} = c. \quad (164)$$

This type of flow in two dimensions was discussed and illustrated in Secs. 94 and 95 and in Probs. 88 to 114 of Exercises V (page 248).

129. References.   Among the many texts with title *Vector Analysis*, we call to the reader's attention the classical lectures of Willard Gibbs, edited by E. B. Wilson, the brief account of J. G. Coffin which emphasizes physical applications, and the work of H. B. Phillips which presents the subject in the form applicable to theoretical electricity and hydrodynamics. Students of the latter subject may also consult with profit the two volumes by L. Prandtl and G. O. Tietjens, *Fundamentals of Hydro- and Aeromechanics* and *Applied Hydro- and Aeromechanics*.

EXERCISES VIII

For each given $f(x,y,z)$, find the gradient ∇f:

1. $x^2y^3z^4$. **2.** $x^2 - y^2 + 2z^2$. **3.** $\log (x^2 + 2y^2 - 3z^2)$.

For each given $\mathbf{Q}(x,y,z)$, find the divergence $\nabla \cdot \mathbf{Q}$ and the curl $\nabla \times \mathbf{Q}$:

4. $x\mathbf{i} + y\mathbf{j} + z\mathbf{k}$. **5.** $(2z - 3y)\mathbf{i} + (3x - z)\mathbf{j} + (y - 2x)\mathbf{k}$.

With subscripts on ∇ indicating the vector or vectors on which ∇ acts, deduce from the identity $\mathbf{a} \times (\mathbf{b} \times \mathbf{c}) = (\mathbf{a} \cdot \mathbf{c})\mathbf{b} - (\mathbf{a} \cdot \mathbf{b})\mathbf{c}$, proved in Prob. 58 of Exercises III (page 136), that

6. $\nabla \times (\mathbf{P} \times \mathbf{Q}) = (\nabla_{\mathbf{PQ}} \cdot \mathbf{Q})\mathbf{P} - (\nabla_{\mathbf{PQ}} \cdot \mathbf{P})\mathbf{Q}$
$$= (\mathbf{Q} \cdot \nabla)\mathbf{P} + \mathbf{P}(\nabla \cdot \mathbf{Q}) - (\mathbf{P} \cdot \nabla)\mathbf{Q} - \mathbf{Q}(\nabla \cdot \mathbf{P}).$$

7. $\mathbf{P} \times (\nabla \times \mathbf{Q}) = \nabla_{\mathbf{Q}}(\mathbf{P} \cdot \mathbf{Q}) - (\mathbf{P} \cdot \nabla_{\mathbf{Q}})\mathbf{Q}$,
$$\mathbf{Q} \times (\nabla \times \mathbf{P}) = \nabla_{\mathbf{P}}(\mathbf{P} \cdot \mathbf{Q}) - (\mathbf{Q} \cdot \nabla_{\mathbf{P}})\mathbf{P}, \text{ and hence}$$
$$\nabla(\mathbf{P} \cdot \mathbf{Q}) = \nabla_{\mathbf{Q}}(\mathbf{P} \cdot \mathbf{Q}) + \nabla_{\mathbf{P}}(\mathbf{P} \cdot \mathbf{Q})$$
$$= \mathbf{P} \times (\nabla \times \mathbf{Q}) + (\mathbf{P} \cdot \nabla)\mathbf{Q} + \mathbf{Q} \times (\nabla \times \mathbf{P}) + (\mathbf{Q} \cdot \nabla)\mathbf{P}.$$

8. $\nabla \times (\nabla \times \mathbf{Q}) = \nabla(\nabla \cdot \mathbf{Q}) - \nabla \cdot \nabla\mathbf{Q} = \nabla(\nabla \cdot \mathbf{Q}) - \nabla^2\mathbf{Q}$, where
$$\nabla \cdot \nabla\mathbf{Q} = \nabla^2\mathbf{Q} \text{ is the vector } \nabla^2Q_x\mathbf{i} + \nabla^2Q_y\mathbf{j} + \nabla^2Q_z\mathbf{k}.$$

Compute the directional derivative of

9. xyz at $(0,1,2)$ in the direction of $2\mathbf{i} + 3\mathbf{j} + 4\mathbf{k}$.
10. $x^2 + 2y^2 + 3z^2$ at $(1,1,0)$ in the direction of $\mathbf{i} - \mathbf{j} + 2\mathbf{k}$.
11. $x^2y^2z^3$ at $(1,1,1)$ in the direction of $2\mathbf{i} - 3\mathbf{j} + \mathbf{k}$.

12. Prove that $f(x,y,z)$ is constant in any volume throughout which $\nabla f = 0$. HINT: Notice either that $\dfrac{\partial f}{\partial x} = \dfrac{\partial f}{\partial y} = \dfrac{\partial f}{\partial z} = 0$ or that $\dfrac{df}{ds} = 0$ in every direction.

13. Prove that $\nabla \cdot \mathbf{Q} = 0$ if $\mathbf{Q} = \nabla \times \mathbf{F}$. For a converse, see Prob. 14.

14. Let $F_x = f(x,y,z)$, $F_y = \displaystyle\int^x \left(\dfrac{\partial f}{\partial y} + Q_z \right) dx + g(y,z)$, and let

$$F_z = \int^{x,y} \left\{ \left(\dfrac{\partial f}{\partial z} - Q_y \right) dx + \left[Q_x + \int^x \left(\dfrac{\partial^2 f}{\partial y\, \partial z} + \dfrac{\partial Q_z}{\partial z} \right) dx + \dfrac{\partial g}{\partial y} \right] dy \right\}$$

$+ h(z)$. In each integration the variables not indicated in the limits are to be kept constant. The integral in x and y is independent of the path if $\nabla \cdot \mathbf{Q} = 0$, where $\mathbf{Q}(x,y,z) = Q_x\mathbf{i} + Q_y\mathbf{j} + Q_z\mathbf{k}$. Show that in this case the vector $\mathbf{F} = F_x\mathbf{i} + F_y\mathbf{j} + F_z\mathbf{k}$ has $\nabla \times \mathbf{F} = \mathbf{Q}$ for any choice of f, g, h.

Verify that each given vector $\mathbf{Q}$ has $\nabla \cdot \mathbf{Q} = 0$. Use Prob. 14 with simplest indefinite integrals and $f = g = h = 0$ to find a vector $\mathbf{F}$ such that $\mathbf{Q} = \nabla \times \mathbf{F}$.

15. $2\mathbf{i} + 3\mathbf{j} + 5\mathbf{k}$.   **16.** $x\mathbf{i} - 2y\mathbf{j} + z\mathbf{k}$.

17. $yz\mathbf{i} + zx\mathbf{j} + xy\mathbf{k}$.   **18.** $3y^2\mathbf{i} + z^2\mathbf{j} + 3x^2\mathbf{k}$.

Let $\bar{x},\bar{y},\bar{z}$ be the center of gravity of a homogeneous solid of volume V. If $\mathbf{n} = \cos\alpha\,\mathbf{i} + \cos\beta\,\mathbf{j} + \cos\gamma\,\mathbf{k}$ is the outer normal to S, the closed surface which bounds the solid, show that

19. $\displaystyle\int_S (x\cos\alpha + y\cos\beta + z\cos\gamma)dS = 3V.$

20. $\displaystyle\int_S (2x\cos\alpha + 3y\cos\beta + 5z\cos\gamma)dS = 10V.$

21. $\displaystyle\int_S (xz\cos\alpha + 2yz\cos\beta + 3z^2\cos\gamma)dS = 9V\bar{z}.$

22. $\displaystyle\int_S (y^2\cos\alpha + 2xy\cos\beta - xz\cos\gamma)dS = V\bar{x}.$

23. $\displaystyle\int_S (Q_x\cos\alpha + Q_y\cos\beta + Q_z\cos\gamma)dS = 0,$ if $\mathbf{Q}$ is any vector such that $\nabla \cdot \mathbf{Q} = 0$, *e.g.*, the vectors of Probs. 15 to 18.

24. Demonstrate that $\displaystyle\int_V \dfrac{\partial Q_x}{\partial x}\, dV = \int_V \dfrac{\partial Q_x}{\partial x}\, dx\, dy\, dz = \int_S \pm\, Q_x dy\, dz$ $= \displaystyle\int_S Q_x \cos\alpha\, dS$, by a method like that used to prove Eq. (18) in Sec. 81. Written as $\displaystyle\int_V \nabla_x f\, dV = \int_S n_x f\, dS$, this leads to the result $\displaystyle\int_V L(\nabla)dV = \int_S L(\mathbf{n})dS$, where L is any linear function.

From Prob. 24, deduce that in particular

25. $\int_V \nabla \cdot \mathbf{Q}\, dV = \int_S \mathbf{n} \cdot \mathbf{Q}\, dS.$

26. $\int_V \nabla \times \mathbf{Q}\, dV = \int_S \mathbf{n} \times \mathbf{Q}\, dS.$

27. $\int_V \nabla f\, dV = \int_S \mathbf{n} f\, dS.$

28. $\int_V \nabla \cdot (f\mathbf{Q})dV = \int_S \mathbf{n} \cdot (f\mathbf{Q})dS$ or

$$\int_V (f\nabla \cdot \mathbf{Q}) + \nabla f \cdot \mathbf{Q})dV = \int_S f\mathbf{Q} \cdot \mathbf{n}\, dS.$$

29. Prove $\int_V f\,\nabla^2 g\, dV + \int_V \nabla f \cdot \nabla g\, dV = \int_S f\,\dfrac{dg}{dn}\, dS.$ HINT: Use Prob. 28, and put $\mathbf{Q} = \nabla g$.

30. From Prob. 29, deduce Green's Theorem,

$$\int_V (f\,\nabla^2 g - g\,\nabla^2 f)dV = \int_S \left(f\,\frac{dg}{dn} - g\,\frac{df}{dn}\right) dS.$$

31. Prove $\int_S \dfrac{dg}{dn}\, dS = \int_V \nabla^2 g\, dV.$ HINT: Put $f = 1$ in Prob. 29.

32. Demonstrate $\int_S g\,\dfrac{dg}{dn}\, dS = \int_V |\nabla g|^2 dV + \int_V g\,\nabla^2 g\, dV.$ HINT: Put $f = g$ in Prob. 29.

Let C be a closed curve and S the portion of any surface bounded by C. Show that

33. $\int_C \nabla f \cdot d\mathbf{s} = 0$ and hence $\int_C f\,\nabla g \cdot d\mathbf{s} = -\int_C g\,\nabla f \cdot d\mathbf{s}.$

34. $\int_S \mathbf{n} \cdot (\nabla f \times \mathbf{Q} + f\,\nabla \times \mathbf{Q})dS = \int_C f\mathbf{Q} \cdot d\mathbf{s}.$

35. $\int_S \mathbf{Q} \cdot \mathbf{n}\, dS$ depends on C only, and not on S if $\nabla \cdot \mathbf{Q} = 0$.   HINT: The $\mathbf{F}$ of Prob. 14 has $\nabla \times \mathbf{F} = \mathbf{Q}$. Hence $\int_S \mathbf{Q} \cdot \mathbf{n}\, dS = \int_C \mathbf{F} \cdot d\mathbf{s}.$

36. Illustrate Prob. 35 for C the circle $x^2 + y^2 = 1$, $z = 0$, and $\mathbf{Q} = 2\mathbf{i} + 3\mathbf{j} + 5\mathbf{k}$. By Prob. 15 $\mathbf{Q} = \nabla \times [5x\mathbf{j} + (2y - 3x)\mathbf{k}]$. Hence

$$\int_S (2\cos\alpha + 3\cos\beta + 5\cos\gamma)dS = \int_C 5x\, dy = 5\pi.$$

Let S bound the volume V, and $V \to P_0$ mean that V shrinks to zero while including P_0 as an interior point. Show that at P_0

37. $\operatorname{div} \mathbf{Q} = \nabla \cdot \mathbf{Q} = \lim\limits_{V \to P_0} \dfrac{\int_S \mathbf{Q} \cdot \mathbf{n}\, dS}{V}.$

38. $\operatorname{curl} \mathbf{Q} = \nabla \times \mathbf{Q} = \lim\limits_{V \to P_0} \dfrac{\int_S \mathbf{n} \times \mathbf{Q}\, dS}{V}.$ HINT: Use Prob. 26.

39. Show that at P_0 curl $\mathbf{Q} = \nabla \times \mathbf{Q}$ is a vector whose component normal to any plane T through P_0 is $(\nabla \times \mathbf{Q}) \cdot \mathbf{n} = \lim\limits_{S \to P_0 \text{ in } T} \dfrac{\int_C \mathbf{Q} \cdot d\mathbf{s}}{S}$, where C bounds the area S, and $S \to P_0$ in T means that S shrinks to zero on some surface tangent to T at P_0 while including P_0 as an interior point.

For each given $\mathbf{F}(x,y,z)$, verify that $\nabla \times \mathbf{F} = 0$ and find an $f(x,y,z)$ such that $\mathbf{F} = \nabla f$.

40. $2xy^3z^4\mathbf{i} + 3x^2y^2z^4\mathbf{j} + 4x^2y^3z^3\mathbf{k}$.   **41.** $e^z[(2y + 3z)\mathbf{i} + 2\mathbf{j} + 3\mathbf{k}]$.

42. $3(x - y + 2z)^2(\mathbf{i} - \mathbf{j} + 2\mathbf{k})$.   **43.** $4(x^2 + y^2 + z^2)(x\mathbf{i} + y\mathbf{j} + z\mathbf{k})$.

44. Let df/ds_1, df/ds_2, df/ds_3 denote the derivatives of f in the directions of $\mathbf{i}_1$, $\mathbf{i}_2$, $\mathbf{i}_3$. If these are the unit vectors of Sec. 123, show that $\nabla f = \dfrac{df}{ds_1}\mathbf{i}_1 + \dfrac{df}{ds_2}\mathbf{i}_2 + \dfrac{df}{ds_3}\mathbf{i}_3$ and $|\text{grad } f|^2 = \left(\dfrac{df}{ds_1}\right)^2 + \left(\dfrac{df}{ds_2}\right)^2 + \left(\dfrac{df}{ds_3}\right)^2$ Deduce that these relations hold if $\mathbf{i}_1$, $\mathbf{i}_2$, $\mathbf{i}_3$ are any three mutually perpendicular unit vectors.

For cylindrical coordinates, $ds^2 = dr^2 + r^2d\theta^2 + dz^2$, show that

45. $\nabla f = \dfrac{\partial f}{\partial r}\mathbf{i}_1 + \dfrac{1}{r}\dfrac{\partial f}{\partial \theta}\mathbf{i}_2 + \dfrac{\partial f}{\partial z}\mathbf{i}_3$.

46. $\nabla \cdot \mathbf{Q} = \dfrac{1}{r}\dfrac{\partial(rQ_1)}{\partial r} + \dfrac{1}{r}\dfrac{\partial Q_2}{\partial \theta} + \dfrac{\partial Q_3}{\partial z}$.

47. $\nabla \times \mathbf{Q} = \left(\dfrac{1}{r}\dfrac{\partial Q_3}{\partial \theta} - \dfrac{\partial Q_2}{\partial z}\right)\mathbf{i}_1 + \left(\dfrac{\partial Q_1}{\partial z} - \dfrac{\partial Q_3}{\partial r}\right)\mathbf{i}_2$
$$+ \left(\dfrac{1}{r}\dfrac{\partial(rQ_2)}{\partial r} - \dfrac{1}{r}\dfrac{\partial Q_1}{\partial \theta}\right)\mathbf{i}_3.$$

48. $\nabla^2 f = \dfrac{1}{r}\dfrac{\partial}{\partial r}\left(r\dfrac{\partial f}{\partial r}\right) + \dfrac{1}{r^2}\dfrac{\partial^2 f}{\partial \theta^2} + \dfrac{\partial^2 f}{\partial z^2}$.

49. With the terms in z omitted and $Q_3 = 0$, the expressions of Probs. 45 to 48 hold for polar coordinates in the plane. Use this fact to check the results of Probs. 24, 46, 98, and 99 of Exercises V (page 245).

Use Eq. (108) to find the gradient of each given $f(r,\phi,\theta)$:

50. $\log r$.   **51.** $r^{-\frac{1}{2}}$.   **52.** r^n.

Find the divergence and curl of each given $\mathbf{Q}(r,\phi,\theta)$:

53. $r\mathbf{i}_1$.   **54.** $\mathbf{i}_1$.   **55.** $r\mathbf{i}_2$.

56. Check Prob. 43 by writing $\mathbf{F} = 4r^3\mathbf{i}_1$, and using Prob. 52.

57. Show that $\nabla \times [f(r)\mathbf{i}_1] = 0$, and deduce that a force directed toward a center and equal to any function of the distance from that center is conservative.

Any solution of Laplace's equation is called a *harmonic function*. Let S bound the volume V lying in a region R throughout which U is harmonic. That is $\nabla \cdot \nabla U = \nabla^2 U = 0$ in R. Show that

58. $\int_S \dfrac{dU}{dn} dS = 0$.   HINT: Use Prob. 31.

59. $\int_S U \dfrac{dU}{dn} dS = \int_V |\nabla U|^2 dV$, and hence $\int_S U \dfrac{dU}{dn} dS > 0$ unless U is constant in V.   HINT: Use Probs. 32 and 12.

60. Let S_r be a sphere of radius r with center at $P_0 = (x_0, y_0, z_0)$ lying in R. Put $U_0 = U(x_0, y_0, z_0)$. Then $U_0 = \dfrac{1}{4\pi a^2} \int_{S_a} U \, dS$, the average of U on S_a.   HINT: Take P_0 as an origin of spherical coordinates and set $I_r = \dfrac{1}{4\pi} \int_{S_r} U(r, \phi, \theta) \sin \phi \, d\phi \, d\theta$. Then $I_a =$ average of U on S_a and $I_r \to U_0$ when $r \to 0$. But by differentiating I_r we may deduce that $\dfrac{dI_r}{dr} = \dfrac{1}{4\pi} \int_{S_r} \dfrac{\partial U}{\partial r} \sin \phi \, d\phi \, d\theta = \dfrac{1}{4\pi r^2} \int_{S_r} \dfrac{dU}{dn} dS = 0$ by   Prob.   58. Hence $I_a - I_r = 0$, and on letting $r \to 0$, $U_0 = I_a$.

61. Unless constant in R, U cannot have a maximum or minimum value at a point P_0 inside R.   HINT: Assume $U = M$, its maximum value, at some point in R. Then either $U = M$ throughout R, or with the notation of Prob. 60 there is a point P_0 at which $U_0 = M$, and such that $U \neq M$ at some points on S_a. But in this case $U_0 \geqq U(a, \phi, \theta)$ for all ϕ, θ and is greater for some values, so that by taking averages $U_0 > I_a$, which contradicts Prob. 60 since $U_0 = I_a$.

62. If $U = 0$ on S, then $U = 0$ throughout V.   HINT: If U were greater than 0 at any point of V, its values in V would have a positive maximum at some inside point. And if U were less than 0 at any point of V, its values in V would have a positive minimum at some inside point. Either case contradicts Prob. 61, and $U = 0$ in V.

63. If $U_2 = U_1$ on S, then $U_2 = U_1$ throughout V.   HINT: Apply Prob. 62 to the harmonic function $U_2 - U_1$.

64. If $dU/dn = 0$ on S, U is constant in V.   HINT: Use Prob. 59.

65. If $dU_1/dn = dU_2/dn$ on S, $U_2 - U_1$ is constant throughout V. HINT: Apply Prob. 64 to the harmonic function $U_2 - U_1$.

In Eq. (111), $\mathbf{i}_1 \cdot \mathbf{n}/r^2 dS$ is the solid angle at O subtended by dS. By a geometric argument, deduce that $\int_S \dfrac{\mathbf{i}_1 \cdot \mathbf{n}}{r^2} dS$

66. Is 0 for O outside V and is 4π for O inside V.

67. Is 2π if O is a point on S at which the surface S is smooth.

68. Taken over the surface of a cube, is $\pi/2$ if O is a vertex, π if O is on an edge, and 2π if O is on a face.

69. With the notation of Eq. (111), derive the following relation:
$\int_S r\mathbf{i}_1 \cdot \mathbf{n}\, dS = 3V$. Use this to check Prob. 19.

70. From Eq. (110), $\nabla \cdot (\rho\mathbf{i}_1) = \dfrac{1}{r^2} \dfrac{\partial}{\partial r} (r^2 \rho) = \dfrac{2\rho}{r} + \dfrac{\partial \rho}{\partial r}$. And from the divergence theorem (38), $\int_V \nabla \cdot (\rho\mathbf{i}_1) dV = \int_S \rho\mathbf{i}_1 \cdot \mathbf{n}\, dS$. Deduce that the potential at O due to charge density ρ inside V bounded by S is
$\int_V \dfrac{\rho}{r}\, dV = \dfrac{1}{2} \int_S \rho\mathbf{i}_1 \cdot \mathbf{n}\, dS - \dfrac{1}{2} \int_V \dfrac{\partial \rho}{\partial r}\, dV$.

71. The potential at $P_0 = (r,O,\theta)$ due to a charge of surface density σ on the element of spherical surface $dS = R^2 \sin \phi\, d\phi\, d\theta$ at $P = (R,\phi,\theta)$ is $\sigma\, dS/|P_0P|$, where $|P_0P| = \sqrt{R^2 + r^2 - 2rR \cos \phi}$. For the whole sphere $0 \leqq \phi \leqq \pi$, $0 \leqq \theta \leqq 2\pi$. Show that the potential due to a uniformly charged spherical shell of radius R at a point inside the shell, $r < R$, is $4\pi R\sigma$, and at a point outside the shell, $r > R$, is $4\pi R^2\sigma/r$.

72. The gravitational potential of a spherical shell of uniform density ρ and thickness dR may be found by replacing σ by $\rho\, dR$ in the expressions of Prob. 71. Show that the potential $U(r,\phi,\theta)$ due to a homogeneous solid sphere of radius a and mass m gravitational units is
$\int_0^a \dfrac{4\pi R^2 \rho\, dR}{r} = \dfrac{4\pi \rho a^3}{3r} = \dfrac{m}{r}$ at a point outside the sphere, $r > a$, and is
$\int_0^r \dfrac{4\pi R^2 \rho\, dR}{r} + \int_r^a 4\pi R\rho\, dR = 2\pi\rho a^2 - \dfrac{2}{3} \pi\rho r^2 = \dfrac{3m}{2a} - \dfrac{mr^2}{2a^3}$ at a point inside the sphere, $r < a$. Here U is a force potential.

73. Using $\mathbf{F} = \nabla U$, find the attraction of the sphere of Prob. 72 on unit gravitational mass at (r,ϕ,θ).

74. For the potential U of Prob. 72, verify the $\nabla^2 U = 0$ if $r > a$ and $\nabla^2 U = -4\pi\rho$ if $r < a$, in accord with Poisson's equation.

75. For any closed circuit B_S bounding a portion of a surface S,
$\int_{B_S} \mathbf{E} \cdot d\mathbf{s} = -\dfrac{\mu}{c} \dfrac{\partial}{\partial t} \int_S \mathbf{H} \cdot \mathbf{n}\, dS$ and $\int_{B_S} \mathbf{H} \cdot d\mathbf{s} = \dfrac{\epsilon}{c} \dfrac{\partial}{\partial t} \int_S \mathbf{E} \cdot \mathbf{n}\, dS$, where $\mathbf{E}$ is the electric intensity vector and $\mathbf{H}$ is the magnetic intensity vector. Using Stokes's theorem (54), show that these may be transformed into
$\int_S \left(\nabla \times \mathbf{E} + \dfrac{\mu}{c} \dfrac{\partial \mathbf{H}}{\partial t} \right) \cdot \mathbf{n}\, dS = 0$ and $\int_S \left(\nabla \times \mathbf{H} - \dfrac{\epsilon}{c} \dfrac{\partial \mathbf{E}}{\partial t} \right) \cdot \mathbf{n}\, dS = 0$.
From the arbitrariness of S and $\mathbf{n}$, deduce Maxwell's equations, namely,
$$\nabla \times \mathbf{E} = -\frac{\mu}{c} \frac{\partial \mathbf{H}}{\partial t}, \qquad \nabla \times \mathbf{H} = \frac{\epsilon}{c} \frac{\partial \mathbf{E}}{\partial t}.$$

76. In the absence of charges or permanent magnets $\nabla \cdot \mathbf{E} = 0$ and $\nabla \cdot \mathbf{H} = 0$. Using these relations, Prob. 8, and Maxwell's equations as stated in Prob. 75, show that each component of $\mathbf{E}$ and $\mathbf{H}$ satisfies the equation $\nabla^2 U = \dfrac{\epsilon\mu}{c^2} \dfrac{\partial^2 U}{\partial t^2}$. This represents wave motion with velocity $c/\sqrt{\epsilon\mu}$ and is fundamental in the electromagnetic theory of light.

77. For steady flow of heat along radii from O, show that the temperature U satisfies the equation $\dfrac{d}{dr}\left(r^2\dfrac{dU}{dr}\right) = 0$.

78. The faces of a homogeneous spherical shell $r = r_1$ and $r = r_2$ are kept at fixed temperatures U_1 and U_2. Use Prob. 77 to show that $r^2\dfrac{dU}{dr} = k$ and $U = -\dfrac{k}{r} + c$. Also show that the rate of heat flow outward through the shell is $-4\pi Kr^2\dfrac{dU}{dr} = -4\pi Kk = 4\pi Kr_1r_2\dfrac{U_1 - U_2}{r_2 - r_1}$.

79. Use Prob. 48 to show that for steady flow of heat normal to concentric cylinders the temperature U satisfies the equation $\dfrac{d}{dr}\left(r\dfrac{dU}{dr}\right) = 0$.

80. The faces of a long homogeneous cylindrical pipe $r = r_1$ and $r = r_2$ are kept at fixed temperatures U_1 and U_2. Using Prob. 79, show that $r\dfrac{dU}{dr} = k$, $U = k\log r + c$. Also show that the rate of heat flow outward through a length L of the pipe is given by the expression

$$-2\pi KLr\frac{dU}{dr} = -2\pi KLk = 2\pi KL\frac{U_1 - U_2}{\log r_2 - \log r_1}.$$

81. If a fluid is rotating like a rigid body with constant vector angular velocity $\mathbf{a}$, show that the rotation $\frac{1}{2}(\nabla \times \mathbf{q}) = \mathbf{a}$ at all points. Hint: Let (x_0, y_0, z_0) be any point on the axis of rotation and define the vector $\mathbf{r} = (x - x_0)\mathbf{i} + (y - y_0)\mathbf{j} + (z - z_0)\mathbf{k}$. Then by Sec. 52, observe that $\mathbf{q}(x,y,z) = \mathbf{a} \times \mathbf{r}$. And by Prob. 6, $\nabla \times \mathbf{q} = \mathbf{a}(\nabla \cdot \mathbf{r}) - (\mathbf{a} \cdot \nabla)\mathbf{r} = 2\mathbf{a}$.

82. In an incompressible viscous fluid the internal friction force vector on an element dS has a component along the x axis equal to $\mu\mathbf{n} \cdot \nabla u\, dS$, where $\mu = \nu\rho$ slugs/ft. sec. is the coefficient of viscosity. Show that $\displaystyle\int_S \mu\mathbf{n} \cdot \nabla u\, dS = \int_V \mu\nabla \cdot \nabla u\, dV$ and deduce that the first equation of motion for viscous flow may be obtained from Eq. (149) by adding $\nu\,\nabla^2 u$ to the right member. Similarly $\nu\,\nabla^2 v$ and $\nu\,\nabla^2 w$ must be added to the right members of (150) and (151) for viscous flow with ρ constant.

83. If no body force acts, $X = Y = Z = 0$ in Eqs. (149) to (152). Assume that u, v, w as well as the x, y, z partial derivatives of u, v, w, and ρ are small and neglect second-order products of these quantities. Show that if $p - p_0 = k(\rho - \rho_0)$ the equations may be written in the form $\dfrac{\partial \mathbf{q}}{\partial t} = -k\,\nabla(\log \rho)$ and $\nabla \cdot \mathbf{q} = -\dfrac{\partial(\log \rho)}{\partial t}$. Use $\nabla \cdot \dfrac{\partial \mathbf{q}}{\partial t} = \dfrac{\partial(\nabla \cdot \mathbf{q})}{\partial t}$ to eliminate $\mathbf{q}$ and deduce the equation $\dfrac{\partial^2(\log \rho)}{\partial t^2} = k\,\nabla^2(\log \rho)$.

84. For changes of pressure in air so rapid that no heat is exchanged, the adiabatic relation $p/p_0 = (\rho/\rho_0)^{1.4}$ was derived in Prob. 28 of

Exercises V (page 245).   If $\rho = \rho_0(1 + s)$, for small s, $\log \rho = \log \rho_0 + s$ approximately, and we may replace the derivatives of $\log \rho$ by those of s. Also at ρ_0, $dp/d\rho = 1.4\ p_0/\rho_0 = k$ in Prob. 83, since by Taylor's series $p = p_0 + (dp/d\rho)_0(\rho - \rho_0)$, approximately.   Deduce the equation for sound waves in air, $\partial^2 s/\partial t^2 = k \nabla^2 s$.   The velocity of sound in air is $\sqrt{k} = \sqrt{1.4\ p_0/\rho_0} = 1{,}120$ ft./sec. for standard pressure and temperature 15°C.   Since p_0/ρ_0 is proportional to absolute temperature T, the velocity of sound varies as $\sqrt{T}$.

CHAPTER IX
DIFFERENTIAL EQUATIONS

Earlier in this book we often encountered physical and geometric problems that led to equations involving derivatives or differentials. And in many cases these differential equations were solved by appropriate special devices. In this chapter we classify the principal useful types of solvable differential equations and describe a convenient method of solving each type.

130. Definition of Terms. Any equation that involves differentials or derivatives is a *differential equation*. Thus

$$\frac{dy}{dx} - y = 0 \qquad \text{or} \qquad dy - y\,dx = 0, \tag{1}$$

$$\left(y - x\frac{dy}{dx}\right)^2 = \sqrt{\frac{dy}{dx}} \qquad \text{or} \qquad \left(y - x\frac{dy}{dx}\right)^4 = \frac{dy}{dx}, \tag{2}$$

$$2\frac{d^2y}{dx^2} - 7\frac{dy}{dx} + 3y = 4\sin x, \tag{3}$$

$$\frac{\partial^2 u}{\partial x^2} + \frac{\partial^2 u}{\partial y^2} + \frac{\partial^2 u}{\partial z^2} = 0 \tag{4}$$

are differential equations. If the equation contains any partial derivatives, *e.g.*, Eq. (4), it is a *partial differential equation*. If it does not, *e.g.*, Eqs. (1) to (3), it is an *ordinary differential equation*.

The *order* of the differential equation is the same as the order of the derivative of highest order in the equation. Thus Eqs. (1) and (2) are each of the first order, while (3) and (4) are each of the second order.

Suppose that a differential equation is reducible to a form in which each member is a polynomial in all the derivatives that occur. Then the *degree* of the equation is the largest exponent of the highest derivative in the reduced form. Thus (2) is of the fourth degree, while (1), (3), and (4) are each of the first degree.

A differential equation is *linear* if it is a first-degree algebraic equation in the set of variables made up of the dependent variables together with all of their derivatives. Thus (1) and (3) are each linear in y, and (4) is linear in u.

131. Integral Curves. The differential equation (1) may be written in the form

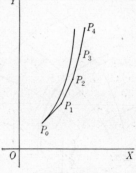

Fig. 134.

$$\frac{dy}{dx} = y. \qquad (5)$$

This associates a value of dy/dx, or a slope, with each point in the plane. Starting at any point P_0, we may construct a polygon $P_0P_1P_2 \cdots$ by choosing any small number h and constructing the sides successively of length h and with the slope at the first end point. A sequence of values of $h \to 0$ leads to a series of polygons approaching a curve C. The curve passes through P_0 and has at each point values of x, y, dy/dx that satisfy the differential equation. Consequently the equation of C, written explicity as

$$y = \psi(x), \qquad \text{or implicitly as} \quad \phi(x,y) = 0, \qquad (6)$$

is called a *solution* of the differential equation. And C itself, which is the graph of a solution, is called an *integral curve*. The discussion suggests that the differential equation (5) has a solution, or integral curve passing through any given point.

Every differential equation of the first order, when solved for dy/dx, takes the form

$$\frac{dy}{dx} = f(x,y). \qquad (7)$$

The geometric process carried out for Eq. (5) may be applied to this equation and suggests that there is an integral curve passing through any point P_0 that is not a singular point of $f(x,y)$. In fact, the geometric process may be used to obtain a rough graph of the integral curve. One practical procedure is as follows. Plot the curves of constant slope, or *isoclines*,

$$f(x,y) = \text{constant} \qquad (8)$$

that pass near P_0. On each of these curves mark a series of short parallel line segments to show the appropriate slope.

Then sketch the curve through P_0 which appears to cut each isocline with the indicated slope.

Supplementing such graphical methods, there are numerical and mechanical methods of solving differential equations. With

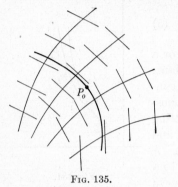

a sufficient expenditure of time, these may be made to give reasonable accuracy. Though tedious, the approximate methods must be resorted to in many cases where a practical problem leads to a differential equation not of a solvable type.

132. General Solution. Since the initial point P_0 may be varied, the differential equation (7) will have a whole family of

Fig. 135.

integral curves. The equation of such a family will involve one constant c. Solved for the constant, it may be written

$$F(x,y) = c. \tag{9}$$

We may eliminate the constant from this form by differentiation,

$$dF = \frac{\partial F}{\partial x}\,dx + \frac{\partial F}{\partial y}\,dy = 0, \quad \text{or} \quad \frac{\partial F}{\partial x} + \frac{\partial F}{\partial y}\frac{dy}{dx} = 0. \tag{10}$$

Either differential equation in (10) is called *exact* and has (9) as its solution. More generally, any first-order differential equation of the form

$$dF = dG \quad \text{or} \quad \frac{dF}{dx} = \frac{dG}{dx} \tag{11}$$

is called *exact*. Here dF and dG are exact differential expressions as defined in Sec. 82, and the functions $F(x,y)$ and $G(x,y)$ of which they are the total differentials may be found by the method given in that section. The general solution of the exact equation (11) is

$$F(x,y) = G(x,y) + c. \quad \text{And} \quad \begin{aligned} F(x,y) - F(x_0,y_0) \\ = G(x,y) - G(x_0,y_0) \end{aligned} \tag{12}$$

is the equation of the integral curve that passes through $P_0 = x_0, y_0$. A few types of first-order equations that can easily be made exact and hence solved are discussed in Sec. 133.

If the family of integral curves is given in the form $g(x,y,c) = 0$, the differential equation having this as its general solution may be found by eliminating the constant c from

$$g(x,y,c) = 0 \qquad \text{and} \qquad \frac{\partial g}{\partial x} + \frac{\partial g}{\partial y}\frac{dy}{dx} = 0. \tag{13}$$

For example, if $g(x,y,c)$ is $y - cx - c^2$, we have

$$y = cx + c^2, \qquad \frac{dy}{dx} = c, \qquad \text{and} \qquad y = x\frac{dy}{dx} + \left(\frac{dy}{dx}\right)^2. \tag{14}$$

Suppose that a given equation contains two independent constants. Then we may obtain three equations from which they may be eliminated by differentiating twice. Thus from

$$y = c_1 e^x + c_2 e^{2x}, \qquad \frac{dy}{dx} = c_1 e^x + 2c_2 e^{2x},$$

$$\frac{d^2 y}{dx^2} = c_1 e^x + 4c_2 e^{2x}. \tag{15}$$

By solving any two of these for c_1 and c_2, and substituting the values in the third equation, we find

$$\frac{d^2 y}{dx^2} - 3\frac{dy}{dx} + 2y = 0. \tag{16}$$

Similarly, if an equation contains n independent constants, successive differentiation and elimination of the constants will lead to a differential equation of the nth order. And, conversely, an ordinary differential equation of the nth order will have a *general solution* containing n constants of integration.

133. First Order and First Degree. A differential equation of the first order and first degree may be put in the form

$$M(x,y)dx + N(x,y)dy = 0 \qquad \text{or}$$

$$M(x,y) + N(x,y)\frac{dy}{dx} = 0. \tag{17}$$

We consider some solvable types that are easy to recognize.

Type I. *Variables Separable.* Here M and N are products of factors, where each factor is either a function of x alone, or a function of y alone. Divide the equation by the factor of M containing y and by the factor of N containing x. The equation then assumes the form

$$f(x)dx - g(y)dy = 0 \qquad \text{or} \qquad f(x)dx = g(y)dy \tag{18}$$

in which the variables are *separated*. The solution is

$$\int f(x)dx - \int g(y)dy = c \qquad \text{or} \qquad \int_{x_0}^{x} f(x)dx = \int_{y_0}^{y} g(y)dy, \quad (19)$$

if $y = y_0$ when $x = x_0$.

Type II. *Linear in* y. Here N is a function of x alone, and M is a first-degree polynomial in y. Thus the equation is

$$[B(x)y - C(x)]dx + A(x)dy = 0 \qquad \text{or}$$

$$A(x)\frac{dy}{dx} + B(x)y = C(x). \quad (20)$$

Divide by $A(x)$. With new notation, the equation becomes

$$\frac{dy}{dx} + P(x)y = Q(x). \quad (21)$$

Multiply by $I(x)dx$, where $I(x)$ is a function of x to be determined presently. The result is

$$I(x)dy + I(x)P(x)y \, dx = I(x)Q(x)dx. \quad (22)$$

By Sec. 82, the left member will be an exact expression if

$$\frac{\partial}{\partial x}[I(x)] = \frac{\partial}{\partial y}[I(x)P(x)y], \qquad \text{or} \qquad \frac{dI}{dx} = IP. \quad (23)$$

This is a separable equation, Type I. We solve it by writing

$$\frac{dI}{I} = P(x)dx, \qquad \log I = \int P(x)dx, \qquad \text{and} \qquad I = e^{\int P \, dx}. \quad (24)$$

With any choice of constant in the integral, this makes

$$dI = IP \, dx \quad \text{and} \quad d(Iy) = I \, dy + y \, dI = I \, dy + IPy \, dx. \quad (25)$$

Consequently, by Eq. (12), the solution of Eq. (22) is

$$Iy = \int IQ \, dx + c, \quad \text{or} \quad y = \frac{1}{I(x)}\left[\int I(x)Q(x)dx + c\right]. \quad (26)$$

And the solution for which $y = y_0$ when $x = x_0$ is

$$I(x)y - I(x_0)y_0 = \int_{x_0}^{x} I(x)Q(x)dx. \quad (27)$$

If multiplication of a differential equation by a factor reduces the equation to either exact form (11), we call the factor an *integrating factor* of the equation. Thus Eq. (21) admits the I of (24) as an integrating factor.

To integrate a given linear equation, first reduce it to the form (21) and compute the integrating factor by (24). Then either multiply in the factor to make the equation exact or use Eq. (27) as a formula for the desired solution.

As an example, consider

$$x^2 \frac{dy}{dx} + 3xy = 5x^3 + 2, \qquad \text{or} \qquad \frac{dy}{dx} + \frac{3}{x} y = 5x + \frac{2}{x^2}. \quad (28)$$

Here the integrating factor is found from

$$\int \frac{3}{x} dx = 3 \log x \text{ to be } I = e^{3 \log x} = x^3. \quad (29)$$

And the exact equation

$$x^3 dy + 3x^2 y \, dx = (5x^4 + 2x) dx \text{ leads to } x^3 y = x^5 + x^2 + c. \quad (30)$$

Type III. *Reducible to Linear.* Consider the Bernoulli equation

$$A(x) \frac{dy}{dx} + B(x)y = C(x)y^n. \quad (31)$$

This differs from the linear equation only by the presence of y^n in the term on the right. Multiply by $(1 - n)y^{-n}/A(x)$. Put

$$u = y^{1-n}, \qquad \frac{du}{dx} = (1 - n)y^{-n} \frac{dy}{dx}, \quad (32)$$

and the equation becomes

$$\frac{du}{dx} + (1 - n) \frac{B(x)}{A(x)} u = (1 - n) \frac{C(x)}{A(x)}. \quad (33)$$

This may be solved by the method used above for Eq. (21).

Again, we may interchange the roles of x and y and so solve an equation linear in x,

$$A(y)dx + [B(y)x - C(y)]dy = 0 \qquad \text{or}$$
$$A(y) \frac{dx}{dy} + B(y)x = C(y). \quad (34)$$

More generally we may use the procedure of Type II whenever we observe new variables $u(x,y)$ and $t(x,y)$ which reduce the given differential equation to the form

$$A(t)\frac{du}{dt} + B(t)u = C(t). \tag{35}$$

Type IV. *Homogeneous.* Homogeneous functions were defined and examples given in Probs. 10 to 18 of Exercises II (page 70). We recall that $M(x,y)$ is homogeneous of the nth degree if multiplication of x and y each by a factor k multiplies the function by k^n. That is,

$$M(kx,ky) = k^n M(x,y). \tag{36}$$

Such a function is x^n times a function of y/x, since if $k = 1/x$,

$$M\left(1,\frac{y}{x}\right) = x^{-n}M(x,y) \qquad \text{and} \qquad M(x,y) = x^n M\left(1,\frac{y}{x}\right). \tag{37}$$

The differential equation (17) is homogeneous if M and N are each homogeneous of the same degree, say n. Then the equation is

$$x^n M\left(1,\frac{y}{x}\right) dx + x^n N\left(1,\frac{y}{x}\right) dy = 0. \tag{38}$$

Divide by x^n. Put $y = vx$, so that

$$dy = v\,dx + x\,dv, \tag{39}$$

and the equation takes the separable form

$$[M(1,v) + vN(1,v)]dx + xN(1,v)dv = 0. \tag{40}$$

The solution of this which makes $y = y_0$ when $x = x_0$ is

$$\log x - \log x_0 = -\int_{y_0/x_0}^{y/x} \frac{N(1,v)dv}{M(1,v) + vN(1,v)}. \tag{41}$$

Type V. *Exact Equations.* $M\,dx + N\,dy$ will equal dF if

$$\frac{\partial M}{\partial y} = \frac{\partial N}{\partial x} \tag{42}$$

by Sec. 82, where we showed how to find the function F. When the condition (42) is satisfied, Eq. (17) becomes the exact equation (10), whose solution is (9), or $F = c$.

An exact expression dF remains exact when multiplied by any function of F. This sometimes enables us to discover an integrating factor of a differential equation.   For example, consider

$$y \, dx - x \, dy = x^6 y^4 (3y \, dx + 2x \, dy). \tag{43}$$

The coefficients 3 and 2 in the right member suggest forming

$$d(x^3 y^2) = 3x^2 y^2 dx + 2x^3 y \, dy = x^2 y(3y \, dx + 2x \, dy). \tag{44}$$

This will remain exact when multiplied by any function of $(x^3 y^2)$. The coefficients 1 and -1 in the left member suggest forming

$$d(xy^{-1}) = y^{-1} dx - xy^{-2} dy = y^{-2}(y \, dx - x \, dy). \tag{45}$$

This will remain exact when multiplied by any function of (x/y), in particular $(x/y)^n$.   Let us multiply Eq. (43) by

$$y^{-2} \left(\frac{x}{y} \right)^n = x^n y^{-n-2}$$

and write the resulting equation in the form

$$\left(\frac{x}{y} \right)^n d \left(\frac{x}{y} \right) = x^{n+4} y^{-n+1} d(x^3 y^2). \tag{46}$$

The factor multiplying $d(x^3 y^2)$ will be a power of $(x^3 y^2)$ if

$$\frac{n+4}{3} = \frac{-n+1}{2}, \qquad 2n + 8 = -3n + 3, \qquad \text{and}$$
$$n = -1. \tag{47}$$

On putting $n = -1$ in Eq. (46), the integral is found to be

$$\log \left(\frac{x}{y} \right) = \frac{1}{2} (x^3 y^2)^2 + c. \tag{48}$$

The procedure just used will succeed with any equation

$$x^p y^q (Ay \, dx + Bx \, dy) = x^r y^s (Cy \, dx + Dx \, dy). \tag{49}$$

When D (or C) is zero, this equation could be treated as a Bernoulli equation in y (or in x) by the method of Type III, but the method just given is shorter.

134. Envelope of a Family of Curves.   In the xy plane, let

$$g(x,y,c) = 0 \tag{50}$$

be the equation of a family of curves G_c. Let E be a curve in the plane tangent to each curve G_c at some point P_c.   Then, if each point of E is a point P_c at which some curve G_c touches E, we call E the *envelope* of the curves G_c. We may use c as a parameter for the envelope E and write

$$x = x(c), \qquad y = y(c). \tag{51}$$

Since these relations make Eq. (50) an indentity, we have at any P_c,

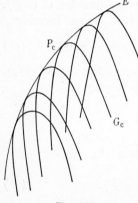

$$\frac{\partial g}{\partial x}\frac{dx}{dc} + \frac{\partial g}{\partial y}\frac{dy}{dc} + \frac{\partial g}{\partial c} = 0. \tag{52}$$

On any one curve G_c, c is constant. Hence the equation

$$\frac{\partial g}{\partial x} + \frac{\partial g}{\partial y}\frac{dy}{dx} = 0, \tag{53}$$

found by differentiating (50) with c constant, determines the slope dy/dx at any point on G_c, and hence in particular at P_c. At P_c, G_c has the same slope as E. Hence in Eq. (53)

Fig. 136.

$$\frac{dy}{dx} = \frac{dy/dc}{dx/dc} \qquad \text{and} \qquad \frac{\partial g}{\partial x}\frac{dx}{dc} + \frac{\partial g}{\partial y}\frac{dy}{dc} = 0. \tag{54}$$

A comparison of Eqs. (52) and (54) shows that at points P_c,

$$\frac{\partial g}{\partial c} = 0. \tag{55}$$

This leads to the rule for finding the parametric equations of the envelope of the family (50). Solve Eqs. (50) and (55) for x and y in terms of c.

When the functions are regular, if the expressions for x and y in terms of c do not make $\partial g/\partial x$ and $\partial g/\partial y$ both zero, this process necessarily gives an envelope. For example, consider

$$(x - 5c)^2 + y^2 = 16c^2, \qquad \text{or} \qquad x^2 + y^2 - 10cx + 9c^2 = 0, \tag{56}$$

the family of circles shown in Fig. 137. On differentiating partially with respect to c, we find

$$-10x + 18c = 0, \qquad \text{or} \qquad x = \frac{9c}{5}. \tag{57}$$

Hence the parametric equations of the envelope are

$$x = \frac{9c}{5} \qquad \text{and} \qquad y = \pm \frac{12c}{5}, \tag{58}$$

since the x and y partial derivatives of the left member of (56),

$$2x - 10c = -\frac{32c}{5} \qquad \text{and} \qquad 2y = \pm \frac{24c}{5}, \tag{59}$$

do not in general vanish.   Note that they are both zero for $c = 0$,

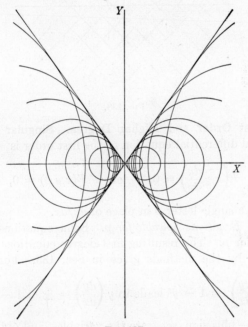

FIG. 137.

and the point $P_0 = (0,0)$ is not a point of contact, since for $c = 0$ the circle (56) degenerates to a point.

On the other hand, consider the family

$$(x - c)^2 = y^2, \tag{60}$$

for which

$$g(x,y,c) = (x - c)^2 - y^2. \tag{61}$$

Here $\partial g / \partial c = 0$ leads to

$$2(x - c) = 0, \qquad x = c \qquad \text{and} \qquad y = 0. \tag{62}$$

But these make $\partial g/\partial x = 0$ and $\partial g/\partial y = 0$. There is no envelope here. Equation (60) represents the pairs of straight lines, and $y = 0$ the locus of their intersections shown in Fig. 138.

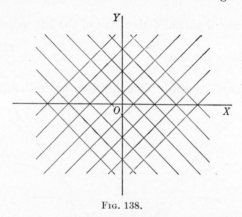

Fɪɢ. 138.

135. First Order and Higher Degree. Singular Solutions.
The general differential equation of the first order is

$$F\left(x,y,\frac{dy}{dx}\right) = 0, \qquad \text{or} \qquad F(x,y,p) = 0, \tag{63}$$

if we write a single letter p in place of dy/dx.

Type I. *Equations Solvable for p.* Some equations (63) may be solved for p. The resulting first-degree equations may then be treated by the methods given in Sec. 133. For example,

$$y^2\left(\frac{dy}{dx}\right)^2 = 1 - y^2 \text{ leads to } y\left(\frac{dy}{dx}\right) = \pm\sqrt{1 - y^2}. \tag{64}$$

We take the plus sign, separate the variables, and obtain

$$\frac{y\,dy}{\sqrt{1 - y^2}} = dx, \qquad -\sqrt{1 - y^2} = x - c, \qquad \text{or}$$

$$y^2 + (x - c)^2 = 1. \tag{65}$$

This last includes the result that would have been obtained by taking the minus sign. It is the general solution of (64) and is the family of circles shown in Fig. 139. These circles have an envelope consisting of the two lines $y = \pm 1$. This is evident from the figure and could be found by applying the method of Sec. 134 to the last equation in (65). Direct substitution shows that $y = 1$ and $y = -1$ are each solutions of the differential equation (64). They are called *singular solutions* because they cannot be obtained from any general solution by specializing the constant. In separating the variables, we divided by $\sqrt{1 - y^2}$, a permissible operation unless $y^2 = 1$. Thus Eq. (64) implies either (65) and the general solution, or else that $y^2 = 1$, the

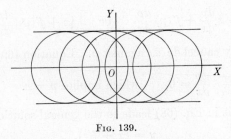

singular solutions, since $y = \pm 1$ happens to solve the original equation.

A differential equation of the first order will always have a general solution, consisting of a one-parameter infinite family of curves. If the differential equation is of the first degree, there will be one slope and one of these curves through each point. For equations of higher degree, there will be more than one slope at some points and the curves of the general solution may have an envelope at which two values of the slope coincide. Since x,y,p have the same values at each point of the envelope as they have for the tangent integral curve, the envelope will be a solution of the differential equation. Usually the envelope will not be a curve of the general solution but will be a singular solution.

Points at which Eq. (63), regarded as an equation in p, has coincident roots satisfy

$$F(x,y,p) = 0 \quad \text{and} \quad \frac{\partial F}{\partial p} = 0. \tag{66}$$

The envelope of the family of curves $g(x,y,c) = 0$ which make up the general solution will satisfy Eqs. (50) and (55) or

$$g(x,y,c) = 0 \quad \text{and} \quad \frac{\partial g}{\partial c} = 0. \tag{67}$$

Thus singular solutions may be found by testing which curves obtained from (66), or from (67), satisfy the differential equation.

Type II.   *Clairaut's Form.*   Clairaut's equation is

$$y = x\frac{dy}{dx} + f\left(\frac{dy}{dx}\right) \qquad \text{or} \qquad y = px + f(p), \qquad (68)$$

where f is any function of one variable.   To solve it, differentiate with respect to x.   The result is

$$\frac{dy}{dx} = p + x\frac{dp}{dx} + f'(p)\frac{dp}{dx} \qquad \text{or} \qquad [x + f'(p)]\frac{dp}{dx} = 0, \quad (69)$$

since we may cancel dy/dx against p.   Equation (69) will hold if

$$\frac{dp}{dx} = 0, \qquad \text{which implies } p = c. \qquad (70)$$

Inserting this in Eq. (68) leads to the general solution

$$y = cx + f(c). \qquad (71)$$

This represents a family of straight lines.   They have an envelope given in terms of the parameter c by

$$y = cx + f(c) \qquad \text{and} \qquad x + f'(c) = 0. \qquad (72)$$

This is the singular solution.   Replacing c by p gives

$$y = px + f(p) \qquad \text{and} \qquad x + f'(p) = 0. \qquad (73)$$

The equations in this form might have been obtained by observing that Eq. (69) would hold if the factor $x + f'(p)$ were zero, and combining $x + f'(p) = 0$ with Eq. (68).   We also note that Eqs. (66) and (67), applied to the problem under discussion, lead to (72) and (73), respectively.

Most equations of the first order and higher degree with simple solutions are reducible to Clairaut's form on introducing new variables u and t.   For example, consider

$$y\left(\frac{dy}{dx}\right)^2 - 2x\frac{dy}{dx} + y = 0. \qquad (74)$$

Multiply by y and put $y^2 = u$, $2y\,dy/dx = du/dx$, obtaining

$$\frac{1}{4}\left(\frac{du}{dx}\right)^2 - x\frac{du}{dx} + u = 0 \qquad \text{or} \qquad u = x\frac{du}{dx} - \frac{1}{4}\left(\frac{du}{dx}\right)^2. \qquad (75)$$

This is Clairaut's form, so that the general solution is

$$u = cx - \frac{c^2}{4} \qquad \text{or} \qquad y^2 = cx - \frac{c^2}{4}. \qquad (76)$$

The singular solution is given by

$$y^2 = cx - \frac{c^2}{4} \quad \text{and} \quad 0 = x - \frac{c}{2}, \quad \text{or} \quad y = \pm x. \quad (77)$$

136. Second Order with One Letter Absent. The general differential equation of the second order is

$$F\left(x, y, \frac{dy}{dx}, \frac{d^2y}{dx^2}\right) = 0. \quad (78)$$

Sometimes one of the letters x, y is absent from the function F. In either case the substitution $dy/dx = p$ reduces the equation to one of the first order.

Type I. *Letter y Absent.* If y is missing, we put

$$\frac{dy}{dx} = p, \quad \frac{d^2y}{dx^2} = \frac{dp}{dx} \quad (79)$$

and

$$F\left(x, \frac{dy}{dx}, \frac{d^2y}{dx^2}\right) = 0 \text{ becomes } F\left(x, p, \frac{dp}{dx}\right) = 0. \quad (80)$$

The solution of this first-order equation in the variables x and p may be written

$$p = G(x, c_1) \quad \text{or} \quad \frac{dy}{dx} = G(x, c_1). \quad (81)$$

This is a separable differential equation whose solution is

$$y = \int G(x, c_1) dx + c_2. \quad (82)$$

For example, consider the linear equation

$$x \frac{d^2y}{dx^2} + 2 \frac{dy}{dx} = 12x^2, \quad \text{or} \quad x \frac{dp}{dx} + 2p = 12x^2. \quad (83)$$

This is linear in p, Type II of Sec. 133. Hence we write

$$\frac{dp}{dx} + \frac{2}{x} p = 12x, \quad \int \frac{2}{x} dx = 2 \log x, \quad e^{2 \log x} = x^2. \quad (84)$$

Multiplying by $x^2 \, dx$ and integrating, we obtain

$$x^2 dp + 2xp \, dx = 12x^3 dx \quad \text{and} \quad px^2 = 3x^4 + c_1. \quad (85)$$

We might have discovered that x was an integrating factor of Eq. (83) and so written down (85) directly, by reasoning as we did for Eq. (43). To complete the solution of the second-order equation, we replace p by dy/dx in (85) and deduce

$$dy = (3x^2 + c_1x^{-2})dx \qquad \text{so that } y = x^3 - c_1x^{-1} + c_2. \quad (86)$$

Type II. *Letter x Absent.* Suppose that x is missing. If

$$\frac{dy}{dx} = p, \qquad \frac{d^2y}{dx^2} = \frac{dp}{dx} = \frac{dp}{dy}\frac{dy}{dx} = p\frac{dp}{dy}. \quad (87)$$

Thus we may replace dy/dx by p, and d^2y/dx^2 by $p\, dp/dy$ in

$$F\left(y,\frac{dy}{dx},\frac{d^2y}{dx^2}\right) = 0 \text{ to obtain } F\left(y,p,p\frac{dp}{dy}\right) = 0. \quad (88)$$

The solution of this first-order equation in the variables y and p may be written

$$p = G(y,c_1) \qquad \text{or} \qquad \frac{dy}{dx} = \quad (y,c_1). \quad (89)$$

This is a separable differential equation whose solution is

$$x = \int \frac{dy}{G(y,c_1)} + c_2. \quad (90)$$

For example, consider the equation

$$\frac{d^2y}{dx^2} = \frac{1}{y^3} \qquad \text{or} \qquad p\frac{dp}{dy} = \frac{1}{y^3}. \quad (91)$$

This is a separable equation, so that we may solve it by writing $2p\, dp = 2y^{-3}dy,$ $\qquad p^2 = -y^{-2} + c_1,$ $\qquad$ or

$$p = \pm\sqrt{c_1 - y^{-2}}. \quad (92)$$

Replace p by dy/dx, separate, and integrate. With the plus sign

$$c_1dx = \frac{c_1y\, dy}{\sqrt{c_1y^2 - 1}}, \qquad c_1x + c_2 = \sqrt{c_1y^2 - 1}, \qquad \text{or}$$

$$(c_1x + c_2)^2 = c_1y^2 - 1. \quad (93)$$

The last equation includes the result of taking the minus sign.

If initial conditions are given, it may be convenient to find c_1 before integrating a second time. Thus, if we wished the solution of (91) for which $p = 0$ and $y = 1$ when $x = 0$, we would find $c_1 = 1$ in (92), and hence throughout (93). Then we would take $c_2 = 0$ to make $y = 1$ when $x = 0$. Consequently, the particular solution required is $x^2 = y^2 - 1$.

137. Linear Equations of Higher Order. The general linear differential equation of order n is

$$a_n(x) \frac{d^n y}{dx^n} + a_{n-1}(x) \frac{d^{n-1} y}{dx^{n-1}} + \cdots + a_1(x) \frac{dy}{dx} + a_0(x)y = \beta(x).$$
$$(94)$$

The right member $\beta(x)$ and the *coefficients* $a_0(x)$, $a_1(x)$, $\cdots$, $a_n(x)$ are given functions of x. Since the order is n, $a_n(x)$ is not identically zero. If $\beta(x) = 0$, the equation is *homogeneous*. Thus the general homogeneous linear equation of the nth order is

$$L(y) = a_n(x) \frac{d^n y}{dx^n} + a_{n-1}(x) \frac{d^{n-1} y}{dx^{n-1}} + \cdots + a_1(x) \frac{dy}{dx} + a_0(x)y$$
$$= 0. \quad (95)$$

We use $L(y)$ to denote the result of substituting any function y in the left member of Eq. (94) or (95). Since multiplying y by a constant multiplies each term by a constant,

$$L(cy_1) = cL(y_1), \quad \text{and} \quad L(cy_1) = 0, \quad \text{if } L(y_1) = 0. \quad (96)$$

Again, replacing y by $y_1 + y_2$ replaces each term in y by the sum of two similar terms, one in y_1 and one in y_2. Hence

$$L(y_1 + y_2) = L(y_1) + L(y_2), \quad \text{and} \quad L(y_1 + y_2) = 0,$$
$$\text{if } L(y_1) = 0, L(y_2) = 0. \quad (97)$$

Consequently the sum of two solutions, or the product of one solution by a constant, is again a solution of the homogeneous equation (95).

Now suppose that u_1, u_2, $\cdots$, u_n are n functions of x each of which is a solution of (95). Then

$$y = c_1 u_1 + c_2 u_2 + \cdots + c_n u_n \quad (98)$$

is also a solution, by the properties just mentioned. This solution may be made to take on any given values of y, and its first $n - 1$ derivatives for any value x_0 if we can solve the equations

$$
\begin{aligned}
y_0 &= c_1 u_1 + c_2 u_2 + \cdots + c_n u_n \\
y_0{}' &= c_1 u_1{}' + c_2 u_2{}' + \cdots + c_n u_n{}' \\
&\cdots \cdots \cdots \cdots \cdots \cdots \cdots \cdots \\
y_0{}^{(n-1)} &= c_1 u_1{}^{(n-1)} + c_2 u_2{}^{(n-1)} + \cdots + c_n u_n{}^{(n-1)}
\end{aligned}
\quad (99)
$$

for the coefficients c.   Here primes denote differentiation with respect to x, the subscripts $_0$ on y, y', etc., denote that we use the values given for x_0, and the functions u_j as well as their derivatives are to be evaluated at x_0.   By Sec. 27, Eqs. (99) have a unique solution if the determinant of the coefficients of the c_j is not zero.

This leads us to consider the function $W(x)$ defined by

$$W(x) = \begin{vmatrix} u_1 & u_2 & \cdots & u_n \\ u_1' & u_2' & \cdots & u_n' \\ \cdots\cdots\cdots\cdots\cdots\cdots \\ u_1^{(n-1)} & u_2^{(n-1)} & \cdots & u_n^{(n-1)} \end{vmatrix}, \tag{100}$$

called the *Wronskian* of the n functions u_j.   If for all values of x, the Wronskian $W(x)$ is different from zero, the n functions u_j are *linearly independent*.   In this case Eqs. (99) can always be solved since $W(x_0) \neq 0$, and Eq. (98) is the general solution of (95).

But it may be proved that the Wronskian of a set of n solutions of a homogeneous linear differential equation of order n is either never zero or always zero.   And when $W(x)$ is always zero, some one of the solutions, say u_n, may be expressed in terms of the rest by a relation of the form

$$u_n = k_1 u_1 + k_2 u_2 + \cdots + k_{n-1} u_{n-1}. \tag{101}$$

In this case the functions u_j are *linearly dependent*, and the expression (98) is equivalent to

$$y = (c_1 + c_n k_1)u_1 + (c_2 + c_n k_2)u_2 + \cdots \\ + (c_{n-1} + c_n k_{n-1})u_{n-1}. \tag{102}$$

Hence it really involves at most $n - 1$ independent constants, namely the $n - 1$ parentheses, and at most $n - 1$ independent functions.   Thus when $W(x) = 0$ for all values, (98) is not the general solution.

We call any n linearly independent solutions of (95) a *fundamental system* of solutions u_j.   The expression (98) provides the general solution of any linear homogeneous equation of order n for which a fundamental system of solutions is known.

Consider next the nonhomogeneous equation (94) or

$$L(y) = \beta(x), \qquad \text{with } \beta(x) \neq 0. \tag{103}$$

Suppose that u is a solution of this equation, and u_1 is a solution of the corresponding homogeneous equation.   Then

$$L(u) = \beta(x) \qquad \text{and} \qquad L(u_1) = 0. \tag{104}$$

It follows from this and the first equation in (97) that

$$L(u + u_1) = L(u) + L(u_1) = \beta(x), \tag{105}$$

so that $u + u_1$ is a solution of (103).   Hence the sum of the general solution of the homogeneous equation and any particular solution of the nonhomogeneous equation,

$$y = u + c_1 u_1 + c_2 u_2 + \cdots + c_n u_n \tag{106}$$

is a solution of (103).   There are no other solutions.   For, if y is any solution of (103) and u is the particular solution just used, it follows from Eqs. (96) and (97) that

$$L(y - u) = L(y) - L(u) = \beta(x) - \beta(x) = 0.$$

Thus $y = u + (y - u)$ equals u plus a solution of the homogeneous equation.   To recapitulate, the expression (106) provides the general solution of any linear equation of order n in terms of a particular solution of the nonhomogeneous equation and a fundamental system of solutions of the corresponding homogeneous equation.   The particular solution is called the *particular integral*.   The remaining terms in (106) make up the *complementary function*.

138. Linear Equations with Constant Coefficients.   The general homogeneous linear differential equation of order n, with constant coefficients, is

$$a_n \frac{d^n y}{dx^n} + a_{n-1} \frac{d^{n-1} y}{dx^{n-1}} + \cdots + a_1 \frac{dy}{dx} + a_0 y = 0. \tag{107}$$

The coefficients $a_0, a_1, \cdots, a_n$ are here constants, with $a_n \neq 0$. In discussing such equations it is convenient to represent d/dx by a single letter D.   Thus

$$\frac{dy}{dx} = Dy, \qquad \frac{d^2 y}{dx^2} = D^2 y, \text{ etc.} \tag{108}$$

And Eq. (107) may be written

$$(a_n D^n + a_{n-1} D^{n-1} + \cdots + a_1 D + a_0) y = 0. \tag{109}$$

Let us seek solutions of the form e^{rx}.   Since

$$D(e^{rx}) = r e^{rx}, \qquad D^2(e^{rx}) = r^2 e^{rx}, \text{ etc.}, \tag{110}$$

the result of putting $y = e^{rx}$ in Eq. (109) is

$$(a_n r^n + a_{n-1} r^{n-1} + \cdots + a_1 r + a_0) e^{rx} = 0. \qquad (111)$$

Thus e^{rx} will be a solution of Eq. (109) if

$$a_n r^n + a_{n-1} r^{n-1} + \cdots + a_1 r + a_0 = 0. \qquad (112)$$

This equation, which is easily written down by replacing D by r in the parenthesis of Eq. (109) or directly from the original form (107), is called the *auxiliary* equation.

If the auxiliary equation has n real and distinct roots, r_1, r_2, $\cdots$, r_n, then the corresponding exponentials form a fundamental system of solutions, and the general solution of (107) is

$$y = c_1 e^{r_1 x} + c_2 e^{r_2 x} + \cdots + c_n e^{r_n x}. \qquad (113)$$

When the a_j are all real, complex roots will occur in conjugate pairs. Suppose that $a \pm bi$ are a pair of conjugate roots, where $i = \sqrt{-1}$. To get the terms of the solution for them to add up to a real quantity, we use conjugate complex constants $p \pm qi$ as coefficients. Then by Sec. 2,

$$(p + qi) e^{(a+bi)x} + (p - qi) e^{(a-bi)x}$$
$$= 2e^{ax} \left(p \frac{e^{ibx} + e^{-ibx}}{2} - q \frac{e^{ibx} - e^{-ibx}}{2i} \right)$$
$$= 2p e^{ax} \cos bx - 2q e^{ax} \sin bx. \qquad (114)$$

Calling $2p$ and $-2q$ new constants c_1 and c_2, we see that a pair of conjugate complex roots of the auxiliary equation

$$a \pm bi \text{ lead to } c_1 e^{ax} \cos bx + c_2 e^{ax} \sin bx \qquad (115)$$

in the general solution, where c_1 and c_2 are real constants.

If the auxiliary equation (112) has repeated roots, the additional terms are obtained by multiplying in powers of x. Specifically, two equal real roots of the auxiliary equation

$$s, s \text{ lead to } c_1 e^{sx} + c_2 x e^{sx} \text{ or } e^{sx}(c_1 + c_2 x). \qquad (116)$$

Three equal real roots of the auxiliary equation

$$s, s, s \text{ lead to } c_1 e^{sx} + c_2 x e^{sx} + c_3 x^2 e^{sx}, \qquad (117)$$

and so on if there are more than three equal real roots.

Equal complex roots are treated similarly. Thus two equal pairs,

$a \pm bi, a \pm bi$ lead to
$$(c_1 + c_2 x) e^{ax} \cos bx + (c_3 + c_4 x) e^{ax} \sin bx. \qquad (118)$$

We shall verify (117). Here the auxiliary equation may be written in the form $P(r)(r - s)^3 = 0$, where $P(r)$ is a polynomial in r. The same calculation that shows this proves that the differential equation may be written

$$P(D)(D - s)^3 y = 0. \tag{119}$$

But if we replace D by d/dx and expand we find that

$$(D - s)x^m e^{sx} = m x^{m-1} e^{sx} \qquad \text{so that } (D - s)e^{sx} = 0. \tag{120}$$

And by repeated use of the first relation,
$$(D - s)^2 x e^{sx} = (D - s)e^{sx} = 0,$$
$$(D - s)^3 x^2 e^{sx} = (D - s)^2 2x e^{sx} = 0. \tag{121}$$

These relations show that $x e^{sx}$ and $x^2 e^{sx}$ as well as e^{sx} are particular solutions of the differential equation (119) with three equal roots s. The verification of (116), (118), and other cases of equal roots is similar.

Consider next the general nonhomogeneous linear differential equation of order n, with constant coefficients, or

$$a_n \frac{d^n y}{dx^n} + a_{n-1} \frac{d^{n-1} y}{dx^{n-1}} + \cdots + a_1 \frac{dy}{dx} + a_0 y = \beta(x), \tag{122}$$

with $\beta(x)$ not identically zero. By Sec. 137 we may write the general solution of this equation by adding any *particular integral* to the *complementary function*. Methods of finding a particular integral will be given in Secs. 139 and 140. The complementary function of Eq. (122) is the general solution of Eq. (107), obtained by replacing the right member $\beta(x)$ by zero. Hence the complementary function is the sum on the right of Eq. (113), modified when necessary as indicated in Eqs. (115) to (118).

To illustrate our remarks we shall solve

$$\frac{d^5 y}{dx^5} - 4 \frac{d^4 y}{dx^4} + 13 \frac{d^3 y}{dx^3} = 12 e^{2x}. \tag{123}$$

The auxiliary equation is

$$r^5 - 4r^4 + 13r^3 = 0 \qquad \text{or} \qquad r^3(r^2 - 4r + 13) = 0. \tag{124}$$

This has three roots equal to 0 and a pair of complex roots $2 \pm \sqrt{-3}$ or $2 \pm 3i$. Hence, since $e^0 = 1$, the complementary function is found from Eqs. (117) and (115) to be

$$c_1 + c_2 x + c_3 x^2 + c_4 e^{2x} \cos 3x + c_5 e^{2x} \sin 3x. \tag{125}$$

We may find a particular integral by substituting $y = Ae^{2x}$ in Eq. (123). The result is

$$(2^5 - 4 \times 2^4 + 13 \times 2^3)Ae^{2x} = 72Ae^{2x} = 12e^{2x}. \quad (126)$$

This equation will hold if

$$72A = 12 \quad \text{or} \quad A = \tfrac{1}{6}. \quad (127)$$

Hence $\tfrac{1}{6}e^{2x}$ is a particular integral. And

$$y = \tfrac{1}{6}e^{2x} + c_1 + c_2x + c_3x^2 + c_4e^{2x}\cos 3x + c_5e^{2x}\sin 3x \quad (128)$$

is the general solution of Eq. (123).

139. Method of Undetermined Coefficients. In many practical cases the right member of Eq. (122), $\beta(x)$, is a sum of terms each of which is of the type

$$kx^m e^{ax}, \quad kx^m e^{ax}\cos bx, \quad \text{or} \quad kx^m e^{ax}\sin bx. \quad (129)$$

Here m is zero or a positive integer, and a and b are any real numbers. For example, as particular cases we have

$$3, \ 2x^3, \ 3e^{2x}, \ 5xe^{2x}, \ 4\cos 3x, \ 5x\sin 3x, \ 7e^x\sin x, \ 5xe^x\cos x. \quad (130)$$

In such cases a particular integral may be found by the method of undetermined coefficients, used to integrate functions of this type in Sec. 70. We consider separately the cases where $\beta(x)$ has a single term and where $\beta(x)$ is a sum of terms.

Case I. *A Single Term.* With any one term T of the type under consideration we associate the simplest polynomial in D, $Q(D)$ such that the differential relation $Q(D)T = 0$ holds. This is easily done by using in reverse the rules for forming the complementary function typified by Eqs. (113), (115) to (118). The polynomials associated with the terms of (130) are

$$D, D^4, (D - 2), (D - 2)^2, (D^2 + 9), (D^2 + 9)^2, (D^2 - 2D + 2),$$
$$(D^2 - 2D + 2)^2. \quad (131)$$

As these illustrate, $Q(D)$ will always be some power of a first- or second-degree factor. And we may write

$$Q(D) = F^q \quad \text{where } F = D - a \text{ or}$$
$$F = D^2 - 2aD + a^2 + b^2. \quad (132)$$

Now consider any particular integral I of Eq. (122), which we rewrite in the form $P(D)y = T(x)$. Since I is a solution of

$$P(D)y = T, \quad P(D)I = T. \quad \text{But} \quad Q(D)T = 0. \quad (133)$$

It follows that I is a solution of

$$Q(D)P(D)y = 0, \qquad \text{since } Q(D)P(D)I = Q(D)T = 0. \quad (134)$$

This enables us to predict the form of I.   Since any term that is in the solution of $P(D)y = 0$ is of no help in making $P(D)y = T$, we may assume I a linear combination with unknown coefficients of those terms in the solution of $Q(D)P(D)y = 0$ and not in the solution of $P(D)y = 0$.   This leads to the following rule:

Let the right member of (122) consist of a single term associated with the polynomial $Q(D) = F^q$.   If F is *not* a factor of $P(D)$, try

$$I = (Ax^{q-1} + Bx^{q-2} + \cdots + L)e^{ax}$$
$$\text{when } F = D - a, \quad (135)$$

and try

$$I = (Ax^{q-1} + Bx^{q-2} + \cdots + L)e^{ax} \cos bx$$
$$+ (Mx^{q-1} + Nx^{q-2} + \cdots + R)e^{ax} \sin bx$$
$$\text{when } F = D^2 - 2aD + a^2 + b^2. \quad (136)$$

If F *is* a factor of $P(D)$ and the highest power of F which is a divisor of $P(D)$ is F^p, try the

$$I \text{ of (135) or (136) multiplied by } x^p. \quad (137)$$

Case II.   *A Sum of Terms*.   With each term in $\beta(x)$ associate a polynomial $Q(D) = F^q$ as before.   Arrange in one group all terms that have the same F.   The particular integral of the given equation will be the sum of solutions of equations each of which has one group on the right.   For any one such equation, the form of the particular integral is given by Eqs. (135) to (137) where q is the highest power of F associated with any term of the group on the right.

For example, suppose that $\beta(x)$ consists of the sum of all the terms in (130).   From (131) we see that these fall into four separate groups, each made up of two consecutive terms.   And if $P(D)$ is not divisible by D, $(D - 2)$, $(D^2 + 9)$, or $(D^2 - 2D + 2)$ we try

$$Ax^3 + Bx^2 + Cx + D \qquad \text{for } 3 + 2x^3, \quad (138)$$
$$(Ax + B)e^{2x} \qquad \text{for } 3e^{2x} + 5xe^{2x}, \quad (139)$$
$$(Ax + B)\cos 3x + (Cx + D)\sin 3x \qquad \text{for } 4\cos 3x + 5x\sin 3x, \quad (140)$$
$$(Ax + B)e^x \cos x + (Cx + D)e^x \sin x$$
$$\text{for } 7e^x \sin x + 5xe^x \cos x. \quad (141)$$

On the other hand, if $P(D)$ were $D^2(D - 2)(D - 5)$ we would use

$$Ax^5 + Bx^4 + Cx^3 + Dx^2 \qquad \text{for } 3 + 2x^3, \qquad (142)$$
$$(Ax^2 + Bx)e^{2x} \qquad \text{for } 3e^{2x} + 5xe^{2x}, \qquad (143)$$

and (140) and (141) as before.

To illustrate a tabular form that minimizes the amount of writing, we work out two examples in detail.

EXAMPLE 1. $\dfrac{d^2y}{dx^2} + 4y = 8 \cos 2x.$ $\qquad\qquad\qquad (144)$

Here $Q = F = D^2 + 4$, and $P(D) = D^2 + 4$. Here $p = 1$ in (137), and $q = 1$, $a = 0$, $b = 2$ in (136) so that we try x times $A \cos 2x + B \sin 2x$. Thus,

4	$y =$	A	$x \cos 2x +$	B	$x \sin 2x$			
0	$\dfrac{dy}{dx} =$	$2B$	$-2A$			$+ A$	$\cos 2x +$	$B \sin 2x$
1	$\dfrac{d^2y}{dx^2} = -4A$		$-4B$		$+4B$	$-4A$		
Totals		0	0		4B	$-4A$		
Should be		0	0		8	0		

The coefficients of the given equation are written on the left, and these are multiplied into each column and the results added. Under these totals we write the coefficients in the right member, to which the totals should be equal if the equation is to hold. Hence

$$4B = 8, \qquad -4A = 0, \qquad \text{so that } B = 2, A = 0, \text{ and}$$
$$y = 2x \sin 2x \quad (145)$$

is a particular solution. The roots of the auxiliary equation,

$$r^2 + 4 = 0, \qquad r = \pm 2i \text{ lead to } c_1 \cos 2x + c_2 \sin 2x. \quad (146)$$

Consequently the general solution of (144) is

$$y = 2x \sin 2x + c_1 \cos 2x + c_2 \sin 2x. \qquad (147)$$

EXAMPLE 2. $\dfrac{d^3y}{dx^3} + \dfrac{d^2y}{dx^2} = 6e^{3x} + 6x^2 + 12x.$ $\qquad (148)$

Here there are two groups. For $6e^{3x}$, $Q = F = D - 3$, which is not a factor of $P(D) = D^3 + D^2$. Hence by (135) with $q = 1$, $a = 3$, we try

$$y = Ae^{3x}, \qquad (D^3 + D^2)Ae^{3x} = (3^3 + 3^2)Ae^{3x} = 36Ae^{3x} = 6e^{3x}.$$
$$(149)$$

It follows that

$$36A = 4, \qquad A = \tfrac{1}{9}, \tag{150}$$

and $\tfrac{1}{9}e^{3x}$ is a part of the particular integral.

For $6x^2$, $Q = D^3$, and for $12x$, $Q = D^2$. These form one group, for which (135) with $q = 3$, $a = 0$ suggests $Ax^2 + Bx + C$. However, $F = D$ and D^2 is a factor of $P(D) = D^3 + D^2$. Hence, we multiply by x^2, and try $Ax^4 + Bx^3 + Cx^2$. The tabular arrangement is

0	$y = A$	$x^4 +$ B	$x^3 +$ C	x^2	
0	$\dfrac{dy}{dx} =$	$4A$	$+ 3B$	$+ 2C$	x
1	$\dfrac{d^2y}{dx^2} =$		$12A$	$+ 6B$	$+2C$
1	$\dfrac{d^3y}{dx^3} =$			$24A$	$+6B$
Totals	0	0	$12A$	$6B + 24A$	$2C + 6B$
Should be	0	0	6	12	0

The totals will be as desired if

$$12A = 6, \qquad 6B + 24A = 12, \qquad 2C + 6B = 0, \qquad \text{or}$$
$$A = \tfrac{1}{2}, \qquad B = 0, \qquad C = 0. \tag{151}$$

It follows that $\tfrac{1}{2}x^4$ is a part of the particular integral.

The complementary function is found from

$$r^3 + r^2 = 0, \qquad r = 0, 0, -1, \text{ to be } c_1 + c_2x + c_3e^{-x}. \tag{152}$$

Adding our results, we find that the general solution of (148) is

$$y = \tfrac{1}{9}e^{3x} + \tfrac{1}{2}x^4 + c_1 + c_2x + c_3e^{-x}. \tag{153}$$

140. Method of Variation of Parameters. We may determine a particular integral of any linear differential equation (94), provided that we already know a fundamental system of solutions of the corresponding homogeneous equation (95). The process, due to Lagrange, is known as the *method of variation of parameters* because it depends on replacing the constants c_j in the complementary function by variables v_j. We first describe the process as applied to a particular case, namely, the equation

$$(1 - x^2)\frac{d^2y}{dx^2} + 2x\frac{dy}{dx} - 2y = 6(1 - x^2)^2. \tag{154}$$

Suppose we already know that the complementary function is

$$c_1x + c_2(1 + x^2). \tag{155}$$

Then we replace c_j by v_j and assume as the form of y

$$y = v_1x + v_2(1 + x^2). \tag{156}$$

We shall use primes to mean x derivatives. Then

$$y' = v_1'x + v_2'(1 + x^2) + v_1 + 2xv_2. \tag{157}$$

We equate the part of this containing v_1' and v_2' to zero,

$$xv_1' + (1 + x^2)v_2' = 0, \tag{158}$$

so that

$$y' = v_1 + 2xv_2 \quad \text{and} \quad y'' = v_1' + 2xv_2' + 2v_2. \tag{159}$$

On substituting from (156) and (159) in Eq. (154), we find

$$(1 - x^2)(v_1' + 2xv_2') = 6(1 - x^2)^2, \quad \text{or}$$
$$v_1' + 2xv_2' = 6(1 - x^2). \tag{160}$$

We now solve this and (158) as a pair of simultaneous equations of the first degree in v_1' and v_2'. The solution is

$$v_1' = 6 + 6x^2, \qquad v_2' = -6x. \tag{161}$$

Integration of these expressions gives

$$v_1 = 6x + 2x^3 + c_1, \qquad v_2 = -3x^2 + c_2. \tag{162}$$

These values, inserted in (156), lead to the general solution

$$y = 3x^2 - x^4 + c_1x + c_2(1 + x^2). \tag{163}$$

Now consider the general equation (94), or as in (103),

$$L(y) = \beta(x), \tag{164}$$

where $L(y)$ is defined by (95). Suppose we already know the complementary function,

$$\sum_{j=1}^{n} c_ju_j, \qquad \text{where } L(u_j) = 0. \tag{165}$$

We replace the c_j by variables v_j and impose the condition that the terms involving v_j' which appear in each of the first $n - 1$

derivatives of y add up to zero.   Then

$$y = \sum_{j=1}^{n} v_j u_j, \qquad y' = \sum_{j=1}^{n} v_j u_j', \qquad \text{since } \sum_{j=1}^{n} v_j' u_j = 0, \quad (166)$$

$$y'' = \sum_{j=1}^{n} v_j u_j'', \qquad \text{since } \sum_{j=1}^{n} v_j' u_j' = 0, \quad (167)$$

and so on down to

$$y^{(n-1)} = \sum_{j=1}^{n} v_j u_j^{(n-1)}, \qquad \text{since } \sum_{j=1}^{n} v_j' u_j^{(n-2)} = 0. \quad (168)$$

And for the nth derivative

$$y^{(n)} = \sum_{j=1}^{n} [v_j' u_j^{(n-1)} + v_j u_j^{(n)}]. \quad (169)$$

On substituting from Eqs. (166) to (169) in Eq. (164), we find

$$\sum_{j=1}^{n} v_j L(u_j) + a_n(x) \sum_{j=1}^{n} v_j' u_j^{(n-1)} = \beta(x). \quad (170)$$

In view of the second equation in (165) the terms in v_j drop out and

$$a_n(x) \sum_{j=1}^{n} v_j' u_j^{(n-1)} = \beta(x). \quad (171)$$

The $n - 1$ imposed conditions with right member zero [Eqs. (166) to (168)] together with this relation may be regarded as a set of n simultaneous equations of the first degree in the v_j'. The determinant of the system is $a_n(x)W(x)$. Since the Wronskian $W(x)$ of (100) is never zero for a fundamental system u_j, and $a_n(x)$ is not zero in any interval where Eq. (94) remains of the nth order, by Sec. 27 the simultaneous equations may be solved for the v_j'. We may then integrate to get the v_j. The first equation in (166) then provides a solution of our original equation. It will be the general solution if we keep the constants of integration in the v_j. If we omit these constants, we find a particular integral, which is all we needed to add to the known complementary function.

Suppose that we select the constants of integration in such a way that each $v_j = 0$ for $x = 0$. Then Eqs. (166) to (168) show that $y, y', y'', \cdots, y^{(n-1)}$ will each equal zero when $x = 0$.   And the solution found from (166) will satisfy these conditions. Thus, for example, the v_1 and v_2 of (162) are each zero when $x = 0$ if $c_1 = 0$ and $c_2 = 0$. Hence the result of putting these values in (163), $y = 3x^2 - x^4$ is the particular solution of (154) which is zero together with its first derivative when $x = 0$.

The method of variation of parameters could be used to find a particular integral of any linear equation with constant coefficients (122) after we have obtained the complementary function by the rules of Sec. 138. This procedure is useful in a few cases where $\beta(x)$ is not a sum of terms each of type (129). But the method of undetermined coefficients is preferable whenever it is applicable.

141. Simultaneous Differential Equations. We sometimes have to solve a system of linear differential equations with constant coefficients containing one independent variable, but more than one dependent variable. We illustrate a method of reducing the problem to an equation of type (122) by solving the system

$$2\frac{dx}{dt} + \frac{dy}{dt} + 5x + y = e^{3t},$$
$$3\frac{dx}{dt} + 2\frac{dy}{dt} + 9x + y = -2e^{3t}. \tag{172}$$

Replace d/dt by D, and rewrite the equations as

$$(2D + 5)x + (D + 1)y = e^{3t},$$
$$(3D + 9)x + (2D + 1)y = -2e^{3t}. \tag{173}$$

If D were a number, we could eliminate y by multiplying the first equation by $(2D + 1)$ and the second by $(D + 1)$ and then subtracting. This suggests that we form the new equations:

$$(2D + 1)(2D + 5)x + (2D + 1)(D + 1)y = (2D + 1)e^{3t} = 7e^{3t},$$
$$(D + 1)(3D + 9)x + (D + 1)(2D + 1)y = (D + 1)(-2e^{3t})$$
$$= -8e^{3t}, \tag{174}$$

where the simplified right members are obtained by recalling that D is d/dt. The terms in y are the same, so that on multiplying out the operators affecting x and subtracting, we find

$$(D^2 - 4)x = 15e^{3t}. \tag{175}$$

The complementary function is found from

$$r^2 - 4 = 0, \qquad r = 2, -2 \text{ to be } c_1e^{2t} + c_2e^{-2t}. \tag{176}$$

And on trying Ae^{3t} in Eq. (175) we find

$$(D^2 - 4)Ae^{3t} = 5Ae^{3t} = 15e^{3t}. \tag{177}$$

Hence $5A = 15$, $A = 3$, and $3e^{3t}$ is a particular integral. Consequently,

$$x = 3e^{3t} + c_1e^{2t} + c_2e^{-2t}. \tag{178}$$

If y were found by a similar process, it would seem to involve two new constants. If we substituted the value of x in either equation of (172) and solved for y, one apparently new constant would appear. But these additional constants are expressible in terms of c_1 and c_2 by relations that could be found by substituting the values of x and y in both equations of (172). It is simpler to eliminate dy/dt from the equations by multiplying the first equation by 2 and subtracting the second. The result is

$$\frac{dx}{dt} + x + y = 4e^{3t}, \qquad \text{or} \qquad y = 4e^{3t} - \frac{dx}{dt} - x. \tag{179}$$

By substituting the value (178) in the right member, we find

$$y = -8e^{3t} - 3c_1e^{2t} + c_2e^{-2t}. \tag{180}$$

To illustrate an alternative procedure, we outline the solution of the system (172) by the use of undetermined coefficients. Try $x = Ae^{3t}$, $y = Be^{3t}$ in the original equations. There results

$$(11A + 4B)e^{3t} = e^{3t}, \qquad (18A + 7B)e^{3t} = -2e^{3t}. \tag{181}$$

These will hold if

$$11A + 4B = 1, \qquad 18A + 7B = -2,$$
$$\text{from which } A = 3, \ B = -8. \tag{182}$$

This shows that $x = 3e^{3t}$, $y = -8e^{3t}$ is a particular solution. The complementary part of the solution may be found by trying

$$x = ae^{rt}, \qquad y = be^{rt} \tag{183}$$

in the homogeneous system, that is, Eqs. (172), or (173), with right members replaced by zero. This leads to

$$\left. \begin{array}{l} [(2r + 5)a + (r + 1)b]e^{rt} = 0 \\ [(3r + 9)a + (2r + 1)b]e^{rt} = 0 \end{array} \right\}$$

or

$$\left. \begin{array}{l} (2r + 5)a + (r + 1)b = 0 \\ (3r + 9)a + (2r + 1)b = 0 \end{array} \right\}. \tag{184}$$

By Sec. 27, for any r such that the determinant

$$\begin{vmatrix} 2r+5 & r+1 \\ 3r+9 & 2r+1 \end{vmatrix} = (2r+5)(2r+1) - (3r+9)(r+1)$$
$$= r^2 - 4 \tag{185}$$

was not equal to zero, these would have a unique solution for a and b, namely $a = 0$, $b = 0$. Since we seek a solution not identically zero, we must use a value of r for which

$$r^2 - 4 = 0, \qquad \text{that is, } r = 2 \text{ or } r = -2. \tag{186}$$

For either of these values, Eqs. (184) are equivalent to a single equation which determines the ratio of b to a as

$$\frac{b}{a} = -\frac{2r+5}{r+1} = -\frac{3r+9}{2r+1} = -3, \qquad \text{if } r = 2 \text{ and}$$
$$= 1 \text{ when } r = -2. \tag{187}$$

Let us write $a = c_1$ when $r = 2$. Then $b = -3c_1$, and

$$x = c_1 e^{2t}, \qquad y = -3c_1 e^{2t} \tag{188}$$

is one solution of the homogeneous system. And we write $a = c_2$ when $r = -2$. Then $b = c_2$ and a second solution is

$$x = c_2 e^{-2t}, \qquad y = c_2 e^{-2t}. \tag{189}$$

Adding the particular solution found from (182) to the complementary parts found in (188) and (189) gives

$$x = 3e^{3t} + c_1 e^{2t} + c_2 e^{-2t},$$
$$y = -8e^{3t} - 3c_1 e^{2t} + c_2 e^{-2t}. \tag{190}$$

This agrees with (178) and (180).

When the determinant in r equated to zero has multiple roots, or roots corresponding to exponentials that appear in one or more right members, the functions to be tried are no longer simple exponentials and it is better to fall back on the method of elimination. But such cases are rarely met. Systems with the right member zero, or sums of terms like $E_0 \sin (\omega t + \alpha)$, containing more than two equations occur in discussions of mechanical vibrations or of currents in electrical networks. It is customary here to replace $E_0 \sin (\omega t + \alpha)$ by $E_0 e^{i\alpha} e^{i\omega t}$, use undetermined coefficients to find the solution in complex form, and then take the imaginary part of the result as the solution of the original real problem.

142. References. For information on numerical methods we refer the reader to Bennett, Milne, Bateman, Ford, *Numerical Integration of Differential Equations*. Of the many texts on the formal solution of solvable types, A. R. Forsyth's *Treatise on Differential Equations* is still one of the most exhaustive.

An introduction to the theory of differential equations, including proofs of the existence of general solutions, is given in Chap. XV of the author's *Treatise on Advanced Calculus*. For a comprehensive theoretical treatment, the reader may consult *Ordinary Differential Equations*, by E. L. Ince.

EXERCISES IX

1. Plot the isoclines of $dy/dx = x^2 + y^2$ with slopes equal to $1, 1.2, 1.4, \cdots, 2.8, 3$ and use them to sketch a portion of the integral curve that passes through $(1,1)$.

Find the differential equation whose general solution is

2. $2x^2 + y^2 = c^2$. **3.** $y = cx^4$. **4.** $y^2 = 4cx$.

5. $cy = c^2x + 1$. **6.** $y^2 = cx^2 + c^2$. **7.** $x = cy + c^2xy$.

8. $y = c_1e^x + c_2e^{-x}$. **9.** $y = c_1 \sin x + c_2 \cos x$.

10. $y = c_1x^2 + c_2x^4$. **11.** $y = c_1 + c_2x + c_3x^2$.

Solve the separable differential equations:

12. $y^3dx + x^3dy = 0$. **13.** $\sec x \cos^2 y\, dx = \cos x \sin y\, dy$.

14. $x\, dx + y\, dy = xy(x\, dy - y\, dx)$. **15.** $e^{x-y}dx = e^{y-x}dy$.

16. Let $p = dy/dx$. Show that the solutions of $f(x,y,1/p) = 0$ cut the solutions of $f(x,y,p) = 0$ at right angles.

Use Prob. 16 to find the *orthogonal trajectories*, or curves that cut at right angles, the curves of each of the systems:

17. $y = cx^2$. **18.** $y = cx$. **19.** $x^2 + 3y^2 = c^2$.

The following equations are linear in y. Solve them.

20. $x\dfrac{dy}{dx} = 2(x + y)$. **21.** $\dfrac{dy}{dx} + y \tan x = \sec x$.

22. $x\dfrac{dy}{dx} = 3y + 6x$. **23.** $x\dfrac{dy}{dx} + y = 3x^2$.

The following equations are linear in x. Solve them.

24. $y\, dx = (x + 3y^4)dy$. **25.** $y\, dx = (3x + 12y)dy$.

Solve the following Bernoulli equations:

26. $x^3\dfrac{dy}{dx} + 2x^2y = y^3$. **27.** $x^2dy = y(x - y)dx$.

If $f(x,y)$ takes the form $0/0$ when $x = 0$, $y = 0$, the origin $O = (0,0)$ is a *singular point* of the differential equation $dy/dx = f(x,y)$. The expansion of the numerator and denominator of $f(x,y)$ in power series will in general start with first-order terms. We may sketch the form of the integral curves near O by dropping the higher order terms, and solving the resulting equation $\dfrac{dy}{dx} = \dfrac{Ax + By}{Cx + Dy}$ which is homogeneous. Solve, and sketch the curves near O for each of the following reduced equations:

28. $\dfrac{dy}{dx} = \dfrac{y}{x}$.   **29.** $\dfrac{dy}{dx} = \dfrac{2y}{x}$.   **30.** $\dfrac{dy}{dx} = -\dfrac{y}{x}$.

31. $\dfrac{dy}{dx} = -\dfrac{x}{y}$.   **32.** $\dfrac{dy}{dx} = -\dfrac{2x}{y}$.   **33.** $\dfrac{dy}{dx} = \dfrac{-x + y}{x + y}$.

Solve the following exact equations:

34. $(3x^2y - y^3)dx - (3y^2x - x^3)dy = 0$.
35. $\cos 2y\, dx - 2x \sin 2y\, dy = 0$.

Find the envelope of each given family of curves:

36. $x \cos c + y \sin c = 1$.   **37.** $(1 - c)x + cy = c - c^2$.
38. $x \sin c + y \cos c = \sin c \cos c$.   **39.** $x^2 + c^2y^2 = c$.
40. $y = cx - (1 + c^2)x^2$.   **41.** $cx^2 + (1 - c)y^2 = c - c^2$.

In each case solve the equivalent first-degree equations obtained by solving for $p = dy/dx$:

42. $p^2 + x(y + 1)p + x^2y = 0$.   **43.** $p^2 = 2px + 3x^2$.
44. $p^2y^2 = 1 + y^2$.   **45.** $p^2 + xy = (x + y)p$.
46. $xy(p^2 + 1) = (x^2 + y^2)p$.   **47.** $x^2p^2 + pxy = 2y^2$.

Solve the following Clairaut equations:

48. $y = px + 1 + p^2$.   **49.** $p^2 + y = px$.
50. $(y - px)^2 = p^3$.   **51.** $y + \log p = px$.

Reduce to Clairaut form by putting $y^2 = u$, and solve:

52. $p^2y + 2px = y$.   **53.** $y = 2px - 4p^2y$.

Reduce to Clairaut form by putting $x^2 = t$, and solve:

54. $x + 2py = p^2x$.   **55.** $xp^2 + 4x = 2py$.

The following equations have x absent. Solve them.

56. $y\dfrac{d^2y}{dx^2} + \left(\dfrac{dy}{dx}\right)^2 + 4 = 0$.   **57.** $\dfrac{d^2y}{dx^2} + \left(\dfrac{dy}{dx}\right)^2 + 9 = 0$.

58. $\dfrac{d^2y}{dx^2} = \left(1 + \left(\dfrac{dy}{dx}\right)^2\right)^{3/2}.$　　　**59.** $y\dfrac{d^2y}{dx^2} + \left(\dfrac{dy}{dx}\right)^2 = 0.$

60. $\dfrac{d^2y}{dx^2} = \left(\dfrac{dy}{dx}\right)^2.$　　　**61.** $\dfrac{d^2y}{dx^2} = \dfrac{1}{y^3}.$

The following equations have y absent.　Solve them.

62. $x\dfrac{d^2y}{dx^2} + x\left(\dfrac{dy}{dx}\right)^2 = \dfrac{dy}{dx}.$　　　**63.** $(1 + x^2)\dfrac{d^2y}{dx^2} + 1 + \left(\dfrac{dy}{dx}\right)^2 = 0.$

Use the procedure of Sec. 138 to solve:

64. $\dfrac{dy}{dx} = 4y.$　　　**65.** $\dfrac{d^2y}{dx^2} + 2\dfrac{dy}{dx} + 2y = 0.$

66. $\dfrac{d^2y}{dx^2} = \dfrac{dy}{dx} + 2y.$　　　**67.** $\dfrac{d^2y}{dx^2} + 3y = 4\dfrac{dy}{dx}.$

68. $\dfrac{d^2y}{dx^2} + y = 2\dfrac{dy}{dx}.$　　　**69.** $\dfrac{d^2y}{dx^2} + 5y = 2\dfrac{dy}{dx}.$

70. $\dfrac{d^2y}{dx^2} + 16y = 0.$　　　**71.** $\dfrac{d^4y}{dx^4} + 8\dfrac{d^2y}{dx^2} + 16y = 0.$

72. $\dfrac{d^3y}{dx^3} = 8y.$　　　**73.** $\dfrac{d^4y}{dx^4} + 3\dfrac{d^2y}{dx^2} = 4y.$

74. $\dfrac{d^4y}{dx^4} + 4\dfrac{d^2y}{dx^2} = 0.$　　　**75.** $\dfrac{d^5y}{dx^5} = \dfrac{dy}{dx}.$

Use the method of Sec. 139 to solve:

76. $\dfrac{dy}{dx} + 2x = 2y + 1.$　　　**77.** $\dfrac{dy}{dx} = y + e^x.$

78. $\dfrac{d^2y}{dx^2} + y = 4x + 4e^x.$　　　**79.** $\dfrac{d^2y}{dx^2} = 4y + 4e^{2x}.$

80. $\dfrac{d^2y}{dx^2} - 2\dfrac{dy}{dx} + 5y = 10\cos x.$　　　**81.** $\dfrac{d^3y}{dx^3} = 4\dfrac{dy}{dx} + 12x.$

82. $\dfrac{d^2y}{dx^2} - 9\dfrac{dy}{dx} + 20y = 4x^2e^{3x}.$　　　**83.** $\dfrac{d^4y}{dx^4} = y + x^3 + 3x.$

Solve as simultaneous each pair of equations:

84. $\dfrac{dx}{dt} = y + 1,\ \dfrac{dy}{dt} = x + 1.$　　　**85.** $\dfrac{d^2y}{dt^2} = 9x,\ \dfrac{d^2x}{dt^2} = 9y.$

86. $\dfrac{d^2x}{dt^2} = 3x + 4y,\ \dfrac{d^2y}{dt^2} + x + y = 0.$

87. $3\dfrac{dx}{dt} + 3x + 2y = e^t,\ 4x - 3\dfrac{dy}{dt} + 3y = 6t.$

88. $2\dfrac{d^2y}{dt^2} - \dfrac{dx}{dt} - 4y = 12t,\ 4\dfrac{dx}{dt} + 2\dfrac{dy}{dt} = 3x.$

Use the method of Sec. 140 to solve:

89. $\dfrac{d^2y}{dx^2} + y = \tan x.$ **90.** $\dfrac{d^2y}{dx^2} + y = \sec x.$

91. Show that the substitution $x = e^t$ transforms

$$k_n x^n \frac{d^n y}{dx^n} + k_{n-1} x^{n-1} \frac{d^{n-1}y}{dx^{n-1}} + \cdots + k_1 x \frac{dy}{dx} + k_0 y = K(x) \text{ into a linear}$$

equation with constant coefficients.   The original equation is known as *Euler's*, or *Cauchy's differential equation.*

Use Prob. 91 to solve the following equations:

92. $x^2 \dfrac{d^2y}{dx^2} - 4x \dfrac{dy}{dx} + 6y = 12x.$ **93.** $x^2 \dfrac{d^2y}{dx^2} + 2x \dfrac{dy}{dx} - 2y = 4x^2.$

94. $x^2 \dfrac{d^2y}{dx^2} - x \dfrac{dy}{dx} + y = x.$ **95.** $x^3 \dfrac{d^3y}{dx^3} + x \dfrac{dy}{dx} - y = x \log x.$

96. The *compound interest equation* is $dy/dx = ky$, where k is a positive or negative constant.   Show that $y = ce^{kx}$.   And if x_1, y_1 and x_2, y_2 are corresponding values, $y = y_1 e^{-kx_1} e^{kx}$, and $k = \dfrac{\log y_2 - \log y_1}{x_2 - x_1}$.   For applications, see Probs. 98 to 103.

97. If $dy/dx = Ay + B$, $A \neq 0$, show that $y = -B/A + ce^{Ax}$. For applications, see Probs. 104 to 107.

In each case, find the solution with the given initial value:

98. $dA = \dfrac{P}{100} A\, dt$, $A = A_0$ for $t = 0$.   Here A is the amount of money after t years, with interest at P per cent per annum continuously compounded.

99. $ds = -\dfrac{s}{V}\, dw$, $s = s_0$ for $w = 0$.   Here s is the amount of salt in a solution of volume V after an amount w of water has run through.

100. $dT = \mu T\, d\theta$, $T = T_0$ for $\theta = 0$.   Here T is the tension at angle θ in a rope wound around a snubbing post, with μ the coefficient of friction between the rope and the post.

101. $dp = -\rho dh = -kp\, dh$, $p = p_0$ for $h = 0$.   Here p is the pressure in the atmosphere at height h, with $\rho = kp$ the density.

102. $R \dfrac{dI}{dt} + \dfrac{1}{C} I = 0$, $I = I_0$ for $t = 0$.   Here I is the current t sec. after discharge of a condenser of capacity C through a circuit of resistance R.

103. $du = -ku\, dt$, $u = u_0$ for $t = 0$.   Here u is the amount of decomposing radium at time t, or untransformed substance in any *first-order chemical reaction.*

104. $dA = \dfrac{P}{100} A \, dt \pm F \, dt$, $A = A_0$ for $t = 0$. Here A is the amount in a fund, with interest as in Prob. 98, and continuous payments of F dollars per annum into or from the fund.

105. $dT = k(T_a - T)dt$, $T = T_0$ for $t = 0$. Here T is the temperature of a small object cooling in air at temperature T_a.

106. $L \dfrac{dI}{dt} + RI = E_0$, $I = I_0$ for $t = 0$. Here I is the current at time t in a circuit with inductance L and resistance R in series.

107. $\dfrac{dx}{dt} = k(A - x)$, $x = 0$ for $t = 0$. Here x is the amount of substance tranformed at time t in a *first-order chemical reaction*.

108. $\dfrac{dx}{dt} = k(A - x)(B - x)$, $A \neq B$, $x = 0$ for $t = 0$. Here x is the amount of substance transformed at time t in a *second-order chemical reaction*. The equation is *not* linear but is separable.

109. If $\dfrac{d^2s}{dt^2} = -\omega^2 s$, $\omega \neq 0$, show that $s = c_1 \cos \omega t + c_2 \sin \omega t$. Derive the alternative form $s = C_1 \sin (\omega t + C_2)$, which shows that the solution is a *simple harmonic motion*. Also deduce from the first form that if $s = s_0$, $v = \dfrac{ds}{dt} = v_0$ at $t = 0$, $s = s_0 \cos \omega t + \dfrac{v_0}{\omega} \sin \omega t$.

110. Given $\dfrac{d^2y}{dx^2} + 2A \dfrac{dy}{dx} + (A^2 + B^2)y = K \sin \omega x$, $A \neq 0$, $B \neq 0$, find the solution with $y = 0$, $dy/dx = 0$ when $x = 0$. This equation is met in the study of electric circuits, where if $I = \dfrac{dq}{dt}$, for the charge q $L \dfrac{d^2q}{dt^2} + R \dfrac{dq}{dt} + \dfrac{q}{C} = E_0 \sin \omega t$, as well as in the study of forced mechanical vibrations where $m \dfrac{d^2s}{dt^2} + \beta \dfrac{ds}{dt} + ks = F_0 \sin \omega t$.

111. The equation $\dfrac{d^2y}{dx^2} = \pm n^2 y + Ax^2 + Bx + C$ is a type encountered in studying small deflections of beams ($n = 0$), columns under compression (minus sign), or members under tension (plus sign). Find the general solution for each of the three cases.

112. The equations for the *catenary*, or curve of equilibrium of a hanging chain or heavy flexible cable, take the form $d(T \cos \tau) = 0$, $d(T \sin \tau) = w \, ds$, where $\tan \tau = \dfrac{dy}{dx}$. Hence $T \cos \tau = H$, a constant, and if $a = \dfrac{H}{w}$, $a \dfrac{d^2y}{dx^2} = \left[1 + \left(\dfrac{dy}{dx} \right)^2 \right]^{\frac{1}{2}}$. If $p = \dfrac{dy}{dx} = 0$ at x_0, y_0, deduce $a \sinh^{-1} p = x - x_0$, and hence $y = y_0 + a \cosh \dfrac{x - x_0}{a} - a$.

113. In the equation of motion with t absent, $m \dfrac{d^2s}{dt^2} = F(s)$, put $v = \dfrac{ds}{dt}$ and deduce that $m \dfrac{v^2}{2} - m \dfrac{v_0^2}{2} = \displaystyle\int_{s_0}^{s} F(s)\,ds$. This is the energy relation.

Compare Probs. 55 and 56 of Exercises VI (page 269) and Eq. (33) of Sec. 106.

114. The equation of motion $m \dfrac{d^2s}{dt^2} = f\left(\dfrac{ds}{dt}\right)$ has s and t both absent. Put $v = ds/dt$ and deduce that if $v = v_0$ and $s = 0$ when $t = 0$, then $t = m \displaystyle\int_{v_0}^{v} \dfrac{dv}{f(v)}$ and $s = m \displaystyle\int_{v_0}^{v} \dfrac{v\,dv}{f(v)}$.

Complete the solutions in Prob. 114, and in the case of Probs. 115 to 117 check by using Sec. 139, if $f(v)$ is

115. $-\alpha$.   **116.** $-\beta v$.   **117.** $-\alpha - \beta v$.

118. $-\beta v^2$.   **119.** $\beta(v^2 - V^2)$, $v_0 < V$.   **120.** $-\beta(v^2 + V^2)$.

CHAPTER X

LEGENDRE POLYNOMIALS AND BESSEL FUNCTIONS

Many problems of mathematical physics lead to linear differential equations of the second order. It is sometimes useful to obtain special solutions of such equations in the form of series of powers. The general solution may then be expressed in terms of the special solutions. We first present this as a general method. We apply the process to Legendre's differential equation and study some of the properties of the special solutions known as *Legendre polynomials*. We apply a modification of the process to Bessel's differential equation and discuss the particular solutions which are known as *Bessel functions*. Finally we describe certain general classes of differential equations whose solutions may be expressed simply in terms of Bessel's functions.

143. Second-order Linear Differential Equations. The linear differential equation of the second order is

$$a_2(x) \frac{d^2y}{dx^2} + a_1(x) \frac{dy}{dx} + a_0(x)y = \beta(x). \tag{1}$$

The corresponding homogeneous equation is

$$L(y) = a_2(x) \frac{d^2y}{dx^2} + a_1(x) \frac{dy}{dx} + a_0(x)y = 0. \tag{2}$$

Here, as in Sec. 137, $L(y)$ denotes the left member of Eq. (1).

Whenever a single solution of (2) is known, the general solution of (2) may be found as follows. Let $u(x)$ be the known solution. Then, using primes to denote differentiation with respect to x,

$$L(u) = a_2(x)u'' + a_1(x)u' + a_0(x)u = 0. \tag{3}$$

Put $y = uv$, so that

$$y' = uv' + u'v, \quad \text{and} \quad y'' = uv'' + 2u'v' + u''v. \tag{4}$$

It follows that

$$L(y) = L(uv) = vL(u) + a_2(x)(uv'' + 2u'v') + a_1(x)uv'. \tag{5}$$

371

In view of Eq. (3), $L(u) = 0$ and the term $vL(u)$ drops out. Hence $y = uv$ will be a solution of $L(y) = 0$, provided that

$$a_2(x)uv'' + [2a_2(x)u' + a_1(x)u]v' = 0. \tag{6}$$

This will hold if

$$\frac{v''}{v'} = -2\frac{u'}{u} - \frac{a_1(x)}{a_2(x)}, \qquad \text{or if}$$

$$\log v' = -2 \log u - \int \frac{a_1(x)}{a_2(x)} dx. \tag{7}$$

Let us define a function $A(x)$ by the relation

$$A(x) = e^{\int_{x_0}^{x} \frac{a_1(x)}{a_2(x)} dx}, \qquad \text{or} \qquad \log A(x) = \int_{x_0}^{x} \frac{a_1(x)}{a_2(x)} dx. \tag{8}$$

Then the indefinite integral in (7) differs from this definite integral only by a constant which we write as a logarithm. Thus

$$\log v' = -2 \log u - \log A(x) + \log c_1 \qquad \text{and}$$

$$v' = \frac{c_1}{u^2 A(x)}. \tag{9}$$

A second integration gives $v = c_1 \int_{x_1}^{x} \frac{dx}{u^2 A(x)} + c_2$. Hence,

$$y = uv = c_1 u \int_{x_1}^{x} \frac{dx}{u^2 A(x)} + c_2 u \tag{10}$$

is a solution of $L(y) = 0$. It is the general solution that we were seeking.

Given one particular solution u of Eq. (2), we need merely calculate $A(x)$ from Eq. (8) and then U from

$$U = u \int_{x_1}^{x} \frac{dx}{u^2 A(x)} \tag{11}$$

to obtain a second particular solution.

If we wish to solve Eq. (1) and know one solution of Eq. (2), we first find U from Eq. (11) and may then complete the solution of (1) by the method of variation of parameters given in Sec. 140. To recapitulate our results, the general solution of any linear differential equation of the second order may be found whenever we know one solution of the corresponding homogeneous equation.

144. Regular Solutions. If a differential equation has a solution that is analytic at $x = 0$, the solution has an expansion in powers of x of the form

$$y = b_0 + b_1x + b_2x^2 + \cdots + b_mx^m + \cdots . \qquad (12)$$

Suppose that the coefficients in the differential equation are either polynomials or can themselves be expanded in ascending powers of x. Then the values of the b_j in (12) may be found by using undetermined coefficients. That is, we substitute the assumed expansion (12) in the differential equation and determine the b_j so that the resulting equation holds.

For example, consider

$$x \frac{d^2y}{dx^2} - \frac{dy}{dx} + 4x^3y = 0 \qquad \text{or} \qquad xy'' - y' + 4x^3y = 0. \qquad (13)$$

From the assumed form of solution (12) we calculate

$$y' = b_1 + 2b_2x + 3b_3x^2 + \cdots + mb_mx^{m-1} + \cdots , \qquad (14)$$
$$y'' = 2b_2 + 6b_3x + 12b_4x^2 + \cdots$$
$$+ m(m - 1)b_mx^{m-2} + \cdots . \qquad (15)$$

Next multiply by the coefficients of Eq. (13).

$$xy'' = \qquad 2b_2x + 6b_3x^2 + 12b_4x^3 + \cdots$$
$$+ m(m - 1)b_mx^{m-1} + \cdots , \qquad (16)$$
$$-y' = -b_1 - 2b_2x - 3b_3x^2 - 4b_4x^3 - \cdots$$
$$- mb_mx^{m-1} - \cdots , \qquad (17)$$
$$4x^3y = \qquad 4b_0x^3 + \cdots$$
$$+ 4b_{m-4}x^{m-1} + \cdots . \qquad (18)$$

The series (12) will be a solution of (13) if the series obtained by adding the three series just written has all its coefficients zero. That is,

$$-b_1 = 0, \qquad 3b_3 = 0, \qquad 8b_4 + 4b_0 = 0, \qquad \cdots . \qquad (19)$$

For greater subscripts the general relation is

$$(m^2 - 2m)b_m + 4b_{m-4} = 0 \qquad \text{or} \qquad b_m = -\frac{4}{m(m - 2)} b_{m-4},$$
$$m > 3. \qquad (20)$$

An arbitrary value given to b_0 determines

$$b_4 = -\frac{b_0}{2}, \qquad b_8 = -\frac{b_4}{12} = \frac{b_0}{2 \cdot 3 \cdot 4}, \qquad \cdots ,$$
$$b_{4m} = \frac{(-1)^m}{(2m)!} b_0. \qquad (21)$$

Similarly an arbitrary value given to b_2 determines

$$b_6 = -\frac{b_2}{6}, \qquad b_{10} = -\frac{b_6}{20} = \frac{b_0}{2 \cdot 3 \cdot 4 \cdot 5}, \qquad \cdots,$$

$$b_{4m+2} = \frac{(-1)^m b_2}{(2m+1)!}. \quad (22)$$

The first two equations in (19) show that $b_1 = 0$ and $b_3 = 0$. These values and Eq. (20) determine successively

$$b_5 = 0, \qquad \cdots, \qquad b_{4m+1} = 0; \qquad b_7 = 0, \qquad \cdots,$$

$$b_{4m+3} = 0. \quad (23)$$

The result of substituting the values found in Eqs. (21) to (23) in the expression for the solution (12) is

$$y = b_0 \left[1 - \frac{x^4}{2} + \frac{x^8}{4!} - \cdots + \frac{(-1)^m x^{4m}}{(2m)!} + \cdots \right]$$
$$+ b_2 \left[x^2 - \frac{x^6}{3!} + \cdots + \frac{(-1)^m x^{4m+2}}{(2m+1)!} + \cdots \right]. \quad (24)$$

This is a solution of Eq. (13). It is the general solution, and each of the brackets is one particular solution. Usually when we use the method of series, the values of the solutions must be calculated from the series. In this case, however, the series are recognizable as the expansions of simple functions and (24) is equivalent to

$$y = b_0 \cos x^2 + b_2 \sin x^2. \quad (25)$$

145. Legendre's Differential Equation. Let us attempt to find regular solutions of *Legendre's differential equation*

$$(1 - x^2) \frac{d^2y}{dx^2} - 2x \frac{dy}{dx} + n(n+1)y = 0, \quad (26)$$

in which the parameter n is a real constant. Assume a solution (12), deduce (14) and (15), and multiply in the coefficients of (26). Then

$$y'' = 2b_2 + 6b_3 x + 12b_4 x^2 + \cdots$$
$$+ m(m-1)b_m x^{m-2} + \cdots, \quad (27)$$

$$-x^2 y'' = \qquad - 2b_2 x^2 - \cdots$$
$$- (m-2)(m-3)b_{m-2} x^{m-2} + \cdots, \quad (28)$$

$$-2xy' = \qquad - 2b_1 x - 4b_2 x^2 - \cdots$$
$$- 2(m-2)b_{m-2} x^{m-2} + \cdots, \quad (29)$$

$$n(n + 1)y = n(n + 1)b_0 + n(n + 1)b_1x + n(n + 1)b_2x^2$$
$$+ \cdots + n(n + 1)b_{m-2}x^{m-2} + \cdots . \quad (30)$$

On summing these series and equating each of the coefficients of the resulting series to zero we find

$$2b_2 + n(n + 1)b_0 = 0, \qquad 6b_3 + (n^2 + n - 2)b_1 = 0,$$
$$12b_4 + (n^2 + n - 6)b_2 = 0, \cdots . \quad (31)$$

For greater subscripts the general relation is

$$m(m - 1)b_m + [n^2 + n - (m - 2)(m - 1)]b_{m-2} = 0, \quad m > 1. \quad (32)$$

This may be written

$$b_m = -\frac{(n - m + 2)(n + m - 1)}{m(m - 1)}b_{m-2}. \quad (33)$$

An arbitrary value given to b_0 determines

$$b_2 = -\frac{n(n + 1)}{2}b_0, \qquad b_4 = -\frac{(n - 2)(n + 3)}{12}b_2$$
$$= \frac{n(n - 2)(n + 1)(n + 3)}{1 \cdot 2 \cdot 3 \cdot 4}b_0, \cdots . \quad (34)$$

And an arbitrary value given to b_1 determines

$$b_3 = -\frac{(n - 1)(n + 2)}{6}b_1, \qquad b_5 = -\frac{(n - 3)(n + 4)}{20}b_3$$
$$= \frac{(n - 1)(n - 3)(n + 2)(n + 4)}{2 \cdot 3 \cdot 4 \cdot 5}b_1, \cdots . \quad (35)$$

With these values, the assumed solution (12) becomes

$$y = b_0\left[1 - \frac{n(n + 1)}{2!}x^2 + \frac{n(n - 2)(n + 1)(n + 3)}{4!}x^4 - \cdots\right]$$
$$+ b_1\left[x - \frac{(n - 1)(n + 2)}{3!}x^3 + \frac{(n - 1)(n - 3)(n + 2)(n + 4)}{5!}x^5\right.$$
$$\left. - \cdots\right]. \quad (36)$$

Each of the series in brackets is a particular solution. The coefficient of y'' in Legendre's equation is $(1 - x^2)$. Because this is not zero in the interval $-1 < x < 1$, each of the particular series just found converges in this interval. And for $|x| < 1$, Eq. (36) gives the general solution of (26).

When n is a positive integer, or zero, one of the series in brackets reduces to a polynomial. For the factor $n - m + 2$ in Eq. (33) is zero if $m = n + 2$. This makes $b_{n+2} = 0$. Hence $b_{n+4}, b_{n+6}, \cdots$, all vanish. Thus, if n is an odd integer, the bracket multiplying b_1 in (36) is a polynomial of degree n. Similarly, if n is an even integer (or zero), the bracket multiplying b_0 in (36) is a polynomial of degree n (or a constant). In

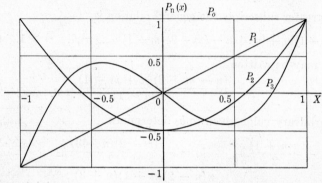

Legendre polynomials.
FIG. 140.

either case the other bracket is not a polynomial but an infinite series.

The bracket that gives the polynomial solution, multiplied by such a constant that its value is 1 when $x = 1$, is called the *nth Legendre polynomial* and is denoted by $P_n(x)$. The first few polynomials are

$$P_0(x) = 1, \qquad P_1(x) = x, \qquad P_2(x) = \tfrac{3}{2}x^2 - \tfrac{1}{2},$$
$$P_3(x) = \tfrac{5}{2}x^3 - \tfrac{3}{2}x. \quad (37)$$

An expression for $P_n(x)$ in descending powers is

$$P_n(x) = \frac{(2n-1)(2n-3)\cdots 3\cdot 1}{n!}\left[x^n - \frac{n(n-1)}{2(2n-1)}x^{n-2}\right.$$
$$\left. + \frac{n(n-1)(n-2)(n-3)}{2\cdot 4(2n-1)(2n-3)}x^{n-4} - \cdots\right]. \quad (38)$$

Rodrigues's formula for $P_n(x)$,

$$P_n(x) = \frac{1}{2^n n!}\frac{d^n(x^2-1)^n}{dx^n}, \quad (39)$$

is proved in Prob. 21.

146. Zonal Harmonics. Any solution of Laplace's equation

$$\nabla^2 U = \frac{\partial^2 U}{\partial x^2} + \frac{\partial^2 U}{\partial y^2} + \frac{\partial^2 U}{\partial z^2} = 0 \tag{40}$$

is called a *harmonic function*. Several properties of such functions were discussed in Probs. 58 to 65 of Exercises VIII (page 332). In spherical polar coordinates, Laplace's equation is

$$\frac{1}{r^2} \frac{\partial}{\partial r} \left(r^2 \frac{\partial U}{\partial r} \right) + \frac{1}{r^2 \sin \phi} \frac{\partial}{\partial \phi} \left(\sin \phi \frac{\partial U}{\partial \phi} \right)$$
$$+ \frac{1}{r^2 \sin^2 \phi} \frac{\partial^2 U}{\partial \theta^2} = 0, \quad (41)$$

by Eq. (110) of Sec. 124. $U = 1/r = 1/|OP|$ is a solution of this equation. Since changing the origin does not affect the form of Eq. (40), $1/|AP|$ is a harmonic function where $|AP|$ is the distance from any fixed point A to the variable point $P = (x,y,z)$. Let A be the point at which $r = 1$, $\phi = 0$. Then the distance AP is, by the law of cosines,

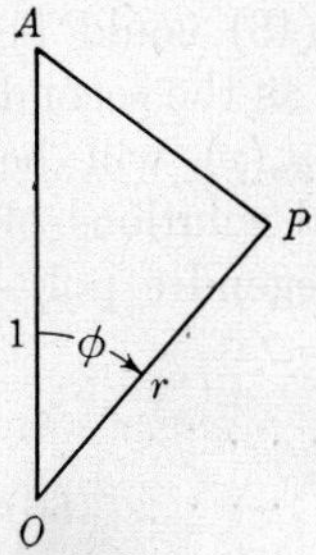

$$AP = \sqrt{1 + r^2 - 2r \cos \phi}. \tag{42}$$

It follows that the reciprocal of this is a solution of Eq. (41). If we put $x = \cos \phi$, our result is that

$$U = \frac{1}{\sqrt{1 + r^2 - 2rx}} = (1 - 2rx + r^2)^{-\frac{1}{2}} \tag{43}$$

is a solution of

$$\frac{1}{r^2} \frac{\partial}{\partial r} \left(r^2 \frac{\partial U}{\partial r} \right) + \frac{1}{r^2} \frac{\partial}{\partial x} (1 - x^2) \frac{\partial U}{\partial x} = 0. \tag{44}$$

Suppose that this equation has a solution of the special form $U = r^n y(x)$. Then

$$\frac{\partial U}{\partial r} = n r^{n-1} y \quad \text{and} \quad \frac{\partial U}{\partial x} = r^n y'. \tag{45}$$

And since Eq. (44) is satisfied,

$$n(n + 1)r^{n-2}y + r^{n-2} \frac{d}{dx} [(1 - x^2)y'] = 0. \tag{46}$$

Fig. 141.

If we carry out the differentiation and divide by r^{n-2}, we find

$$(1 - x^2)y'' - 2xy' + n(n + 1)y = 0, \qquad (47)$$

which is Legendre's equation.

Next expand the U of Eq. (43) in ascending powers of r,

$$U = y_0(x) + y_1(x)r + y_2(x)r^2 + \cdots + y_n(x)r^n + \cdots. \quad (48)$$

This series converges for $|r| < 1$ if $-1 \leqq x \leqq 1$. But for $x = 1$,

$$U = (1 - 2r + r^2)^{-\frac{1}{2}} = (1 - r)^{-1} = 1 + r + r^2 + \cdots$$
$$+ r^n + \cdots. \quad (49)$$

Hence $y_n(1) = 1$. Substituting Eq. (48) in (44) gives a true equation. Since the different powers of r cannot combine, each term separately is a solution of (44), and $y_n(x)$ is a solution of Eq. (47). Finally we note that the expansion (48) could be found from the binomial theorem, with $-2rx + r^2$ as the second term of the binomial. Hence the coefficients $y_n(x)$ will be polynomials in x. Since they are the polynomial solutions of (47) which equal 1 when $x = 1$, they are the Legendre polynomials, and

$$(1 - 2rx + r^2)^{-\frac{1}{2}} = P_0(x) + P_1(x)r + P_2(x)r^2 + \cdots$$
$$+ P_n(x)r^n + \cdots. \quad (50)$$

The Legendre polynomials are sometimes called *Legendre coefficients*, that is, the coefficients of powers of r in (50). They are also called *zonal harmonics*, because they are helpful in the problem of finding a harmonic function with values given on a spherical zone.

147. Bessel Functions of the First Kind. *Bessel's differential equation* is

$$x^2 \frac{d^2y}{dx^2} + x \frac{dy}{dx} + (x^2 - p^2)y = 0. \qquad (51)$$

The parameter p is either zero or a positive constant. We refer to (51) as Bessel's equation of order p. When p is an integer, Eq. (51) has one particular solution of the form (12). We may obtain solutions that hold for fractional as well as integral values of p by using the more general form

$$y = x^c(b_0 + b_1x + b_2x^2 + \cdots)$$
$$= b_0x^c + b_1x^{c+1} + b_2x^{c+2} + \cdots. \qquad (52)$$

By differentiating this, we find that

$$y' = cb_0x^{c-1} + (c+1)b_1x^c + (c+2)b_2x^{c+1} + \cdots, \quad (53)$$
$$y'' = c(c-1)b_0x^{c-2} + (c+1)cb_1x^{c-1} + (c+2)(c+1)b_2x^c + \cdots. \quad (54)$$

On multiplying by the coefficients of (51), we find that the lowest power of x present is x^c. And the sum of the terms in x^c is

$$c(c-1)b_0x^c + cb_0x^c - p^2b_0x^c = (c^2 - p^2)b_0x^c. \quad (55)$$

This must be zero, and for a solution of the form (52) with $b_0 \neq 0$, we must have

$$c^2 = p^2, \quad c = p \quad \text{or} \quad c = -p. \quad (56)$$

We recall that $p \geqq 0$, and consider first the case $c = p$. Then on replacing c by p in Eqs. (52) to (54), and multiplying by the coefficients of (51), we find

$$x^2y'' = p(p-1)b_0x^p + (p+1)pb_1x^{p+1} + (p+2)(p+1)b_2x^{p+2} + \cdots, \quad (57)$$
$$xy' = pb_0x^p + (p+1)b_1x^{p+1} + (p+2)b_2x^{p+2} + \cdots, \quad (58)$$
$$x^2y = b_0x^{p+2} + \cdots, \quad (59)$$
$$-p^2y = -p^2b_0x^p - p^2b_1x^{p+1} - p^2b_2x^{p+2} + \cdots. \quad (60)$$

On adding these series and equating the coefficient of each power of x in the sum to zero, we find

$$[(p+1)^2 - p^2]b_1 = 0, \quad [(p+2)^2 - p^2]b_2 + b_0 = 0, \quad \cdots. \quad (61)$$

The general relation for higher powers, obtained from the term in x^{p+m} is

$$[(p+m)^2 - p^2]b_m + b_{m-2} = 0, \quad m > 1. \quad (62)$$

This may be written

$$b_m = -\frac{b_{m-2}}{m(2p+m)}. \quad (63)$$

An assumed value of b_0 determines in succession

$$b_2 = -\frac{b_0}{2(2p+2)}, \quad b_4 = -\frac{b_2}{4(2p+4)} = \frac{b_0}{2 \cdot 4(2p+2)(2p+4)}, \quad (64)$$

and

$$b_{2k} = \frac{(-1)^k b_0}{2 \cdot 4 \cdot 6 \cdots (2k)(2p+2)(2p+4) \cdots (2p+2k)}$$
$$= \frac{(-1)^k b_0}{2^{2k} k! (p+1)(p+2) \cdots (p+k)} = \frac{(-1)^k b_0 \Gamma(p+1)}{2^{2k} k! \Gamma(p+k+1)}, \quad (65)$$

by Eq. (13) of Sec. 97 with p, n replaced by $p+1$, $k+1$.

The first equation in (61) is

$$[(p+1)^2 - p^2]b_1 = 0, \quad \text{or} \quad (2p+1)b_1 = 0. \quad (66)$$

Since $p \geqq 0$, $2p+1 > 0$, and this relation can hold only if $b_1 = 0$. It then follows from the relation (63) that

$$b_1 = 0, \qquad b_3 = 0, \qquad b_5 = 0, \qquad \cdots b_{2k+1} = 0, \qquad \cdots . \quad (67)$$

With c replaced by p and the terms with zero coefficients omitted, the solution (52) reduces to

$$y = b_0 x^p + b_2 x^{p+2} + b_4 x^{p+4} + \cdots + b_{2k} x^{p+2k} + \cdots . \quad (68)$$

This is a solution of Eq. (51) if b_{2k} is determined in terms of b_0 by Eq. (65). The *Bessel function* $J_p(x)$ is obtained by choosing

$$b_0 = \frac{1}{2^p \Gamma(p+1)}, \qquad \text{so that } b_{2k} = \frac{(-1)^k}{2^{p+2k} k! \Gamma(p+k+1)}. \quad (69)$$

Consequently, we may write

$$J_p(x) = \sum_{k=0}^{\infty} (-1)^k \frac{x^{p+2k}}{2^{p+2k} k! \Gamma(p+k+1)} = \sum_{k=0}^{\infty} \frac{(-1)^k (x/2)^{p+2k}}{k! \Gamma(p+k+1)}. \quad (70)$$

The simplification of the last form written was the reason for the choice of b_0 made in Eq. (69). We note that $0! = 1$.

When $p = n$, a positive integer or zero, we may replace $\Gamma(n+k+1)$ by $(n+k)!$. For example,

$$J_0(x) = 1 - \frac{x^2}{2^2} + \frac{x^4}{2^4 (2!)^2} - \frac{x^6}{2^6 (3!)^2} + \frac{x^8}{2^8 (4!)^2} - \cdots . \quad (71)$$

$$J_1(x) = \frac{x}{2} - \frac{x^3}{2^3 2!} + \frac{x^5}{2^5 2! 3!} - \frac{x^7}{2^7 3! 4!} + \frac{x^9}{2^9 4! 5!} - \cdots . \quad (72)$$

A solution of Eq. (51) which is finite for $x = 0$ is called a Bessel function of the first kind of order p. It can differ by a constant factor only from $J_p(x)$. The function $J_p(x)$ of Eq. (70) is referred to as the Bessel function of order p of the first kind.

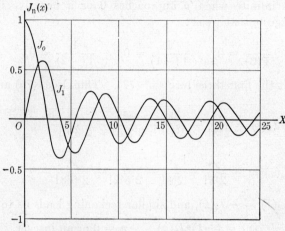

Bessel functions of the first kind.
Fig. 142.

148. Bessel Functions of the Second Kind. When p is not zero or an integer, the function

$$J_{-p}(x) = \sum_{k=0}^{\infty} (-1)^k \frac{x^{-p+2k}}{2^{-p+2k}k!\,\Gamma(-p+k+1)}, \tag{73}$$

obtained from (70) by replacing p by $-p$, is a second solution of (51). Hence for nonintegral values of p,

$$y = c_1 J_p(x) + c_2 J_{-p}(x), \qquad p \neq 0 \text{ or an integer,} \tag{74}$$

is the general solution of Eq. (51).

To see why we excepted integral values of p, let us study a particular case, $p = 3$. For $p = 3$, Eq. (70) becomes

$$J_3(x) = \frac{x^3}{2^3\Gamma(4)} - \frac{x^5}{2^5 1!\,\Gamma(5)} + \frac{x^7}{2^7 2!\,\Gamma(6)} - \cdots . \tag{75}$$

And, formally, for $p = -3$ we have

$$J_{-3}(x) = \frac{x^{-3}}{2^{-3}\Gamma(-2)} - \frac{x^{-1}}{2^{-1}1!\,\Gamma(-1)} + \frac{x}{2\ 2!\,\Gamma(0)} - \frac{x^3}{2^3 3!\,\Gamma(1)} + \cdots . \tag{76}$$

By Sec. 97, Eq. (9),

$$\Gamma(1) = 1, \qquad \Gamma(2) = 1, \qquad \Gamma(3) = 2!, \qquad \Gamma(4) = 3!, \text{ etc.} \quad (77)$$

And we deduced from Eq. (13) or Fig. 117 of Sec. 97 that $\Gamma(p)$ becomes infinite when p approaches 0 or a negative integer. This suggests that we set

$$\frac{1}{\Gamma(0)} = 0, \qquad \frac{1}{\Gamma(-1)} = 0, \qquad \frac{1}{\Gamma(-2)} = 0, \quad (78)$$

and omit the first three terms of (77). Thus Eqs. (75) and (76) become

$$J_3(x) = \frac{x^3}{2^3 3!} - \frac{x^5}{2^5 4!} + \frac{x^7}{2^7 2! 5!} - \frac{x^9}{2^9 3! 6!} + \cdots \quad (79)$$

and

$$J_{-3}(x) = -\frac{x^3}{2^3 3!} + \frac{x^5}{2^5 4!} - \frac{x^7}{2^7 5! 2!} + \frac{x^9}{2^9 6! 3!} - \cdots \quad (80)$$

Thus $J_{-3}(x) = -J_3(x)$, and similar reckoning leads us to write

$$J_{-n}(x) = (-1)^n J_n(x), \qquad n = 0 \text{ or an integer.} \quad (81)$$

This relation is the definition of $J_{-n}(x)$ when n is a positive integer. It then holds when n is a negative integer and is an identity for $n = 0$. It may be proved that (81) and (73) together make $J_{-p}(x)$ a continuous function of p for any fixed positive value of x. We note that for integral or zero values of the subscript, $J_{-p}(x)$ is a function of the first kind.

When the parameter p is an integer n, or zero, a second solution of the differential equation (51) can be found in terms of $J_n(x)$ by using Eqs. (8) and (11). Here $a_1(x) = x$, $a_2(x) = x^2$. Hence with $x_0 = 1$,

$$\log A(x) = \int_1^x \frac{a_1(x)}{a_2(x)} \, dx = \int_1^x \frac{dx}{x} = \log x, \qquad A(x) = x. \quad (82)$$

And a second solution is given by

$$U = J_n(x) \int_{x_1}^x \frac{dx}{x J_n^2}. \quad (83)$$

By Eq. (70) the leading term in the power series expansion of $J_n(x)$ is x^n. Hence $x J_n^2$ has a power series expansion starting with x^{2n+1}. And the integrand of (83) may be expanded in ascending integral powers starting with x^{-2n-1}. That is,

$$\frac{1}{xJ_n{}^2} = c_0x^{-2n-1} + c_1x^{-2n} + \cdots + c_{2n}x^{-1} + \cdots . \quad (84)$$

The integral of this series will start with a term in x^{-2n}. And the term in x^{-1} will give rise to a logarithm. Thus there is a second solution of the form

$$y = aJ_n(x) \log x + x^{-n}(a_0 + a_1x + a_2x^2 + \cdots). \quad (85)$$

It is possible to find a second solution by substituting this in the differential equation and proceeding as in Sec. 147. The equations determine the later coefficients in terms of a and a_0. We omit the lengthy calculations and merely mention that one choice of a and a_0 gives

$$\pi Y_n(x) = 2J_n(x) \log \frac{x}{2} - \sum_{k=0}^{\infty} \frac{(-1)^k x^{n+2k}}{2^{n+2k}k!(n+k)!} [\psi(k+n) + \psi(k)]$$

$$- \sum_{r=0}^{n-1} \frac{(n-r-1)!x^{-n+2r}}{2^{-n+2r}r!}, \quad (86)$$

where for the integral values of the argument used here

$$\psi(k) = 0.5772157 \cdots + 1 + \frac{1}{2} + \frac{1}{3} + \cdots + \frac{1}{k}. \quad (87)$$

This choice of the constants is such that if

$$Y_p(x) = \frac{1}{\sin p\pi} [\cos p\pi J_p(x) - J_{-p}(x)], \quad (88)$$

for nonintegral p, $Y_p(x)$ is a continuous function of p for any fixed positive value of x.

A solution of Eq. (51) which is infinite for $x = 0$ is called a Bessel function of the second kind of order p. Any combination

$$y = c_1J_p(x) + c_2Y_p(x) \quad (89)$$

with $c_2 \neq 0$ is an example of such a solution. As the standard function of the second kind of order p, we take $Y_p(x)$ when p is zero or an integer and $J_{-p}(x)$ when p is nonintegral. This is the usual choice and notation. Other functions have been taken as standard by some writers and the notation is not uniform. For example Jahnke-Emde uses $N_p(x)$ to denote our $Y_p(x)$. Each standard function of the second kind arises from a choice of the constants a and a_0 in (85) and can be obtained from (89) by a suitable choice of c_1 and c_2.

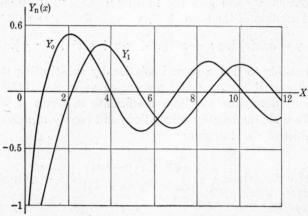

Bessel functions of the second kind.
Fig. 143.

149. Bessel's Differential Equation. The general solution of Bessel's differential equation of order p,

$$x^2 \frac{d^2y}{dx^2} + x \frac{dy}{dx} + (x^2 - p^2)y = 0, \qquad (90)$$

is a linear combination of two Bessel functions of order p, one of the first kind and one of the second kind. Following Jahnke-Emde, we let $Z_p(x)$ denote any solution of (90). Then we may write

$$Z_p(x) = c_1 J_p(x) + c_2 J_{-p}(x), \qquad p \text{ nonintegral}, \qquad (91)$$

and

$$Z_p(x) = c_1 J_p(x) + c_2 Y_p(x), \qquad p \text{ an integer or zero.} \quad (92)$$

With a proper choice of c_1 and c_2, these expressions may be made to represent any given or desired particular solution. And with arbitrary constants c_1 and c_2 they represent the general solution.

If the conditions of the problem make the solution finite for $x = 0$, then c_2 must be zero, and we need determine only the constant c_1.

We shall find $Z_p(x)$ a convenient abbreviation in the following sections where our discussion applies to integral and nonintegral values of p. In specific applications, p is known and $Z_p(x)$ may be replaced by the expansion (91) if p is nonintegral and by the expansion (92) if p is integral.

150. Differential Equations That Lead to Bessel Functions. Some differential equations reduce to that of Bessel after a simple transformation of variables. A general equation of this kind is

$$x^2 \frac{d^2y}{dx^2} + [(1 - 2A)x - 2BCx^{c+1}] \frac{dy}{dx} + [(A^2 - E^2p^2) + BC(2A - C)x^c + B^2C^2x^{2c} + E^2D^2x^{2E}]y = 0. \quad (93)$$

This becomes Bessel's equation of order p,

$$X^2 \frac{d^2Z}{dX^2} + X \frac{dZ}{dX} + (X^2 - p^2)Z = 0, \qquad (94)$$

if we make the substitution

$$y = x^A e^{Bx^C} Z, \qquad X = Dx^E. \qquad (95)$$

The verification is easily made by the method of Sec. 24, if we start with Bessel's equation (94). It follows that the solution of Eq. (93) is

$$y = x^A e^{Bx^C} Z_p(Dx^E), \qquad (96)$$

where $Z_p(X)$ is to be interpreted by Eqs. (91) and (92).

We consider some important special cases. Equation

$$x^2 \frac{d^2y}{dx^2} + (1 - 2A)x \frac{dy}{dx} + [(A^2 - E^2p^2) + E^2D^2x^{2E}]y = 0 \quad (97)$$

has as its solution

$$y = x^A Z_p(Dx^E). \qquad (98)$$

And the solution of the equation

$$x^2 \frac{d^2y}{dx^2} + x \frac{dy}{dx} + (D^2x^2 - p^2)y = 0 \qquad (99)$$

is

$$y = Z_p(Dx).$$

As an application of these results, consider the equation

$$\frac{d^2y}{dx^2} + kx^n y = 0 \qquad \text{or} \qquad x^2 \frac{d^2y}{dx^2} + kx^{n+2}y = 0, \qquad k > 0. \quad (100)$$

This may be obtained from (97) by putting

$$1 - 2A = 0, \qquad A^2 - E^2 p^2 = 0, \qquad E^2 D^2 = k, \qquad 2E = n + 2.$$

One solution of these equations is

$$A = \frac{1}{2}, \qquad E = \frac{n+2}{2}, \qquad p = \frac{1}{n+2}, \qquad D = \frac{2\sqrt{k}}{n+2}. \quad (101)$$

Thus the solution (98) becomes

$$y = \sqrt{x}\, Z_{1/(n+2)} \left(\frac{2\sqrt{k}}{n+2}\, x^{(n+2)/2} \right), \qquad n \neq -2. \quad (102)$$

When $n = -2$, Eq. (100) is an Euler-Cauchy equation which may be solved in terms of elementary functions by the method described in Prob. 91 of Exercises IX (page 368). This procedure is sometimes effective in other cases where the attempt to reduce a given equation by the formulas of this section fails because of zero denominators.

If k were negative in the differential equation (100), the solution (102) would involve Bessel functions of imaginary arguments. It could be expressed in real form in terms of the modified Bessel functions described in Sec. 155.

151. Cylindrical Harmonics. The form of Laplace's equation (40) in cylindrical coordinates is

$$\nabla^2 U = \frac{1}{r} \frac{\partial}{\partial r} \left(r \frac{\partial U}{\partial r} \right) + \frac{1}{r^2} \frac{\partial^2 U}{\partial \theta^2} + \frac{\partial^2 U}{\partial z^2} = 0 \quad (103)$$

by Prob. 48 of Exercises VIII (page 331). Let us attempt to find solutions of this equation, or harmonic functions, of the form

$$U = y(r)(c_1' \cos m\theta + c_2' \sin m\theta)(c_1'' e^{az} + c_2'' e^{-az}). \quad (104)$$

Here a, m, and the coefficients c_1', etc., are constants. We may take $a > 0$, $m > 0$. The assumed form of U leads to the relations

$$\frac{\partial^2 U}{\partial r^2} = \frac{y''}{y}\, U, \qquad \frac{\partial U}{\partial r} = \frac{y'}{y}\, U, \qquad \frac{\partial^2 U}{\partial \theta^2} = -m^2 U,$$

$$\frac{\partial^2 U}{\partial z^2} = a^2 U. \quad (105)$$

Hence the U of (104) will be a solution of Eq. (103) if

$$\frac{y''}{y} U + \frac{1}{r} \frac{y'}{y} U - \frac{m^2}{r^2} U + a^2 U = 0 \qquad \text{or}$$

$$\frac{y''}{y} + \frac{y'}{ry} - \frac{m^2}{r^2} + a^2 = 0. \quad (106)$$

This is equivalent to

$$r^2 \frac{d^2 y}{dr^2} + r \frac{dy}{dr} + (a^2 r^2 - m^2) y = 0. \qquad (107)$$

But this is Eq. (99) with r, a, m in place of x, D, p. Hence the solution of the differential equation (107) is

$$y(r) = Z_m(ar) = c_1 J_m(ar) + c_2 Y_m(ar). \qquad (108)$$

And the most general harmonic function of the form sought is obtained by inserting this in (104). The coefficients of the expanded product involve the six quantities c_1, etc., but could be expressed in terms of four independent constants, *e.g.*, the ratios c_2/c_1, c_2'/c_1', c_2''/c_1'', and one factor of proportionality.

If the solution is finite at infinity, $c_1'' = 0$. If the solution is finite for $r = 0$, $c_2 = 0$. And, if the solution is single-valued, it must not change when θ is increased by 2π, so that m must be an integer. Thus with these restrictions we may write

$$U = J_m(ar)(A \cos m\theta + B \sin m\theta) e^{-az},$$
$$m = 0, 1, 2, \cdots . \quad (109)$$

Bessel functions are sometimes called *cylindrical harmonics* because they are helpful in the problem of finding a harmonic function with values given on the surface of a right circular cylinder.

152. Asymptotic Expansions. In Eq. (93) let us put

$$A = \frac{1}{2}, \qquad B = \frac{1}{2}, \qquad C = 1, \qquad D = -\frac{i}{2}, \qquad E = 1,$$
$$\text{where } i = \sqrt{-1}, \quad (110)$$

and replace x by t. Then we obtain the equation

$$t^2 \frac{d^2 y}{dt^2} - t^2 \frac{dy}{dt} + \left(\frac{1}{4} - p^2 \right) y = 0, \qquad \text{or}$$

$$\frac{d^2 y}{dt^2} - \frac{dy}{dt} + \frac{1 - 4p^2}{4t^2} y = 0. \quad (111)$$

By Eq. (96) the solution of this is

$$y = \sqrt{t}\, e^{t/2} Z_p\left(-\frac{it}{2}\right). \tag{112}$$

The second form of Eq. (111) shows that for large t, one solution is approximated by a constant. This leads us to attempt to find a solution in the form

$$y = b_0 + \frac{b_1}{t} + \frac{b_2}{t^2} + \cdots + \frac{b_m}{t^m} + \cdots. \tag{113}$$

A procedure similar to that used in Sec. 144 shows that

$$b_n = \frac{4p^2 - (2n-1)^2}{4n}\, b_{n-1}. \tag{114}$$

Hence if $b_0 = 1$, we have the expansion of one solution

$$S_p(t) = 1 + \frac{4p^2 - 1}{1!4t} + \frac{(4p^2-1)(4p^2-9)}{2!(4t)^2}$$
$$+ \frac{(4p^2-1)(4p^2-9)(4p^2-25)}{3!(4t)^3} + \cdots. \tag{115}$$

For a suitable choice of constants c_1 and c_2 in Z_p,

$$S_p(t) = \sqrt{t}\, e^{t/2} Z_p\left(-\frac{it}{2}\right), \quad \text{or}$$
$$Z_p(x) = (-2ix)^{-\frac{1}{2}} e^{-ix} S_p(2ix). \tag{116}$$

By a lengthy analysis involving integrals in the complex plane, the proper choice of the constants is determined. We omit the proof but state the result which is equivalent to

$$J_p(x) - iY_p(x) = i^{p+\frac{1}{2}} 2^{\frac{1}{2}} (\pi x)^{-\frac{1}{2}} e^{-ix} S_p(2ix). \tag{117}$$

Define the abbreviation ϕ_p by

$$\phi_p = x - \frac{2p+1}{4}\,\pi. \tag{118}$$

Then we have

$$i^{p+\frac{1}{2}} e^{-ix} = e^{-i\phi_p} = \cos\phi_p - i\sin\phi_p. \tag{119}$$

Also let P_p and Q_p be real series such that

$$S_p(2ix) = P_p(x) - iQ_p(x). \tag{120}$$

Then from (115) the series for P_p and Q_p are found to be

$$P_p(x) = 1 - \frac{(4p^2 - 1)(4p^2 - 9)}{2!(8x)^2}$$
$$+ \frac{(4p^2 - 1)(4p^2 - 9)(4p^2 - 25)(4p^2 - 49)}{4!(8x)^4} - \cdots \quad (121)$$

and

$$Q_p(x) = \frac{4p^2 - 1}{8x} - \frac{(4p^2 - 1)(4p^2 - 9)(4p^2 - 25)}{3!(8x)^3}$$
$$+ \cdots \quad (122)$$

From Eqs. (117) to (120) we may deduce that

$$J_p(x) - iY_p(x) =$$
$$2^{1/2}(\pi x)^{-1/2} (\cos \phi_p - i \sin \phi_p)(P_p - iQ_p). \quad (123)$$

For real values of x, J_p, Y_p, ϕ_p, P_p, and Q_p are all real. By expanding the right member of (123) and equating the real and imaginary parts, we find

$$J_p(x) = 2^{1/2}(\pi x)^{-1/2}(P_p \cos \phi_p - Q_p \sin \phi_p), \quad (124)$$

and

$$Y_p(x) = 2^{1/2}(\pi x)^{-1/2}(P_p \sin \phi_p + Q_p \cos \phi_p). \quad (125)$$

The series for $S_p(t)$, $P_p(x)$, and $Q_p(x)$ given above are usually divergent, but asymptotic as defined in Sec. 76. Hence, like the series of Sec. 103, they may be used for numerical computation whenever the arguments are large enough to make one of the early terms small.

153. Order Half an Odd Integer. Suppose that p has the form

$$p = \frac{2n + 1}{2} = n + \frac{1}{2}, \qquad n \text{ an integer or zero.} \quad (126)$$

Then the Bessel functions of order p reduce to elementary functions. This may be seen from the expansions of Sec. 152. For Eqs. (126) and (114) have as a consequence

$$4p^2 = (2n + 1)^2 \qquad \text{and}$$
$$b_{n+1} = \frac{4p^2 - (2n + 1)^2}{4(n + 1)} b_n = 0. \quad (127)$$

Hence all the b_m with subscripts greater than n are zero in the expansion (115), and similarly in the expansions (121) and (122).

These expansions accordingly break off. For example, from Eqs. (121) and (122) we find

$$P_{1/2}(x) = 1, \qquad P_{3/2}(x) = 1; \qquad Q_{1/2}(x) = 0,$$

$$Q_{3/2}(x) = \frac{1}{x}. \quad (128)$$

And from Eq. (118),

$$\phi_{1/2} = x - \frac{\pi}{2}, \qquad \phi_{3/2} = x - \pi, \qquad \phi_{-1/2} = x,$$

$$\phi_{-3/2} = x + \frac{\pi}{2}. \quad (129)$$

It then follows from Eqs. (124) and (125) that

$$J_{1/2}(x) = 2^{1/2}(\pi x)^{-1/2} \sin x,$$

$$J_{-1/2}(x) = -Y_{1/2}(x) = 2^{1/2}(\pi x)^{-1/2} \cos x,$$

$$J_{3/2}(x) = 2^{1/2}(\pi x)^{-1/2}\left(-\cos x + \frac{\sin x}{x}\right),$$

$$J_{-3/2}(x) = Y_{3/2}(x) = 2^{1/2}(\pi x)^{-1/2}\left(-\sin x - \frac{\cos x}{x}\right). \quad (130)$$

We note that when (126) holds, $\cos p\pi = 0$, $\sin p\pi = (-1)^n$. Hence, from Eq. (88),

$$Y_p(x) = (-1)^{n+1} J_{-p}(x), \qquad \text{if } p = n + \tfrac{1}{2}. \quad (131)$$

This is illustrated for $n = 0$ and 1 in (130).

154. Identities. Roots of $J_p(x) = 0$. The Bessel functions satisfy a number of identities. For example,

$$\frac{d}{dx}[x^p J_p(x)] = x^p J_{p-1}(x) \qquad \text{and} \qquad \frac{d}{dx}[x^{-p} J_p(x)]$$

$$= -x^{-p} J_{p+1}(x). \quad (132)$$

We may verify these by using the series expansions (70) and (73).

By differentiating the products, we may deduce that

$$\frac{dJ_p}{dx} = -\frac{p}{x}J_p + J_{p-1} \qquad \text{and} \qquad \frac{dJ_p}{dx} = \frac{p}{x}J_p - J_{p+1}. \quad (133)$$

If we add these and then divide by 2, we find

$$\frac{dJ_p}{dx} = \frac{1}{2}(J_{p-1} - J_{p+1}). \quad (134)$$

And, if we subtract the two equations, we may deduce that

$$J_{p-1} + J_{p+1} = \frac{2p}{x} J_p. \tag{135}$$

The relations (132) to (135) continue to hold if we replace J_p by Y_p or by Z_p with the same constants c_1 and c_2 used throughout. For Y_p this follows from Eq. (88) directly when p is not zero or an integer and by taking limits for these special values. It then follows for Z_p from Eqs. (91) and (92).

The asymptotic formula (124) suggests that for each p Eq. $J_p(x) = 0$ has an infinite number of real roots, and that the larger roots approximate those of $\cos [x - (2p + 1)/4] = 0$, or $\frac{3 + 2p}{4} \pi \pm k\pi$, k a positive integer. This is the case, so that the numerically large roots of $J_p(x) = 0$ separate those of $J_{p+1}(x) = 0$. In fact the relation of separation holds for all the roots. We give the argument for positive roots. Let a and b be two positive roots of $J_p(x) = 0$. Then the function $x^{-p}J_p(x)$ is zero for $x = a$ and $x = b$. Hence, by Rolle's theorem of Sec. 10, the derivative of the function is zero for some value ξ between a and b. It then follows from the second equation in (132) that $J_{p+1}(\xi) = 0$. Next replace p in the first equation of (132) by $p + 1$ to obtain

$$\frac{d}{dx} [x^{p+1}J_{p+1}(x)] = x^{p+1}J_p(x). \tag{136}$$

Similar reasoning applied to this equation shows that there is a root of $J_p(x) = 0$ between any two positive roots of $J_{p+1}(x) = 0$.

The same argument shows that the positive roots of $Y_p(x) = 0$ separate those of $Y_{p+1}(x) = 0$, and conversely. And similarly for $Z_p(x) = 0$ and $Z_{p+1}(x) = 0$, if Z_p and Z_{p+1} are formed with the same constants c_1 and c_2. The separation also holds for the negative roots. Thus the arrangement of the roots in Figs. 142 and 143 is typical of those of any two similar Bessel functions whose orders differ by unity.

155. Modified Bessel Functions. As noted at the end of Sec. 150, the method of that section may lead us to Bessel functions of imaginary arguments. As the simplest case of this kind, let us consider

$$x^2 \frac{d^2y}{dx^2} + x \frac{dy}{dx} - (x^2 + p^2)y = 0, \tag{137}$$

in which p is real. By Eq. (99), this has as its solution

$$y = Z_p(ix), \qquad \text{where } i = \sqrt{-1}. \qquad (138)$$

The standard solution of the first kind of Eq. (137) is taken as

$$I_p(x) = i^{-p}J_p(ix), \quad \text{where } i^{-p} = e^{-pi\pi/2} = \cos\frac{p\pi}{2} - i\sin\frac{p\pi}{2}. \quad (139)$$

The added factor i^{-p} makes the solution real for real x. It also makes $I_p(x)$ satisfy the relations

$$\frac{d}{dx}[x^p I_p(x)] = x^p I_{p-1}(x), \qquad \frac{d}{dx}[x^{-p} I_p(x)] = x^{-p} I_{p+1}(x), \quad (140)$$

$$\frac{dI_p}{dx} = \frac{1}{2}(I_{p-1} + I_{p+1}) \qquad \text{and} \qquad I_{p-1} - I_{p+1} = \frac{2p}{x} I_p. \quad (141)$$

These may be obtained from the identities (132) to (135) by using the relation (139). They hold for negative values of p if we extend the defining relation (139) to negative values.

The standard solution of the second kind for Eq. (137) may be taken as $I_{-p}(x)$ or

$$K_p(x) = \frac{\pi}{2 \sin p\pi} [I_{-p}(x) - I_p(x)], \qquad p \text{ nonintegral.} \quad (142)$$

For $p = n$, zero, or an integer, $I_{-n}(x) = I_n(x)$ is a function of the first kind. But when $p \to n$, $K_p(x)$ approaches a limiting function

$$K_n(x) = (-1)^{n+1}I_n(x) \log\frac{x}{2} + \frac{1}{2}\sum_{r=0}^{n-1}\frac{(n-r-1)!(-1)^r}{2^{-n+2r}r!} x^{-n+2r}$$

$$+ (-1)^n \frac{1}{2}\sum_{k=0}^{\infty}\frac{x^{n+2k}}{2^{n+2k}k!(n+k)!}[\psi(k+n) + \psi(k)], \quad (143)$$

where $\psi(k)$ is defined by Eq. (87).

The asymptotic expansions of the modified Bessel functions analogous to Eqs. (124) and (125) are

$$I_p(x) \cong (2\pi x)^{-\frac{1}{2}}e^x S_p(-2x), \qquad K_p(x) \cong \pi^{\frac{1}{2}}(2x)^{-\frac{1}{2}}e^{-x}S_p(2x),$$
$$(144)$$

where $S_p(t)$ is defined by Eq. (115). Here $\cong$ means "equal with small percentage error when x is large and positive."

The graph of $I_0(x)$ and $K_0(x)$ for positive values of x is given in Fig. 144. For positive values of x, the graphs of the modified functions of any order have the same character.

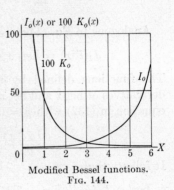

In electrical problems we often treat $E_0 \sin (\omega t + \alpha)$ as the imaginary part of $E_0 e^{i\alpha} e^{i\omega t}$. Compare the remark at the end of Sec. 141. This sometimes leads to imaginary coefficients and, in particular, to an equation of the form

Modified Bessel functions.
Fig. 144.

$$x \frac{d^2 y}{dx^2} + \frac{dy}{dx} - ia^2 xy = 0, \qquad i = \sqrt{-1},\, a > 0. \quad (145)$$

This is equivalent to Eq. (99) with

$$p = 0, \quad \text{and} \quad D^2 = -ia^2 \quad \text{or} \quad D = ai^{3/2}. \quad (146)$$

To specify a particular square root, we interpret $i^{3/2}$ by

$$i^{3/2} = (e^{i\pi/2})^{3/2} = e^{3\pi i/4} = \cos \frac{3\pi}{4} + i \sin \frac{3\pi}{4}. \quad (147)$$

Then by Eq. (99), the solution of (145) is

$$y = Z_0(i^{3/2} ax). \quad (148)$$

In many applications the solution sought is finite at $x = 0$, so that only the solution of the first kind is required. The standard form for this, with $a = 1$, is taken as

$$J_0(i^{3/2} x) = \text{ber } x + i \text{ bei } x = M_0(x) e^{i\theta_0(x)}. \quad (149)$$

For x real, the function is complex with real component "ber" (Bessel-real) and imaginary component "bei" (Bessel-imaginary). From the series (71), with $i^{3/2} x$ in place of x, we find

$$\text{ber } x = 1 + \sum_{k=1}^{\infty} (-1)^k \frac{x^{4k}}{2^2 4^2 6^2 \cdots (4k)^2}, \quad (150)$$

$$\text{bei } x = \sum_{k=0}^{\infty} (-1)^k \frac{x^{4k+2}}{2^2 4^2 6^2 \cdots (4k+2)^2}. \tag{151}$$

Analogous to Eq. (149) we may write

$$J_1(i^{3/2}x) = \text{ber}_1 x + i \text{ bei}_1 x = M_1(x)e^{i\theta_1(x)}. \tag{152}$$

The functions defined by this equation are useful when the derivatives of ber x and bei x are required. For from the second equation in (132) with $p = 0$, $J_0'(x) = -J_1(x)$. Hence

$$\frac{dJ_0(i^{3/2}x)}{dx} = -i^{3/2}J_0(i^{3/2}x). \tag{153}$$

It follows that

$$\text{ber}' x + i \text{ bei}' x = -i^{3/2}M_1(x)e^{i\theta_1(x)} = M_1(x)e^{i[\theta_1(x) - \pi/4]}. \tag{154}$$

For x between 0 and 20 the values of ber x, bei x, $M_0(x)$, $\theta_0(x)$ of (149), as well as the values of ber' x, bei' x, $M_1(x)$, $\theta_1(x) - \pi/4$ are tabulated in H. B. Dwight's *Mathematical Tables*.

Similar functions may be defined for any order,

$$\text{ber}_p x + i \text{ bei}_p x = J_p(i^{3/2}x) = i^p I_p(i^{1/2}x). \tag{155}$$

And there are similar functions of the second kind

$$\text{ker}_p x + i \text{ kei}_p x = i^{-p}K_p(i^{1/2}x). \tag{156}$$

For x between 0 and 10 and p between 0 and 5 the functions defined by Eqs. (155) and (156), together with their derivatives are tabulated in H. B. Dwight's *Tables of Integrals and Other Mathematical Data*.

156. References. Jahnke-Emde's *Tables of Functions* includes many data on Legendre polynomials and Bessel functions in numerical and graphical form. An introduction to the theory of the functions as well as applications to problems of mathematical physics will be found in A. G. Webster's *Partial Differential Equations of Mathematical Physics*, edited by S. J. Plimpton. N. W. McLachlan's *Bessel Functions for Engineers* includes many applications to practical problems.

For the theory of Legendre polynomials and related functions the reader may consult E. W. Hobson's *Theory of Spherical and Ellipsoidal Harmonics*. Among the treatises on Bessel functions we may mention the *Theory of Bessel Functions* by G. N. Watson and the *Treatise on Bessel Functions*, by Gray, Mathews, and MacRobert.

EXERCISES X

Verify that the given function is one solution and, using this fact, find the complete solution of the given equation:

1. e^x, $x \dfrac{d^2y}{dx^2} - (2x + 1) \dfrac{dy}{dx} + (x + 1)y = 0$.

2. x, $(1 - x) \dfrac{d^2y}{dx^2} + x \dfrac{dy}{dx} - y = 0$.

3. e^{-x}, $x \dfrac{d^2y}{dx^2} + (2x + 2) \dfrac{dy}{dx} + (x + 2)y = 0$.

4. x^2, $x^2 \dfrac{d^2y}{dx^2} - 4x \dfrac{dy}{dx} + 6y = 0$.

5. 1, $\cos x \dfrac{d^2y}{dx^2} + \sin x \dfrac{dy}{dx} = 0$.

6. $x + 1$, $(1 + x)^2 \dfrac{d^2y}{dx^2} - 2(1 + x) \dfrac{dy}{dx} + 2y = 0$.

Find series solutions of the equations:

7. $\dfrac{d^2y}{dx^2} = xy$.   **8.** $\dfrac{d^2y}{dx^2} = x^2 \dfrac{dy}{dx} + xy$.   **9.** $\dfrac{d^2y}{dx^2} = x^2y$.

Find series solutions of the following equations and identify them with elementary functions:

10. $\dfrac{d^2y}{dx^2} = 4y$.   **11.** $\dfrac{d^2y}{dx^2} = -y$.   **12.** $\dfrac{dy}{dx} = 2xy$.

Prove that U of Eq. (43) satisfies the relations:

13. $(1 + r^2 - 2rx) \dfrac{\partial U}{\partial r} = (x - r)U$.   **14.** $r \dfrac{\partial U}{\partial r} = (x - r) \dfrac{\partial U}{\partial x}$.

From Eq. (50), and Probs. 13 and 14 above, deduce that

15. $nP_n - (2n - 1)xP_{n-1} + (n - 1)P_{n-2} = 0$.

16. (a) $x \dfrac{dP_{n-1}}{dx} - \dfrac{dP_{n-2}}{dx} = (n - 1)P_{n-1}$, or

     (b) $x \dfrac{dP_n}{dx} - \dfrac{dP_{n-1}}{dx} = nP_n$.

17. By differentiating the result of Prob. 15 and using Prob. 16(a), deduce that $\dfrac{dP_n}{dx} - x \dfrac{dP_{n-1}}{dx} = nP_{n-1}$.

18. From Probs. 16(b) and 17 deduce that

$$(1 - x^2) \dfrac{dP_n}{dx} = n(P_{n-1} - xP_n),$$

and

$$(1 - x^2)\frac{dP_{n-1}}{dx} = n(xP_{n-1} - P_n).$$

19. If u and v are each functions of x, Leibniz's rule for the nth derivative of a product states that $\frac{d^n(uv)}{dx^n} = (D_u + D_v)^n uv$, where the power is to be expanded by the binomial theorem and the terms interpreted similarly to $15D_u{}^4D_v{}^2uv = 15\frac{d^4u}{dx^4}\frac{d^2v}{dx^2}$. Verify that the rule holds for $n = 2$ and $n = 3$.

20. Use the rule of Leibniz given in Prob. 19 to show that, if f is a function of x, $\frac{d^m(xf)}{dx^m} = x\frac{d^mf}{dx^m} + m\frac{d^{m-1}f}{dx^{m-1}}$, and also derive the relation $\frac{d^m(x^2f)}{dx^m} = x^2\frac{d^mf}{dx^m} + 2mx\frac{d^{m-1}f}{dx^{m-1}} + m(m-1)\frac{d^{m-2}f}{dx^{m-2}}$.

21. If $u = (x^2 - 1)^n$, $(x^2 - 1)\frac{du}{dx} = 2nxu$. Use Prob. 20 to show that the result of differentiating this equation $(n + 1)$ times reduces to $(x^2 - 1)\frac{d^{n+2}u}{dx^{n+2}} + 2x\frac{d^{n+1}u}{dx^{n+1}} - n(n + 1)\frac{d^nu}{dx^n} = 0$. Hence the derivative d^nu/dx^n is a solution of Legendre's equation (26). Since it is a polynomial, it must equal $cP_n(x)$. And to make the coefficient of x^n agree with that in Eq. (38), $c = 2^nn!$. This proves Rodrigues's formula, Eq. (39).

22. Use Prob. 20 to show that the result of differentiating Legendre's equation (26) m times is

$$(1 - x^2)\frac{d^{m+2}y}{dx^{m+2}} - 2x(m + 1)\frac{d^{m+1}y}{dx^{m+1}} + (n - m)(n + m + 1)\frac{d^my}{dx^m} = 0.$$

Also show that, if we put $d^my/dx^m = w(1 - x^2)^{-m/2}$ in this, it becomes

$$(1 - x^2)\frac{d^2w}{dx^2} - 2x\frac{dw}{dx} + \left[n(n + 1) - \frac{m^2}{1 - x^2}\right]w = 0.$$

This is the *associated Legendre equation*. If $m \leqq n$, it admits as one solution the *associated Legendre polynomial* defined by

$$P_n{}^m = (1 - x^2)^{m/2}\frac{d^m}{dx^m}P_n(x) = \frac{(1 - x^2)^{m/2}}{2^nn!}\frac{d^{m+n}}{dx^{m+n}}(x^2 - 1)^n.$$

Use the series (71) and (72) to verify the tabulated values:

23. $J_0(0.1) = 0.9975$.   **24.** $J_0(1) = 0.7652$.
25. $J_0(2) = 0.2239$.   **26.** $J_1(0.1) = 0.0499$.
27. $J_1(1) = 0.4401$.   **28.** $J_1(2) = 0.5767$.

29. Show that $J_p(-x) = (-1)^p J_p(x)$. Hence, in particular, we have $J_0(-x) = J_0(x)$ but $J_1(-x) = -J_1(x)$.

Find series of the form (52) which are solutions of

30. $(x - x^2) \dfrac{d^2y}{dx^2} - 3 \dfrac{dy}{dx} + 2y = 0.$

31. $2x^2 \dfrac{d^2y}{dx^2} - x \dfrac{dy}{dx} + (1 - x^2)y = 0.$

Find series of the form (52) which are solutions of each of the following equations, and identify them with elementary functions:

32. $2x \dfrac{d^2y}{dx^2} + \dfrac{dy}{dx} = 2y.$ **33.** $4x \dfrac{d^2y}{dx^2} + 2 \dfrac{dy}{dx} + y = 0.$

34. Let n be zero or a positive integer. Then by Eq. (70), we have

$$J_n(x) = \sum_{k=0}^{\infty} (-1)^k \frac{x^{n+2k}}{2^{n+2k} k! (n+k)!}.$$ From Eq. (81) deduce the relation

$$J_{-n}(x) = \sum_{k=0}^{\infty} (-1)^{n+k} \frac{x^{n+2k}}{2^{n+2k} k! (n+k)!}.$$

35. Use the series of Prob. 34 to verify that $J_{-5}(4) = -0.1321$.

36. From the Maclaurin's series for e^z, deduce that the exponential

$$e^{xt/2} = 1 + \frac{x}{2} t + \frac{x^2}{2^2} \frac{1}{2!} t^2 + \cdots + \frac{x^r}{2^r} \frac{1}{r!} t^r + \cdots$$ and also show that

$$e^{-\frac{x}{2}\frac{1}{t}} = 1 - \frac{x}{2} t^{-1} + \frac{x^2}{2^2} \frac{1}{2!} t^{-2} + \cdots + (-1)^s \frac{x^s}{2^s} \frac{1}{s!} t^{-s} + \cdots .$$

37. From the expansions of Probs. 34 and 36 deduce the relation

$$e^{\frac{x}{2}\left(t - \frac{1}{t}\right)} = \sum_{n=-\infty}^{\infty} J_n(x) t^n.$$

38. Multiply the expansion of Prob. 37 by that obtained from it when x is replaced by y. Hence show that

$$J_n(x + y) = \sum_{k=-\infty}^{\infty} J_k(x) J_{n-k}(y).$$

39. From Prob. 38, with $n = 0$ and $y = -x$, deduce the identity
$$[J_0(x)]^2 + 2[J_1(x)]^2 + 2[J_2(x)]^2 + \cdots = 1.$$

Use Probs. 23 and 26 and Eq. (86) to verify that

40. $Y_0(0.1) = -1.534.$ **41.** $Y_1(0.1) = -6.46.$

Express the general solution of each of the following equations in terms of Bessel functions:

42. $4 \dfrac{d^2y}{dx^2} + 9xy = 0.$ **43.** $x \dfrac{d}{dx}\left(x \dfrac{dy}{dx}\right) + 25x^2 y = 0.$

44. $x \dfrac{d^2y}{dx^2} + 3 \dfrac{dy}{dx} + 4xy = 0.$ **45.** $x \dfrac{d^2y}{dx^2} + \dfrac{dy}{dx} + y = 0.$

46. $x \dfrac{d^2y}{dx^2} + 17 \dfrac{dy}{dx} + xy = 0.$ **47.** $x \dfrac{d^2y}{dx^2} + 3 \dfrac{dy}{dx} + y = 0.$

48. $4x^2 \dfrac{d^2y}{dx^2} + (4x^2 - 15)y = 0.$ **49.** $\dfrac{d^2y}{dx^2} + 27x^4 y = 0.$

Express the general solution of each of the following equations in terms of modified Bessel functions:

50. $x^2 \dfrac{d^2y}{dx^2} + x \dfrac{dy}{dx} = (x^2 + 4)y.$ **51.** $x \dfrac{d^2y}{dx^2} + \dfrac{dy}{dx} = 9y.$

52. $x^2 \dfrac{d^2y}{dx^2} + x \dfrac{dy}{dx} = (x + 1)y.$ **53.** $x \dfrac{d^2y}{dx^2} + 5 \dfrac{dy}{dx} = 16x^5 y.$

54. $4x^2 \dfrac{d^2y}{dx^2} + 4x^2 \dfrac{dy}{dx} + y = 0.$ **55.** $4 \dfrac{d^2y}{dx^2} = 9xy.$

56. A vertical column of uniform cross section A ft.^{2} has specific weight w lb./ft.^{3} and flexural rigidity EI lb./ft.^{2} If it supports its own weight, the (small) angle of deflection θ at distance x ft. from the top satisfies the differential equation $EI \dfrac{d^2\theta}{dx^2} = -Awx\theta.$ Show that

$$\theta = x^{1/3} Z_{1/3}\left(\frac{2}{3}\sqrt{\frac{wA}{EI}}\, x^{3/2}\right).$$

57. Given $\theta = x^{1/3} Z_{1/3}(kx^{3/2})$. From Eqs. (91), (70), and (73) deduce that $\theta = c_1(A_1 x + B_1 x^4 + \cdots) + c_2(A_2 + B_2 x^3 + \cdots)$, where $A_1 \neq 0$. Hence if $d\theta/dx = 0$ for $x = 0$, $c_1 = 0$ and $\theta = c_2 x^{1/3} J_{-1/3}(kx^{3/2})$. And if $\theta = 0$ for $x = L$, $J_{-1/3}(kL^{3/2}) = 0$.

58. If L ft. is a critical length of the column of Prob. 56, the boundary conditions are as given in Prob. 57. From tables, the smallest root of $J_{-1/3}(z) = 0$ is $z_0 = 1.8663$. Deduce that the first critical length is $L_0 = 1.986 \, (EI/wA)^{1/3}$.

59. For a circular cross section, of radius r, $I = \pi r^4/4$, and the ratio $I/A = r^2/4$. Use this fact and Prob. 58 to compute the critical length for a steel wire of diameter 0.02 in. if its density is 480 lb./ft.^{3} and $E = 3 \times 10^7$ lb./in.^{2}

60. The problem of a linearly tapered or conical column, supporting its own weight, leads to a differential equation which assumes the form $\dfrac{d^2y}{dx^2} + k^2 \dfrac{y}{x^4} = 0.$ Express the general solution in terms of Bessel functions of the type considered in Sec. 153. Hence express the solution in terms of elementary functions.

61. If a cooling fin has a triangular cross section, with suitable choice of variables, the equation governing temperature distribution reduces to

$\dfrac{d}{dx}\left(x\,\dfrac{du}{dx}\right) = k^2 u$, where $\dfrac{du}{dx} = 0$ for $x = 0$. Show that the solution is $u = c_1 I_0(2k\sqrt{x})$.

Use the asymptotic formulas (124) and (125) to verify that

62. $J_0(10) = -0.2459.$ **63.** $J_1(10) = 0.0435.$

64. $Y_0(10) = 0.0557.$ **65.** $Y_1(10) = 0.2490.$

Show that

66. $J_{5/2}(x) = 2^{1/2}(\pi x)^{-1/2}\left(\dfrac{3 - x^2}{x^2}\sin x - \dfrac{3}{x}\cos x\right).$

67. $J_{-5/2}(x) = -Y_{5/2}(x) = 2^{1/2}(\pi x)^{-1/2}\left(\dfrac{3}{x}\sin x + \dfrac{3 - x^2}{x^2}\cos x\right).$

68. Using the values given in Eq. (130), verify by direct substitution that Eq. (132) hold when $p = \frac{1}{2}$.

69. Check the value for $J_{1/2}(x)$ given in Eq. (130) by comparing its Maclaurin's series with the series (70) for $p = \frac{1}{2}$.

70. Assuming the value of $J_{1/2}(x)$ and $J_{-1/2}(x)$ given in Eq. (130), check the value of $J_{3/2}(x)$ by putting $p = \frac{1}{2}$ in Eq. (135).

From Eq. (134) deduce that

71. $2^2\,\dfrac{d^2 J_p}{dx^2} = J_{p-2} - 2J_p + J_{p+2}.$

72. $2^3\,\dfrac{d^3 J_p}{dx^3} = J_{p-3} - 3J_{p-1} + 3J_{p+1} - J_{p-3}.$

73. Check Prob. 71 for the special case when p is an integer n by using the expansions of Prob. 34.

From Eqs. (139) and (130) deduce that

74. $I_{1/2}(x) = 2^{1/2}(\pi x)^{-1/2}\sinh x = (2\pi x)^{-1/2}(e^x - e^{-x}).$

75. $I_{-1/2}(x) = 2^{1/2}(\pi x)^{-1/2}\cosh x = (2\pi x)^{-1/2}(e^x + e^{-x}).$

76. From Eq. (142) and Probs. 74 and 75 deduce the similar result $K_{1/2}(x) = \pi^{1/2}(2x)^{-1/2}e^{-x}.$

77. Show that Prob. 76 agrees exactly with Eq. (144), but that Prob. 74 differs from Eq. (144) by the term in e^{-x}, which for x large and positive is negligibly small compared to e^x.

Use the series (150) and (151) to verify that

78. ber $1 = 0.9844.$ **79.** bei $1 = 0.2496.$

Differentiate the series (150) and (151) and verify that

80. ber$'$ $1 = -0.0624.$ **81.** bei$'$ $1 = 0.4974.$

From Eq. (149) and Probs. 78 and 79 deduce that

82. $M_0(1) = 1.016.$ **83.** $\theta_0(1) = 14.23°.$

From Eq. (154) and Probs. 80 and 81 deduce that

84. $M_1(1) = 0.5013.$ **85.** $\theta_1(1) = 142.16°.$

86. If $a = 1$, Eq. (145) may be written $\dfrac{d}{dx}(xy') = ixy$. From Eq. (149) deduce that $y = \text{ber } x + i \text{ bei } x$ satisfies this relation.

If $y = \text{ber } x + i \text{ bei } x$, $dy/dx = y' = \text{ber}' x + i \text{ bei}' x$. By substituting these values in the relation of Prob. 86 and equating real and imaginary parts, deduce that

87. $\dfrac{d}{dx}(x \text{ ber}' x) = -x \text{ bei } x.$

88. $\dfrac{d}{dx}(x \text{ bei}' x) = x \text{ ber } x.$

89. If u is any function of x, from Prob. 86 deduce the relations
$\dfrac{d}{dx}(uxy') = u'xy' + u\dfrac{d}{dx}(xy') = u'xy' + uixy$, or

$$xuy' \Big|_0^k = \int_0^k x(u'y' + iuy)dx.$$

Let $u = \text{ber } x - i \text{ bei } x$. Substitute this value and its conjugate $y = \text{ber } x + i \text{ bei } x$ in the last relation of Prob. 89. And by equating real and imaginary parts, deduce that

90. $\displaystyle\int_0^k x[(\text{ber}' x)^2 + (\text{bei}' x)^2]dx = k(\text{ber } k \text{ ber}' k + \text{bei } k \text{ bei}' k).$

91. $\displaystyle\int^k x[(\text{ber } x)^2 + (\text{bei } x)^2]dx = k(\text{ber } k \text{ bei}' k - \text{bei } k \text{ ber}' k).$

The expression for the power loss in a solenoid due to eddy currents involves an integral of the type evaluated in Prob. 90.

CHAPTER XI

FOURIER SERIES AND
PARTIAL DIFFERENTIAL EQUATIONS

Equations that involve partial derivatives of the unknown functions are called *partial differential equations*. Poisson's equation for the potential, the equation governing heat flow, and the equations governing fluid flow, derived in Secs. 126 to 128, are illustrations.

In most practical applications of differential equations, the required particular solution must satisfy certain initial or boundary conditions as well as the differential equation. For ordinary differential equations, as we saw in Chap. IX, the natural procedure is first to find the general solutions involving arbitrary constants and then to use the boundary conditions to determine these constants. But the general solution of a partial differential equation contains one or more arbitrary functions. And it is not easy to find the particular values of these functions from the boundary conditions even when the general solution is known.

It is often possible to solve a specific partial differential equation problem in the form of a series of terms, each of which satisfies some of the boundary conditions. In the cases discussed, the sum of the series satisfies these same boundary conditions for arbitrary values of certain coefficients. And the problem is solved by determining these coefficients so that the remaining boundary conditions are satisfied. This chapter is devoted to such series methods. Since these methods frequently depend on the Fourier expansion of a function in a series of sine and cosine terms, we begin with a brief discussion of Fourier series.

157. Fourier's Theorem for Periodic Functions. A function $f(x)$ is said to be *periodic*, of period p, if

$$f(x + p) = f(x). \tag{1}$$

For example, $\sin (2\pi x/p)$ and $\cos (2\pi x/p)$ are each periodic of period p, since

$$\sin \frac{2\pi}{p} (x + p) = \sin \left(\frac{2\pi x}{p} + 2\pi \right) = \sin \frac{2\pi x}{p}, \qquad (2)$$

and

$$\cos \frac{2\pi}{p} (x + p) = \cos \left(\frac{2\pi x}{p} + 2\pi \right) = \cos \frac{2\pi x}{p}. \qquad (3)$$

More generally, $\sin (2n\pi x/p)$ and $\cos (2n\pi x/p)$ are each periodic of period p if n is any positive integer. Hence, if the infinite series

$$a + a_1 \cos \frac{2\pi x}{p} + b_1 \sin \frac{2\pi x}{p} + a_2 \cos \frac{4\pi x}{p} + b_2 \sin \frac{4\pi x}{p} + \cdots$$

$$+ a_n \cos \frac{2\pi n x}{p} + b_n \sin \frac{2\pi n x}{p} + \cdots \qquad (4)$$

or

$$a + \sum_{k=1}^{\infty} \left(a_k \cos \frac{2\pi k x}{p} + b_k \sin \frac{2\pi k x}{p} \right) \qquad (5)$$

is convergent, it represents a function of period p.

If a function $f(x)$ is single-valued and continuous on a finite interval and its graph on this interval has finite arc length, we call the function or its graph *regular*. We call a single-valued function $f(x)$ *piecewise regular* if its graph on any finite interval is made up of a finite number of pieces, each of which is a regular arc or an isolated point.

For example, on the interval $0 \leqq x < 4$, the relations

$$f(0) = 2, \qquad f(x) = 3 \quad \text{if } 0 < x < 2, \qquad f(2) = 2,$$
$$f(x) = 1 \quad \text{if } 2 < x < 4, \qquad (6)$$

define a piecewise regular function. And, if we add the condition

$$f(x + 4) = f(x), \qquad (7)$$

the function is defined for all values of x as a piecewise regular function of period 4. Its graph is shown in Fig. 145. We use the notation $f(x-)$ to mean the value at x approached from the left and $f(x+)$ to mean the value at x approached from the right. Thus at $x = 2$ these values are $f(2-) = 3$ and $f(2+) = 1$.

Suppose that $f(x)$ is any piecewise regular periodic function of period p. Then it may be proved that there are coefficients for which the series (5) converges to $f(x)$ at all points of continuity, and to $\frac{1}{2}[f(x+) + f(x-)]$ at the points of discontinuity. Furthermore, correct relations will be obtained from the equation

$$f(x) = a + \sum_{k=1}^{\infty} \left(a_k \cos \frac{2\pi kx}{p} + b_k \sin \frac{2\pi kx}{p} \right), \qquad (8)$$

by termwise integration after multiplication by any function of x.

If we use as multipliers 1, $\cos (2\pi nx/p)$, $\sin (2\pi nx/p)$, respectively, where n is any positive integer, and integrate from c to

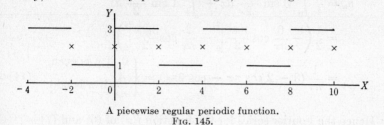

A piecewise regular periodic function.
FIG. 145.

$c + p$, where c is any constant, the results, as shown in Probs. 1 to 8 are

$$\int_c^{c+p} f(x)dx = pa, \qquad \text{or } a = \frac{1}{p} \int_c^{c+p} f(x)dx. \qquad (9)$$

$$\int_c^{c+p} f(x) \cos \frac{2n\pi x}{p} \, dx = \frac{1}{2} pa_n, \qquad \text{or}$$

$$a_n = \frac{2}{p} \int_c^{c+p} f(x) \cos \frac{2n\pi x}{p} \, dx, \qquad (10)$$

$$\int_c^{c+p} f(x) \sin \frac{2n\pi x}{p} \, dx = \frac{1}{2} pb_n, \qquad \text{or}$$

$$b_n = \frac{2}{p} \int_c^{c+p} f(x) \sin \frac{2n\pi x}{p} \, dx. \qquad (11)$$

To recapitulate, if $f(x)$ is any piecewise regular periodic function of period p, and a, the a_n and the b_n are found from Eqs. (9) to (11), the series (5) will converge to $f(x)$ at all points of continuity, and to $\frac{1}{2}[f(x+) + f(x-)]$ at all points of discontinuity. This is known as *Fourier's theorem for periodic functions.*

Let us illustrate the procedure for the function defined by the relations (6) and (7). Here $p = 4$. We take $c = 0$ and, since the expression for the function changes at 2, calculate the integrals from 0 to 4 as the sum of those from 0 to 2 and from 2 to 4. Thus we find

$$a = \tfrac{1}{4}\left(\int_0^2 3 \, dx + \int_2^4 1 \, dx \right) = \tfrac{1}{4}(6 + 2) = 2. \tag{12}$$

$$a_n = \frac{2}{4}\left(\int_0^2 3 \cos \frac{n\pi x}{2} \, dx + \int_2^4 1 \cos \frac{n\pi x}{2} \, dx \right)$$

$$= \frac{1}{2}\left(\frac{6}{n\pi} \sin \frac{n\pi x}{2} \Big|_0^2 + \frac{2}{n\pi} \sin \frac{n\pi x}{2} \Big|_2^4 \right) = 0. \tag{13}$$

$$b_n = \frac{2}{4} \int_0^2 3 \sin \frac{n\pi x}{2} \, dx + \int_2^4 1 \sin \frac{n\pi x}{2} \, dx$$

$$= \frac{1}{2}\left(-\frac{6}{n\pi} \cos \frac{n\pi x}{2} \Big|_0^2 - \frac{2}{n\pi} \cos \frac{n\pi x}{2} \Big|_2^4 \right)$$

$$= \frac{1}{n\pi} (3 - 2 \cos n\pi - \cos 2n\pi) = \begin{cases} 0, & \text{if } n \text{ is even,} \\ \dfrac{4}{n\pi}, & \text{if } n \text{ is odd.} \end{cases} \tag{14}$$

Hence the Fourier series for the function $f(x)$ of (6) and (7) is

$$2 + \frac{4}{\pi}\left(\sin \frac{\pi x}{2} + \frac{1}{3} \sin \frac{3\pi x}{2} + \frac{1}{5} \sin \frac{5\pi x}{2} + \cdots \right). \tag{15}$$

The defining relations (6) and (7) happen to make the value of the function equal to $\tfrac{1}{2}[f(x+) + f(x-)]$ at the points of discontinuity. For example, $f(4) = \tfrac{1}{2}[f(4+) + f(4-)]$, since

$$2 = \tfrac{1}{2}(3 + 1).$$

Hence Fig. 145 is the graph of the sum of the series (15) for all values of x. Had we taken other values for $f(x)$ as the definition at the points of discontinuity, we would still have found the same Fourier series since the values $f(0)$ and $f(2)$ were not used in Eqs. (12) to (14). We may always obtain the graph of the Fourier series which represents any piecewise regular function by plotting the regular arcs, together with the midpoints of the vertical segments determined by consecutive arcs. In Fourier series problems, we shall frequently define the regular arcs only and give no values at the discontinuities, since these last do not affect the Fourier series.

If the function $f(x)$ is known only graphically or is expressed in terms of complicated functions, the coefficients can be found by methods like those described in Secs. 77 and 78. There are instruments known as *harmonic analyzers*, somewhat similar to planimeters, by which the coefficients a_n and b_n can be obtained from a plot, to suitable scale, of $f(x)$ itself. Several efficient arrangements of the application of a modified trapezoidal rule to the integrals in question, known as schedules for harmonic analysis, will be found in Scarborough's *Numerical Analysis* and

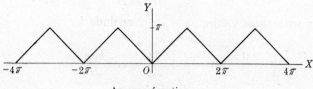

An even function.
FIG. 146.

Lipka's *Graphical and Mechanical Computation*, Vol. II.

158. Fourier Cosine Series and Fourier Sine Series. Let us put $p = 2L$ and $c = -L$ in Eqs. (9) to (11). They then become

$$a = \frac{1}{2L} \int_{-L}^{L} f(x)dx, \qquad a_n = \frac{1}{L} \int_{-L}^{L} f(x) \cos \frac{n\pi x}{L} \, dx, \quad (16)$$

$$b_n = \frac{1}{L} \int_{-L}^{L} f(x) \sin \frac{n\pi x}{L} \, dx.$$

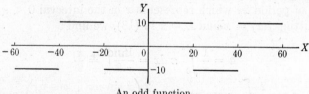

An odd function.
FIG. 147.

An *even* function of x is one for which $f(-x) = f(x)$. An inspection of the graph of an even function (Fig. 146) shows that the integral of an even function from $-L$ to L is twice the integral of the same function from 0 to L.

An *odd* function of x is one for which $f(-x) = -f(x)$. An inspection of the graph of an odd function (Fig. 147) shows that the integral of an odd function from $-L$ to L is zero.

We note that $\cos(n\pi x/L)$ is an even function, while $\sin(n\pi x/L)$ is an odd function. For

$$\cos\left(-\frac{n\pi x}{L}\right) = \cos \frac{n\pi x}{L}, \qquad \text{but} \qquad \sin\left(-\frac{n\pi x}{L}\right) = -\sin \frac{n\pi x}{L}. \quad (17)$$

Again, the product of two even functions or of two odd functions is even, while the product of an odd and an even function is odd.

From the facts stated, we may conclude from Eq. (16) that if $f(x)$ is an even function, $b_n = 0$ and

$$a = \frac{1}{L} \int_0^L f(x)dx, \qquad a_n = \frac{2}{L} \int_0^L f(x) \cos \frac{n\pi x}{L} \, dx. \qquad (18)$$

Hence with these values

$$f(x) = a + \sum_{k=1}^{\infty} a_k \cos \frac{k\pi x}{L}. \qquad (19)$$

For *any* given function $f(x)$ in $0 < x < L$, Eqs. (18) and (19) may be used to find a *Fourier cosine series of period* $2L$ which represents $f(x)$ in $0 < x < L$. For, from $f(x)$ in $0 < x < L$, we may form an even function of period $2L$ equal to the given function for $0 < x < L$. The series (19), with coefficients calculated by (18) will then represent the even periodic function for all x. Hence in particular it will represent the given $f(x)$ for $0 < x < L$, assumed to be piecewise regular.

We illustrate the procedure by finding the Fourier cosine series of period 2π which represents x in the interval $0 < x < \pi$. On putting $f(x) = x$ and $L = \pi$ in (18), we find

$$a = \frac{1}{\pi} \int_0^\pi x \, dx = \frac{1}{\pi} \frac{x^2}{2} \Big|_0^\pi = \frac{\pi}{2}. \qquad (20)$$

$$a_n = \frac{2}{\pi} \int_0^\pi x \cos nx \, dx = \frac{2}{\pi} \left(\frac{x \sin nx}{n} + \frac{\cos nx}{n^2} \right) \Big|_0^\pi$$

$$= \frac{2}{\pi n^2} (\cos n\pi - 1) = \begin{cases} 0, & \text{if } n \text{ is even,} \\ -\dfrac{4}{\pi n^2}, & \text{if } n \text{ is odd.} \end{cases} \qquad (21)$$

It follows that, for $0 < x < \pi$,

$$x = \frac{\pi}{2} - \frac{4}{\pi} \left(\cos x + \frac{1}{3^2} \cos 3x + \frac{1}{5^2} \cos 5x + \cdots \right). \qquad (22)$$

The graph of the right member of (22) is as shown in Fig. 146. Hence Eq. (22) holds for $x = 0$, or $x = \pi$ but not for $x < 0$ or $x > \pi$.

Next suppose that $f(x)$ is an odd function. Then, from the facts mentioned above, combined with Eqs. (16), we may conclude that $a = a_n = 0$ and

$$b_n = \frac{2}{L} \int_0^L f(x) \sin \frac{n\pi x}{L} \, dx. \tag{23}$$

Hence with these values

$$f(x) = \sum_{k=1}^{\infty} b_k \sin \frac{k\pi x}{L}. \tag{24}$$

For *any* given function $f(x)$ in $0 < x < L$, Eqs. (23) and (24) may be used to find a *Fourier sine series of period* $2L$ which represents $f(x)$ in $0 < x < L$. For, from $f(x)$ in $0 < x < L$, we may form an odd function of period $2L$ equal to the given function for $0 < x < L$. The series (24), with coefficients calculated by (23) will then represent the odd periodic function for all x. Hence in particular it will represent the given $f(x)$ for $0 < x < L$, assumed to be piecewise regular.

We illustrate the procedure by finding the Fourier sine series of period 40 which represents 10 in the interval $0 < x < 20$. On putting $f(x) = 10$ and $L = 20$ in (23) we find

$$b_n = \frac{1}{10} \int_0^{20} 10 \sin \frac{n\pi x}{20} \, dx = -\frac{20}{n\pi} \cos \frac{n\pi x}{20} \Big|_0^{20}$$

$$= \frac{20}{n\pi} (1 - \cos n\pi) = \begin{cases} 0, \text{ if } n \text{ is even,} \\ \dfrac{40}{n\pi}, \text{ if } n \text{ is odd.} \end{cases} \tag{25}$$

It follows that, for $0 < x < 20$,

$$10 = \frac{40}{\pi} \left(\sin \frac{\pi x}{20} + \frac{1}{3} \sin \frac{3\pi x}{20} + \frac{1}{5} \sin \frac{5\pi x}{20} + \cdots \right). \tag{26}$$

The graph of the right member of (26) is as shown in Fig. 147. Hence Eq. (26) does not hold for $x = 0$ or $x = 20$.

159. Laplace's Equation. It was shown in Sec. 126 that in space free of charges the electrical potential satisfies Laplace's equation,

$$\frac{\partial^2 U}{\partial x^2} + \frac{\partial^2 U}{\partial y^2} + \frac{\partial^2 U}{\partial z^2} = 0. \tag{27}$$

This equation is also satisfied by the temperature in a steady-state distribution (Sec. 127) and the velocity potential for the irrotational motion of an incompressible fluid (Sec. 128). Since the temperatures on the surface of a body determine the steady-state distribution inside, physical considerations suggest that there is a unique solution of Eq. (27) taking on given boundary values if these are sufficiently regular. That there is at most one solution when the body is finite is in accord with Prob. 63 of Chap. VIII.

In temperature distribution or potential problems in a plane, taken as the xy plane, Laplace's equation becomes

$$\frac{\partial^2 U}{\partial x^2} + \frac{\partial^2 U}{\partial y^2} = 0. \tag{28}$$

It was shown in Sec. 87 that the real or imaginary part of any analytic function of $(x + iy)$ satisfies this equation. And this fact was used in Secs. 94 and 95 to find the velocity potential for certain types of fluid flow in a plane.

We shall now present a method of solving Laplace's equation by combining particular solutions. For definiteness, we shall use the language of heat flow.

160. Temperatures in a Rectangular Plate. If a homogeneous plane plate has its faces insulated and its edges kept at prescribed temperatures, its steady-state temperatures will be determined. In particular let us consider a rectangle $ABCD$, with sides AD and BC so long compared with AB and CD that we may treat them as infinite. Let the prescribed boundary temperatures be 0° for AD, DC, and BC and 10° along AB, and assume

$$AB = 20 \text{ cm.}$$

Take the origin at A, and the axes of x and y along AB and AD, respectively. Then the boundary conditions are

$$U(0,y) = 0, \qquad U(20,y) = 0, \qquad U(x,\infty) = 0,$$
$$U(x,0) = 10. \tag{29}$$

Our problem is to find the solution of Eq (28) which satisfies the conditions (29).

We begin by seeking solutions of (28) in the form

$$U = X(x) \cdot Y(y), \quad \text{or} \quad U = XY, \quad (30)$$

where $X(x)$ or more briefly X is a function of x alone and $Y(y)$ or more briefly Y is a function of y alone. By differentiating Eq. (30) partially we find

$$\frac{\partial U}{\partial x} = Y \frac{dX}{dx}, \quad \frac{\partial^2 U}{\partial x^2} = Y \frac{d^2 X}{dx^2}, \quad \frac{\partial U}{\partial y} = X \frac{dY}{dy},$$

$$\frac{\partial^2 U}{\partial y^2} = X \frac{d^2 Y}{dy^2}. \quad (31)$$

Thus, if Eq. (28) is satisfied, we must have

$$\frac{\partial^2 U}{\partial x^2} + \frac{\partial^2 U}{\partial y^2} = Y \frac{d^2 X}{dx^2} + X \frac{d^2 Y}{dy^2} = 0. \quad (32)$$

We may rewrite the last equation in the form

$$-\frac{1}{X} \frac{d^2 X}{dx^2} = \frac{1}{Y} \frac{d^2 Y}{dy^2}. \quad (33)$$

Since the left member of this equation does not involve y, it does not change when y changes. Similarly, the right member does not involve x and so does not change when x changes. As the two members are equal, their common value cannot change when either variable changes and so must be a constant. This constant may be positive, negative or zero. As the case useful for our problem, we assume the constant positive and write it as K^2. Then

$$-\frac{1}{X} \frac{d^2 X}{dx^2} = \frac{1}{Y} \frac{d^2 Y}{dy^2} = K^2, \quad \text{or} \quad \frac{d^2 X}{dx^2} + K^2 X = 0 \quad \text{and}$$

$$\frac{d^2 Y}{dy^2} - K^2 Y = 0. \quad (34)$$

By the method of Sec. 138 the solutions of these equations are found to be

$$X = c_1 \cos Kx + c_2 \sin Kx \quad \text{and} \quad Y = c_3 e^{Ky} + c_4 e^{-Ky}. \quad (35)$$

Thus for any value of K and c_1, c_2, c_3, c_4,

$$U = (c_1 \cos Kx + c_2 \sin Kx)(c_3 e^{Ky} + c_4 e^{-Ky}) \quad (36)$$

will be a particular solution of Eq. (28).

By specializing the constants in (36) we may satisfy the first three conditions (29). In fact, if $c_3 = 0$, the second factor will be zero for $y = +\infty$. And if $c_1 = 0$ the first factor will reduce to $c_2 \sin Kx$ and so be zero for $x = 0$. It will also be zero for $x = 20$ if

$$\sin 20K = 0, \qquad 20K = n\pi \qquad \text{or} \qquad K = \frac{n\pi}{20}, \qquad (37)$$

where n is any positive integer. If we write B_n for the product $c_2 c_4$ which goes with a particular n, we have

$$B_n e^{-n\pi y/20} \sin \frac{n\pi x}{20}, \qquad n = 1, 2, 3 \cdots \qquad (38)$$

as a set of terms each of which satisfies Eq. (28) and the first three boundary conditions of (29).

The same will be true of a sum, or infinite series of such terms, and to solve our problem it merely remains to determine the coefficients of a series

$$U(x,y) = \sum_{n=1}^{\infty} B_n e^{-n\pi y/20} \sin \frac{n\pi x}{20}, \qquad (39)$$

so that the fourth conditions of (29) will be satisfied. That is,

$$10 = U(x,0) = \sum_{n=1}^{\infty} B_n \sin \frac{n\pi x}{20}, \qquad \text{for } 0 < x < 20. \quad (40)$$

Accordingly the B_n are the coefficients b_n of the expansion of 10 in a Fourier sine series of period 40. These were found in Eq. (25). Replacing the B_n in (39) by these values, we have as the solution of our problem

$$U(x,y) = \frac{40}{\pi} \left(e^{-\pi y/20} \sin \frac{\pi x}{20} + \frac{1}{3} e^{-3\pi y/20} \sin \frac{3\pi x}{20} \right.$$
$$\left. + \frac{1}{5} e^{-5\pi y/20} \sin \frac{5\pi x}{20} + \cdots \right). \quad (41)$$

The series may be used for practical computation when y is not too small compared with 20, since the first few terms will then give a good approximation. For example, when $x = 10$, $y = 10$,

$$U(10,10) = \frac{40}{\pi} \left(e^{-\pi/2} - \frac{1}{3} e^{-3\pi/2} + \frac{1}{5} e^{-5\pi/2} - \cdots \right)$$
$$= \frac{40}{\pi} (0.2079 - 0.0030 + 0.0001) = 2.61. \quad (42)$$

161. Temperatures in a Circular Plate. Let us next find the steady-state temperature distribution of a circular plate whose faces are insulated and whose circumference is kept at prescribed temperatures. In particular, let one diameter of the circle be AB, and let the radius $OA = 10$ cm. Let the temperature be $0°$ at A and $100°$ at B, and increase linearly along the circumference between these points. Thus in Fig. 149 at C on the

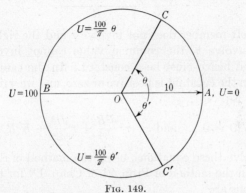

Fig. 149.

upper semicircle $U = 100\theta/\pi$, and at C' on the lower semicircle $U = 100\theta'/\pi$. If we use polar coordinates, $\theta' = -\theta$, and the boundary conditions are

$$U(10,\theta) = \frac{100\theta}{\pi}, \qquad \text{if } 0 < \theta < \pi,$$
$$= -\frac{100\theta}{\pi}, \qquad \text{if } -\pi < \theta < 0. \tag{43}$$

Since U must satisfy Laplace's equation, $U(r,\theta)$ is a solution of

$$\frac{\partial^2 U}{\partial r^2} + \frac{1}{r^2}\frac{\partial^2 U}{\partial \theta^2} + \frac{1}{r}\frac{\partial U}{\partial r} = 0, \tag{44}$$

by Eq. (85) of Sec. 25.

We begin by seeking solutions of Eq. (44) in the form

$$U = R(r) \cdot \Theta(\theta), \qquad \text{or} \qquad U = R\Theta, \tag{45}$$

where $R(r)$ or R is a function of r alone and $\Theta(\theta)$ or Θ is a function of θ alone. It follows from Eq. (45) that

$$\frac{\partial U}{\partial r} = \Theta\frac{dR}{dr}, \qquad \frac{\partial^2 U}{\partial r^2} = \Theta\frac{d^2R}{dr^2}, \qquad \text{and} \qquad \frac{\partial^2 U}{\partial \theta^2} = R\frac{d^2\Theta}{d\theta^2}. \tag{46}$$

On inserting these values in Eq. (44) we find

$$\Theta \frac{d^2R}{dr^2} + \frac{1}{r^2} R \frac{d^2\Theta}{d\theta^2} + \frac{1}{r} \Theta \frac{dR}{dr} = 0. \tag{47}$$

This may be rewritten in the form

$$-\frac{\dfrac{d^2\Theta}{d\theta^2}}{\Theta} = \frac{r^2 \dfrac{d^2R}{dr^2} + r \dfrac{dR}{dr}}{R}. \tag{48}$$

Since the left member does not involve r and the right member does not involve θ, the common value cannot involve either variable and hence must be a constant. In the case useful for our problem the constant is positive or zero, and we write it as K^2. Then from Eq. (48),

$$\frac{d^2\Theta}{d\theta^2} + K^2\Theta = 0 \quad \text{and} \quad r^2 \frac{d^2R}{dr^2} + r \frac{dR}{dr} - K^2R = 0. \tag{49}$$

We may solve these equations, using the method of Sec. 138 for the first and the method of Prob. 91 of Chap. IX for the second. The solutions are

$$\Theta = c_1 \cos K\theta + c_2 \sin K\theta \quad \text{and} \quad R = c_3 r^K + c_4 r^{-K},$$
$$\text{when } K \neq 0. \tag{50}$$

Hence for any value of K and c_1, c_2, c_3, c_4

$$U = (c_1 \cos K\theta + c_2 \sin K\theta)(c_3 r^K + c_4 r^{-K}) \tag{51}$$

will be a solution of Eq. (44). Although (50) is no longer the general solution when $K = 0$, it does include the solution we need in that case.

From the nature of polar coordinates, $U(r,\theta)$ will be periodic of period 2π. Hence we make the particular solutions (51) of period 2π by putting $K = n$, where n is zero or a positive integer. And since r^{-K} is infinite for $r = 0$, we take $c_4 = 0$. Also we write A_n for the c_1c_3 and B_n for the c_2c_3 which goes with a particular n. Then

$$A_0 \text{ and } A_n r^n \cos n\theta + B_n r^n \sin n\theta, \qquad n = 1,2,3, \cdots \tag{52}$$

is a set of particular solutions of period 2π, and we write

$$U(r,\theta) = A_0 + \sum_{n=1}^{\infty} (A_n r^n \cos n\theta + B_n r^n \sin n\theta). \tag{53}$$

This will satisfy the boundary condition (43) if

$$U(10,\theta) = A_0 + \sum_{n=1}^{\infty} (A_n 10^n \cos n\theta + B_n 10^n \sin n\theta). \quad (54)$$

Thus $A_0 = a$, $A_n 10^n = a_n$, $B_n 10^n = b_n$, the coefficients in the Fourier series of period 2π which represents $U(10,\theta)$. Since $U(10,\theta)$ is an even function, the b_n and hence the B_n will all be zero. Also a and the a_n may be found from (18) with $L = \pi$. In fact, since the graph of $U(10,\theta)$ against θ differs from Fig. 146 only by a change in the vertical scale, the coefficients may be obtained from those of Eq. (22) by multiplication by $100/\pi$. Hence

$$A_0 = a = 50, \qquad A_n = 10^{-n}a_n = -\frac{400}{\pi^2 n^2} 10^{-n}, \text{ if } n \text{ is odd.} \quad (55)$$

Thus the solution of our problem in series form is

$$U(r,\theta) = 50 - \frac{400}{\pi^2} \left(\frac{r}{10} \cos\theta + \frac{r^3}{3^2 \cdot 10^3} \cos 3\theta \right.$$
$$\left. + \frac{r^5}{5^2 \cdot 10^5} \cos 5\theta + \cdots \right). \quad (56)$$

162. Temperatures in a Solid Sphere. We shall next find the steady-state temperature distribution inside a solid sphere when its surface is kept at prescribed temperatures, symmetrical about a diameter. In particular, let AB be the diameter and let the radius OA be 20 cm. Take the z axis along OA, as shown in Fig. 150. Let the prescribed temperatures at the surface of the sphere be $U = 100°$ on the upper hemisphere, $z > 0$, and $U = 0°$ on the lower hemisphere, $z < 0$.

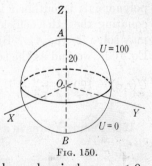

Fig. 150.

It will be convenient to use the spherical polar coordinates r, ϕ, θ of Sec. 59. Since the boundary values are symmetrical about AB or OZ, the temperatures inside the sphere will also be symmetrical about OZ and so will not depend on θ. Thus our solution may be written $U(r,\phi)$ and the boundary conditions are

$$U(20,\phi) = \begin{cases} 100, \text{ if } 0 < \phi < \dfrac{\pi}{2}, \\ 0, \text{ if } \dfrac{\pi}{2} < \phi < \pi. \end{cases} \quad (57)$$

When $\partial^2 U/\partial \theta^2 = 0$, Laplace's equation in spherical coordinates is

$$\frac{1}{r^2}\frac{\partial}{\partial r}\left(r^2\frac{\partial U}{\partial r}\right) + \frac{1}{r^2 \sin \phi}\frac{\partial}{\partial \phi}\left(\sin \phi \frac{\partial U}{\partial \phi}\right) = 0, \qquad (58)$$

by Eq. (110) of Sec. 124. Thus our problem is to find the solution of Eq. (58) which assumes the boundary values (57).

The discussion of Sec. 146 shows that if $x = \cos \phi$, $r^n P_n(x)$, where $P_n(x)$ is the nth Legendre polynomial of Sec. 145, is a solution of Eq. (58). Hence

$$A_n r^n P_n(\cos \phi), \qquad n = 0, 1, 2, \cdots \qquad (59)$$

is a set of particular solutions of Eq. (58) and we write

$$U(r,\phi) = \sum_{n=0}^{\infty} A_n r^n P_n(\cos \phi). \qquad (60)$$

This will satisfy the boundary conditions (57) if

$$U(10,\phi) = \sum_{n=0}^{\infty} A_n (20)^n P_n(\cos \phi). \qquad (61)$$

The method of developing a function in a series of Legendre polynomials is outlined in Probs. 56 to 62. In particular by equating the nth coefficient found in Prob. 62 to $A_n(20)^n$, we may solve for the A_n. By substituting the values thus found in Eq. (60), we find as the solution of our problem

$$U(r,\phi) = 100\left[\frac{1}{2} + \frac{3}{4}\frac{r}{20}P_1(\cos \phi) - \frac{7}{16}\frac{r^3}{20^3}P_3(\cos \phi) + \cdots\right].$$
$$(62)$$

163. Temperatures in a Solid Cylinder. We shall next find the

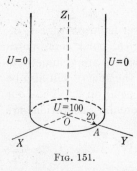
Fig. 151.

steady-state temperature distribution inside a solid right cylinder whose surfaces are kept at prescribed temperatures, symmetrical about the axis of the cylinder. We take the axis of the cylinder as OZ, one face of the cylinder as the xy plane, and assume that the cylinder is so long compared with its radius $OA = 20$ cm. that we may treat the other end as at infinity. Let the prescribed temperatures be $U = 0°$ on the lateral surface and the end at infinity, and let $U = 100°$ on the end in the xy plane.

It will be convenient to use cylindrical coordinates r, θ, z. Since the boundary values are symmetrical about OZ, the temperatures inside will also be symmetrical about OZ and so will not depend on θ. Thus our solution may be written $U(r,z)$, and the boundary conditions are

$$U(r,0) = 100, \qquad U(r,\infty) = 0, \qquad U(20,z) = 0. \qquad (63)$$

When $\partial^2 U/\partial\theta^2 = 0$, Laplace's equation in cylindrical coordinates is

$$\frac{1}{r}\frac{\partial}{\partial r}\left(r\frac{\partial U}{\partial r}\right) + \frac{\partial^2 U}{\partial z^2} = 0, \qquad (64)$$

by Prob. 48 of Exercises VIII (page 331). Thus our problem is to find the solution of (64) which assumes the boundary values (63).

In Sec. 151 we found a particular solution (109) of Laplace's equation in cylindrical coordinates (103). It will be independent of θ if $m = 0$, so that

$$AJ_0(ar)e^{-az} \qquad (65)$$

is a particular solution of (64). It already satisfies the second condition (63) and will satisfy the third if

$$J_0(20a) = 0, \qquad \text{or} \qquad 20a = \alpha_n, \qquad (66)$$

where α_n is one of the infinitely many real roots of $J_0(x) = 0$ mentioned in Sec. 154. Hence

$$A_nJ_0\left(\frac{\alpha_n}{20}r\right)e^{-\alpha_nz/20}, \quad n = 1,2,3, \cdots \qquad (67)$$

is a set of particular solutions of Eq. (64) and we write

$$U(r,z) = \sum_{n=1}^{\infty} A_nJ_0\left(\frac{\alpha_n}{20}r\right)e^{-\alpha_nz/20}. \qquad (68)$$

This will satisfy the remaining boundary condition if

$$100 = U(r,0) = \sum_{n=1}^{\infty} A_nJ_0\left(\frac{\alpha_n}{20}r\right). \qquad (69)$$

The method of developing a function in a series of Bessel's functions of this kind is outlined in Probs. 63 to 68. In particular, the A_n of (69) are 100 times the coefficients found in Prob. 68. Using these values in (68), we find as the solution of our problem

$$U(r,z) = 200 \sum_{n=1}^{\infty} \frac{1}{\alpha_n J_1(\alpha_n)} J_0 \left(\frac{\alpha_n}{20} r \right) e^{-\alpha_n z/20}. \tag{70}$$

164. Cooling of a Rod.   If a thin uniform rod AB has its sides insulated, the temperature at any cross section C will depend only on the distance $AC = x$ and the time t.   Thus we may put

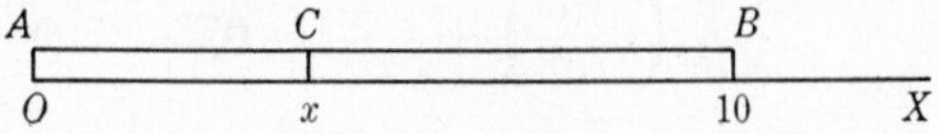

FIG. 152.

$\partial^2 U/\partial y^2 = 0$ and $\partial^2 U/\partial z^2 = 0$ in Eq. (135) of Sec. 127 to obtain the equation governing the flow of heat in the rod.   The result is

$$\frac{\partial U}{\partial t} = a^2 \frac{\partial^2 U}{\partial x^2}, \tag{71}$$

as the equation satisfied by the temperature $U(x,t)$.

Consider in particular a rod AB 10 cm. long, of material for which $a^2 = 2$ cm.²/sec.   Suppose that originally all points of the rod were at 100° but that at times $t = 0$ the ends of the rod A and B had their temperatures suddenly changed to 0° and kept at this temperature.   We wish to find $U(x,t)$.   The initial and boundary conditions are

$$U(x,0) = 100, \qquad U(0,t) = 0, \qquad U(10,t) = 0. \tag{72}$$

We begin by seeking solutions of Eq. (71) in the form

$$U = X(x) \cdot T(t) \qquad \text{or} \qquad U = XT. \tag{73}$$

From Eqs. (73) and (71), by a procedure similar to that used to derive Eqs. (34), we find that

$$\frac{d^2X/dx^2}{X} = \frac{dT/dt}{a^2 T} = -K^2, \qquad \text{or}$$

$$\frac{d^2X}{dx^2} + K^2 X = 0 \qquad \text{and} \qquad \frac{dT}{dt} + a^2 K^2 T = 0. \tag{74}$$

We have written the constant as $-K^2$, since it is negative in the case useful for our problem.   The solution of Eqs. (74) by the method of Sec. 138 leads to

$$U = (c_1 \cos Kx + c_2 \sin Kx) c_3 e^{-a^2 K^2 t} \tag{75}$$

as a particular solution of Eq. (71).

The second condition (72) will be satisfied if $c_1 = 0$. And the third condition will be satisfied if

$$\sin 10K = 0, \quad \text{or} \quad K = \frac{n\pi}{10} \quad \text{and} \quad a^2K^2 = 0.02n^2\pi^2, \quad (76)$$

where n is any positive integer. We write B_n for the product c_2c_3 which goes with a particular n, and have

$$B_n \sin \frac{n\pi x}{10} e^{-0.02n^2\pi^2 t}, \qquad n = 1,2,3, \cdots \qquad (77)$$

as a set of terms each of which satisfies Eq. (71) and the last two conditions of (72). Hence we put

$$U(x,t) = \sum_{n=1}^{\infty} B_n \sin \frac{n\pi x}{10} e^{-0.02n^2\pi^2 t}. \qquad (78)$$

The remaining initial condition will be satisfied if

$$100 = U(x,0) = \sum_{n=1}^{\infty} B_n \sin \frac{n\pi x}{10}. \qquad (79)$$

This shows that the B_n are the coefficients of the Fourier sine series of period 20 which represents 100. They may be calculated as the b_n of Eq. (23) with $f(x) = 100, L = 10$. On computing them and substituting the values in Eq. (78), we obtain as the solution of our problem

$$U(x,t) = \frac{400}{\pi} \left(\sin \frac{\pi x}{10} e^{-0.02\pi^2 t} + \frac{1}{3} \sin \frac{3\pi x}{10} e^{-0.18\pi^2 t} + \cdots \right). \quad (80)$$

The process used above requires modification if the ends of the rod are suddenly changed to fixed temperatures different from zero. We illustrate the revised procedure by solving the following problem.

Suppose that the rod of Fig. 152 has end A kept at 30° and end B kept at 100° until temperatures indistinguishable from the steady state are reached. At some time thereafter, let us suddenly lower the temperature of A to 20° and that of B to 40°, and from then on maintain these temperatures. We wish to find $U(x,t)$, where t is measured from the sudden change.

We must make use of the steady-state solution of Eq. (71). Since this is independent of t, it will be a solution of

$$\frac{d^2U}{dx^2} = 0, \quad \text{or} \quad U = c_1x + c_2. \tag{81}$$

We first determine the constants c_1 and c_2 so that this takes on the original end values, 30 at A, $x = 0$ and 100 at B, $x = 10$. Hence

$$30 = c_2, \quad 100 = 10c_1 + c_2 \quad \text{and} \quad c_2 = 30, \quad c_1 = 7. \tag{82}$$

This shows that $7x + 30$ was the temperature before the sudden change and, for our problem, the initial condition is

$$U(x,0) = 7x + 30. \tag{83}$$

The temperatures for our problem will approach the steady-state solution for the changed end values, 20 at A, $x = 0$ and 40 at B, $x = 10$. The values of c_1 and c_2 which make (81) take on these values are found from

$$20 = c_2, \quad 40 = 10c_1 + c_2 \text{ to be } c_2 = 20, \quad c_1 = 2. \tag{84}$$

This shows that the steady-state solution

$$U_S = 2x + 20 \tag{85}$$

satisfies the changed boundary conditions for our problem

$$U(0,t) = 20, \quad U(10,t) = 40. \tag{86}$$

Mathematically considered, our problem is to find a solution of Eq. (71) that satisfies the initial condition (83) and the boundary conditions (86). We transform this to a problem with end values zero by putting

$$U = U_S + U_T = 2x + 20 + U_T. \tag{87}$$

This makes the new function U_T satisfy the relation

$$U_T = U - U_S = U - 2x - 20. \tag{88}$$

Since U and U_S are each solutions of Eq. (71), their difference U_T is also a solution. It follows from the way in which U_S was determined, and may be verified from Eqs. (86) and (88) that

$$U_T(0,t) = 0, \quad U_T(10,t) = 0. \tag{89}$$

Also from Eqs. (83) and (88) we may deduce that

$$U_T(x,0) = U(x,0) - 2x - 20 = 5x + 10. \tag{90}$$

The problem of finding $U_T(x,t)$, a solution of Eq. (71) which satisfies the initial conditions (90) and boundary condition (89), is similar in type to the first problem solved in this section. To solve it, we begin with the relation similar to (78),

$$U_T(x,t) = \sum_{n=1}^{\infty} B_n \sin \frac{n\pi x}{10} \, e^{-0.02 n^2 \pi^2 t}. \tag{91}$$

This satisfies the differential equation (71) and the end conditions (89). The initial condition (90) will be satisfied if

$$5x + 10 = U_T(x,0) = \sum_{n=1}^{\infty} B_n \sin \frac{n\pi x}{10}. \tag{92}$$

The coefficients of this expansion in a sine series of period 20 may be found from Eq. (23) or from Prob. 32. On substituting their values in (91) and making use of (87), we find as the solution of our problem

$$U(x,t) = 2x + 20 + \frac{1}{\pi} \left(140 \sin \frac{x}{10} \, e^{-0.02\pi^2 t} - 50 \sin \frac{2\pi x}{10} \, e^{-0.08\pi^2 t} \right.$$
$$\left. + \frac{140}{3} \sin \frac{3\pi x}{10} \, e^{-0.18\pi^2 t} - \cdots \right). \tag{93}$$

165. The Vibrating String. In Example 1 of Sec. 175 the equation governing the small transverse displacements of a taut, vibrating string is found to be

$$\frac{\partial^2 u}{\partial x^2} = \frac{1}{s^2} \frac{\partial^2 u}{\partial t^2}. \tag{94}$$

Here x is distance along the string, u is transverse displacement, and $s^2 = Tg/D$, where T is tension, D weight per unit length, and g the acceleration of gravity. Thus s has the units of velocity, or of x/t.

In particular consider the string AB of length 100 units, and measure x from A. Denote the displacement by $u(x,t)$ and the velocity by $u_t(x,t) = \partial u / \partial t$. Then, if the ends are fixed,

$$u(0,t) = 0, \qquad u(100,t) = 0. \tag{95}$$

Suppose that we wish to determine the motion when the initial displacement and velocity were

$$u(x,0) = 2 \sin \frac{\pi x}{50}, \qquad u_t(x,0) = 3 \sin \frac{\pi x}{25}. \tag{96}$$

We begin by seeking solutions of Eq. (94) of the form

$$u = X(x) \cdot T(t) \qquad \text{or} \qquad u = XT. \tag{97}$$

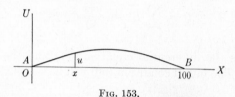

Fig. 153.

From Eqs. (97) and (94), by a procedure similar to that used to derive Eqs. (34), we find that

$$\frac{d^2X/dx^2}{X} = \frac{d^2T/dt^2}{s^2T} = -K^2, \qquad \text{or}$$

$$\frac{d^2X}{dx^2} + K^2X = 0 \qquad \text{and} \qquad \frac{d^2T}{dt^2} + s^2K^2T = 0. \tag{98}$$

We have written the constant as $-K^2$, since it is negative in the case useful for our problem. The solution of Eqs. (98) by the method of Sec. 138 leads to

$$u = (c_1 \cos Kx + c_2 \sin Kx)(c_3 \cos Kst + c_4 \sin Kst). \tag{99}$$

The first condition of (95) will be satisfied if $c_1 = 0$, and the second will be satisfied if

$$\sin 100K = n\pi, \qquad \text{or} \qquad K = \frac{n\pi}{100}, \tag{100}$$

where n is any positive integer. In place of the products c_2c_3 and c_2c_4 which go with a particular n, we write C_n and D_n, respectively. Thus

$$\sin \frac{n\pi x}{100} \left(C_n \cos \frac{n\pi st}{100} + D_n \sin \frac{n\pi st}{100} \right), \qquad n = 1,2,3, \cdots \tag{101}$$

are a set of terms each of which satisfies Eq. (94) and the boundary conditions (95). Hence, we put

$$u(x,t) = \sum_{n=1}^{\infty} \sin \frac{n\pi x}{100} \left(C_n \cos \frac{n\pi st}{100} + D_n \sin \frac{n\pi st}{100} \right). \quad (102)$$

The initial conditions (96) will be satisfied if

$$u(x,0) = 2 \sin \frac{\pi x}{50} = \sum_{n=1}^{\infty} C_n \sin \frac{n\pi x}{100}, \quad (103)$$

and

$$u_t(x,0) = 3 \sin \frac{\pi x}{25} = \sum_{n=1}^{\infty} \frac{n\pi s}{100} D_n \sin \frac{n\pi x}{100}. \quad (104)$$

Ordinarily at this point we would expand the given values of $u(x,0)$ and $u_t(x,0)$ in Fourier sine series of period $2L$, where L is the length of the string, by using Eq. (23). But here this is unnecessary, since the values are already Fourier sine series of period 200, of one term. Thus

$$2 = C_2, \quad 3 = \frac{\pi s}{25} D_4, \quad \text{or} \quad C_2 = 2, \quad D_4 = \frac{75}{\pi s}, \quad (105)$$

and the other C_n and D_n are zero. On putting these values in Eq. (102), we find as the solution of our problem

$$u(x,t) = 2 \sin \frac{\pi x}{50} \cos \frac{\pi st}{50} + \frac{75}{\pi s} \sin \frac{\pi x}{25} \cos \frac{\pi st}{25}. \quad (106)$$

166. Flow of Electricity in a Cable. When an electric current flows in a long cable, of series resistance R(ohms per mile) and inductance L(henrys per mile), the loss of current due to the

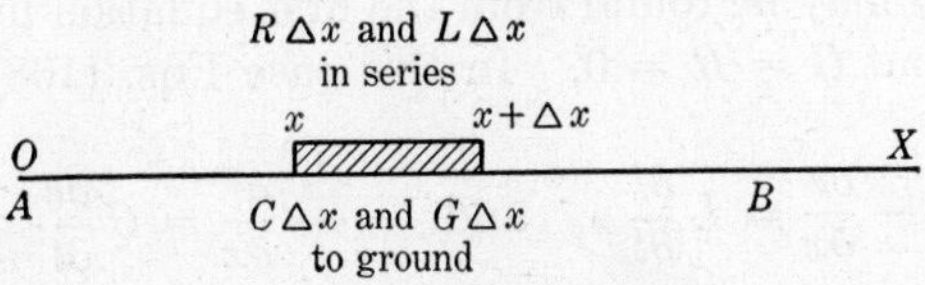

FIG. 154.

imperfection of the insulation depends on the capacitance to ground C(farads per mile) and conductance to ground G(mhos per mile). Note that each of the four quantities R, L, G, C is here taken per unit of length. If x (miles) is the distance along the cable, the e.m.f. e (volts), and the current i (amperes)* will depend on x as well as on the time t (seconds). That is,

$$e = e(x,t), \qquad i = i(x,t). \tag{107}$$

The e.m.f. decreases with distance in accord with the relation

$$-\frac{\partial e}{\partial x} = Ri + L\frac{\partial i}{\partial t}, \tag{108}$$

while the current decreases with distance in accord with

$$-\frac{\partial i}{\partial x} = Ge + C\frac{\partial e}{\partial t}. \tag{109}$$

These relations are consequences of the definition of the quantities R, L, G, and C.

If we make certain simplifying assumptions, the equations may be solved by methods previously discussed. Let us first put $G = L = 0$. In this case the equations become

$$-\frac{\partial e}{\partial x} = Ri \quad \text{and} \quad -\frac{\partial i}{\partial x} = C\frac{\partial e}{\partial t}. \tag{110}$$

These are known as the *telegraph equations*, because they are approximately satisfied in telegraph signaling, where the leakage and inductance are negligible. By differentiating the first equation in (110) with respect to x, we may deduce that

$$\frac{\partial^2 e}{\partial x^2} = RC\frac{\partial e}{\partial t}. \tag{111}$$

Since the equation just written has the same form as the equation for one dimensional heat flow [Eq. (71)], it may be solved by the methods for that equation discussed in Sec. 164. After e has been found, i may be found from the first equation in (110).

We next put $G = R = 0$. In this case Eqs. (108) and (109) become

$$-\frac{\partial e}{\partial x} = L\frac{\partial i}{\partial t} \quad \text{and} \quad -\frac{\partial i}{\partial x} = C\frac{\partial e}{\partial t}. \tag{112}$$

These are known as the *radio equations*, because they roughly approximate the situation when the frequencies are high, and the

---

* Electrical engineers habitually use i for current intensity and e for electromotive force and avoid confusion with the mathematical meaning of these symbols by writing j for $\sqrt{-1}$ and ϵ for $2.71828 \cdots$.

terms in the time derivative are large compared with the undifferentiated terms. By differentiating the first equation in (112) with respect to x and the second with respect to t, we may deduce that

$$\frac{\partial^2 e}{\partial x^2} = LC \frac{\partial^2 e}{\partial t^2}. \tag{113}$$

This has the same form as the equation for the vibrating string [Eq. (94)] and may be solved by the methods used for that equation in Sec. 165. After e has been found, we may find the partial derivatives of i from Eqs. (112) and hence determine i by the procedure illustrated by Eqs. (34) to (38) of Sec. 82.

167. References. Additional illustrations of the methods of this chapter will be found in Byerly's *Fourier Series and Spherical Harmonics*, Carslaw's *Theory of the Conduction of Heat*, and the author's *Differential Equations for Electrical Engineers*.

An introduction to the theory of Fourier series will be found in Chap. XIV of the author's *Treatise on Advanced Calculus*.

The simplest justification of the validity of the series solutions of partial differential equations rests on the theory of integral equations and will be found in such comprehensive works as Frank and Von Mises, *Differential- und Integralgleichungen der Mechanik und Physik* or Courant-Hilbert, *Methoden der mathematischen Physik*.

EXERCISES XI

Verify that, for any positive integer n,

1. $\displaystyle\int_c^{c+p} \cos \frac{2n\pi x}{p}\, dx = \frac{p}{2n\pi} \sin \frac{2n\pi x}{p} \Big|_c^{c+p} = 0.$

2. $\displaystyle\int_c^{c+p} \sin \frac{2n\pi x}{p}\, dx = -\frac{p}{2n\pi} \cos \frac{2n\pi x}{p} \Big|_c^{c+p} = 0.$

From Probs. 1 and 2 and the appropriate one of the relations.

$$\cos A \cos B = \tfrac{1}{2}[\cos (A - B) + \cos (A + B)],$$
$$\sin A \sin B = \tfrac{1}{2}[\cos (A - B) - \cos (A + B)],$$
$$\sin A \cos B = \tfrac{1}{2}[\sin (A + B) + \sin (A - B)],$$

deduce that for any positive integers k and n,

3. $\displaystyle\int_c^{c+p} \cos \frac{2n\pi x}{p} \cos \frac{2k\pi x}{p}\, dx = 0,$ if $k \neq n$ and

$$= \frac{p}{2}, \text{ if } k = n.$$

4. $\int_c^{c+p} \sin \dfrac{2n\pi x}{p} \sin \dfrac{2k\pi x}{p} \, dx = 0$, if $k \neq n$ and

$$= \frac{p}{2}, \text{ if } k = n.$$

5. $\int_c^{c+p} \sin \dfrac{2k\pi x}{p} \cos \dfrac{2n\pi x}{p} \, dx = 0.$

6. Using Probs. 1 and 2, deduce that the result of integrating Eq. (8) termwise from c to $c + p$ is Eq. (9).

7. Using Probs. 1, 3, and 5, deduce that the result of multiplying Eq. (8) by $\cos (2n\pi x/p)$ and then integrating termwise from c to $c + p$ is Eq. (10).

8. Using Probs. 2, 4, and 5 with k and n interchanged, deduce that the result of multiplying Eq. (8) by $\sin (2n\pi x/p)$ and then integrating termwise from c to $c + p$ is Eq. (11).

Find the Fourier series of period 2π which in the interval $-\pi < x < \pi$ represents

9. x.   **10.** x^2.   **11.** x^3.   **12.** e^x.   **13.** $x \sin x$.   **14.** $x \cos x$.
15. $f(x) = \pi$ if $-\pi < x < 0$ and $f(x) = 0$ if $0 < x < \pi$.
16. $f(x) = x$ if $-\pi < x < 0$ and $f(x) = 0$ if $0 < x < \pi$.

Find the Fourier series of period 2π which in the interval $0 < x < 2\pi$ represents

17. x.   **18.** x^2.   **19.** x^3.   **20.** e^x.   **21.** $x \sin x$.   **22.** $x \cos x$.
23. $f(x) = \pi$ if $0 < x < \pi$ and $f(x) = 0$, if $\pi < x < 2\pi$.
24. $f(x) = x$ if $0 < x < \pi$ and $f(x) = 0$, if $\pi < x < 2\pi$.

Find the Fourier series of period π which represents the periodic function

25. $|\sin x|$.   **26.** $|\cos x|$.   **27.** $\sin^2 x$.   **28.** $\cos^2 x$.

Verify that for $0 < x < L$,

29. $1 = \dfrac{4}{\pi} \left(\sin \dfrac{\pi x}{L} + \dfrac{1}{3} \sin \dfrac{3\pi x}{L} + \dfrac{1}{5} \sin \dfrac{5\pi x}{L} + \cdots \right).$

30. $x = \dfrac{2L}{\pi} \left(\sin \dfrac{\pi x}{L} - \dfrac{1}{2} \sin \dfrac{2\pi x}{L} + \dfrac{1}{3} \sin \dfrac{3\pi x}{L} - \cdots \right).$

31. $x = \dfrac{L}{2} - \dfrac{4L}{\pi^2} \left(\cos \dfrac{\pi x}{L} + \dfrac{1}{3^2} \cos \dfrac{3\pi x}{L} + \dfrac{1}{5^2} \cos \dfrac{5\pi x}{L} + \cdots \right).$

32. From Probs. 29 and 30, deduce that for $0 < x < L$,

$$Ax + B = \frac{1}{\pi} \left[(4B + 2LA) \sin \frac{\pi x}{L} - \frac{2LA}{2} \sin \frac{2\pi x}{L} \right.$$
$$\left. + \frac{4B + 2LA}{3} \sin \frac{3\pi x}{L} - \frac{2LA}{4} \sin \frac{4\pi x}{L} + \cdots \right].$$

33. Check the terms of Prob. 31, other than the constant term, by integrating the series of Prob. 29 termwise.

By the method used in Probs. 3 and 4, verify that

34. $\int_0^L \cos \dfrac{n\pi x}{L} \cos \dfrac{k\pi x}{L} \, dx = 0$, if $k \neq n$ and

$$= \dfrac{L}{2}, \text{ if } k = n.$$

35. $\int_0^L \sin \dfrac{n\pi x}{L} \sin \dfrac{k\pi x}{L} \, dx = 0$, if $k \neq n$ and

$$= \dfrac{L}{2}, \text{ if } k = n.$$

36. Square both sides of Eq. (19) and integrate from 0 to L. Using Prob. 34 to evaluate the terms on the right, deduce that

$$\int_0^L [f(x)]^2 dx = a^2 L + \frac{L}{2}(a_1{}^2 + a_2{}^2 + a_3{}^2 + \cdots).$$

37. Square both sides of Eq. (24) and integrate from 0 to L. Using Prob. 35 to evaluate the terms on the right, deduce that

$$\int_0^L [f(x)]^2 dx = \frac{L}{2}(b_1{}^2 + b_2{}^2 + b_3{}^2 + \cdots).$$

38. From Probs. 29 and 37 deduce the validity of the equation
$\dfrac{\pi^2}{8} = \dfrac{1}{1^2} + \dfrac{1}{3^2} + \dfrac{1}{5^2} + \cdots$ and check this by putting $x = 0$ in Prob. 31.

39. From Probs. 30 and 37 deduce that

$$\frac{\pi^2}{6} = \frac{1}{1^2} + \frac{1}{2^2} + \frac{1}{3^2} + \frac{1}{4^2} + \cdots.$$

40. From Probs. 31 and 36 deduce that

$$\frac{\pi^4}{96} = \frac{1}{1^4} + \frac{1}{3^4} + \frac{1}{5^4} + \cdots.$$

A long rectangular plate has its surfaces insulated and the two long sides, as well as one of the short sides, maintained at 0°. Find an expression for the steady-state temperature $U(x,y)$ if

41. The other short side, $y = 0$, is kept at 40° and is 30 cm. long.

42. $U(x,0) = 8x$, and the short side is 6 cm. long.

43. $U(x,0) = 2x - 4$, and the short side is 4 cm. long.

44. $U(x,0) = 2 \sin \dfrac{\pi x}{10}$, and the short side is 10 cm. long.

45. $U(x,0) = 5 \sin \dfrac{\pi x}{3} + 3 \sin \dfrac{\pi x}{4}$, and the short side is 12 cm. long.

46. $U(x,0) = c$, and the short side is L cm. long.

47. $U(x,0) = px$, and the short side is L cm. long.

48. A rectangular plate is bounded by the lines $x = 0$, $x = a$, $y = 0$, $y = b$. Its surfaces are insulated, and the temperatures along the edges are $U(0,y) = 0$, $U(a,y) = 0$, $U(x,b) = 0$, $U(x,0) = f(x)$. By restricting the constants in the expression (36), deduce the particular solution that satisfies the first three conditions, $C_n \sin \dfrac{\pi n x}{a} \sinh \dfrac{n\pi(y - b)}{a}$, where sinh means the hyperbolic sine of Sec. 4.

49. Using a series of the particular solutions of Prob. 48, find $U(x,y)$ when $f(x) = 100$.

Find $U(r,\theta)$, the steady-state temperature distribution of a circular plate of radius a whose faces are insulated, if

50. $a = 20$ and $U(20,\theta) = 1$, if $0 < \theta < \pi$, and $= 0$, if $-\pi < \theta < 0$.

51. $a = 15$ and $U(15,\theta) = 45 \sin \theta + 450 \sin 2\theta$.

52. $a = 1$ and $U(1,\theta) = 2\theta$, $0 < \theta < 2\pi$.

53. A plate in the form of a circular sector is bounded by the lines $\theta = 0$, $\theta = \alpha$, $r = a$. Its surfaces are insulated, and the temperatures along the boundary are $U(r,0) = 0$, $U(r,\alpha) = 0$, $U(a,\theta) = f(\theta)$. By restricting the constants in the solution (51), deduce the particular solution that satisfies the first two conditions, $C_n \sin \dfrac{\pi n \theta}{\alpha}\, r^{\pi n/\alpha}$.

54. Using a series of the particular solutions of Prob. 53, find $U(r,\theta)$ if $\alpha = \pi/3$ and $f(\theta) = 100$.

55. A plate in the form of a ring is bounded by the lines $r = 2$, $r = 4$. Its surfaces are insulated, and the temperatures along the boundary are $U(2,\theta) = 10 \sin \theta + 6 \cos \theta$, $U(4,\theta) = 17 \sin \theta + 15 \cos \theta$. Using a series of particular solutions of the following appropriate form, $(C_n r^n + D_n r^{-n}) \cos n\theta + (E_n r^n + F_n r^{-n}) \sin n\theta$, find the steady-state temperature in the ring, $U(r,\theta)$.

56. Use Leibniz's rule for the derivative of a product as stated in Prob. 19 of Exercises X (page 396) to show that each of the first $n - 1$ derivatives of $(x^2 - 1)^n = (x - 1)^n(x + 1)^n$ is zero when $x = 1$ or -1.

57. Verify the integral identity $\displaystyle\int_{-1}^{1} \frac{d^n}{dx^n}(x^2 - 1)^n \frac{d^m}{dx^m}(x^2 - 1)^m dx$
$= (-1)^n \displaystyle\int_{-1}^{1}(x^2 - 1)^n \frac{d^{m+n}}{dx^{m+n}}(x^2 - 1)dx^m$, by integrating by parts n times and noting that each time the integrated part is zero at the limits by Prob. 56.

58. Show that $\displaystyle\int_{-1}^{1} P_n(x)P_m(x)dx = 0$, if $m \neq n$. HINT: Use Rodrigues's formula, $P_n(x) = \dfrac{1}{2^n n!}\dfrac{d^n}{dx^n}(x^2 - 1)^n$, Eq. (39) of Sec. 145, to reduce the integral to a constant times the integral of Prob. 57. Let $n > m$. Then $m + n > 2m$ and since the term of highest degree in $(x^2 - 1)^m$ is x^{2m} its $2m$th derivative is $(2m)!$, and its $(m + n)$th derivative is zero.

59. Show that $\int_{-1}^{1} [P_n(x)]^2 dx = \dfrac{2}{2n + 1}$. HINT: Use of the hint to Prob. 58 and Prob. 57 with $m = n$ leads to the simplified expression $\dfrac{(-1)^n (2n)!}{2^{2n}(n!)^2} \int_{-1}^{1} (x^2 - 1)^n dx$. And by Eq. (55) of Sec. 100, we deduce

$$\int_{-1}^{1} (x + 1)^n (1 - x)^n dx = 2^{2n+1} \frac{\Gamma(n + 1)\Gamma(n + 1)}{\Gamma(2n + 2)} = 2^{2n+1} \frac{(n!)^2}{(2n + 1)!}.$$

60. If $f(x)$ is piecewise regular for $-1 < x < 1$, it may be represented by a series whose terms are constants times the Legendre polynomials, $f(x) = A_0 P_0(x) + A_1 P_1(x) + A_2 P_2(x) + \cdots$. With regard to convergence inside the interval and possibility of termwise integration, the behavior is analogous to that for Fourier series described in Sec. 157. Following the procedure of that section, and using Probs. 58 and 59, show that

$$\int_{-1}^{1} f(x) P_n(x) dx = \frac{2A_n}{2n + 1} \qquad \text{and} \qquad A_n = \frac{2n + 1}{2} \int_{-1}^{1} f(x) P_n(x) dx.$$

61. Using Eq. (37) of Sec. 145, verify that the value of $\int_{0}^{1} P_n(x) dx$ for $n = 0, 1, 2, 3$ is $1, \frac{1}{2}, 0, -\frac{1}{8}$.

62. Use Probs. 60 and 61 to deduce that the development of a function $f(x) = 0$ for $-1 < x < 0$ and 100 for $0 < x < 1$ is

$$100[\tfrac{1}{2} + \tfrac{3}{4}P_1(x) - \tfrac{7}{16}P_3(x) + \cdots].$$

63. By Eq. (99) of Sec. 150, $y = J_0(ax)$ is a solution of the equation $x^2 \dfrac{d^2 y}{dx^2} + x \dfrac{dy}{dx} + a^2 x^2 y = 0$ or $\dfrac{d}{dx}\left(x \dfrac{dy}{dx}\right) = -a^2 xy$. We also note that $z = J_0(bx)$ is a solution of $\dfrac{d}{dx}\left(x \dfrac{dz}{dx}\right) = -b^2 xz$. By multiplying the first equation by z and the second by $-y$ and adding, deduce that $\dfrac{d}{dx}\left(xz \dfrac{dy}{dx} - xy \dfrac{dz}{dx}\right) = (b^2 - a^2)xyz$ and, by integrating this, show that $\left[z \dfrac{dy}{dx} - y \dfrac{dz}{dx}\right]_{x=1} = (b^2 - a^2) \int_{0}^{1} xyz \, dx$. From Eq. (132) of Sec. 154, $\dfrac{d}{dx}[J_0(x)] = -J_1(x)$, so that $\dfrac{dy}{dx} = -aJ_1(ax)$ and similarly we deduce $\dfrac{dz}{dx} = -bJ_1(bx)$. From the relation between y and z found above, deduce that $\int_{0}^{1} x J_0(ax) J_0(bx) dx = \dfrac{bJ_0(a)J_1(b) - aJ_0(b)J_1(a)}{b^2 - a^2}$.

64. Show that if α_n and α_m are any two distinct roots of $J_0(x) = 0$, $\int_0^1 xJ_0(\alpha_n x)J_0(\alpha_m x)dx = 0$.   HINT: Use the result of Prob. 63.

65. When $b \to a$, the limit of the fraction in the right member of the result of Prob. 63 may be found by differentiating numerator and denominator with respect to b and by putting $b = a$, by l'Hospital's rule of Sec. 16.   Apply this process to the case when $a = \alpha_n$ is one root of $J_0(x) = 0$, and $b \to \alpha_n$, and so deduce that $\int_0^1 xJ_0(\alpha_n x)^2 dx = \frac{1}{2}[J_1(\alpha_n)]^2$.

66. From Eq. (132) of Sec. 154, $\dfrac{d}{dx}[xJ_1(x)] = xJ_0(x)$.   Deduce from this that $\dfrac{d}{dx}[xJ_1(ax)] = axJ_0(ax)$ and

$$\int_0^1 xJ_0(ax)dx = \frac{1}{a}xJ_1(ax)\Big|_0^1 = \frac{1}{a}J_1(a).$$

67. If $f(x)$ is piecewise regular for $0 < x < 1$, it may be represented by a series whose terms are multiples of $J_0(\alpha_n)x$, where the α_n are the roots of $J_0(x) = 0$.   Thus

$$f(x) = A_1J_0(\alpha_1 x) + A_2J_0(\alpha_2 x) + A_3J_0(\alpha_3 x) + \cdots.$$

With regard to convergence inside the interval and possibility of termwise integration the behavior is analogous to that for Fourier series described in Sec. 157.   Following the procedure of that section, but multiplying in an extra factor x and using Probs. 64 and 65, show that

$$\int_0^1 f(x)xJ_0(\alpha_n x)dx = \frac{1}{2}A_n[J_1(\alpha_n)]^2$$

and

$$A_n = \frac{2}{[J_1(\alpha_n)]^2}\int_0^1 xf(x)J_0(\alpha_n x)dx.$$

68. Use Prob. 66 to evaluate the integrals of Prob. 67 when $f(x) = 1$, and so deduce that for $0 < x < 1$

$$1 = \frac{2}{\alpha_1}\frac{J_0(\alpha_1 x)}{J_1(\alpha_1)} + \frac{2}{\alpha_2}\frac{J_0(\alpha_2 x)}{J_1(\alpha_2)} + \frac{2}{\alpha_3}\frac{J_0(\alpha_3 x)}{J_1(\alpha_3)} + \cdots.$$

The ends A and B of a rod 50 cm. long have their temperatures kept at $0°$ and $100°$, respectively, until the temperatures are indistinguishable from those for the steady state.   At some time after this, there is a sudden charge.   Find the temperature of any point in the rod, $U(x,t)$, as a function of x cm., the distance from A, and t sec., the time elapsed after the sudden change, if the new temperatures maintained at A and B are

69. $0°$ at A, $0°$ at B.   **70.** $100°$ at A, $100°$ at B.

71. $0°$ at A, $50°$ at B.   **72.** $50°$ at A, $0°$ at B.

73. $25°$ at A, $75°$ at B.   **74.** $50°$ at A, $150°$ at B.

Find the temperature of a point 12.5 cm. from A of the rod of Prob. 73, 5 min. after the sudden change if

75. The rod is of silver, for which $a^2 = 1.74$.
76. The rod is of wrought iron, for which $a^2 = 0.173$.
77. The rod is of glass, for which $a^2 = 0.00571$.

78. The ends of a rod 60 cm. long are insulated so that $\partial U/\partial x = 0$ at $x = 0$ and $\partial U/\partial x = 0$ at $x = 60$. Show that for any zero or integral value of n, $A_n \cos \dfrac{n\pi x}{60} e^{-a^2 n^2 \pi^2 t/3,600}$ is a particular solution of Eq. (71) satisfying the end conditions.

79. Suppose that the rod of Prob. 78 had its temperatures kept at $0°$ and $180°$ until the steady state was approximated, and the ends were then suddenly insulated at $t = 0$. Derive the proper initial condition $U(x,0) = 3x$ and, using a series of particular solutions of the type found in Prob. 78, find $U(x,t)$.

Find the displacement $u(x,t)$ of a tightly stretched string of length a vibrating between fixed end points if the initial velocity was zero and the initial displacement $u(x,0)$ was

80. $p \sin \dfrac{5\pi x}{a}$.   **81.** $p \sin^3 \dfrac{\pi x}{a}$.   **82.** $apx - px^2$.

83. $\dfrac{2px}{a}$, if $0 < x < \dfrac{a}{2}$, and $2p - \dfrac{2px}{a}$, if $\dfrac{a}{2} < x < a$.

Find the displacement $u(x,t)$ of a tightly stretched string of length a vibrating between fixed end points if the string was initially in the equilibrium position, $u(x,0) = 0$, and the initial velocity $\partial u/\partial t$ at $t = 0$ or $u_t(x,0)$ was

84. $q \sin \dfrac{3\pi x}{a}$.   **85.** $q \sin^3 \dfrac{\pi x}{a}$.   **86.** $aqx - qx^2$.

87. A cable is a miles long and has negligible L and G. Find $e(x,t)$ and $i(x,t)$ t sec. after the ends are grounded, if initially $e(x,0) = Ex/a$, the steady-state condition due to one end being grounded and the other at the constant e.m.f. E.

88. A cable is a miles long and has negligible L and G. Both ends are grounded, so that $e(x,0) = 0$. But, at $t = 0$, the end $x = a$ is suddenly connected to a constant e.m.f. E. Find $e(x,t)$ and $i(x,t)$. In particular show that at the receiving end

$$i(0,t) = -\frac{E}{Ra}[1 - 2(\epsilon^{-\pi^2 t/a^2 RC} - \epsilon^{-4\pi^2 t/a^2 RC} + \epsilon^{-9\pi^2 t/a^2 RC} - \cdots)].$$

89. If, for the cable in Prob. 88, we take $a = 3,142 = 1,000\pi$ miles, $R = 3$ ohms/mile, and $C = \frac{1}{3}$ microfarad/mile or $\frac{1}{3} \cdot 10^{-6}$ farad/mile, show that after 2 sec. $i(0,t)$ is about 73 per cent of its maximum value.

90. Neglecting R and G, find the current $i(x,t)$ and the e.m.f. $e(x,t)$ in a line a miles long, t sec. after the ends were suddenly grounded if initially $i(x,0) = I_0$, so that $\partial e/\partial t = 0$ at $t = 0$, and $e(x,0) = Ex/a$, the steady-state condition due to one end's being grounded and the other at potential E.

91. The equation for the flow of heat in a rod with radiating surfaces is $\dfrac{\partial U}{\partial t} = a^2 \dfrac{\partial^2 U}{\partial x^2} - b^2(U - U_0)$. Show that if $U_0 = 0$, for any value of K, $e^{-(a^2K^2+b^2)t}(C \cos Kx + D \sin Kx)$ is a particular solution.

92. Find the temperature $U(x,t)$ of the rod of Prob. 91 if $U_0 = 0$, $U(0,t) = U(10,t) = 0$, $U(x,0) = x$. HINT: Use a sum of particular solutions with $C = 0$, $K = n\pi/10$.

93. The differential equation of a vibrating string with viscous damping is $\dfrac{\partial^2 u}{\partial t^2} = s^2 \dfrac{\partial^2 u}{\partial x^2} - b \dfrac{\partial u}{\partial t}$. Show that this has particular solutions of the form $e^{-bt/2}(A \sin Kx + B \cos Kx)(C \sin Mt + D \cos Mt)$ if $M = \sqrt{K^2s^2 - (b^2/4)}$.

94. The differential equation for the transverse vibrations of an elastic beam is $EI \dfrac{\partial^4 u}{\partial x^4} + m \dfrac{\partial^2 u}{\partial t^2} = 0$. Show that this has particular solutions of the form

$$(A \sin Kx + B \cos Kx + C \sinh Kx + D \cosh Kx)$$
$$\times (E \sin Mt + F \cos Mt), \text{ if } M = K^2 \sqrt{EI/m}.$$

95. The differential equation for the vibrations of a membrane is $\dfrac{1}{s^2} \dfrac{\partial^2 u}{\partial t^2} = \dfrac{\partial^2 u}{\partial x^2} + \dfrac{\partial^2 u}{\partial y^2} = \dfrac{1}{r} \dfrac{\partial}{\partial r}\left(r \dfrac{\partial u}{\partial r}\right) + \dfrac{1}{r^2} \dfrac{\partial^2 u}{\partial \theta^2}$. Following the method of Sec. 151, deduce as particular solutions of this equation the expression $J_m(ar)(A \cos m\theta + B \sin m\theta)(C \sin ast + D \cos ast)$.

96. For the symmetrical vibrations of a circular membrane, the displacement depends on r and t only. If the membrane is fixed on the edge and has radius L, $u(L,t) = 0$. Show that the particular solutions of Prob. 95 which apply here are

$$J_0\left(\frac{\alpha_n r}{L}\right)\left(C \sin \frac{\alpha_n st}{L} + D \cos \frac{\alpha_n st}{L}\right), \text{ where } J_0(\alpha_n) = 0.$$

97. Suppose that the membrane of Prob. 96 was initially at rest, and its displacement was $u(r,0) = f(r/L)$, where $f(x)$ is the function of Prob. 67. Show that the displacement at any time is

$$u(r,t) = \sum_{n=1}^{\infty} A_n \cos \frac{\alpha_n st}{L} J_0\left(\frac{\alpha_n r}{L}\right).$$

98. In quantum mechanics, the energy levels are the values of E for which Schrödinger's equation $\nabla^2 \psi + \dfrac{8\pi^2 m}{h^2} (E - V)\psi = 0$ has regular solutions. Let $V = 0$, and use the cylindrical coordinates of Prob. 48 of Exercises VIII (page 331). For ψ dependent on θ only, and $r = a$, show that the equation takes the form $\dfrac{1}{a^2} \dfrac{d^2 \psi}{d\theta^2} + \dfrac{8\pi^2 m}{h^2} E\psi$.

99. Show that the last equation of Prob. 98 has solutions of period 2π and, hence single-valued, of the form

$$A \cos n\theta + B \sin n\theta \text{ if } E = n^2 h^2 / 8\pi^2 m a^2.$$

100. Suppose that $V = 0$ and we use the spherical coordinates of Eq. (110) of Sec. 124. Show that for ψ dependent on ϕ only and $r = a$, the Schrödinger equation of Prob. 98 takes the form

$$\frac{1}{a^2 \sin \phi} \frac{d}{d\phi} \left(\sin \phi \frac{d}{d\phi} \right) + \frac{8\pi^2 m}{h^2} E = 0.$$

101. Show that the equation of Prob. 97 has regular solutions

$$\psi = A P_n (\cos \phi) \text{ if } E = \frac{n(n+1)h^2}{8\pi^2 m a^2}.$$

CHAPTER XII

THE CALCULUS OF VARIATIONS AND LAGRANGE'S EQUATIONS

In the simplest typical problem of the calculus of variations, we seek an unknown function $y(x)$ for which the integral of a known function of x, $y(x)$, and one or more derivatives of $y(x)$, is a minimum. A necessary condition is given by Euler's differential equation, which we derive for this case. We indicate the nature of the condition when we are dealing with several functions or with multiple integrals.

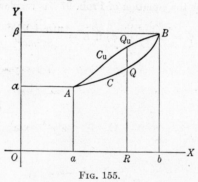

Fig. 155.

In many branches of physics variational methods may be used to give a succinct statement of general laws in a form readily applicable to any system of coordinates. To illustrate this we discuss Lagrange's equations for the motion of a system of particles and their relation to Hamilton's integral. We also describe the generalization to continuous mass distributions and use it to set up the partial differential equations that govern the elastic vibrations of strings, beams, and membranes.

168. The Least Value of an Integral. Let $F(x,y,y')$ be a given twice differentiable function of three variables. And let

$$A = (a,\alpha)$$

and $B = (b,\beta)$ be two fixed points in the xy plane. Then, if

432

A and B are joined by any curve C, $y = f(x)$, we shall have

$$\alpha = f(a), \qquad \beta = f(b). \tag{1}$$

At each point Q of C,

$$y' = \frac{dy}{dx} = f'(x). \tag{2}$$

Thus the curve C determines a value of

$$I = \int_a^b F(x,y,y')dx = \int_a^b F[x,f(x),f'(x)]dx. \tag{3}$$

Since I depends on C, its value will usually change when we replace C by a new curve joining A and B. We wish to study this variation of I with C, in particular as a means of finding for what curve C the integral I is a minimum (or a maximum).

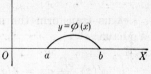

Fig. 156.

We may form a restricted set of varied curves, C_u, as follows. First select any curve

$$y = \phi(x) \text{ such that } \phi(a) = 0 \qquad \text{and} \qquad \phi(b) = 0. \tag{4}$$

Then for any value of the parameter u, the curve C_u,

$$Y = Y(x) = f(x) + u\phi(x), \text{ will have } Y(a) = \alpha \qquad \text{and}$$
$$Y(b) = \beta, \tag{5}$$

by Eqs. (1) and (4). Hence it will pass through A and B. On the curve C_u of Eq. (5)

$$Y' = \frac{dY}{dx} = f'(x) + u\phi'(x). \tag{6}$$

For any value of u, we have a curve C_u and may form the value of I along this curve by substituting the values from (5) and (6) in

$$I(u) = \int_a^b F(x,Y,Y')dx. \tag{7}$$

We shall next differentiate this function with respect to u. By Eq. (44) of Sec. 65 we may differentiate under the integral sign. As x does not contain u, we may consider $F(x,Y,Y')$ as a composite function of the two variables Y and Y', each of which is a function of u, and apply the total derivative rule of Sec. 21. This gives

$$\frac{\partial F}{\partial u} = \frac{\partial F}{\partial Y}\frac{\partial Y}{\partial u} + \frac{\partial F}{\partial Y'}\frac{\partial Y'}{\partial u}. \tag{8}$$

But from Eqs. (5) and (6) we find

$$\frac{\partial Y}{\partial u} = \phi(x) \quad\text{and}\quad \frac{\partial Y'}{\partial u} = \phi'(x), \tag{9}$$

so that

$$\frac{\partial F}{\partial u} = \phi(x) \frac{\partial F}{\partial Y} + \phi'(x) \frac{\partial F}{\partial Y'}. \tag{10}$$

It follows that

$$\frac{dI}{du} = \int_a^b \left[\phi(x) \frac{\partial F}{\partial Y} + \phi'(x) \frac{\partial F}{\partial Y'} \right] dx. \tag{11}$$

Let us transform the second term by integrating by parts. We have

$$\int_a^b \phi'(x) \frac{\partial F}{\partial Y'} dx = \phi(x) \frac{\partial F}{\partial Y'} \Big|_a^b - \int_a^b \phi(x) \frac{d}{dx} \left(\frac{\partial F}{\partial Y'} \right) dx. \tag{12}$$

The integrated part is zero because of the condition that

$$\phi(a) = \phi(b) = 0.$$

Thus the new form of Eq. (11) is

$$\frac{dI}{du} = \int_a^b \phi(x) \left[\frac{\partial F}{\partial Y} - \frac{d}{dx} \left(\frac{\partial F}{\partial Y'} \right) \right] dx. \tag{13}$$

Let us next suppose that there is a twice differentiable curve for which the value of I is least and that we take this as the curve C. Then the value of I on C, or $I(0)$, will be less than the value of $I(u)$ for any other curve C_u. Hence $I(u)$ will assume a minimum value for $u = 0$. As our continuity assumptions assure the continuity of dI/du, this will be zero at the minimum, or when $u = 0$. But when $u = 0$, from Eqs. (5) and (6), $Y = y$ and $Y' = y'$. Thus on putting $u = 0$ in (13), and $I'(0) = 0$, we find

$$\int_a^b \phi(x) \left[\frac{\partial F}{\partial y} - \frac{d}{dx} \left(\frac{\partial F}{\partial y'} \right) \right] dx = 0. \tag{14}$$

Because the function $\phi(x)$ is arbitrary, except for the end conditions, and the factor in brackets is continuous, we may conclude that the bracket is zero for every x such that $a \leqq x \leqq b$. For, if the bracket were positive at any point, there would be some small interval including this point, say $p < x < q$, in which it remained positive. And, by taking the function of Fig. 157 as $\phi(x)$, the integrand of (14) would be zero except for $p < x < q$, and positive for these values. Hence the integral would be positive and not zero as required. And, if the bracket were negative at any point, a similar contradiction would follow. Thus we have proved the theorem:

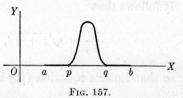

Fig. 157.

If the integral I of (3) *has a minimum* (or a maximum) *along any sufficiently regular curve C joining A and B, with equation $y = f(x)$, then $y = f(x)$ will be a solution of the differential equation*

$$\frac{\partial F}{\partial y} - \frac{d}{dx}\left(\frac{\partial F}{\partial y'}\right) = 0. \tag{15}$$

This is called *Euler's equation*. The partial derivatives are taken on the assumption that x, y, and y' are three independent variables. But in computing the derivative indicated by d/dx, we must recall that $y = f(x)$ and $y' = dy/dx = f'(x)$ are functions of x. If we carry out the x differentiation, we obtain the expanded form

$$\frac{\partial F}{\partial y} - \frac{\partial^2 F}{\partial x \, \partial y'} - \frac{\partial^2 F}{\partial y \, \partial y'}\frac{dy}{dx} - \frac{\partial^2 F}{\partial y'^2}\frac{d^2 y}{dx^2} = 0. \tag{16}$$

This is a second-order differential equation. Hence its solution contains two arbitrary constants. These are to be determined by the requirement that the curve pass through the points A and B.

Any curve corresponding to a solution of Euler's equation, (15) or (16) is called an *extremal*.

Even in simple problems, it may be impossible to pass an extremal through A and B for all possible positions. However, in many cases it is physically evident that there can be no maximum. In such cases if two points A and B are taken as the end of a sufficiently short arc of an extremal, this will be a minimizing arc.

As an example, let us find the arc C that minimizes S, the area of the surface of revolution generated by the rotation of C about OX. This surface area is

$$S = 2\pi \int_a^b y \, ds = 2\pi \int_a^b y \sqrt{1 + y'^2} \, dx. \tag{17}$$

Since S will be least when $S/2\pi$ is least, we take

$$I = \int_a^b y \sqrt{1 + y'^2}\, dx, \qquad F(x,y,y') = y \sqrt{1 + y'^2}. \quad (18)$$

It follows that

$$\frac{\partial F}{\partial y} = \sqrt{1 + y'^2}, \qquad \frac{\partial F}{\partial y'} = \frac{yy'}{\sqrt{1 + y'^2}}, \quad (19)$$

so that Euler's equation (15) is

$$\sqrt{1 + y'^2} - \frac{d}{dx} \frac{yy'}{\sqrt{1 + y'^2}} = 0, \qquad \text{or} \qquad 1 + y'^2 - yy'' = 0. \quad (20)$$

By the method of Sec. 136, Type II, we find successively

$$\frac{dy}{y} = \frac{p\, dp}{1 + p^2}, \qquad \log y = \frac{1}{2} \log (1 + p^2) + \log c_1,$$

$$dx = \frac{c_1\, dy}{\sqrt{y^2 - c_1{}^2}}. \quad (21)$$

From this the solution is found as

$$x = c_1 \cosh^{-1} \frac{y}{c_1} + c_2 \qquad \text{or} \qquad y = c_1 \cosh \frac{x - c_2}{c_1}. \quad (22)$$

Thus the extremals are catenaries, with base the axis of x. If α and β are not too small compared with $b - a$, the constants c_1 and c_2 can be found which make (22) pass through A and B and provide the minimizing arc.

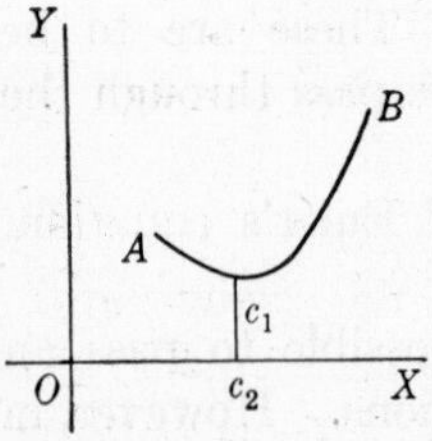

Fig. 158.

169. Higher Derivatives, Several Variables. The Euler equation which gives a necessary condition for

$$I = \int_a^b F(x,y,y',y'')dx \quad (23)$$

to be a minimum is

$$\frac{\partial F}{\partial y} - \frac{d}{dx}\left(\frac{\partial F}{\partial y'}\right) + \frac{d^2}{dx^2}\left(\frac{\partial F}{\partial y''}\right) = 0. \quad (24)$$

This is obtained by applying two integrations by parts to the additional term

$$\int_a^b \phi''(x) \frac{\partial F}{\partial y''} dx = \phi'(x) \frac{\partial F}{\partial y''}\Big|_a^b - \int_a^b \phi'(x) \frac{d}{dx}\left(\frac{\partial F}{\partial y''}\right) dx$$

$$= \left[\phi'(x) \frac{\partial F}{\partial y''} - \phi(x) \frac{d}{dx}\left(\frac{\partial F}{\partial y''}\right)\right]_a^b$$

$$+ \int_a^b \phi(x) \frac{d^2}{dx^2}\left(\frac{\partial F}{\partial y''}\right) dx, \quad (25)$$

and applying the additional restriction to $\phi(x)$ that $\phi'(a) = 0$ and $\phi'(b) = 0$, so that both integrated parts vanish.

If the integral depends on two functions, as

$$I = \int_a^b F(x,y,z,y',z')dx, \tag{26}$$

there are two Euler equations,

$$\frac{\partial F}{\partial y} - \frac{d}{dx}\left(\frac{\partial F}{\partial y'}\right) = 0 \quad \text{and} \quad \frac{\partial F}{\partial z} - \frac{d}{dx}\left(\frac{\partial F}{\partial z'}\right) = 0. \tag{27}$$

To derive these, introduce two functions $\phi(x)$ and $\psi(x)$ and two parameters u and v, and put

$$Y = y + u\phi(x), \qquad Z = z + v\psi(x). \tag{28}$$

Substitution of these in Eq. (26) makes $I(u,v)$ a function of the two parameters u and v. A necessary condition for a minimum is that $\partial I/\partial u = 0$ and $\partial I/\partial v = 0$, and on treating each of these as we did $du/dI = 0$ in Sec. 168, Eqs. (27) are obtained.

The Euler equations for an integral containing any number of dependent variables, and higher derivatives of any order, may be found by similar methods or written down by analogy.

170. Variational Notation. Since $y = f(x)$, Eq. (5) may be written

$$Y = y + u\phi(x) \quad \text{or} \quad Y - y = u\phi(x). \tag{29}$$

The difference $Y - y$ or QQ_u in Fig. 155 is the change in Y, starting from y, the value for $u = 0$. Hence $u\phi(x) = Y - y$ is called the *variation* of y and is denoted by δy. It may also be defined as the differential of Y, for differentiation with respect to u at $u = 0$. For, at $u = 0$, $du = u - 0 = u$ and

$$\frac{dY}{du} = \phi(x), \quad \text{so that} \left(\frac{dY}{du}\right) du = \phi(x)u = \delta y. \tag{30}$$

Again, since $y' = f'(x)$, Eq. (6) may be written

$$Y' = y' + u\phi'(x) \quad \text{or} \quad Y' - y' = u\phi'(x). \tag{31}$$

The term $u\phi'(x) = Y' - y'$ is the variation of y' and is denoted by $\delta y'$. It is the differential of Y', for u differentiation, at $u = 0$. For, at $u = 0$, $du = u$ and

$$\frac{dY'}{du} = \phi'(x), \qquad \text{so that} \left(\frac{dY'}{du}\right) du = \phi'(x)u = \delta y'. \quad (32)$$

It follows from the definitions that

$$\frac{d(\delta y)}{dx} = \delta\left(\frac{dy}{dx}\right) \qquad \text{or} \qquad (\delta y)' = \delta(y'). \quad (33)$$

That is, the operators δ and d/dx are commutative.

The variations of y'' and the higher derivatives of y are defined similarly.

For any function of x,y and its derivatives the variation is defined as the total differential for differentiation with respect to u at $u = 0$. Hence from Sec. 21, for $F(x,y,y')$,

$$\delta F = \frac{\partial F}{\partial y}\,\delta y + \frac{\partial F}{\partial y'}\,\delta y'. \quad (34)$$

From Eq. (13) we find as the value of $\delta I = (dI/du)_{u=0}du$,

$$\delta I = \int_a^b \left[\frac{\partial F}{\partial y} - \frac{d}{dx}\left(\frac{\partial F}{\partial y'}\right)\right] \delta y\, dx, \quad (35)$$

when the variations at the end points are zero.

For the I of Eq. (23), whose integrand is $F(x,y,y',y'')$,

$$\delta I = \int_a^b \left[\frac{\partial F}{\partial y} - \frac{d}{dx}\left(\frac{\partial F}{\partial y'}\right) + \frac{d^2}{dx^2}\left(\frac{\partial F}{\partial y''}\right)\right] \delta y\, dx, \quad (36)$$

when the variations are restricted as indicated after Eq. (25).

Let us next consider the I of Eq. (26), whose integrand is $F(x,y,z,y',z')$, containing the two independent variables y and z. We recall Eqs. (28) and define the variations as total differentials, formed for differentiation with respect to the independent variables u and v, at $u = 0$, $v = 0$ where $du = u$ and $dv = v$. Hence

$$\delta y = u\phi(x), \qquad \delta y' = u\phi'(x), \qquad \delta z = v\psi(x), \qquad \delta z' = v\psi'(x). \quad (37)$$

And for the function $F(x,y,z,y',z')$ we have

$$\delta F = \frac{\partial F}{\partial y}\,\delta y + \frac{\partial F}{\partial y'}\,\delta y' + \frac{\partial F}{\partial z}\,\delta z + \frac{\partial F}{\partial z'}\,\delta z'. \quad (38)$$

For *I*, the integral of such a function,

$$\delta I = \int_a^b \left[\frac{\partial F}{\partial y} - \frac{d}{dx}\left(\frac{\partial F}{\partial y'} \right) \right] \delta y \, dx$$
$$+ \int_a^b \left[\frac{\partial F}{\partial z} - \frac{d}{dx}\left(\frac{\partial F}{\partial z'} \right) \right] \delta z \, dx, \quad (39)$$

when δy and δz are zero at the end points.

It is sometimes convenient to introduce a new parameter t as the independent variable and to regard x and y (or x, y, and z) as the dependent variables. Thus consider the integrand $F(x,y,y')$. If we use dots for the t derivatives, we may write

$$y' = \frac{\dot{y}}{\dot{x}} \quad \text{and} \quad F(x,y,y')dx = F\left(x,y, \frac{\dot{y}}{\dot{x}} \right) \dot{x} \, dt. \quad (40)$$

Let $x = a$ when $t = t_1$, $x = b$ when $t = t_2$, and put

$$H(x,y,\dot{x},\dot{y}) = F\left(x,y, \frac{\dot{y}}{\dot{x}} \right) \dot{x}. \quad (41)$$

Then

$$I = \int_a^b F(x,y,y')dx = \int_{t_1}^{t_2} H(x,y,\dot{x},\dot{y})dt. \quad (42)$$

And by Eq. (39), with x,y,z replaced by t,x,y, we have

$$\delta I = \int_{t_1}^{t_2} \left[\frac{\partial H}{\partial x} - \frac{d}{dt}\left(\frac{\partial H}{\partial \dot{x}} \right) \right] \delta x \, dt$$
$$+ \int_{t_1}^{t_2} \left[\frac{\partial H}{\partial y} - \frac{d}{dt}\left(\frac{\partial H}{\partial \dot{y}} \right) \right] \delta y \, dt, \quad (43)$$

for δx and δy zero at t_1 and t_2.

171. Constraints. We sometimes desire to minimize the integral

$$I = \int_a^b F(x,y,y')dx, \quad (44)$$

taken between fixed end points, while keeping a second integral constant,

$$J = \int_a^b G(x,y,y')dx = K. \quad (45)$$

In such a case, as shown in Prob. 51, the desired curves satisfy the Euler equation for minimizing

$$\int_a^b [F(x,y,y') - \lambda G(x,y,y')]dx, \quad (46)$$

where λ is a constant. From Eq. (15) the condition is

$$\frac{\partial F}{\partial y} - \lambda \frac{\partial G}{\partial y} - \frac{d}{dx}\left(\frac{\partial F}{\partial y'}\right) + \lambda \frac{d}{dx}\left(\frac{\partial G}{\partial y'}\right) = 0. \tag{47}$$

In this case the values of the two constants of integration and

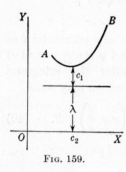

FIG. 159.

the constant λ are determined by the three conditions that the curve pass through the fixed end points and that the second integral J have the given constant value K.

As an example, let us find the arc C of given length L which minimizes S, the area of the surface of revolution generated by the rotation of C about OX. From Eqs. (17) and (18) we see that we are to make

$$I = \frac{S}{2\pi} = \int_a^b y \sqrt{1 + y'^2}\, dx$$

a minimum for $\int_a^b \sqrt{1 + y'^2}\, dx = L. \tag{48}$

The extremals satisfy Euler's equation for

$$\int_a^b (y - \lambda) \sqrt{1 + y'^2}\, dx, \tag{49}$$

or

$$\sqrt{1 + y'^2} - \frac{d}{dx}\left[\frac{(y - \lambda)y'}{\sqrt{1 + y'^2}}\right] = 0 \quad \text{or}$$

$$1 + y'^2 - (y - \lambda)y'' = 0. \tag{50}$$

By steps analogous to (21) and (22), with $y - \lambda$ in place of y, we find

$$y = \lambda + c_1 \cosh \frac{x - c_2}{c_1}. \tag{51}$$

Thus the extremals are catenaries, with base lines parallel to the axis of x. Minimizing catenaries may be found if L is greater than the distance between the end points and is not too large.

Only slight modifications are necessary if there are more constraints, or more independent variables. For example, to minimize

$$\int_a^b F(x,y,z,y',z')dx \tag{52}$$

taken between fixed end points, while keeping constant

$$\int_a^b G(x,y,z,y',z')dx = K \qquad \text{and} \qquad \int_a^b H(x,y,z,y',z')dx = L, \quad (53)$$

we use the two Euler equations (27) formed for the integral

$$\int_a^b [F(x,y,z,y',z') - \lambda G(x,y,z,y',z') - \mu H(x,y,z,y',z')]dx. \quad (54)$$

When there are two independent variables, the constraint may not involve an integral. Thus we may desire to minimize

$$I = \int_a^b F(x,y,z,y',z')dx \quad (55)$$

taken between fixed end points, while x,y,z satisfy the relation

$$G(x,y,z) = 0. \quad (56)$$

In this case, as shown in Prob. 54, the desired curves satisfy the Euler equations (27) formed for the integral

$$\int_a^b [F(x,y,z,y',z') - \lambda(x)G(x,y,z)]dx, \quad (57)$$

where $\lambda(x)$ is a *function of the independent variable*, here x. That is,

$$\frac{\partial F}{\partial y} - \frac{d}{dx}\left(\frac{\partial F}{\partial y'}\right) - \lambda(x)\frac{\partial G}{\partial y} = 0 \qquad \text{and}$$

$$\frac{\partial F}{\partial z} - \frac{d}{dx}\left(\frac{\partial F}{\partial z'}\right) - \lambda(x)\frac{\partial G}{\partial z} = 0. \quad (58)$$

As an example, let us find the arc C joining two points on the sphere $x^2 + y^2 + z^2 = a^2$ whose length is a minimum. Here it is convenient to introduce a parameter t and use dots for t derivatives, as in Eq. (40), so that we are to make

$$\int_a^b \sqrt{\dot{x}^2 + \dot{y}^2 + \dot{z}^2}\, dt \text{ a minimum while } x^2 + y^2 + z^2 - a^2 = 0. \quad (59)$$

The extremals satisfy the Euler equations for

$$\int_a^b [\sqrt{\dot{x}^2 + \dot{y}^2 + \dot{z}^2} - \lambda(t)(x^2 + y^2 + z^2 - a^2)]dt. \quad (60)$$

The first of the three equations is

$$-2\lambda(t)x - \frac{d}{dt}\left[\frac{\dot{x}}{\sqrt{\dot{x}^2 + \dot{y}^2 + \dot{z}^2}}\right] = 0, \qquad \text{or}$$

$$-2\lambda(t)x - \frac{d}{dt}\left(\frac{dx}{ds}\right) = 0. \quad (61)$$

And the other two equations may be reduced to

$$-2\lambda(t)y - \frac{d}{dt}\left(\frac{dy}{ds}\right) = 0 \qquad \text{and} \qquad -2\lambda(t)z - \frac{d}{dt}\left(\frac{dz}{ds}\right) = 0. \quad (62)$$

Elimination of $\lambda(t)$ from the equations in x and y leads to the relation

$$y\,d\left(\frac{dx}{ds}\right) - x\,d\left(\frac{dy}{ds}\right) = 0 \qquad \text{or} \qquad d\left(y\frac{dx}{ds} - x\frac{dy}{ds}\right) = 0. \quad (63)$$

This gives the integral

$$y\frac{dx}{ds} - x\frac{dy}{ds} = c_1; \qquad \text{and} \qquad z\frac{dx}{ds} - x\frac{dz}{ds} = c_2 \quad (64)$$

follows by applying the same process to the equations in x and z. We may deduce from Eqs. (64) that

$$c_2\frac{y\,dx - x\,dy}{x^2} = c_1\frac{z\,dx - x\,dz}{x^2} \qquad \text{or} \qquad c_2\,d\left(\frac{y}{x}\right) = c_1\,d\left(\frac{z}{x}\right), \quad (65)$$

and it follows by integration that

$$c_2\frac{y}{x} = c_1\frac{z}{x} + c_3, \qquad \text{or} \qquad c_3 x - c_2 y + c_1 z = 0. \quad (66)$$

As this has no constant term, it is a plane through the origin or center of the sphere $x^2 + y^2 + z^2 = a^2$. Hence it cuts the sphere in a great circle to give the minimizing arc.

172. Hamilton's Principle. In a conservative force field, as defined in Sec. 122, there is a potential energy function $U(x,y,z)$ whose partial derivatives, prefixed by a minus sign, equal the components of force acting on a particle at x,y,z. Hence by Newton's law, the equations of motion for a particle of mass m in the field are

$$m\frac{d^2x}{dt^2} = -\frac{\partial U}{\partial x}, \qquad m\frac{d^2y}{dt^2} = -\frac{\partial U}{\partial y}, \qquad m\frac{d^2z}{dt^2} = -\frac{\partial U}{\partial z}. \quad (67)$$

For any conservative mechanical system, with kinetic energy T and potential energy U, the difference

$$L = T - U \tag{68}$$

is called the *Lagrangian function*. The integral of this function with respect to the time t between two fixed limits is known as *Hamilton's integral*,

$$I = \int_{t_1}^{t_2} L \, dt = \int_{t_1}^{t_2} (T - U) dt. \tag{69}$$

For the motion of one particle described above,

$$T = \frac{m}{2} v^2 = \frac{m}{2} (\dot{x}^2 + \dot{y}^2 + \dot{z}^2) \qquad U = U(x,y,z), \tag{70}$$

so that

$$I = \int_{t_1}^{t_2} \left[\frac{m}{2} (\dot{x}^2 + \dot{y}^2 + \dot{z}^2) - U(x,y,z) \right] dt. \tag{71}$$

Consider the problem of making this integral, a function of the independent variable t and three dependent variables x,y,z, a minimum, when the variations δx, δy, δz are zero at the end points. The extremals satisfy three Euler equations similar to (27). The first is

$$\frac{\partial L}{\partial x} - \frac{d}{dt} \left(\frac{\partial L}{\partial \dot{x}} \right) = 0 \qquad \text{or} \qquad - \frac{\partial U}{\partial x} - \frac{d}{dt} (m\dot{x}). \tag{72}$$

This may be rewritten as

$$m \frac{d^2 x}{dt^2} = - \frac{\partial U}{\partial x}, \tag{73}$$

which is the first of Eqs. (67). Similarly the Euler equations for y and z are, essentially, the second and third equations in (67). For the case of one particle, this proves *Hamilton's principle*:

The equations of motion define an extremal for the problem of minimizing Hamilton's integral (69).

Suppose, next, that the particle in the force field is constrained to lie on a surface whose equation is

$$F(x,y,z) = 0, \tag{74}$$

by additional forces normal to the surface, with components

$$-\lambda \frac{\partial F}{\partial x}, \qquad -\lambda \frac{\partial F}{\partial y}, \qquad -\lambda \frac{\partial F}{\partial z}. \tag{75}$$

Then the equations of motion become

$$m \frac{d^2x}{dt^2} = -\frac{\partial U}{\partial x} - \lambda \frac{\partial F}{\partial x}, \qquad m \frac{d^2y}{dt^2} = -\frac{\partial U}{\partial y} - \lambda \frac{\partial F}{\partial y},$$

$$m \frac{d^2z}{dt^2} = -\frac{\partial U}{\partial z} - \lambda \frac{\partial F}{\partial z}. \quad (76)$$

Here the variable λ is to be so determined that Eq. (74) is satisfied. That is, the normal forces are exactly those required to keep the path in the surface. Since the path is in the surface, by Sec. 49,

$$\frac{\partial F}{\partial x} dx + \frac{\partial F}{\partial y} dy + \frac{\partial F}{\partial z} dz = 0. \quad (77)$$

Hence, by Sec. 122, the work done by the normal forces is zero, and they do not affect the potential energy. Thus Hamilton's integral (69) again takes the form (71).

Now consider the problem of making this integral a minimum, with variations zero at the end points, subject to the constraint (74). By analogy with (57), the Euler equations are found as those for the integral

$$\int_{t_1}^{t_2} \left[\frac{m}{2} (\dot{x}^2 + \dot{y}^2 + \dot{z}^2) - U(x,y,z) - \lambda(t)F(x,y,z) \right] dt. \quad (78)$$

But these are found to be equivalent to Eqs. (76), the equations of motion for our problem.

Similar calculations show that Hamilton's principle is valid for systems of particles, acted on by any combination of conservative forces and constraining forces that do no work. For rigid bodies the laws of motion and the definition of energy are obtained by replacing the sums that appear in the discussion of a set of particles by integrals in the continuous case. When this has been done, it is again found that Hamilton's principle leads to the equations of motion.

173. Lagrange's Equations. Suppose that a function of several variables has its partial derivatives with respect to each of these variables equal to zero for a particular set of values, *e.g.*, at $P_0 = (x_0, y_0, z_0)$ for three variables x, y, z. Then this will be the case for the partial derivatives with respect to any new set of variables for the corresponding set of values, *e.g.*, at $P_0 = (q_{10}, q_{20}, q_{30})$, for new variables q_1, q_2, q_3 and

$$q_{i0} = f_i(x_0, y_0, z_0) \text{ obtained from } q_i = f_i(x,y,z). \quad (79)$$

This follows from the relations like

$$\frac{\partial F}{\partial q_1} = \frac{\partial F}{\partial x}\frac{\partial x}{\partial q_1} + \frac{\partial F}{\partial y}\frac{\partial y}{\partial q_1} + \frac{\partial F}{\partial z}\frac{\partial z}{\partial q_1}, \tag{80}$$

obtained in Sec. 24.

Similarly, if an integral has its variations equal to zero along a particular curve for one set of coordinates, these will be zero along that same curve for any other set of coordinates. This property of the variations, and Hamilton's principle, enable us to set up the equations of motion for a conservative mechanical system in any system of coordinates. We need merely express the Lagrangian function $T - U$ in the new coordinates and write down the Euler equations for minimizing Hamilton's integral. When the system has n degrees of freedom, it is convenient to use n independent coordinates, often denoted by $q_1, q_2, \cdots, q_n$. Then

$$T - U = L(q_1, q_2, \cdots, q_n; \dot{q}_1, \dot{q}_2, \cdots, \dot{q}_n) \quad \text{or} \quad L(q_k, \dot{q}_k). \tag{81}$$

And the Euler equation for the kth coordinate is

$$\frac{\partial L}{\partial q_k} - \frac{d}{dt}\left(\frac{\partial L}{\partial \dot{q}_k}\right) = 0. \tag{82}$$

The q_k are called *Lagrangian* or *generalized coordinates*, and Eqs. (82) are *Lagrange's equations*.

For example, suppose a particle is moving on a sphere

$$x^2 + y^2 + z^2 = a^2$$

under no forces. For the spherical polar coordinates r, ϕ, θ, on the sphere $r = a$ and

$$x = a \cos\theta \sin\phi, \qquad y = a \sin\theta \sin\phi, \qquad z = a \cos\phi. \tag{83}$$

Also from

$$ds^2 = a^2(d\phi^2 + \sin^2\phi\, d\theta^2), \qquad v^2 = \dot{s}^2 = a^2(\dot{\phi}^2 + \sin^2\phi\dot{\theta}^2). \tag{84}$$

Since there are no forces, $U = 0$ and

$$L = T = \frac{m}{2}a^2(\dot{\phi}^2 + \sin^2\phi\dot{\theta}^2). \tag{85}$$

Hence we may take ϕ and θ as the two Lagrangian coordinates. And the equations of motion (82) for them are

$$\frac{\partial L}{\partial \phi} - \frac{d}{dt}\left(\frac{\partial L}{\partial \dot{\phi}}\right) = 0 \quad \text{and} \quad \frac{\partial L}{\partial \theta} - \frac{d}{dt}\left(\frac{\partial L}{\partial \dot{\theta}}\right) = 0. \tag{86}$$

Using the value of L from (85), we may reduce these to

$$\sin \phi \cos \phi \; \dot{\theta}^2 - \ddot{\phi} = 0, \qquad - \frac{d}{dt} (\sin^2 \phi \; \dot{\theta}) = 0. \qquad (87)$$

From the second equation, by integration

$$\sin^2 \phi \; \dot{\theta} = h, \qquad \text{or} \qquad \dot{\theta} = h \csc^2 \phi. \qquad (88)$$

On substituting this in the first equation of (87), it becomes

$$\ddot{\phi} - h^2 \frac{\cos \phi}{\sin^3 \phi} = 0, \qquad \text{or} \qquad 2\dot{\phi} \, \ddot{\phi} - 2h^2 \cot \phi \csc^2 \phi \, \dot{\phi} = 0. \qquad (89)$$

By integrating this with respect to t, we find

$$\dot{\phi}^2 + h^2 \cot^2 \phi = c^2. \qquad (90)$$

From this and Eqs. (88) and (84) we may deduce that

$$c^2 + h^2 = \dot{\phi}^2 + h^2 \csc^2 \phi = \dot{\phi}^2 + \sin^2 \phi \dot{\theta}^2 = \frac{\dot{s}^2}{a^2}. \qquad (91)$$

This shows that $\dot{s}$, the velocity in the path, is constant.

To find the path itself, we deduce from (88) and (90) that

$$d\theta = h \csc^2 \phi \; dt = \frac{\pm \, h \csc^2 \phi \, d\phi}{\sqrt{c^2 - h^2 \cot^2 \phi}}. \qquad (92)$$

From this, by integration, with $c_2 = k + \pi$ for the plus sign,

$$\theta = \sin^{-1} \frac{h \cot \phi}{c} + k, \qquad h \cot \phi = c \sin (\theta - k). \qquad (93)$$

This may be written

$$ha \cos \phi = ca \sin \theta \sin \phi \cos k - ca \cos \theta \sin \phi \sin k, \qquad (94)$$

or by Eq. (83)

$$hz = c \cos k \, y - c \sin k \, x. \qquad (95)$$

This is the equation of a plane through the origin, the center of the sphere, and shows that the paths are great circles.

174. Multiple or Repeated Integrals. Suppose that

$$F(x,y,z,p,q)$$

is a twice differentiable function of five variables. The dependent variable z is a function of x and y, and $p = \partial z/\partial x$, $q = \partial z/\partial y$. We wish to study the variation of the integral

$$\iint F(x,y,z,p,q) dx \, dy, \qquad (96)$$

over a surface S restricted to pass through a fixed boundary curve B, and in particular as a means of finding for what surface S the integral is a minimum.

Our procedure is similar to that used for the simple integral (3) in Sec. 168. We first select any surface

$$z = \phi(x,y) \text{ such that } \phi(x,y) = 0 \text{ on the curve } B_1, \quad (97)$$

the projection of the curve B in the xy plane. Then if $z(x,y)$ passes through B, for any u the surface S_u given by

$$Z(x,y) = z(x,y) + u\phi(x,y) \quad (98)$$

will also pass through B. On this surface

$$P = \frac{\partial Z}{\partial x} = p + u\phi_x \quad \text{and} \quad Q = \frac{\partial Z}{\partial y} = q + u\phi_y, \quad (99)$$

and our integral is

$$I = \iint F(x,y,Z,P,Q)dx\,dy. \quad (100)$$

Differentiation under the integral sign leads to

$$\frac{dI}{du} = \iint \left(\frac{\partial F}{\partial Z}\phi + \frac{\partial F}{\partial P}\phi_x + \frac{\partial F}{\partial Q}\phi_y \right) dx\,dy. \quad (101)$$

We next deduce from the rule for integration by parts that

$$\int \frac{\partial F}{\partial P}\phi_x\,dx = \frac{\partial F}{\partial P}\phi - \int \frac{\partial}{\partial x}\left(\frac{\partial F}{\partial P}\right)\phi\,dx, \quad (102)$$

and

$$\int \frac{\partial F}{\partial Q}\phi_y\,dy = \frac{\partial F}{\partial Q}\phi - \int \frac{\partial}{\partial y}\left(\frac{\partial F}{\partial Q}\right)\phi\,dy. \quad (103)$$

When these are applied to the parts of the integral (101), with the repeated integration taken in the appropriate order, the integrated parts drop out since they are to be computed at points on the boundary curve in the xy plane B_1, where $\phi(x,y) = 0$. Hence Eq. (101) may be reduced to

$$\frac{dI}{du} = \iint \left[\frac{\partial F}{\partial z} - \frac{\partial}{\partial x}\left(\frac{\partial F}{\partial P}\right) - \frac{\partial}{\partial y}\left(\frac{\partial F}{\partial Q}\right) \right] \phi\,dx\,dy. \quad (104)$$

When $u = 0$, $Z = z$, $P = p$, $Q = q$. And by multiplying the value of the derivation dI/du when $u = 0$ by $du = u - 0 = u$ and writing δz for $u\phi$, we find

$$\delta I = \iint \left[\frac{\partial F}{\partial z} - \frac{\partial}{\partial x}\left(\frac{\partial F}{\partial p}\right) - \frac{\partial}{\partial y}\left(\frac{\partial F}{\partial q}\right) \right] \delta z\,dx\,dy. \quad (105)$$

If $z(x,y)$ is the surface for which I is least, $\delta I = 0$ for arbitrary δz. Since the bracket is continuous, it follows that the bracket must be zero. Hence a necessary condition for a minimum is

$$\frac{\partial F}{\partial z} - \frac{\partial}{\partial x}\left(\frac{\partial F}{\partial p}\right) - \frac{\partial}{\partial y}\left(\frac{\partial F}{\partial q}\right) = 0. \tag{106}$$

This is the Euler equation for our problem, and any surface corresponding to a solution of this equation is an extremal.

In Eq. (106), the derivatives with respect to z, p, and q are calculated with x,y,z,p,q as five independent variables and the other four held fast. But the differentiations with respect to x and y are calculated with x and y as the two independent variables, and $z = z(x,y)$, $p = \partial z/\partial x$, $q = \partial z/\partial y$ all functions of x and y.

The conditions for more independent variables, or higher derivatives, are of a similar nature to those given in Sec. 169. For example, if F involved the derivatives

$$r = \frac{\partial^2 z}{\partial x^2}, \qquad s = \frac{\partial^2 z}{\partial x\,\partial y}, \qquad t = \frac{\partial^2 z}{\partial y^2}, \tag{107}$$

the Euler equation would be

$$\frac{\partial F}{\partial z} - \frac{\partial}{\partial x}\left(\frac{\partial F}{\partial p}\right) - \frac{\partial}{\partial y}\left(\frac{\partial F}{\partial q}\right) + \frac{\partial^2}{\partial x^2}\left(\frac{\partial F}{\partial r}\right) + \frac{\partial^2}{\partial x\,\partial y}\left(\frac{\partial F}{\partial s}\right)$$
$$+ \frac{\partial^2}{\partial y^2}\left(\frac{\partial F}{\partial t}\right) = 0. \tag{108}$$

When there are several dependent variables, there is a separate equation for each dependent variable.

As an example, the condition that the Dirichlet integral

$$I = \int \int \int \left[\left(\frac{\partial U}{\partial x}\right)^2 + \left(\frac{\partial U}{\partial y}\right)^2 + \left(\frac{\partial U}{\partial z}\right)^2\right] dx\,dy\,dz \tag{109}$$

be a minimum is

$$-\frac{\partial}{\partial x}\left(2\frac{\partial U}{\partial x}\right) - \frac{\partial}{\partial y}\left(2\frac{\partial U}{\partial y}\right) - \frac{\partial}{\partial z}\left(2\frac{\partial U}{\partial z}\right) = 0, \tag{110}$$

or

$$\frac{\partial^2 U}{\partial x^2} + \frac{\partial^2 U}{\partial y^2} + \frac{\partial^2 U}{\partial z^2} = 0, \tag{111}$$

which is Laplace's equation.

We may express the Dirichlet integral (109) in spherical polar coordinates by noting that

$$I = \iiint |\nabla U|^2 dV = \iiint |\nabla U|^2 r^2 \sin \phi \, dr \, d\phi \, d\theta, \qquad (112)$$

and by inserting the value of ∇U given in Eq. (108) of Sec. 124. The result is

$$I = \int \int \int \left[\left(\frac{\partial U}{\partial r} \right)^2 + \frac{1}{r^2} \left(\frac{\partial U}{\partial \phi} \right)^2 + \frac{1}{r^2 \sin^2 \phi} \left(\frac{\partial U}{\partial \theta} \right)^2 \right] r^2 \sin \phi \, dr \, d\phi \, d\theta. \qquad (113)$$

In forming the Euler equation for this integral, we must take into account the factor $r^2 \sin \phi$. Doing this we find

$$- \frac{\partial}{\partial r} \left(2r^2 \sin \phi \, \frac{\partial U}{\partial r} \right) - \frac{\partial}{\partial \phi} \left(2 \sin \phi \, \frac{\partial U}{\partial \phi} \right) - \frac{\partial}{\partial \theta} \left(\frac{2}{\sin \phi} \frac{\partial U}{\partial \theta} \right) = 0, \qquad (114)$$

or

$$\sin \phi \, \frac{\partial}{\partial r} \left(r^2 \frac{\partial U}{\partial r} \right) + \frac{\partial}{\partial \phi} \left(\sin \phi \, \frac{\partial U}{\partial \phi} \right) + \frac{1}{\sin \phi} \frac{\partial^2 U}{\partial \theta^2} = 0. \qquad (115)$$

To see the exact relation of the left members of Eqs. (111) and (115), let us denote the former by A and the latter by B. Then

$$\delta I = \iiint - 2A \, \delta U \, dx \, dy \, dz = \iiint - 2B \, \delta U \, dr \, d\phi \, d\theta. \qquad (116)$$

We may equate the two values of δI if δU is formed with the same parameter and the same function, expressed first in x,y,z and then in r,ϕ,θ coordinates, since the total derivative of a composite function does not depend on the intermediate variables used to compute it. But by changing coordinates in the triple integral,

$$\iiint - 2A \, \delta U \, dx \, dy \, dz = \iiint - 2A \, \delta U \, r^2 \sin \phi \, dr \, d\phi \, d\theta. \qquad (117)$$

Hence, from Eqs. (116) and (117), we may conclude that

$$\iiint - 2(Ar^2 \sin \phi - B) \delta U \, dr \, d\phi \, d\theta = 0 \qquad (118)$$

for arbitrary δU. It follows that

$$Ar^2 \sin \phi - B = 0, \qquad \text{and} \qquad A = \frac{1}{r^2 \sin \phi} B. \qquad (119)$$

Combined with the values of A from Eq. (111) and B from Eq. (115), this checks Eq. (110) of Sec. 124.

175. Vibrations of Material Systems. The deduction of Hamilton's principle from Newton's law of motion for systems of particles and rigid bodies was sketched in Secs. 172 and 173. One way of extending the laws of mechanics to nonrigid systems is to give a suitable interpretation to the kinetic and potential energies and accept Hamilton's principle as the basic law. We may then apply it for any system of coordinates as in Sec. 173.

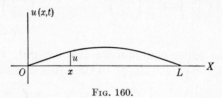

Fig. 160.

We proceed to give some illustrations of this point of view as applied to vibrating systems.

EXAMPLE 1. *The Vibrating String.* Consider a taut string, of length L ft., vibrating between fixed end points. Let $u(x,t)$ be the small longitudinal displacement at time t of a point at $x,0$ in the equilibrium position. Let $m = D/g$ be the density in slugs per foot and T be the tension in pounds. When a portion of the string of length dx is stretched to a length ds, the work done is $T(ds - dx)$. We assume that the slope $\partial u/\partial x = u_x$ is small. Then

$$\frac{ds}{dx} = \sqrt{1 + u_x{}^2} = 1 + \frac{1}{2} u_x{}^2 + \cdots, \qquad \text{and}$$

$$ds = dx + \frac{1}{2} u_x{}^2 dx, \quad (120)$$

if we neglect terms of higher order in u_x. Hence the work is

$$T(ds - dx) = \frac{T}{2} u_x{}^2 dx, \qquad \text{so that} \int_0^L \frac{T}{2} u_x{}^2 dx \quad (121)$$

is the potential energy.

The portion of the string over dx has a mass $m\,dx$ and velocity $\partial u/\partial t = u_t$. Hence the kinetic energy is the integral of $\frac{1}{2}m u_t{}^2 dx$. This leads to the Hamilton's integral of our problem as

$$\int_{t_1}^{t_2} dt \int_0^L \left(\frac{m}{2} u_t{}^2 - \frac{T}{2} u_x{}^2 \right) dx, \quad (122)$$

which is equivalent to a double integral in x and t. The Euler equation for minimizing this is

$$-\frac{\partial}{\partial t}(mu_t) - \frac{\partial}{\partial x}(-Tu_x) = 0, \quad \text{or} \quad -mu_{tt} + Tu_{xx} = 0. \quad (123)$$

Hence the equation for the vibrating string may be written

$$m\frac{\partial^2 u}{\partial t^2} = T\frac{\partial^2 u}{\partial x^2} \quad \text{or} \quad \frac{\partial^2 u}{\partial x^2} = \frac{1}{s^2}\frac{\partial^2 u}{\partial t^2} \quad (124)$$

if $s = \sqrt{T/m} = \sqrt{Tg/D}$, and so has the dimensions of velocity, feet per second.

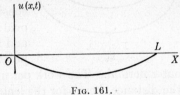

FIG. 161.

EXAMPLE 2. *The Vibrating Beam.* The potential energy of a bent beam is $EI/2\rho^2$ per unit length, where ρ is the radius of curvature. If the longitudinal displacement of the beam is $u(x,t)$, for small displacements the curvature is approximately $\partial^2 u/\partial x^2 = u_{xx}$. And, since we may approximate ds by dx, the potential energy is

$$\int_0^L \frac{EI}{2}u_{xx}^2 dx. \quad (125)$$

If the beam is of density m slugs/ft., and x is in feet, the kinetic energy is the integral of $\frac{1}{2}mu_t^2 dx$. Thus, the Hamilton's integral of our problem is

$$\int_{t_1}^{t_2} dt \int_0^L \left(\frac{m}{2}u_t^2 - \frac{EI}{2}u_{xx}^2\right)dx. \quad (126)$$

The Euler equation for minimizing the equivalent double integral in x and t is

$$-\frac{\partial}{\partial t}(mu_t) + \frac{\partial^2}{\partial x^2}(-EIu_{xx}) = 0, \quad \text{or} \quad -mu_{tt} - EIu_{xxxx} = 0. \quad (127)$$

Hence the equation for the vibrating beam is

$$m\frac{\partial^2 u}{\partial t^2} + EI\frac{\partial^4 u}{\partial x^4} = 0. \quad (128)$$

In this equation, with m in slugs per foot, x in feet, t in seconds, and EI in pounds per square foot times feet to the fourth power or in pounds times square feet, we may measure u either in feet or in inches.   But we must convert EI if given in pounds times square inches.

EXAMPLE 3. *The Vibrating Membrane.* Consider a taut membrane with fixed boundary B, such as a drumhead.   Let the

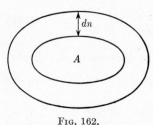

FIG. 162.

tension across any internal arc be T lb. per unit length.   Then the work done in stretching an area A to an area A' is $T(A' - A)$.

We may make this plausible by considering the special case of the oval of Fig. 162, originally of length s and area A, enlarged by having each point moved a distance dn along the outer normal.   The work per unit length is T the force times dn the distance, hence for the length s, the work is

$$sT\, dn = T(s\, dn) = T\, dA, \qquad \text{since } dA = s\, dn. \qquad (129)$$

Let the equilibrium position of the taut membrane be the xy plane and $u(x,y,t)$ be the small transverse displacements.   By Sec. 57, the element of stretched area is

$$dS = \sec \gamma\, dx\, dy, \qquad \text{where } \sec \gamma = \sqrt{1 + u_x^2 + u_y^2}$$
$$= 1 + \tfrac{1}{2}u_x^2 + \tfrac{1}{2}u_y^2 + \cdots . \qquad (130)$$

Hence to terms of the second order in u_x and u_y,

$$dS - dx\, dy = (\sec \gamma - 1)dx\, dy = \tfrac{1}{2}(u_x^2 + u_y^2)dx\, dy. \qquad (131)$$

Multiplied by T, this gives the work of stretching the element of area $dx\, dy$.   Integration then gives the total work, or potential energy, as

$$\iint \frac{T}{2} (u_x^2 + u_y^2)dx\, dy. \qquad (132)$$

The kinetic energy is the integral of $\tfrac{1}{2}mu_t^2 dx\, dy$.   Thus Hamilton's integral for this problem is

$$\int_{t_1}^{t_2} dt \iint \left[\frac{m}{2} u_t^2 - \frac{T}{2} (u_x^2 + u_y^2) \right] dx\, dy. \qquad (133)$$

The double integral in (132) and (133) is taken over the area bounded by B. The Euler equation for the triple integral in t,x,y equivalent to (133) is

$$-\frac{\partial}{\partial t}(mu_t) - \frac{\partial}{\partial x}(-Tu_x) - \frac{\partial}{\partial y}(-Tu_y) = 0 \qquad \text{or}$$

$$-mu_{tt} + Tu_{xx} + Tu_{yy} = 0. \quad (134)$$

Hence the equation for the vibrating membrane is

$$m\frac{\partial^2 u}{\partial t^2} = T\left(\frac{\partial^2 u}{\partial x^2} + \frac{\partial^2 u}{\partial y^2}\right). \quad (135)$$

176. References. For a more extensive treatment of that portion of the calculus of variations which is of interest in applied mathematics, we refer to Hilbert-Courant, *Methoden der mathematischen Physik.*

The Rayleigh or energy method of computing characteristic frequencies is a useful application of variational methods and Hamilton's principle. It is described in Temple and Bickley's *Rayleigh's Principle and Its Applications to Engineering.*

G. A. Bliss's *Carus Monograph on the Calculus of Variations* provides an elementary treatment of the subject as a branch of pure mathematics and a possible introduction to such comprehensive treatises as those of Bolza, Tonelli, and Hadamard.

EXERCISES XII

On any surface, the line of shortest length joining two points may be found by minimizing $\int ds$. The extremals for this problem are called *geodesics.* Find them

1. On a plane, taking $\int ds = \int \sqrt{1 + y'^2}\, dx$.

2. On a plane, taking $\int ds = \int \sqrt{1 + r^2(d\theta/dr)^2}\, dr$.

3. On the cylinder $x^2 + y^2 = a^2$, taking $x = a\cos u$, $y = a\sin u$, $z = v$ so that $ds = \int \sqrt{a^2 + (dv/du)^2}\, du$.

4. On the sphere $x^2 + y^2 + z^2 = a^2$, using spherical coordinates so that $\int ds = \int \sqrt{1 + \sin^2\phi(d\theta/d\phi)^2}\, d\phi$.

5. On the cone $x^2 + y^2 = z^2\tan^2 A$, taking $x = u\cos v$, $y = u\sin v$, $z = u\cot A$ so that $\int ds = \int \sqrt{\csc^2 A + u^2(dv/du)^2}\, du$.

6. On a surface for which $\int ds = \int \sqrt{u[1 + (dv/du)^2]}\, du$.

7. On the helicoid, $x = u\cos v$, $y = u\sin v$, $z = kv$, so that the length $\int ds = \int \sqrt{1 + (u^2 + k^2)(dv/du)^2}\, du$. Merely indicate the last integration.

8. On the catenoid of revolution, $x = u\cos v$, $y = u\sin v$, $z = \cosh^{-1} u$, so that $\int ds = \int u\sqrt{1/u^2 - 1 + (dv/du)^2}\, du$. Merely indicate the last integration.

9. On the surface of revolution, $x = u \cos v$, $y = u \sin v$, $z = f(u)$, so that $\int ds = \int \sqrt{1 + [f'(u)]^2 + u^2(dv/du)^2}\, du$. Merely indicate the last integration.

10. By Sec. 56, on any surface $ds^2 = E\, du^2 + 2F\, du\, dv + G\, dv^2$. Show that the geodesics satisfy the second order differential equation

$$\frac{d}{du}\left(\frac{F + Gv'}{\sqrt{E + 2Fv' + Gv'^2}}\right) = \frac{E_v + 2F_v v' + G_v v'^2}{2\sqrt{E + 2Fv' + Gv'^2}},$$

where primes mean u derivatives and subscripts partial derivatives.

If either variable x or y does not appear explicitly in the integrand of Eq. (3), a first integral of Euler's equation may be found. Specifically, show that the extremals for

11. $\int_a^b F(x,y')dx$ satisfy $\dfrac{\partial F}{\partial y'} = c_1$. Problems 1 to 9 provide examples of this.

12. $\int_a^b F(y,y')dx$ satisfy $F - y'\dfrac{\partial F}{\partial y'} = c_2$. HINT: Verify the relation

$$\frac{d}{dx}\left(F - y'\frac{\partial F}{\partial y'}\right) = y'\left(\frac{\partial F}{\partial y} - \frac{d}{dx}\frac{\partial F}{\partial y'}\right).$$

13. Check Prob. 12 by writing $\displaystyle\int F(y,y')dx = \int F\left(y, \frac{1}{dx/dy}\right)\frac{dx}{dy}\, dy$ and using Prob. 11 with x and y interchanged.

14. Show that for the integral of Prob. 1, Probs. 11 and 12 lead to the same first integral.

15. Check Prob. 2 by taking $\int ds = \int \sqrt{(dr/d\theta)^2 + r^2}\, d\theta$, and using Prob. 12.

16. Check Prob. 4 by taking $\int ds = \int \sqrt{(d\phi/d\theta)^2 + \sin^2 \phi}\, d\theta$, and using Prob. 12.

17. Check Eq. (21) by applying Prob. 12 to the integral of Eq. (18).

18. A ray of light moves between two fixed points in the xy plane with variable velocity, $v(x,y)$. By Fermat's law, its travel time is a minimum. Verify that the travel time is $\displaystyle\int \frac{ds}{v} = \int \frac{\sqrt{1 + y'^2}}{v(x,y)}\, dx$, and that the paths are determined by $\dfrac{vy''}{1 + y'^2} - \dfrac{\partial v}{\partial x}y' + \dfrac{\partial v}{\partial y} = 0$.

19. Suppose that, in Prob. 18, $v(x,y) = f(x)$. Apply Prob. 11 to derive the first integral $\dfrac{y'}{f\sqrt{1 + y'^2}} = c_1 = \dfrac{1}{h}$, and the final solution

$$y - k = \int \frac{f\, dx}{\sqrt{h^2 - f^2}}.$$

Use Prob. 19 to complete the solution of Prob. 18 if the velocity $v(x,y) = f(x) =$

20. 1.   **21.** x.   **22.** $\sqrt{x}$.   **23.** $1/x$.   **24.** $1/\sqrt{x}$.

25. Suppose that, in Prob. 18, $v(x,y) = g(y)$. Apply Prob. 12 to derive the first integral $\dfrac{1}{g\sqrt{1 + y'^2}} = c_1 = \dfrac{1}{h}$, and the final solution

$$x - k = \int \frac{g\,dy}{\sqrt{h^2 - g^2}}.$$

Use Prob. 25 to complete the solution of Prob. 18 if the velocity $v(x,y) = g(y) =$

26. 1.   **27.** y.   **28.** $\sqrt{y}$.   **29.** $1/y$.   **30.** $1/\sqrt{y}$.

31. In the brachystochrone problem it is required to find the curve joining O and B such that a body, starting from rest and sliding under gravity, will reach B in least time. With the y axis downward, $v = \sqrt{2gy}$. Find the extremals. HINT: The time may be expressed as $\int \dfrac{ds}{v} = \int \dfrac{\sqrt{1 + y'^2}}{\sqrt{2gy}}\,dx$, and Prob. 12 is applicable.

32. By Sec. 82, if $\dfrac{\partial P}{\partial y} = \dfrac{\partial Q}{\partial x}$, $I = \displaystyle\int (P + Qy')dx$ taken between fixed end points is independent of the path and so has a variation zero. Show that in this case the Euler equation reduces to an identity, $0 = 0$.

Verify the conclusion of Prob. 32 directly for

33. $\int (y + xy')dx$.   **34.** $\int (x + yy')dx$.
35. $\int (y^2 + 2xyy')dx$.   **36.** $\int y^4 y'\,dx$.

37. From Prob. 32, deduce that in setting up Euler's equation, we may omit any terms from the integral which, collectively, make up an exact integral.

Find the extremals when minimizing

38. $\int (y'^2 + y^2)dx$.   **39.** $\int (y''^2 + y^2)dx$.   **40.** $\int (y'^2 + z'^2 + y^2 + z^2)dx$.

41. Carry out in detail the derivation of Eq. (39) from first principles, and use it to obtain the Euler equations (27).

42. Show that the variation of $I = \int F(x,y,z,y',z',y'',z'')dx$ is the sum of two terms, one like the right member of Eq. (36) and another obtained from this by replacing y by z. Use this to obtain two Euler equations, similar in form to Eq. (24).

When the end points are not fixed, derive the relations

43. $\delta \int_a^b F(x,y,y')dx = \delta y \dfrac{\partial F}{\partial y'} \Big|_a^b + \int_a^b \left[\dfrac{\partial F}{\partial y} - \dfrac{d}{dx}\left(\dfrac{\partial F}{\partial y'} \right) \right] \delta y \, dy.$

44. $\delta \int_{t_1}^{t_2} G(x,y,\dot{x},\dot{y})dt = \delta x \dfrac{\partial G}{\partial \dot{x}} + \delta y \dfrac{\partial G}{\partial \dot{y}} \Big|_{t_1}^{t_2}$

$\qquad + \int_{t_1}^{t_2} \left[\dfrac{\partial G}{\partial x} - \dfrac{d}{dt}\left(\dfrac{\partial G}{\partial \dot{x}} \right) \right] \delta x \, dt + \int_{t_1}^{t_2} \left[\dfrac{\partial G}{\partial y} - \dfrac{d}{dt}\left(\dfrac{\partial G}{\partial \dot{y}} \right) \right] \delta y \, dt.$

45. Suppose that the end point B in Fig. 155 is not fixed but is restricted to lie on a curve K_B. Noting that a minimizing curve C would have to be a minimizing curve when the end point B was fixed at the right place on K_B, show that the Euler equation (15) is still satisfied.

46. From Probs. 1 and 45, the curve C joining a fixed point A with a point on a curve K_B and having least length must be a straight line segment, with $y' = c_1$. If K_B is the line $x = b$, by applying Prob. 43 with $F = \sqrt{1 + y'^2}$, deduce the further condition $\dfrac{\delta y \, y'}{\sqrt{1 + y'^2}} \Big|^b = 0$, or since δy at b is now arbitrary, $y' = c_1 = 0$. Hence the extremal is $y = \alpha$, the line through A parallel to the x axis, or perpendicular to K_B.

47. If in Prob. 46 the fixed curve K_B is $H(x,y) = 0$, from Prob. 44 with $G = \sqrt{\dot{x}^2 + \dot{y}^2}$, deduce the further condition $\dfrac{\delta x \, \dot{x} + \delta y \, \dot{y}}{\sqrt{\dot{x}^2 + \dot{y}^2}} \Big|^{t_2} = 0$. Since, at t_2, δx and δy are now arbitrary except for the condition $\delta x \, H_x + \delta y \, H_y$, $\dfrac{\delta y}{\delta x} = -\dfrac{H_x}{H_y}$ and $\dfrac{\dot{y}}{\dot{x}} = -\dfrac{\delta x}{\delta y}$, so that at t_2, or B, the straight line C is perpendicular to K_B.

48. If in Prob. 18 the end point B is not fixed but restricted to lie on a curve K_B, show that the path C is perpendicular to K_B at B. HINT: Reason as in Prob. 47.

49. Draw conclusions similar to those of Probs. 47 and 48 for the case when B is fixed and A lies on a curve K_A, or when A lies on K_A and B lies on K_B. In the first case C is the extremal through B perpendicular to K_A at A, and in the second the extremal perpendicular to K_A at A and to K_B at B.

50. In $I = \int_a^b F(x,y,y')dx$, put $\delta y = u\phi(x) + v\psi(x)$, and let δI denote the total differential of I formed at $u = 0$ and $v = 0$ where $du = u$ and $dv = v$. Assuming fixed end points and with the abbreviation $F_2 = \dfrac{\partial F}{\partial y} - \dfrac{d}{dx}\left(\dfrac{\partial F}{\partial y'} \right)$, show that in this case the variation is

$$\delta I = du \int_a^b F_2\phi \, dx + dv \int_a^b F_2\psi \, dx.$$

51. Apply Prob. 50 to the integrals I and J of Eqs. (44) and (45). From this and Sec. 34 deduce that if I is to be a minimum when J is constant, $\int_a^b (F_2 - \lambda G_2)\phi \, dx = 0$ and $\int_a^b (F_2 - G_2)\psi \, dx = 0$, or since ϕ and ψ are arbitrary, $F_2 - \lambda G_2 = 0$, which is Eq. (47), the Euler equation for (46).

52. In $I = \int_a^b F(x,y,z,y',z')dx$, put $\delta y = u\phi(x)$ and $\delta z = v\psi(x)$, and let δI denote the total differential of I formed at $u = 0$ and $v = 0$ where $du = u$ and $dv = v$. Assuming fixed end points and with the abbreviations $F_2 = \dfrac{\partial F}{\partial y} - \dfrac{d}{dx}\left(\dfrac{\partial F}{\partial y'}\right)$ and $F_3 = \dfrac{\partial F}{\partial z} - \dfrac{d}{dx}\left(\dfrac{\partial F}{\partial z'}\right)$, show that

$$\delta I = du \int_a^b F_2\phi \, dx + dv \int_a^b F_3\psi \, dx.$$

53. With the notation of Prob. 52 applied to $G(x,y,z)$ we have $G_2 = \partial G/\partial y$, $G_3 = \partial G/\partial z$. Show that $\delta G = du\, G_2 + dv\, G_3$.

54. The condition that the integral I of Eq. (55) be a minimum when Eq. (56) holds is that the δI of Prob. 52 be zero for all du and dv making the δG of Prob. 53 equal to zero. If $\lambda(x)$ is defined by the relation $F_2 - \lambda(x)G_2 = 0$, by forming $\delta I - \lambda(x)\delta G$ and reasoning as in Sec. 34, deduce that $F_3 - \lambda(x)G_3 = 0$. This establishes Eqs. (58), the Euler equations for (57), as necessary conditions.

Find the extremals for the problem of determining a curve C of given length L joining AB and maximizing the area bounded by

55. C, the axis of x and two fixed ordinates, $\int_a^b y \, dx$.

56. C, OA, and OB, $\int_a^b \frac{1}{2}(x \, dy - y \, dx)$.

57. C itself, a closed curve when A and B coincide, $\int \frac{1}{2}(x \, dy - y \, dx)$, taken from a to a along C.

58. Find the extremals for the problem of the curve of given length L, with lowest center of gravity or least $L\bar{y} = \int y \, ds$.

The geodesics, as defined in the remark preceding Prob. 1, on any surface $G(x,y,z) = 0$ may be found by minimizing $\int ds$ subject to this condition. Use the Euler equation for z to show that the geodesics make a constant angle with OZ on the cylinder

59. $x^2 + y^2 = a^2$, taking $\int ds = \int \sqrt{1 + y'^2 + z'^2} \, dx$.

60. $x^2 + y^2 = a^2$, taking $\int ds = \int \sqrt{\dot{x}^2 + \dot{y}^2 + \dot{z}^2} \, dt$.

61. $g(x,y) = 0$, taking $\int ds$ as in Prob. 59 or 60.

62. Using the parameter t, as in Prob. 60, for the geodesics on any surface $G(x,y,z) = 0$ deduce the relations

$$\frac{d^2x/ds^2}{\partial G/\partial x} = \frac{d^2y/ds^2}{\partial G/\partial y} = \frac{d^2z/ds^2}{\partial G/\partial z}.$$

63. Referring to Secs. 49 and 54, interpret the result of Prob. 62 as stating that a geodesic curve on any surface has its principal normal at each point coincident with the normal to the surface at that point.

64. We may use the arc length of a curve s as the parameter, if we introduce the additional constraint $x'^2 + y'^2 + z'^2 = 1$, where primes denote s derivatives. Check Prob. 62 by finding the Euler equations for $\int[1 - \lambda(s)G(x,y,z) - \mu(s)(x'^2 + y'^2 + z'^2 - 1)]ds$. As first found, the Euler equations contain terms in μ'. But if the three equations are multiplied by x', y', and z' respectively and added, in view of the constraints the result is equivalent to $\mu' = 0$. This proves μ constant.

65. Reasoning as in Prob. 64, show that the geodesics of Prob. 10 satisfy the Euler equations for the integral containing the parameter λ, $\int[1 - \lambda(s)(Eu'^2 + 2Fu'v' + Gv'^2 - 1)]ds$, or after λ is proved constant

$$2\frac{d}{ds}(Eu' + Fv') = E_u u'^2 + 2F_u u'v' + G_u v'^2$$

$$\text{and } 2\frac{d}{ds}(Fu' + Gv') = E_v u'^2 + 2F_v u'v' + G_v v'^2.$$

66. Identify the last equation in Prob. 65, where primes are s derivatives, with the equation of Prob. 10, where primes are u derivatives.

67. Show that the result of multiplying the first equation of Prob. 65 by u', the second by v', and adding is equivalent to the exact equation $\frac{d}{ds}(Eu'^2 + 2Fu'v' + Gv'^2) = 0$. Hence since the constraint equation $Eu'^2 + 2Fu'v' + Gv'^2 = 1$ holds, the equations of Prob. 65 are not independent.

68. If we omit the kinetic energy from Hamilton's integral, we obtain the condition for equilibrium, $\delta\int(-U)dt = 0$. Show that for a single particle in a force field with potential energy $U(x,y,z)$, this is equivalent to $\partial U/\partial x = 0$, $\partial U/\partial y = 0$, $\partial U/\partial z = 0$.

69. Suppose that the particle in Prob. 68 is constrained to lie on a surface $G(x,y,z) = 0$. Then the condition is $\delta\int(-U - \lambda G)dt = 0$, where λ, ordinarily a function of t, is a constant because U and G do not contain t. Deduce the conditions $\dfrac{\partial U}{\partial x} = -\lambda\dfrac{\partial G}{\partial x}$, $\dfrac{\partial U}{\partial y} = -\lambda\dfrac{\partial G}{\partial y}$, $\dfrac{\partial U}{\partial z} = -\lambda\dfrac{\partial G}{\partial z}$.

70. Suppose that the particle in Prob. 68 is constrained to lie on a curve, the intersection of two surfaces $G(x,y,z) = 0$ and $H(x,y,z) = 0$. By proceeding as in Prob. 69, deduce three conditions, of which the first is $\dfrac{\partial U}{\partial x} = -\lambda\dfrac{\delta G}{\partial x} - \mu\dfrac{\partial H}{\partial x}$.

When gravity acts and the z axis is upward, $U = mgz$. Show that the equilibrium positions of a particle

71. On the surface $z = f(x,y)$ are given by $\partial f/\partial x = 0$, $\partial f/\partial y = 0$. See Prob. 69.

72. On the curve $z^2 + x^2 = 4$, $y = 0$, are given by $0 = 2\lambda x$, $0 = \mu$, $-mg = 2\lambda z$, and hence $x = 0$, $y = 0$, $z = \pm 2$. See Prob. 70.

Use Lagrange's equations to set up the equations of motion

73. For a simple pendulum, $T = \dfrac{m}{2} L^2 \dot{\theta}^2$, $U = mgL(1 - \cos \theta)$.

74. For a compound pendulum, $T = \dfrac{I}{2} \dot{\theta}^2$, $U = mgL(1 - \cos \theta)$.

75. For the pendulum of Prob. 74 when the oscillations are small, and we approximate $\cos \theta$ by $1 - \frac{1}{2}\theta^2$, or U by $\dfrac{mgL}{2} \theta^2$.

76. For a pendulum with an elastic string of natural length L, so that $T = \dfrac{m}{2} [(L + r)^2\dot{\theta}^2 + \dot{r}^2]$, $U = mg[L - (L + r) \cos \theta] + \dfrac{k}{2} r^2$.

77. The pendulum of Prob. 76 when r and θ are small, and we use the approximations $T = \dfrac{m}{2} (L^2\dot{\theta}^2 + \dot{r}^2)$, $U = mg \left(-r + \dfrac{L}{2} \theta^2 \right) + \dfrac{k}{2} r^2$.

78. A particle in a plane acted on by springs along the x and y axes, $T = \dfrac{m}{2} (\dot{x}^2 + \dot{y}^2)$, $U = \frac{1}{2}(k_1 x^2 + k_2 y^2)$.

79. A particle in a plane acted on by a conservative force field with components F_r and F_θ in the direction of increasing r and θ. Hint: Use $U(r,\theta)$ and deduce from $dU = \dfrac{\partial U}{\partial r} \, dr + \dfrac{\partial U}{\partial \theta} \, d\theta = -F_r \, dr - F_\theta r \, d\theta$ that $\dfrac{\partial U}{\partial r} = -F_r$, $\dfrac{\partial U}{\partial \theta} = -rF_\theta$.

80. A particle in space acted on by a conservative force field with components F_r, F_ϕ, F_θ. Hint: Proceed as in Prob. 79, using $U(r,\phi,\theta)$ and $dU = \dfrac{\partial U}{\partial r} \, dr + \dfrac{\partial U}{\partial \phi} \, d\phi + \dfrac{\partial U}{\partial \theta} \, d\theta = -F_r \, dr - F_\phi r \, d\phi - F_\theta r \sin \phi \, d\theta$.

81. A particle moving on any surface under no forces in the surface. With u and v as in Prob. 10, $T = \dfrac{m}{2} (E\dot{u}^2 + 2F\dot{u}\dot{v} + G\dot{v}^2)$, $U = 0$.

82. The energy integral, $E\dot{u}^2 + 2F\dot{u}\dot{v} + G\dot{v}^2 = c_1$ could be deduced from the Euler equations of Prob. 81 by a calculation like that made in Prob. 67. It shows that the speed in the path ds/dt is constant. From this and a comparison of the equations of Probs. 81 and 65, show that the paths are geodesics.

Find the Euler condition for each of the following integrals to be a minimum:

83. $\displaystyle \int \int (p^2 + q^2)dx \, dy = \int \int \left[\left(\dfrac{\partial z}{\partial x} \right)^2 + \left(\dfrac{\partial z}{\partial y} \right)^2 \right] dx \, dy.$

84. $\int \int \left[\left(\dfrac{\partial U}{\partial r} \right)^2 + \dfrac{1}{r^2} \left(\dfrac{\partial U}{\partial \theta} \right)^2 \right] r \, dr \, d\theta.$

85. $\int \int \left[U^2 + \left(\dfrac{\partial U}{\partial x} \right)^2 + \left(\dfrac{\partial U}{\partial y} \right)^2 \right] dx \, dy.$

86. $\int \int \int \left[\left(\dfrac{\partial U}{\partial r} \right)^2 + \dfrac{1}{r^2} \left(\dfrac{\partial U}{\partial \theta} \right)^2 + \left(\dfrac{\partial U}{\partial z} \right)^2 \right] r \, dr \, d\theta \, dz.$

87. $\int \int \int \left[\dfrac{1}{h_1{}^2} \left(\dfrac{\partial U}{\partial u} \right)^2 + \dfrac{1}{h_2{}^2} \left(\dfrac{\partial U}{\partial v} \right)^2 + \dfrac{1}{h_3{}^2} \left(\dfrac{\partial U}{\partial w} \right)^2 \right] h_1 h_2 h_3 \, du \, dv \, dw,$

where the notation is that of Sec. 124.

88. $\int \int \sqrt{1 + p^2 + q^2} \, dx \, dy = \int \int \sqrt{1 + \left(\dfrac{\partial z}{\partial x} \right)^2 + \left(\dfrac{\partial z}{\partial y} \right)^2} \, dx \, dy.$

89. From Sec. 57 deduce that the integral of Prob. 88 represents the area of the surface $z = f(x,y)$ spanned by the fixed boundary curve B. The surfaces for which the integral is least are called *minimal* surfaces.

90. Carry out in detail the derivation of Eq. (108) as the condition for $I = \int\int F(x,y,z,p,q,r,s,t) dx \, dy$ to be a minimum.

By reasoning like that used to derive Eq. (119), check

91. Equation (85) of Sec. 25, using Probs. 83 and 84.

92. Problem 48 of Exercises VIII (page 331), using Prob. 86.

93. Equation (107) of Sec. 124, using Prob. 87.

94. If a surface $z = f(x,y)$ is spanned over a fixed curve B, its surface area is $A = \int\int \sqrt{1 + p^2 + q^2} \, dx \, dy$, by Prob. 89. The volume under the surface is $V = \int\int z \, dx \, dy$. Find the Euler equation for the problem of making A a minimum when V is constant.

95. Let the string of Example 1, Sec. 175, be subjected to a load parallel to the u axis. If the load on ds is $F(x,t)dx$, there is an additional term in the potential energy, $-\int uF \, dx$. Show that in this case the equation of motion for the string is

$$m \frac{\partial^2 u}{\partial t^2} = T \frac{\partial^2 u}{\partial x^2} + F.$$

96. Reasoning as in Prob. 95, show that if a load $F(x,t)dx$ acts on an element ds of the beam of Example 2, Sec. 175, the equation of motion for the beam is

$$m \frac{\partial^2 u}{\partial t^2} + EI \frac{\partial^4 u}{\partial x^4} = F.$$

97. Reasoning as in Prob. 95, show that if a load $F(x,y,t)dx \, dy$ acts on an element dS of the membrane of Example 3, Sec. 175, the equation of motion for the membrane is

$$m \frac{\partial^2 u}{\partial t^2} = T \left(\frac{\partial^2 u}{\partial x^2} + \frac{\partial^2 u}{\partial y^2} \right) + F.$$

Using Hamilton's principle with the kinetic energy term omitted, as in Prob. 68, obtain the condition for equilibrium

98. Of the string of Prob. 95, $T \dfrac{d^2u}{dx^2} = -F(x)$.

99. Of the beam of Prob. 96, $EI \dfrac{d^4u}{dx^4} = F(x)$.

100. Of the membrane of Prob. 97, $T\left(\dfrac{\partial^2 u}{\partial x^2} + \dfrac{\partial^2 u}{\partial y^2}\right) = -F(x,y)$.

101. Show that in polar coordinates, Hamilton's integral for the membrane [Eq. (133)] becomes

$$\int_{t_1}^{t_2} dt \int \int \left[\frac{m}{2} u_t{}^2 - \frac{T}{2}\left(u_r{}^2 + \frac{1}{r^2} u_\theta{}^2\right)\right] r \, dr \, d\theta,$$

and use this to find the equation for the membrane in polar coordinates.

102. The Hamilton integral for a vibrating plate is

$$\int_{t_1}^{t_2} dt \int \int \left[\frac{m}{2} u_t{}^2 + \frac{A}{2}(u_{xx} + u_{yy})^2 + \frac{B}{2}(u_{xy}{}^2 - u_{xx}u_{yy})\right] dx \, dy.$$

From this deduce the equation of motion for the plate

$$m \frac{\partial^2 u}{\partial t^2} + A\left(\frac{\partial^4 u}{\partial x^4} + 2 \frac{\partial^4 u}{\partial x^2 \partial y^2} + \frac{\partial^4 u}{\partial y^4}\right).$$

103. The Hamilton integral for sound waves or vibrations in air is
$$\int_{t_1}^{t_2} dt \int \int \left[\frac{m}{2} u_t{}^2 - \frac{k}{2}(u_x{}^2 + u_y{}^2 + u_z{}^2)\right] dx \, dy \, dz. \quad \text{Deduce that}$$

$$m \frac{\partial^2 u}{\partial t^2} = k\left(\frac{\partial^2 u}{\partial x^2} + \frac{\partial^2 u}{\partial y^2} + \frac{\partial^2 u}{\partial z^2}\right).$$

104. If the taut string is not vibrating in a plane but has displacements $y(x,t)$ and $z(x,t)$ parallel to OY and OZ, the stretched length ds has components dx, $y_x dx$, and $z_x dx$. Deduce that for y_x and z_x small, the potential energy is approximately $\displaystyle\int \frac{T}{2}(y_x{}^2 + z_x{}^2)dx$, and derive the equations of motion $m \dfrac{\partial^2 y}{\partial t^2} = T \dfrac{\partial^2 y}{\partial x^2}$ and $m \dfrac{\partial^2 z}{\partial t^2} = T \dfrac{\partial^2 z}{\partial x^2}$.

105. For a rod vibrating longitudinally, let u be the displacement of an element originally at distance x from one end. Then the kinetic energy is $\displaystyle\int \frac{m}{2} u_t{}^2 dx$, while the potential energy is $\displaystyle\int EA\, u_x{}^2 dx$. Deduce the equation $m \dfrac{\partial^2 u}{\partial t^2} = EA \dfrac{\partial^2 u}{\partial x^2}$.

106. Assuming that the effect of air resistance, or other viscous damping, on a string is equivalent to a load at any instant equal to $-k\dfrac{\partial u}{\partial t}$, and using Prob. 95, deduce the equation of motion

$$m\frac{\partial^2 u}{\partial t^2} = T\frac{\partial^2 u}{\partial x^2} - k\frac{\partial u}{\partial t}.$$

BIBLIOGRAPHY

BENNETT, A. A., W. E. MILNE, H. BATEMAN, and L. E. FORD: Numerical Integration of Differential Equations, *National Research Council Bulletin* 92, Washington, D. C., 1933.

BLISS, G. A.: "Calculus of Variations," The Open Court Publishing Company, Chicago, 1925.

BÔCHER, M.: "Introduction to Higher Algebra," The Macmillan Company, New York, 1907.

BOLZA, O.: "Vorlesungen über Variationsrechnung," B. G. Teubner, Leipzig, 1909.

BURINGTON, R. S., and C. C. TORRANCE: "Higher Mathematics," McGraw-Hill Book Company, Inc., New York, 1939.

BYERLY, W. E.: "Fourier Series and Spherical Harmonics," Ginn and Company, Boston, 1893.

CARSLAW, H. S.: "Theory of the Conduction of Heat," The Macmillan Company, London, 1921.

CHURCHILL, R. V.: "Fourier Series and Boundary Value Problems," McGraw-Hill Book Company, Inc., New York, 1941.

COFFIN, J. G.: "Vector Analysis," John Wiley & Sons, Inc., New York, 1911.

COURANT, R., and D. HILBERT: "Methoden der mathematischen Physik," Verlag Julius Springer, Berlin, vol. 1, 1931; vol. 2, 1937.

DAVIS, H. T.: "Tables of Higher Mathematical Functions," Principia Press, Bloomington, Ind., vol. 1, 1933.

DICKSON, L. E.: "First Course in the Theory of Equations," John Wiley & Sons, Inc., New York, 1922.

———: "Modern Algebraic Theories," Benj. H. Sanborn & Co., Chicago, 1926.

DWIGHT, H. B.: "Mathematical Tables of Elementary and Some Higher Mathematical Functions," McGraw-Hill Book Company, Inc., New York, 1941.

———: "Tables of Integrals and Other Mathematical Data," The Macmillan Company, New York, 1934.

EISENHART, L. P.: "Treatise on the Differential Geometry of Curves and Surfaces," Ginn and Company, Boston, 1909.

ENNEPER, A.: "Elliptische Funktionen," Nebert, Halle, 1890.

FINE, H. B.: "Calculus," The Macmillan Company, New York, 1937.

———: "College Algebra," Ginn and Company, Boston, 1905.

——— and H. D. THOMPSON: "Coordinate Geometry," The Macmillan Company, New York, 1918.

FORSYTH, A. R.: "Treatise on Differential Equations," Macmillan & Company, Ltd., London, 1885.

463

FRANK, P., and R. VON MISES: "Differential- und Integralgleichungen der Mechanik und Physik," Rosenberg, New York, 1943.

FRANKLIN, P.: "Differential Equations for Electrical Engineers," John Wiley & Sons, Inc., New York, 1933.

————: "A Treatise on Advanced Calculus," John Wiley & Sons, Inc., New York, 1940.

GIBBS, J. W., and E. B. WILSON: "Vector Analysis," Charles Scribner's Sons, New York, 1901.

GLAUERT, H.: "The Elements of Aerofoil and Airscrew Theory," Cambridge University Press, London, 1924.

GRAUSTEIN, W. C.: "Elementary Differential Geometry," The Macmillan Company, New York, 1935.

GRAY, A., G. B. MATHEWS, and T. M. MACROBERT: "A Treatise on Bessel Functions," Macmillan & Co., Ltd., London, 1931.

HADAMARD, J. S.: "Leçons sur le calcul des variations," Hermann & Cie, Paris, 1910.

HOBSON, E. W.: "Theory of Spherical and Ellipsoidal Harmonics," Cambridge University Press, London, 1931.

HURWITZ, A., and R. COURANT: "Vorlesungen über allgemeine Funktionentheorie und elliptische Funktionen," Verlag Julius Springer, Berlin, 1925.

INCE, E. L.: "Ordinary Differential Equations," Longmans, Green and Company, London, 1927.

JAHNKE, E., and F. EMDE: Tables of Functions, B. G. Teubner, Leipzig, 1938.

KÁRMÁN, T. V., and M. A. BIOT: "Mathematical Methods in Engineering," McGraw-Hill Book Company, Inc., New York, 1940.

LIPKA, J.: "Graphical and Mechanical Computation," John Wiley & Sons, Inc., New York, 1918.

MCLACHLAN, N. W.: "Complex Variable and Operational Calculus, with Technical Applications," Cambridge University Press, London, 1939.

OSGOOD, W. F.: "Advanced Calculus," The Macmillan Company, New York, 1929.

PEIRCE, B. O.: "Short Table of Integrals," Ginn and Company, Boston, 1929.

PHILLIPS, H. B.: "Vector Analysis," John Wiley & Sons, Inc., New York, 1933.

PRANDTL, L., and G. O. TIETJENS: "Applied Hydro- and Aeromechanics," McGraw-Hill Book Company, Inc., New York, 1934.

————: "Fundamentals of Hydro- and Aeromechanics," McGraw-Hill Book Company, Inc., New York, 1934.

REDDICK, H. W., and F. H. MILLER: "Advanced Mathematics for Engineers," John Wiley & Sons, Inc., New York, 1938.

ROTHE, R., F. OLLENDORF, and K. POHLHAUSEN: "Theory of Functions as Applied to Engineering Problems," Massachusetts Institute of Technology Press, Cambridge, Mass., 1933.

SCARBOROUGH, J. B.: "Numerical Mathematical Analysis," The Johns Hopkins Press, Baltimore, 1930.

SHERWOOD, T. K., and C. E. REED: "Applied Mathematics in Chemical Engineering," McGraw-Hill Book Company, Inc., New York, 1939.

SOKOLNIKOFF, I. S., and E. S. SOKOLNIKOFF: "Higher Mathematics for Engineers and Physicists," McGraw-Hill Book Company, Inc., New York, 1941.

TEMPLE, G., and W. G. BICKLEY: "Rayleigh's Principle and Its Applications to Engineering," Oxford University Press, New York, 1933.

TONELLI, L.: Fondamenti di calcolo delle variazioni, Zanichelli, Bologna, 1923.

WALKER, M.: "Conjugate Functions for Engineers," Oxford University Press, New York, 1933.

WATSON, G. N.: "Theory of Bessel Functions," Cambridge University Press, London, 1922.

WEBSTER, A. G., and S. J. PLIMPTON: "Partial Differential Equations of Mathematical Physics," G. E. Stechert & Company, New York, 1933.

WILSON, E. B.: "Advanced Calculus," Ginn and Company, Boston, 1912.

WOODS, F. S.: "Advanced Calculus," Ginn and Company, New York, 1934.

ANSWERS

4. $\dfrac{e^{ax}(a \cos bx + b \sin bx)}{a^2 + b^2}$,

$\dfrac{e^{ax}(a \sin bx - b \cos bx)}{a^2 + b^2}$.

5. $3x - 2 \sin 2x + \dfrac{\sin 4x}{4}$.

6. $x - \dfrac{\sin 4x}{4}$.

15. $\dfrac{1 + i}{\sqrt{2}} = 0.707 + 0.707i$.

16. 1.

17. $\cosh 3 = 10.068$.

18. $- \sin 1 \cosh 1 + i \cos 1 \sinh 1$
$= -1.30 + 0.63i$.

19. $\cos 1 \cosh 2 - i \sin 1 \sinh 2$
$= 2.03 - 3.04i$.

20. $\cos 3 = -0.9900$.

21. $\sinh 2 \cos 1 - i \cosh 2 \sin 1$
$= 1.97 - 3.16i$.

22. $\cosh 1 \cos 1 + i \sinh 1 \sin 1$
$= 0.83 + 0.99i$.

33. 0.8657.

38. (a) 4, 0; (b) 9, $-\pi/2$;
(c) 2, $\pi/6$.

39. (a) 1.386; (b) $2.197 - 1.571i$;
(c) $0.693 + 0.524i$.

40. $-4 - i$.

41. $-8 - 2i$.

42. $-17 - 52i$.

43. $8 - 6i$.

44. $1 + 5i$.

45. i.

46. (a) ± 2; (b) $\pm(2.12 - 2.12i)$;
(c) $\pm(1.37 + 0.366i)$.

47. 2,
$-1 \pm \sqrt{3}\, i = -1 \pm 1.732i$.

48. $\pm(\sqrt{2} \pm \sqrt{2}\, i)$
$= \pm(1.414 \pm 1.414i)$.

49. $2i$, $\pm 1.902 + 0.618i$,
$\pm 1.176 - 1.618i$.

50. ± 1, $\pm \dfrac{1 \pm \sqrt{3}\, i}{2}$
$= \pm(0.5 \pm 0.866i)$.

72. 0.7468.

73. 0.3103.

74. 1.1047.

75. 0.4931.

76. 0.19806.

77. -0.41825.

78. 0.3573.

79. 0.739.

80. 1.166.

81. 1.896.

82. n.

83. 1.

84. 1.

85. $-\pi$.

86. 2.

87. $- \sqrt{3}/2$.

89. $\log a - \log b$.

90. 2.

91. 2.

92. ½.

93. 1.

94. -2.

95. 0.

96. 1.

97. 1.

98. 0.

99. e^{-12}.

100. 0.

101. 0.

102. 3.41×10^{-4}.

103. 1.08×10^{-4}.

104. 1.33×10^{-4}.

105. 2.5×10^{-5}.

106. $-1, -3$.

1. $\dfrac{x}{x^2 - y^2}$, $\dfrac{-y}{x^2 - y^2}$.

2. $e^x \cosh y + e^x \sinh y = e^{x+y}$.

3. $\dfrac{y}{x^2 + y^2}, \dfrac{-x}{x^2 + y^2}$.

4. $\dfrac{4(x^2 - y^2 - 4)}{(x^2 + y^2 + 4)^2 - 4x^2}$,

$\dfrac{8xy}{(x^2 + y^2 + 4)^2 - 4x^2}$.

5. $\dfrac{-y}{(x - y)^2}, \dfrac{x}{(x - y)^2}$.

6. 3.9 ft.

8. 9 per cent.

9. 1.25 per cent.

18. With $u = y/x$, $v = z/x$:

(**11**) $x^2 \sqrt{1 - u^2} \sin^{-1} u$;

(**12**) $x^0 \tan^{-1} u$;

(**13**) $x^0 \log (1 + u^2 + v^2)$;

(**14**) $x^2 u, \frac{1}{2}x^2 u, \frac{1}{2}x^2(u + v)$;

(**15**) $x^3 uv, x^3 u, \frac{1}{3}\pi x^3 u$;

(**16**) $ax^n u^q$.

40. $\dfrac{\partial u}{\partial x} = \dfrac{1}{2u} = \dfrac{1}{2} x^{-\frac{1}{2}}, \dfrac{\partial u}{\partial y} = 0$,

$\dfrac{\partial v}{\partial x} = -\dfrac{2}{5u} = -\dfrac{2}{5} x^{-\frac{1}{2}}, \dfrac{\partial v}{\partial y} = \dfrac{1}{5}$.

41. $\dfrac{d^2 z}{dx^2} + 1 = 0$.

42. $x \dfrac{d^2 z}{dx^2} + (2n + 1) \dfrac{dz}{dx} + xz = 0$.

43. $t \dfrac{d^2 z}{dt^2} + (n + 1) \dfrac{dz}{dt} + z = 0$.

44. $\dfrac{d^2 y}{d\theta^2} + \cot \theta \dfrac{dy}{d\theta} + n(n + 1)y = 0$.

49. $\dfrac{dy}{dx} = -\dfrac{x^{n-1}}{y^{n-1}}$

$= -(x^{-n} - 1)^{(1-n)/n}$,

$\dfrac{d^2 y}{dx^2} = (1 - n) \dfrac{x^{n-2}}{y^{2n-1}}$.

50. $\dfrac{3x^2 - y}{x - 3y^2}$.

51. $\dfrac{dx}{dt} = \dfrac{1 - 2t^3}{(1 + t^3)^2}, \dfrac{dy}{dt} = \dfrac{2t - t^4}{(1 + t^3)^2}$.

52. $\dfrac{\partial^2 f}{\partial x^2} + 2 \dfrac{\partial^2 f}{\partial x\, \partial y} \dfrac{dF}{dx} + \dfrac{\partial f}{\partial y} \dfrac{d^2 F}{dx^2}$

$+ \dfrac{\partial^2 f}{\partial y^2} \left(\dfrac{dF}{dx}\right)^2$.

69. -11. **70.** -31. **71.** 37.

72. $x = 4, y = 1$.

73. $x = 2, y = 3, z = 1$.

74. $x = 2, y = 1, z = 3$.

85. $\dfrac{dx}{yz} = \dfrac{dy}{-2xz} = \dfrac{dz}{xy}$.

90. $\dfrac{v - x}{u - v}$.

97. $1 + \dfrac{x^2 y^2}{2} - \dfrac{x^4 y^4}{8} + \cdots$.

98. $x + \dfrac{x(2y - x)}{2}$

$+ \dfrac{x(3y^2 - 3xy + 2x^2)}{6} + \cdots$.

99. $1 + x + \dfrac{x^2 - y^2}{2} + \dfrac{x^3 - 3xy^2}{6}$

$+ \cdots$.

100. $(1,2)$.

101. The median point of the triangle

$\left(\dfrac{x_1 + x_2 + x_3}{3}, \dfrac{y_1 + y_2 + y_3}{3}\right)$.

102. 10 in. by 10 in. by 5 in.

103. Height of cylinder 3 ft., height of cone 6 ft., radius $3 \sqrt{5}$ ft.

106. $\dfrac{AD}{A^2 + B^2 + C^2}, \dfrac{BD}{A^2 + B^2 + C^2}$,

$\dfrac{CD}{A^2 + B^2 + C^2}$.

107. $\frac{1}{2}, \pm 1, \pm 1$ or ∓ 1.

108. $\frac{1}{6}, \frac{1}{3}, \frac{1}{2}$.

109. $u = \dfrac{2aS}{a^2 + b^2 + c^2}$,

$v = \dfrac{2bS}{a^2 + b^2 + c^2}$,

$w = \dfrac{2cS}{a^2 + b^2 + c^2}$.

EXERCISES III (Pages 133 to 143)

1. $(6,6,6)$, $(-6,6,6)$, $(-6,-6,6)$, $(6,-6,6)$, $(6,6,-6)$, $(-6,6,-6)$, $(-6,-6,-6)$, $(6,-6-6)$.

2. $\sqrt{14}$; $\dfrac{1}{\sqrt{14}}, \dfrac{2}{\sqrt{14}}, \dfrac{3}{\sqrt{14}}$.

3. $\sqrt{21}$; $\dfrac{-2}{\sqrt{21}}, \dfrac{-4}{\sqrt{21}}, \dfrac{1}{\sqrt{21}}$.

4. $\sqrt{38}$; $\dfrac{2}{\sqrt{38}}, \dfrac{-3}{\sqrt{38}}, \dfrac{-5}{\sqrt{38}}$.

5. $7, 3 \sqrt{10}, \sqrt{53}$.

6. $\dfrac{x - 1}{3} = \dfrac{y - 2}{6} = \dfrac{z - 3}{2}$,

$$\frac{x-1}{1} = \frac{y-2}{-5} = \frac{z-3}{-8},$$

$$\frac{x+2}{4} = \frac{y+4}{1} = \frac{z-1}{-6}.$$

7. $46.73°$.

8. $3\sqrt{5},\ \sqrt{29},\ \sqrt{3}$.

9. $-5i + 4j - 2k,\ 3\sqrt{5}$.

10. $4i + 6j - 8k,\ 2\sqrt{29}$.

11. $-5i - 5j - 5k,\ 5\sqrt{3}$.

12. $7i - j - 2k,\ 3\sqrt{6}$.

13. $3i - 7j + 6k,\ \sqrt{94}$.

14. $7i - 11j + k,\ 9\sqrt{19}$.

15. $7i - 10j - 5k,\ \sqrt{174}$.

16. 45.

17. -10.

18. -3.

19. -1.

20. 3.

21. 154.

22. $\dfrac{-10}{3\sqrt{145}}$.

25. $4x - y - z = 6$.

26. $\sqrt{2}/3$.

27. $\dfrac{x-2}{1} = \dfrac{y-8}{12} = \dfrac{z-32}{80}$.

31. $\dfrac{x-2}{2} = \dfrac{y-1}{2} = \dfrac{z}{1}$.

33. $2x + y + 2z = 9$.

34. $z + 5 = x + 2y$.

35. $4x + 3y + 5\sqrt{3}\,z = 40$.

36. $\cos^{-1}(4/\sqrt{219}) = 74.3°$.

45. $3i + 4j - 2k$.

46. $-6i - 4j + 2k$.

47. $4i + 8j + 4k$.

48. $-3i - 11j + 2k$.

49. $-2i - 3j + 6k$.

56. $\dfrac{x-1}{3} = \dfrac{y-1}{6} = \dfrac{z-1}{1}$.

60. $\sqrt{3/7}\,[(-4y + 2z)i_1 + (4x - z)j_1 + (-2x + y)k_1]$.

63. 125.

67. t: $\frac13,\ \frac23,\ \frac23$; p: $-\frac23,\ -\frac13,\ \frac23$; b: $\frac23,\ -\frac23,\ \frac13$.

68. $x + 2y + 2z = 13$.

69. $2x - 2y + z = 2$.

70. $\dfrac{x-3}{1} = \dfrac{y-3}{2} = \dfrac{z-2}{2}$.

71. $\frac{2}{27}$.

72. $\frac{2}{27}$.

73. 5.

74. t: $\dfrac{4}{\sqrt{21}},\ \dfrac{1}{\sqrt{21}},\ \dfrac{2}{\sqrt{21}}$;

p: $\dfrac{22}{\sqrt{2121}},\ \dfrac{-26}{\sqrt{2121}},\ \dfrac{31}{\sqrt{2121}}$;

b: $\dfrac{1}{\sqrt{101}},\ \dfrac{8}{\sqrt{101}},\ \dfrac{-6}{\sqrt{101}}$.

75. $4x + y + 2z = 7$.

76. $x + 8y - 6z = 3$.

77. $\dfrac{x-1}{4} = \dfrac{y-1}{1} = \dfrac{z-1}{2}$.

78. $\dfrac{2}{21}\sqrt{\dfrac{101}{21}}$.

79. $12\frac{2}{101}$.

80. t: $\dfrac23,\ \dfrac13,\ \dfrac23$; p: $\dfrac{1}{\sqrt5},\ -\dfrac{2}{\sqrt5},\ 0$;

b: $\dfrac{4}{3\sqrt5},\ \dfrac{2}{3\sqrt5},\ \dfrac{-5}{3\sqrt5}$.

81. $2x + y + 2z = 5$.

82. $4x + 2y - 5z = -8$.

83. $\dfrac{x}{2} = \dfrac{y-1}{1} = \dfrac{z-2}{2}$.

84. $2\sqrt{5}/9$.

85. $-\frac89$.

86. $3(e - 1) = 5.14$.

90. t: $-\sin t \cos \alpha,\ \cos t \cos \alpha,$ $\sin \alpha$; p: $-\cos t,\ -\sin t,\ 0$;

b: $\sin t \sin \alpha,\ -\cos t \sin \alpha,$ $\cos \alpha$.

91. $-x \sin t + y \cos t + z \tan \alpha$ $= a \tan^2 \alpha$.

92. $x \sin t - y \cos t + z \cot \alpha = a$.

93. $\dfrac{x - a \cos t}{-\sin t} = \dfrac{y - a \sin t}{\cos t}$

$= \dfrac{z - a\,(\tan \alpha)t}{\tan \alpha}$.

97. Replace t by $(s \cos \alpha)/a$ in answer to Prob. 90.

100. $ds = \sqrt{a^2 du^2 + dv^2}$; $dS = a\,du\,dv$.

101. $ds = \sqrt{a^2 v^2 du^2 + (a^2 + 1)dv^2}$; $dS = av\sqrt{a^2 + 1}\,du\,dv$.

102. ds

$= \sqrt{a^2v^2du^2 + (a^2 + 4c^2v^2)dv^2}$;

$dS = av\sqrt{a^2 + 4c^2v^2}\,du\,dv.$

103. $ds^2 = a^2\cos^2 v\,du^2$

$+ (a^2\sin^2 v + c^2\cos^2 v)dv^2$;

$dS = a\cos v\,R\,du\,dv$, where

$R^2 = a^2\sin^2 v + c^2\cos^2 v.$

104. $ds^2 = a^2\cosh^2 v\,du^2$

$+ (a^2\sinh^2 v + c^2\cosh^2 v)dv^2$;

$dS = a\cosh v\,R\,du\,dv$, where

$R^2 = a^2\sinh^2 v + c^{2a}\cosh^2 v.$

105. $ds^2 = f^2 du^2 + (f'^2 + g'^2)dv^2$;

$dS = f\sqrt{f'^2 + g'^2}\,du\,dv.$

106. $ds^2 = (a^2\sin^2 u + b^2\cos^2 u)du^2$

$+ dv^2$; $dS = R\,du\,dv$, where

$R^2 = a^2\sin^2 u + b^2\cos^2 u.$

107. $ds^2 = v^2(a^2\sin^2 u$

$+ b^2\cos^2 u)du^2$

$+ 2v\sin u\cos u(b^2 - a^2)du\,dv$

$+ (a^2\cos^2 u + b^2\sin^2 u$

$+ 1)dv^2$; $dS = vR\,du\,dv$,

where $R^2 = a^2b^2 + a^2\sin^2 u$

$+ b^2\cos^2 u.$

108. $ds^2 = v^2(a^2\sin^2 u$

$+ b^2\cos^2 u)du^2$

$+ 2v\sin u\cos u(b^2 - a^2)du\,dv$

$+ (a^2\cos^2 u + b^2\sin^2 u$

$+ 4c^2v^2)dv^2$; $dS = vR\,du\,dv$,

where $R^2 = a^2b^2$

$+ 4c^2v^2(a^2\sin^2 u + b^2\cos^2 u).$

109. $ds^2 = \cos^2 v(a^2\sin^2 u$

$+ b^2\cos^2 u)du^2$

$+ 2\cos v\sin v(a^2 - b^2)du\,dv$

$+ \sin^2 v(a^2\cos^2 u + b^2\sin^2 u)$

$+ c^2\cos^2 v\,dv^2$; dS

$= \cos vR\,du\,dv$, where R^2

$= a^2b^2\sin^2 v$

$+ c^2\cos^2 v(a^2\sin^2 u$

$+ b^2\cos^2 u).$

110. Replace $\cos v$ by $\cosh v$ and $\sin v$ by $\sinh v$ in answer to Prob. 109.

111. $ds^2 = f^2(a^2\sin^2 u$

$+ b^2\cos^2 u)du^2$

$+ 2ff'\sin u\cos u(b^2$

$- a^2)du\,dv + [f'^2(a^2\cos^2 u$

$+ b^2\sin^2 u) + g'^2]dv^2$;

$dS = fR\,du\,dv$, where R^2

$= a^2b^2f'^2 + g'^2(a^2\sin^2 u$

$+ b^2\cos^2 u).$

113. $ds = \sqrt{(v^2 + k^2)du^2 + dv^2}$;

$dS = \sqrt{v^2 + k^2}\,du\,dv.$

114. At $u = 0$, $v = 0$: $ds^2 = c^2\,du^2$

$+ 2c^2\,du\,dv + (a^2 + c^2)dv^2$;

$\cos\theta = c/\sqrt{a^2 + c^2}.$

125. $\frac{1}{12}(5^{3/2} - 1).$

126. $\frac{2\pi}{3}(2\sqrt{2} - 1).$

127. 4.

128. $\pi - 2.$

129. $\frac{\pi - 2}{2n}.$

130. 2.

131. $\frac{20 - 3\pi}{36n}.$

133. $dV = u^2v\,du\,dv\,dw.$

EXERCISES IV (Pages 186 to 197)

11. $64u^5.$

12. $\frac{3}{2}.$

14. 0.

16. $\frac{1}{2}a^{-2}\log(1 + a^2x^2).$

17. $a^{-2}\sqrt{1 - a^2x^2}.$

18. $-6\log x + 3\log(x - 1)$

$+ 3\log(x + 1) + c.$

19. $\frac{1}{2}\log(x - 1) - \frac{1}{4}\log(x^2$

$+ 1) + \frac{1}{2}\tan^{-1}x + c.$

20. $-4\tan^{-1}x - 4/x + c.$

21. $\frac{-3x^2 + 3x - 2}{3(x - 1)^3} + c.$

22. $-\frac{1}{5(x - 1)} + \frac{13}{25}\log(x - 1)$

$+ \frac{6}{25}\log(x^2 + 4)$

$+ \frac{16}{25}\tan^{-1}\frac{x}{2} + c.$

38. 4.

39. 4.

40. $M_x = \frac{9}{5}$, $M_y = \frac{16}{5}$,

$(\bar{x}, \bar{y}) = (\frac{4}{5}, \frac{9}{20}).$

41. See answer to Prob. 40.

42. $I_x = \frac{16}{15}$, $I_y = \frac{8}{3}$, $I_0 = \frac{56}{15}.$

43. See answer to Prob. 42.

44. $(8/3\pi, 8/3\pi).$

45. $I_x = \pi,\ I_y = \pi,\ I_0 = 2\pi.$

46. $16\pi w$ or 3,142 lb.

48. $m\gamma k[-2\sqrt{2}$
$+4 \log (1 + \sqrt{2})].$

49. $\pi a^3/6.$

50. $\pi a^3/6.$

51. $\pi a^3/6.$

52. $\pi a^3/6.$

54. $M_z = \pi k a^4/4.$

EXERCISES V (Pages 244 to 251)

1. $-3\frac{2}{3}$ for C_1, 8 for C_2.

2. 18 for C_1, 15 for C_2.

3. $-2\pi.$

4. $-56\pi.$

5. $-2.$

6. $-5\frac{6}{3}$ for $C_1 - C_2$.

7. 3 for $C_1 - C_2$.

10. $\pi ab.$

11. $3\pi a^2/8.$

12. $\pi^3 a^2/6 + \pi a^2/2.$

13. $a^2 n(n + 1)\pi.$

14. $a^2 n(n - 1)\pi.$

15. $(4 - \pi)a^2/2.$

16. $\frac{1}{4}x^4 + 4x^3 y + y^2.$

17. $\frac{1}{6}(x^2 + y^2)^3.$

18. $e^x + xe^y + e^y.$

19. $\frac{1}{2}x^2 + x \cos y + \frac{1}{2}y^2.$

20. $\frac{1}{2} \tan^{-1} (x/2y).$

21. $\frac{1}{4} \log \dfrac{2x + y}{2x - y}.$

22. $ax^{m+1}y^{n+1}.$

29. $u = 2x - 3y,\ v = 3x + 2y.$

30. $u = 3x^2 - 3y^2,\ v = 6xy.$

31. $u = e^{3x} \cos 3y,\ v = e^{3x} \sin 3y.$

32. $u = y^3 - 3x^2 y,\ v = x^3 - 3xy^2.$

33. $u = \sin 2x \cosh 2y,$
$v = \cos 2x \sinh 2y.$

34. $u = \cos x \cosh y,$
$v = -\sin x \sinh y.$

35. $u = \sinh x \cos y,$
$v = \cosh x \sin y.$

36. $u = \cosh 3x \cos 3y,$
$v = \sinh 3x \sin 3y.$

37. $(1 - 2i)z.$

38. $-3iz^2.$

39. $-ie^z.$

40. $\sin z.$

47. $u = \log r,\ v = \theta.$

48. $u = -4\theta,\ v = 4 \log r.$

49. $u = -3r^2 \sin 2\theta,\ v = 3r^2 \cos 2\theta.$

50. $u = 2r^3 \cos 3\theta,\ v = 2r^3 \sin 3\theta.$

51. $u = \dfrac{\cos \theta}{r},\ v = -\dfrac{\sin \theta}{r}.$

52. $u = \sqrt{r} \cos \dfrac{\theta}{2},\ v = \sqrt{r} \sin \dfrac{\theta}{2}.$

53. $u = 5r \cos (\theta + 2).$
$v = 5r \sin (\theta + 2).$

54. $u = ar^p \cos (p\theta + A),$
$v = ar^p \sin (p\theta + A).$

55. $-1.$

56. $-i/3.$

57. 2.

58. $-\frac{6}{5} - 2\pi i$ for C_1,
$-\frac{6}{5} + 2\pi i$ for C_2.

59. $2 \log \frac{2}{3}$ for C_1 or C_2.

60. $\log \frac{2}{3} - \pi i$ for C_1,
$\log \frac{2}{3} + \pi i$ for C_2.

91. $P = x^2 - 2xy - y^2 - x + y,$
$F = (1 + i)(z^2 - z),\ z = \frac{1}{2}$ or
$(\frac{1}{2}, 0).$

92. $p(0,0) - p(5, 10)$
$= 480\rho$ lb./ft.$^2 = 926$ for (a),
$= 1.14$ for (b).

93. $q_1 = 1,\ q_2 = 0, p = c - \rho/2.$

94. $q_1 = 2x,\ q_2 = -2y,$
$p = c - 2\rho(x^2 + y^2).$

95. $q_1 = e^x \cos y,\ q_2 = -e^x \sin y,$
$p = c - \frac{1}{2}\rho e^{2x}.$

96. $q_1 = \sin x \cosh y,$
$q_2 = -\cos x \sinh y,$
$p = c - \frac{1}{2}\rho(\sin^2 x + \sinh^2 y).$

97. $q_1 = \cosh x \cos y,$
$q_2 = -\sinh x \sin y,$
$p = c - \frac{1}{2}\rho(\cos^2 y + \sinh^2 x).$

102. $q_r = 1/r,\ q_\theta = 0,$
$p = c - \rho/2r^2.$

103. $q_r = 4r^3 \cos 4\theta,\ q_\theta$
$= -4r^3 \sin 4\theta,\ p = c - 8\rho r^6.$

104. $q_r = -r^{-2} \cos \theta,$
$q_\theta = -r^{-2} \sin \theta,$
$p = c - \rho/2r^4.$

105. $q_r = \frac{2}{3}r^{-1/3} \cos (2\theta/3),$
$q_\theta = -\frac{2}{3}r^{-1/3} \sin (2\theta/3),$
$p = c - 2\rho/9r^{2/3}.$

106. $q_r = mr^{m-1} \cos m\theta$,

$q_\theta = -mr^{m-1} \sin m\theta$,

$p = c - \frac{1}{2}\rho m^2 r^{2m-2}$.

EXERCISES VI (Pages 266 to 272)

1. $\Gamma(1.8) = 0.9314$.
2. $\Gamma(2.25) = 1.1330$.
3. $\Gamma(3.667) = 4.012$.
4. $\Gamma(3.8) = 4.694$.
5. $\Gamma(-2.4) = -1.108$.
6. $B(0.8, 0.6) = 1.953$.
13. $a^2/6$.
14. $3\pi a^2/32$.
15. $\pi ab/4$.
16. $\bar{x} = a/5$, $\bar{y} = a/5$.
17. $7Ma^2/64 = 21\pi\rho a^4/2048$.
18. $2\pi a^2 b/3$.
19. $a^6/165$.
20. $M = 21\pi a^4/1024$, $A\bar{x} = A\bar{y}$
$= 12a^5/77$, $\bar{x} = \bar{y}$
$= 3072a/539\pi$.
21. $2Ma^2/5 = 4\pi\rho a^4 b/15$.
22. $a^3/90$.
23. $\pi a^3/70$.
24. $\pi abc/6$.
25. $\sqrt{\pi}\ \Gamma(\frac{1}{4})\Gamma(\frac{1}{6})/48\Gamma(1\frac{1}{12})$.
26. $3a/28$, $3a/28$, $3a/28$.
27. $14Ma^2/143 = \pi\rho a^5/715$.
28. $a^6/11880$.
29. $\frac{2}{27}$.
30. $-\Gamma(\frac{6}{5})$.
31. $\Gamma(\frac{4}{3})$.
32. $\frac{1}{8}\Gamma(\frac{5}{8})$.
33. $\frac{4096}{105}$.
34. $\sqrt{2}\ \pi$.
35. 2π.
36. $\sqrt{\pi}\ \Gamma(\frac{1}{3})/3\Gamma(\frac{5}{6})$.
37. $\sqrt{\pi}\ \Gamma(\frac{1}{4})/4\Gamma(\frac{3}{4})$.
38. $\sqrt{\pi}\ \Gamma(\frac{3}{4})/4\Gamma(\frac{5}{4})$.
39. $\pi \sqrt{2}/4$.
40. $\pi \sqrt{3}/9$.
41. $2\pi \sqrt{3}/9$.
42. $2\Gamma(\frac{4}{3})\Gamma(\frac{7}{6})/3\sqrt{\pi}$.
43. $3\pi \sqrt{2}/8$.
45. $\frac{1}{2}\pi \sec \frac{\pi}{5}$.

46. π.
47. $\pi/\sqrt{2}$.
64. $\sqrt{2}\ \pi/16$.
65. $\bar{x} = \frac{5}{32} \sqrt{2} \csc \frac{3\pi}{8}$,

$\bar{y} = \frac{3}{32} \sqrt{2} \csc \frac{\pi}{8}$.
66. $\frac{1}{16}$.
85. $\Gamma(-1.2) = 4.851$.

EXERCISES VII (Pages 295 to 302)

1. 1.5924.
2. 0.967.
3. 1.879.
4. 0.666.
5. 2.3314.
6. 11.337.
7. 0.1760.
8. 1.5747.
9. 1.5734.
10. 1.5869.
12. 0.786.
13. $F(1/\sqrt{2}, \pi/18) = 0.1750$.
14. $K(1/\sqrt{2}) - F(1/\sqrt{2}, 4\pi/9)$
$= 0.2456$.
15. $1/\sqrt{2}\ [K(\frac{1}{2}) - F(\frac{1}{2}, \pi/4)]$
$= 0.6232$.
16. $\sqrt{2}\ F(1/\sqrt{2}, \pi/4) = 1.1682$.
17. $\sqrt{2}\ [K(1/\sqrt{2}) - F(1/\sqrt{2}, \phi)]$
$= 2.086$, where $\sin \phi$
$= \sqrt{2} \sin \frac{\pi}{12}$.
18. $\sqrt{2}\ K(1/\sqrt{2}) = 2.622$.
20. $a/\sqrt{2}\ F(1/\sqrt{2}, \pi/4)$
$= 0.5841a$, $a/\sqrt{2}\ K(1/\sqrt{2})$
$= 1.311a$.
22. $4K(1/\sqrt{2})\ \sqrt{l/g}$
$= 7.416\ \sqrt{l/g}$.
23. $0.380\ \sqrt{l/g}$, $0.446\ \sqrt{l/g}$,
$1.028\ \sqrt{l/g}$.
25. $7.29\ \sqrt{l/g}$ from the series.
26. $4/\omega_0\ K(\sqrt{3}/2) = 8.6260/\omega_0$.
28. $\frac{1}{2}K(\sqrt{3}/2) = 1.0782$.
29. $\frac{1}{2}K(\sqrt{3}/2) = 1.0782$.
30. $\frac{1}{2}K(\sqrt{3}/2) = 1.0782$.

31. $\frac{1}{2}K(\sqrt{3}/2) = 1.0782$.
32. $\frac{1}{2}K(\frac{1}{2}) = 0.8429$.
33. $\frac{1}{2}K(\frac{1}{2}) = 0.8429$.
34. 1.35566.
35. 0.9345.
36. 1.6666.
37. 0.6143.
38. 1.22963.
39. 8.3679.
40. 0.3057.
41. 1.56686.
42. 1.56938.
43. 1.55497.
45. 0.3927.
46. $12E(\frac{1}{3}) = 18.314$.
47. $8E(\sqrt{3}/2) = 9.6885$.
48. $16E(\sqrt{2}/2) = 21.610$.
49. 0.944.
50. $x = 2.57$, $y = 2.17$.
51. $x = 0.996$, $y = 2.74$.
53. 18.314.
54. $L = 2\sqrt{1 + a^2}\,E(a/\sqrt{1 + a^2})$.
55. 3.8200.
58. 11.7397, 1.6534.
59. $\sqrt{2}\,[2E(1/\sqrt{2}) - K(1/\sqrt{2})]$
$= 1.2082$.
60. $\sqrt{2}\,[2E(1/\sqrt{2}) - K(1/\sqrt{2})]$
$= 1.2082$.
61. $4E(1/\sqrt{2}, \pi/6) = 2.0484$.
63. $K(\sqrt{3}/2) = 2.1565$.
64. $1/\sqrt{2}\,K(1/\sqrt{2}) = 1.311$.
65. $\frac{1}{2}K(1/\sqrt{2}) = 0.9270$.
66. $\sqrt{2}\,K(1/\sqrt{2}) = 2.622$.
67. $K(\sqrt{3}/2) - F(\sqrt{3}/2,$
$\sin^{-1}\sqrt{2/3}) = 1.078$.
68. $3^{-1/4}F(\sin 75°, \phi) = 1.401$.
ϕ radians $= 74.46°$.
69. $\frac{4}{3}K(\frac{1}{3}) = 2.1565$.
71. 0.599.
72. 0.100.
76. 2.194.
78. 8.867.
82. $b = 3.940$, $2a = 0.214$.

EXERCISES VIII (Pages 328 to 335)

1. $2xy^3z^4\mathbf{i} + 3x^2y^2z^4\mathbf{j} + 4x^2y^3z^3\mathbf{k}$.

2. $2x\mathbf{i} - 2y\mathbf{j} + 4z\mathbf{k}$.
3. $\dfrac{2x\mathbf{i} + 4y\mathbf{j} - 6z\mathbf{k}}{x^2 + 2y^2 - 3z^2}$.
4. Div $= 3$, curl $= 0$.
5. Div $= 0$, curl $= 2\mathbf{i} + 4\mathbf{j} + 6\mathbf{k}$.
9. $4/\sqrt{29}$.
10. $-2/\sqrt{6}$.
11. $1/\sqrt{14}$.
15. $5x\mathbf{j} + (2y - 3x)\mathbf{k}$.
16. $zx\mathbf{j} + 2xy\mathbf{k}$.
17. $\frac{1}{2}x^2y\mathbf{j} + \frac{1}{2}z(y^2 - x^2)\mathbf{k}$.
18. $x^3\mathbf{j} + (y^3 - z^2x)\mathbf{k}$.
40. $x^2y^3z^4$.
41. $(2y + 3z)e^x$.
42. $(x - y + 2z)^3$.
43. $(x^2 + y^2 + z^2)^2$.
50. $1/r\ \mathbf{i}_1$.
51. $-\frac{1}{2}r^{-3/2}\mathbf{i}_1$.
52. $nr^{n-1}\mathbf{i}_1$.
53. Div $= 3$, curl $= 0$.
54. Div $= 2/r$, curl $= 0$.
55. Div $= \cot\phi$, curl $= 2\mathbf{i}_3$.
73. $-m/r^2$ if $r > a$, $-mr/a^3$ if
$r < a$.

EXERCISES IX (Pages 365 to 370)

2. $y\,dy/dx + 2x = 0$.
3. $x\,dy/dx = 4y$.
4. $2x\,dy/dx = y$.
5. $y(dy/dx) = x(dy/dx)^2 + 1$.
6. $x^2y = x^3dy/dx + y(dy/dx)^2$.
7. $y^3 = xy^2\,dy/dx + x^4(dy/dx)^2$.
8. $d^2y/dx^2 = y$.
9. $d^2y/dx^2 = -y$.
10. $x^2d^2y/dx^2 - 5x\,dy/dx + 8y$
$= 0$.
11. $d^3y/dx^3 = 0$.
12. $x^2 + y^2 = cx^2y^2$.
13. $\tan x = \sec y + c$.
14. $x^2 - 1 = c(y^2 + 1)$.
15. $e^{2x} = e^{2y} + c$.
17. $x^2 + 2y^2 = c$.
18. $x^2 + y^2 = c$.
19. $y = cx^3$.
20. $y = -2x + cx^2$.
21. $y = \sin x + c\cos x$.
22. $y = -3x + cx^2$.
23. $xy = x^3 + c$.

24. $x = y^4 + cy$.

25. $x = -6y + cy^3$.

26. $3x^2 = y^2 + cx^4y^2$.

27. $2x = y + cx^2y$.

28. $y = cx$, straight lines.

29. $y = cx^2$, parabolas.

30. $xy = c$, rectangular hyperbolas.

31. $x^2 + y^2 = c$, circles.

32. $2x^2 + y^2 = c$, ellipses.

33. $\frac{1}{2} \log (x^2 + y^2) = -\tan^{-1}\frac{y}{x}$
$+ c$, logarithmic spirals.

34. $x^3y - y^3x = c$.

35. $x \cos 2y = c$.

36. $x^2 + y^2 = 1$.

37. $x^{1/2} + y^{1/2} = 1$.

38. $x^{2/3} + y^{2/3} = 1$.

39. $2xy = \pm 1$.

40. $4x^2 = 1 - 4y$.

41. $\pm x + y = 1$ and $\pm x - y = 1$.

42. $2y + x^2 = c$, $2 \log y + x^2 = c$.

43. $2y + x^2 = c$, $2y - 3x^2 = c$.

44. $y^2 + 1 = (x + c)^2$.

45. $2y - x^2 = c$, $y = ce^x$.

46. $y^2 - x^2 = c$, $y = cx$.

47. $y = cx$, $x^2y = c$.

48. $y = cx + 1 + c^2$, $4y = 1 - x^2$.

49. $y = cx - c^2$, $4y = x^2$.

50. $(y - cx)^2 = c^3$, $27y = 4x^3$.

51. $y = cx - \log c$, $y = 1 + \log x$.

52. $y^2 = 2cx + c^2$, singular solution degenerates to $x^2 + y^2 = 0$.

53. $y^2 = cx - c^2$, $x = \pm 2y$.

54. $c^2x^2 = 2cy + 1$, singular solution degenerates to $x^2 + y^2 = 0$.

55. $cy = c^2x^2 + 1$, $y = \pm 2x$.

56. $(2x + c_2)^2 + y^2 = c_1$.

57. $c_1e^y = \sin (3x + c_2)$.

58. $(x + c_2)^2 + (y + c_1)^2 = 1$.

59. $y^2 = c_1x + c_2$.

60. $x = c_1e^{-y} + c_2$.

61. $(c_1{}^2x + c_2)^2 = 1 + c_1{}^2y^2$.

62. $y = \log (x^2 + c_1) + c_2$.

63. $c_1{}^2y = -c_1x$
$+ (1 + c_1{}^2) \log (1 + c_1x)$
$+ c_2$.

64. $y = c_1e^{4x}$.

65. $y = c_1e^x \cos x + c_2e^x \sin x$.

66. $y = c_1e^{2x} + c_2e^{-x}$.

67. $y = c_1e^x + c_2e^{3x}$.

68. $y = c_1e^x + c_2xe^x$.

69. $y = c_1e^x \cos 2x + c_2e^x \sin 2x$.

70. $y = c_1 \cos 4x + c_2 \sin 4x$.

71. $y = c_1 \cos 2x + c_2 \sin 2x$
$+ c_3x \cos 2x + c_4x \sin 2x$.

72. $y = c_1e^{2x} + c_2e^{-x} \cos \sqrt{3}\, x$
$+ c_3e^{-x} \sin \sqrt{3}\, x$.

73. $y = c_1e^x + c_2e^{-x} + c_3 \cos 2x$
$+ c_4 \sin 2x$.

74. $y = c_1 + c_2x + c_3 \cos 2x$
$+ c_4 \sin 2x$.

75. $y = c_1 + c_2e^{ax} \cos ax$
$+ c_3e^{ax} \sin ax + c_4e^{-ax} \cos ax$
$+ c_5e^{-ax} \sin ax$, where
$a = 1/\sqrt{2}$.

76. $y = x + c_1e^{2x}$.

77. $y = xe^x + c_1e^x$.

78. $y = 4x + 2e^x + c_1 \cos x$
$+ c_2 \sin x$.

79. $y = xe^{2x} + c_1e^{2x} + c_2e^{-2x}$.

80. $y = 2 \cos x - \sin x$
$+ c_1e^x \cos 2x + c_2e^x \sin 2x$.

81. $y = -\frac{3}{2}x^2 + c_1 + c_2e^{2x}$
$+ c_3e^{-2x}$.

82. $y = (2x^2 + 6x + 7)e^{3x}$
$+ c_1e^{4x} + c_2e^{5x}$.

83. $y = -x^3 - 3x + c_1e^x + c_2e^{-x}$
$+ c_3 \cos x + c_4 \sin x$.

84. $x = c_1e^t + c_2e^{-t} - 1$,
$y = c_1e^t - c_2e^{-t} - 1$.

85. $x = c_1e^{3t} + c_2e^{-3t} + c_3 \cos 3t$
$+ c_4 \sin 3t$, $y = c_1e^{3t} + c_2e^{-3t}$
$- c_4 \cos 3t - c_3 \sin 3t$.

86. $x = 2c_1e^t + 2c_2te^t + 2c_3e^{-t}$
$+ 2c_4te^{-t}$, $y = (c_2 - c_1)e^t$
$- c_2te^t + (-c_3 - c_4)e^{-t}$
$- c_4te^{-t}$.

87. $x = c_1e^{t/3} + c_2e^{-t/3} - 12t$,
$y = -2c_1e^{t/3} - c_2e^{-t/3}$
$+ \frac{1}{2}e^t + 18t + 18$.

88. $x = c_1e^t + c_2te^t + c_3e^{-3t/2} - 2$,
$y = (-c_1/2 - 3c_2/2)e^t$
$- \frac{1}{2}c_2te^t - 3c_3e^{-3t/2} - 3t$.

89. $y = c_1 \sin x$
$+ [c_2 - \log (\tan x + \sec x)]$
$\cos x.$

90. $y = (\log \cos x + c_1) \cos x$
$+ (x + c_2) \sin x.$

92. $y = 6x + c_1 x^2 + c_2 x^3.$

93. $y = x^2 + c_1 x + c_2 x^{-2}.$

94. $y = \frac{1}{2}x(\log x)^2 + c_1 x$
$+ c_2 x \log x.$

95. $y = \frac{1}{24}x(\log x)^4 + c_1 x$
$+ c_2 x \log x + c_3 x(\log x)^2.$

98. $A = A_0 e^{Pt/100}.$

99. $s = s_0 e^{-w/V}.$

100. $T = T_0 e^{\mu\theta}.$

101. $p = p_0 e^{-kh}.$

102. $I = I_0 e^{-t/RC}.$

103. $u = u_0 e^{-kt}.$

104. $A = \mp 100F/P$
$+ (A_0 \pm 100F/P)e^{Pt/100}.$

105. $T = T_a + (T_0 - T_a)e^{-kt}.$

106. $I = E_0/R$
$+ (I_0 - E_0/R)e^{-Rt/L}.$

107. $x = A - Ae^{-kt}.$

108. $k(B - A)t = \log \dfrac{A(B - x)}{B(A - x)}.$

111. $y = (Ax^4 + 2Bx^3 + 6Cx^2)/12$
$+ c_1 + c_2 x,$
$y = (Ax^2 + Bx + C)/n^2$
$- 2A/n^4 + c_1 \cos x + c_2 \sin x,$
$y = -(Ax^2 + Bx + C)/n^2$
$-2A/n^4 + c_1 e^{nx} + c_2 e^{-nx}.$

115. $t = (v_0 - v)m/\alpha,$
$s = (v_0^2 - v^2)m/2\alpha.$

116. $t = \dfrac{m}{\beta} \log \dfrac{v_0}{v},\ s = \dfrac{m}{\beta} (v_0 - v).$

117. $t = \dfrac{m}{\beta} \log \dfrac{\alpha + \beta v_0}{\alpha + \beta v},$
$s = \dfrac{m}{\beta} (v_0 - v)$
$- \dfrac{m\alpha}{\beta^2} \log \dfrac{\alpha + \beta v_0}{\alpha + \beta v}.$

118. $t = \dfrac{m}{\beta} \left(\dfrac{1}{v} - \dfrac{1}{v_0}\right),\ s = \dfrac{m}{\beta} \log \dfrac{v_0}{v}.$

119. $t =$
$\dfrac{m}{V\beta} \left(\tanh^{-1} \dfrac{v_0}{V} - \tanh^{-1} \dfrac{v}{V}\right),$
$s = \dfrac{m}{2\beta} \log \dfrac{V^2 - v^2}{V^2 - v_0^2}.$

120. $t = \dfrac{m}{V\beta} \left(\tan^{-1} \dfrac{v_0}{V} - \tan^{-1} \dfrac{v}{V}\right),$
$s = \dfrac{m}{2\beta} \log \dfrac{V^2 + v_0^2}{V^2 + v^2}.$

EXERCISES X (Pages 395 to 400)

1. $y = c_1 e^x + c_2 x^2 e^x.$

2. $y = c_1 x + c_2 e^x.$

3. $y = c_1 e^{-x} + c_2 e^{-x}/x.$

4. $y = c_1 x^2 + c_2 x^3.$

5. $y = c_1 + c_2 \sin x.$

6. $y = c_1(x + 1) + c_2(x^2 + x).$

7. $b_0 \left(1 + \dfrac{1}{3!} x^3 + \dfrac{1 \cdot 4}{6!} x^6\right.$
$+ \dfrac{1 \cdot 4 \cdot 7}{9!} x^9 + \cdots \left.\right)$
$+ b_1 \left(x + \dfrac{2}{4!} x^4 + \dfrac{2 \cdot 5}{7!} x^7\right.$
$+ \dfrac{2 \cdot 5 \cdot 8}{10!} x^{10} + \cdots \left.\right).$

8. $b_0 \left(1 + \dfrac{1x^3}{2 \cdot 3} + \dfrac{1 \cdot 4x^6}{2 \cdot 3 \cdot 5 \cdot 6}\right.$
$+ \cdots \left.\right) + b_1 \left(x + \dfrac{2x^4}{3 \cdot 4}\right.$
$+ \dfrac{2 \cdot 5x^7}{3 \cdot 4 \cdot 6 \cdot 7} + \cdots \left.\right).$

9. $b_0 \left(1 + \dfrac{x^4}{3 \cdot 4} + \dfrac{x^8}{3 \cdot 4 \cdot 7 \cdot 8}\right.$
$+ \cdots \left.\right) + b_1 \left(x + \dfrac{x^5}{4 \cdot 5}\right.$
$+ \dfrac{x^9}{4 \cdot 5 \cdot 8 \cdot 9} + \cdots \left.\right).$

10. $b_0 \cosh 2x + b_1 \sinh 2x.$

11. $b_0 \cos x + b_1 \sin x.$

12. $b_0 e^{x^2}.$

30. $c_1(3 + 2x + x^2)$
$+ c_2(x^4 + 2x^5 + 3x^6 + \cdots).$

31. $c_1 \left(x + \dfrac{x^3}{2 \cdot 5} + \dfrac{x^5}{2 \cdot 5 \cdot 4 \cdot 9}\right.$
$+ \cdots \left.\right) + c_2 \left(x^{1/2} + \dfrac{x^{5/2}}{2 \cdot 3}\right.$
$+ \dfrac{x^{9/2}}{2 \cdot 3 \cdot 4 \cdot 7} + \cdots \left.\right).$

32. $c_1 \cosh (2 \sqrt{x})$
$+ c_2 \sinh (2 \sqrt{x});\ c = 0,\ \frac{1}{2}.$

33. $c_1 \cos \sqrt{x} + c_2 \sin \sqrt{x};$
$c = 0, \frac{1}{2}.$

42. $y = \sqrt{x}\ Z_{1/3}(x^{3/2}).$

43. $y = Z_0(5x)$.

44. $y = x^{-1}Z_1(2x)$.

45. $y = Z_0(2x^{1/2})$.

46. $y = x^{-8}Z_8(x)$.

47. $y = x^{-1}Z_2(2x^{1/2})$.

48. $y = x^{1/2}Z_2(x)$.

49. $y = x^{1/2}Z_{1/6}(3^{1/2}x^3)$.

50. $y = c_1I_2(x) + c_2K_2(x)$.

51. $y = c_1I_0(6x^{1/2}) + c_2K_0(6x^{1/2})$.

52. $y = c_1I_2(2x^{1/2}) + c_2K_2(2x^{1/2})$.

53. $y = x^{-2}[c_1I_{2/3}(\tfrac{4}{3}x^3)$
    $+ c_2K_{2/3}(\tfrac{4}{3}x^3)]$.

54. $y = x^{1/2}e^{-x/2}Z_0(ix/2)$.

55. $y = x^{1/2}[c_1I_{1/3}(x^{3/2})$
    $+ c_2K_{1/3}(x^{3/2})]$.

59. 5.958 in.

60. $y = c_1x \cos(k/x)$
    $+ c_2x \sin(k/x)$.

EXERCISES XI (Pages 423 to 431)

In this group of answers, Σ means $\displaystyle\sum_{n=1}^{\infty}$, or sum on n for the values $1, 2, 3, \cdots$.

9. $\Sigma(-1)^{n+1}2n^{-1}\sin nx$.

10. $\pi^2/3 + \Sigma(-1)^n4n^{-2}\cos nx$.

11. $\Sigma(-1)^{n+1}2(\pi^2n^{-1}$
    $- 6n^{-3})\sin nx$.

12. $\dfrac{\sinh \pi}{\pi}\left(1 + \sum u_n\right)$, where u_n
    $= (-1)^n2\dfrac{\cos nx - n\sin nx}{1 + n^2}$.

13. $1 - \tfrac{1}{2}\cos x$
    $+ \sum(-1)^n\dfrac{2\cos(n+1)x}{n^2+2n}$.

14. $-\tfrac{1}{2}\sin x + \Sigma(-1)^{n+1}$
    $\dfrac{2n+2}{n^2+2n}\sin(n+1)x$.

15. $\pi/2 - \Sigma 2k^{-1}\sin kx$, $k = 2n - 1$.

16. $-\pi/4 + \sum\dfrac{2\cos(2n-1)x}{\pi(2n-1)^2}$
    $+ \sum(-1)^{n+1}\dfrac{\sin nx}{n}$.

17. $\pi - \Sigma 2n^{-1}\sin nx$.

18. $\tfrac{4}{3}\pi^2 + \Sigma 4n^{-2}\cos nx$
    $- \Sigma 4\pi n^{-1}\sin nx$.

19. $2\pi^3 + \Sigma 12\pi n^{-1}\cos nx$
    $+ \Sigma(12n^{-3} - 8\pi^2n^{-1})\sin nx$.

20. $(e^{2\pi} - 1)\pi^{-1}(\tfrac{1}{2} + \Sigma u_n)$,
    where $u_n = \dfrac{\cos nx - n\sin nx}{1 + n^2}$.

21. $\pi \sin x - 1 - \dfrac{\cos x}{2}$
    $+ \sum\dfrac{2\cos(n+1)x}{n^2+2n}$.

22. $\pi \cos x - \dfrac{\sin x}{2}$
    $- \sum\dfrac{2n+2}{n^2+2n}\sin(n+1)x$.

23. $\pi/2 + \Sigma 2k^{-1}\sin kx$, $k = 2n - 1$.

24. $\dfrac{\pi}{4} - \sum\dfrac{2\cos nx}{\pi n^2}$
    $+ \sum(-1)^{n+1}\dfrac{\sin nx}{n}$.

25. $\dfrac{2}{\pi} - \sum\dfrac{4\cos 2nx}{\pi(4n^2-1)}$.

26. $\dfrac{2}{\pi} + \sum(-1)^{n+1}\dfrac{4\cos 2nx}{\pi(4n^2-1)}$.

27. $\tfrac{1}{2} - \tfrac{1}{2}\cos 2x$.

28. $\tfrac{1}{2} + \tfrac{1}{2}\cos 2x$.

41. $\displaystyle\sum\dfrac{160}{(2n-1)\pi}\sin\dfrac{(2n-1)\pi x}{30}$
    $e^{\frac{-(2n-1)\pi y}{30}}$

42. $\displaystyle\sum(-1)^{n+1}\dfrac{96}{n\pi}\sin\dfrac{n\pi x}{6}e^{-n\pi y/6}$.

43. $-\displaystyle\sum\dfrac{8}{n\pi}\sin\dfrac{n\pi x}{2}e^{-n\pi y/2}$.

44. $2\sin\dfrac{\pi x}{10}e^{-\pi y/10}$.

45. $5\sin\dfrac{\pi x}{3}e^{-\pi y/3}$
    $+ 3\sin\dfrac{\pi x}{4}e^{-\pi y/4}$.

46. $\displaystyle\sum\dfrac{4c}{(2n-1)\pi}\sin\dfrac{(2n-1)\pi x}{L}$
    $e^{\frac{-(2n-1)\pi y}{L}}$.

47. $\displaystyle\sum\dfrac{2pL(-1)^{n+1}}{n\pi}\sin\dfrac{n\pi x}{L}e^{-\frac{n\pi y}{L}}$.

49. $\displaystyle\sum\dfrac{u_n\sinh\dfrac{(2n-1)\pi(b-y)}{a}}{\pi(2n-1)\sinh\dfrac{n\pi b}{a}}$,
    where $u_n = 400\sin\dfrac{(2n-1)\pi x}{a}$.

50. $\dfrac{1}{2\pi} + \sum \dfrac{2}{n\pi}\left(\dfrac{r}{20}\right)^n \sin n\theta.$

51. $3r \sin \theta + 2r^2 \sin 2\theta.$

52. $2\pi - \Sigma 4n^{-1}r^n \sin n\theta.$

54. $\sum \dfrac{400}{\pi(2n-1)}\left(\dfrac{r}{a}\right)^{6n-3}$
$\sin(6n-3)\theta.$

55. $\left(4r - \dfrac{4}{r}\right)\cos\theta$
$+ \left(4r + \dfrac{4}{r}\right)\sin\theta.$

69. $\sum (-1)^{n+1}\dfrac{200}{n\pi}$
$\sin\dfrac{n\pi x}{50}\, e^{-bn^2t},$
where $b = a^2\pi^2/2500.$

70. $100 - \sum \dfrac{200}{n\pi}\sin\dfrac{n\pi x}{50}\, e^{-bn^2t},$
where $b = a^2\pi^2/2500.$

71. $x + \sum (-1)^{n+1}\dfrac{100}{n\pi}\sin\dfrac{n\pi x}{50}$
$e^{-bn^2t},$
where $b = a^2\pi^2/2500.$

72. $50 - x + \sum \dfrac{100}{n\pi}k_n \sin\dfrac{n\pi x}{50}$
$e^{-bn^2t},$
where $b = a^2\pi^2/2500,$ and
$k_n = 1$ for n odd and -3 for
n even.

73. $25 + x - \sum \dfrac{50}{n\pi}\sin\dfrac{n\pi x}{25}\, e^{-bn^2t},$
where $b = a^2\pi^2/625.$

74. $50 + 2x - \Sigma u_n,$ where u_n
$= \dfrac{200}{(2n-1)\pi}\sin\dfrac{(2n-1)\pi x}{50}$
$e^{-b(2n-1)^2t^2},$
with $b = a^2\pi^2/2500.$

75. $37.5°.$

76. $30.5°.$

77. $25°.$

79. $90 - \Sigma u_n,$ where u_n
$= \dfrac{720}{(2n-1)^2\pi^2}$
$\cos\dfrac{(2n-1)\pi x}{60}\, e^{-v_n},$ with
$v_n = (2n-1)^2a^2\pi^2t^2/3600.$

80. $p \sin\dfrac{5\pi x}{a}\cos\dfrac{5\pi st}{a}.$

81. $\dfrac{p}{4}\left(3\sin\dfrac{\pi x}{a}\cos\dfrac{\pi st}{a}\right.$
$\left. - \sin\dfrac{3\pi x}{a}\cos\dfrac{3\pi st}{a}\right).$

82. $\sum \dfrac{8pa^2}{k_n^3\pi^3}\sin\dfrac{k_n\pi x}{a}\cos\dfrac{k_n\pi st}{a},$
with $k_n = 2n - 1.$

83. $\sum \dfrac{8p(-1)^{n+1}}{k_n^2\pi^2}\sin\dfrac{k_n\pi x}{a}$
$\cos\dfrac{k_n\pi st}{a},$ with $k_n = 2n - 1.$

84. $\dfrac{qa}{3\pi s}\sin\dfrac{3\pi x}{a}\sin\dfrac{3\pi st}{a}.$

85. $\dfrac{qa}{12\pi s}\left(9\sin\dfrac{\pi x}{a}\sin\dfrac{\pi st}{a}\right.$
$\left. - \sin\dfrac{3\pi x}{a}\cos\dfrac{3\pi st}{a}\right).$

86. $\sum \dfrac{8qa^3}{k_n^4\pi^4 s}\sin\dfrac{k_n\pi x}{a}\sin\dfrac{k_n\pi st}{a},$
with $k_n = 2n - 1.$

87. $e = \sum (-1)^{n+1}\dfrac{2E}{n\pi}\sin\dfrac{n\pi x}{a}\epsilon^{-bn^2t},$
$i = \sum (-1)^n\dfrac{2E}{Ra}\cos\dfrac{n\pi x}{a}\epsilon^{-bn^2t},$
where $b = \pi^2/a^2RC.$

88. $e = \dfrac{Ex}{a} - e_1,\ i = -\dfrac{E}{Ra} - i_1,$
where e_1 and i_1 are the e and
i of Prob. 87.

90. $e = \sum \dfrac{2E}{n\pi}(-1)^{n+1}\sin\dfrac{n\pi x}{a}$
$\cos\dfrac{n\pi t}{a\sqrt{LC}},\quad i = I_0$
$+ \sqrt{\dfrac{C}{L}}\sum \dfrac{2E}{n\pi}(-1)^n\cos\dfrac{n\pi x}{a}$
$\sin\dfrac{n\pi t}{a\sqrt{LC}}.$

92. $\sum (-1)^{n+1}\dfrac{20}{n\pi}\sin\dfrac{n\pi x}{10}\, e^{-c_nt},$
where $c_n = \dfrac{a^2n^2\pi^2}{100} + b^2.$

EXERCISES XII (Pages 453 to 462)

1. $y = c_1x + c_2,$ straight lines.

2. $r\cos(\theta - c_2) = c_1$ straight
lines.

3. $v = c_1 u + c_2$.

4. $\cos \phi = c_1 \sin \phi \cos \theta$
$+ c_2 \sin \phi \sin \theta$, great circles.

5. $u \cos [\sin A (v - c_2)] = c_1$.

6. $(v - c_2)^2 = 2c_1 u - c_1^2$.

7. $v = c_2 +$
$$\int \frac{c_1 du}{\sqrt{(u^2 + k^2)(u^2 + k^2 - c^2)}}.$$

8. $v = c_2$
$$+ \int \frac{c_1 du}{\sqrt{(u^2 - 1)(u^2 - c_1^2)}}.$$

9. $v = c_2 + \displaystyle\int \frac{c_1 \sqrt{1 + f'^2}}{u \sqrt{u^2 - c_1^2}}\, du$.

20. $y - k = c_2 x$, straight lines.

21. $(y - k)^2 + x^2 = h^2$, circles.

22. $y - k = h^2 \sin^{-1} \dfrac{\sqrt{x}}{h}$
$- \sqrt{h^2 x - x^2}$, cycloids.

23. $hx = \cosh h(y - k)$, catenaries.

24. $h^4(y - k)^2 = 4h^2 x - 4$,
parabolas.

26. $x - k = c_2 y$, straight lines.

27. $(x - k)^2 + y^2 = h^2$, circles.

28. $x - k = h^2 \sin^{-1} \dfrac{\sqrt{y}}{h}$
$- \sqrt{h^2 y - y^2}$, cycloids.

29. $hy = \cosh h(x - k)$, catenaries.

30. $h^4(x - k)^2 = 4h^2 y - 4$,
parabolas.

31. $x - k = h^2 \sin^{-1} \dfrac{\sqrt{y}}{h}$
$- \sqrt{h^2 y - y^2}$, or $x = k$
$+ \frac{1}{2}h^2(u - \sin u)$,
$y = \frac{1}{2}h^2(1 - \cos u)$, cycloids,
inverted since y axis points
down.

38. $y = c_1 e^x + c_2 e^{-x}$.

39. $y = c_1 e^{ax} \cos ax + c_2 e^{ax} \sin ax$
$+ c_3 e^{-ax} \cos ax + c_4 e^{-ax} \sin ax$,
where $a = 1/\sqrt{2}$.

40. $y = c_1 e^x + c_2 e^{-x}$, $z = c_3 e^x$
$+ c_4 e^{-x}$.

42. $\dfrac{d^2}{dx^2}(F_{y'y'}) - \dfrac{d}{dx}(F_{y'})$
$+ F_y = 0$.

$\dfrac{d^2}{dx^2}(F_{z'z'}) - \dfrac{d}{dx}(F_{z'})$
$+ F_z = 0$.

55. $(x - c_1)^2 + (y - c_2)^2 = \lambda^2$,
c_1, c_2, λ to make circular arc pass
through A and B and have
length L.

56. See answer to Prob. 55.

57. $(x - c_1)^2 + (y - c_2)^2$
$= (L/4\pi)^2$, c_1, c_2 restricted so
circle passes through A.

58. $y = \lambda + c_1 \cosh \dfrac{x - c_2}{c_1}$, c_1, c_2,
λ to make catenary pass
through end points and have
length L.

59. $\dfrac{z'}{\sqrt{1 + y'^2 + z'^2}} = c_1$,
$\cos \gamma = c_1$.

60. $\dfrac{\dot{z}}{\sqrt{\dot{x}^2 + \dot{y}^2 + \dot{z}^2}} = c_1$,
$\cos \gamma = c_1$.

61. See answers to Probs. 59 and
60.

73. $mL^2 d^2\theta/dt^2 + mgL \sin \theta = 0$.

74. $I d^2\theta/dt^2 + mgL \sin \theta = 0$.

75. $mL^2 d^2\theta/dt^2 + mgL\theta = 0$.

76. $m(L + r)^2 \dfrac{d^2\theta}{dt^2}$
$+ 2m(L + r) \dfrac{dr}{dt}\dfrac{d\theta}{dt}$
$+ mg(L + r) \sin \theta = 0$.
$m \dfrac{d^2 r}{dt^2} - m(L + r)\left(\dfrac{d\theta}{dt}\right)^2$
$- mg \cos \theta + kr = 0$.

77. $mL^2 \dfrac{d^2\theta}{dt^2} + mgL\theta = 0$,
$m \dfrac{d^2 r}{dt^2} - mg + kr = 0$.

78. $m \dfrac{d^2 x}{dt^2} + k_1 x = 0$,
$m \dfrac{d^2 y}{dt^2} + k_2 y = 0$.

79. $m(\ddot{r} - r\dot{\theta}^2) = F_r$,
$m \dfrac{d}{dt}(r^2\dot{\theta}) = rF_\theta$.

80. $m[\ddot{r} - r(\dot{\phi}^2 + \sin^2\phi\,\dot{\theta}^2)] = F_r,$

$m\dfrac{d}{dt}(r^2\sin^2\phi\,\dot{\theta}) = r\sin\phi\,F_\theta,$

$m\left[\dfrac{d}{dt}(r^2\dot{\phi})\right.$

$\left. - r^2\sin\phi\cos\phi\,\dot{\theta}^2\right] = rF_\phi.$

81. $\dfrac{d}{dt}m(E\dot{u} + F\dot{v})$

$= \dfrac{m}{2}(E_u\dot{u}^2 + 2F_u\dot{u}\dot{v} + G_u\dot{v}^2),$

$\dfrac{d}{dt}m(F\dot{u} + G\dot{v})$

$= \dfrac{m}{2}(E_v\dot{u}^2 + 2F_v\dot{u}\dot{v} + G_v\dot{v}^2).$

83. $\partial^2 z/\partial x^2 + \partial^2 z/\partial y^2 = 0.$

84. $r\partial^2 U/\partial r^2 + \partial U/\partial r$
$+ 1/r\,\partial^2 U/\partial\theta^2 = 0.$

85. $\partial^2 U/\partial x^2 + \partial^2 U/\partial y^2 - U = 0.$

86. $r\dfrac{\partial^2 U}{\partial r^2} + \dfrac{\partial U}{\partial r} + \dfrac{1}{r}\dfrac{\partial^2 U}{\partial\theta^2}$

$+ r\dfrac{\partial^2 U}{\partial z^2} = 0.$

87. $\dfrac{\partial}{\partial u}\left(\dfrac{h_2 h_3}{h_1}\dfrac{\partial U}{\partial u}\right)$

$+ \dfrac{\partial}{\partial v}\left(\dfrac{h_3 h_1}{h_2}\dfrac{\partial U}{\partial v}\right)$

$+ \dfrac{\partial}{\partial w}\left(\dfrac{h_1 h_2}{h_3}\dfrac{\partial U}{\partial w}\right) = 0.$

88. $r(1 + q^2) - 2pqs + t(1 + p^2)$
$= 0,\ r,\ s,\ t,$ as in Eq. (107).

94. $r(1 + q^2) - 2pqs + t(1 + p^2)$
$+ \lambda(1 + p^2 + q^2)^{3/2} = 0.$

101. $m\dfrac{\partial^2 u}{\partial t^2} = T\left(\dfrac{\partial^2 u}{\partial r^2} + \dfrac{1}{r}\dfrac{\partial u}{\partial r}\right.$

$\left. + \dfrac{1}{r^2}\dfrac{\partial^2 u}{\partial\theta^2}\right).$

INDEX

Numbers in a parenthesis refer to problems, the first of which begins on the page whose number immediately precedes the parenthesis. Other numbers refer to pages.

A

Absolute value, **7**
Acceleration, 116
Adiabatic, 245 (28), 334 (84)
Amplitude of elliptic integrals, 273
Analytic functions, 17, 209
   integrals of, 213
Angle between two segments, 87
Angular velocity, 104
Arc length, 91, 122
Area, 125, 128
Associated Legendre equations, 396 (22)
Asymptotic series, 179, 196 (103–106)
   for Bessel functions, 387
   for the Gamma function, 265
Attraction, 146, 333 (72–74)
Auxiliary equation, 354

B

ber and bei, 393
Bernoulli's equation, 327
Bessel functions, 378, 384
   asymptotic series for, 387
   expansions in, 415, 427 (63–68)
   of first kind, 378
   identities in, 390
   modified, 391
   of order half an odd integer, 389
   roots of, 390
   of second kind, 381
Bessel's differential equation, **378, 384**
Beta function, 255
Binormal, 110
Brachystochrone, 455 (31)

C

Calculus of variations, 432
   constraints in, 439, 456 (50–67)
   higher derivatives in, 436
   multiple integrals in, 446
   several variables in, 436
   variable end points in, 456 (43–49)
Catenary, 369 (112)
   as extremal, 436, 440
Cauchy-Euler differential equation, 368 (91)
Cauchy-Riemann differential equations, 211, 246 (44)
Cauchy's integral formula, 246 (63)
Cauchy's integral theorem, 215
Cauchy's mean value theorem, 14
Chemical reaction, 368 (103, 107)
Circulation, 231, 326
Clairaut's form, 348
Column supporting its own weight, 398 (56–60)
Complementary function, 353
Complex functions, integrals of, 213
Complex number, 2, 9
Complex variable, 1, 17, 209
Components of a vector, 84
Composite functions, differentiation of, 4
Compound-interest equation, 368 (96)
Conformal mapping, 140 (116–124), 212, 235
Conservative force fields, 208, 314, 442, 459 (79, 80)
Constraints in variation problems, 439, 456 (50–67)
Continuity, equation of, 231, 325

481